Introduction to
PHYSIOLOGY

VOLUME 3

Introduction to
PHYSIOLOGY

VOLUME 3

HUGH DAVSON

*Physiology Department, University College
London, England*

M. B. SEGAL

*Sherrington School of Physiology, St. Thomas's Hospital
London, England*

1976

ACADEMIC PRESS · LONDON
GRUNE & STRATTON · NEW YORK

ACADEMIC PRESS INC. (LONDON) LTD.
24/28 Oval Road
London NW1

United States Edition published by
GRUNE & STRATTON INC.
111 Fifth Avenue
New York, New York 10003

Library of Congress Catalog Card Number: 75 5668
ISBN (Academic Press): 0 12 206803-3
ISBN (Grune & Stratton): 0 8089 0898-7

Printed in Great Britain by
The Whitefriars Press Ltd., London and Tonbridge

CONTENTS

Chapter 1 The Control of the Body Temperature

Chapter 2   The Control of the Vascular Circulation

Chapter 3   Control of Respiration

Chapter 4   Control Mechanisms in the Alimentary Process

Chapter 6   Homeostasis in the Nervous System

CHAPTER 1

The Control of the Body Temperature

Chemical and Physical Thermoregulation

Heat Production and Dissipation

In Vol. 1 we have discussed the basic principles of energy consumption, and the dissipation of heat, by the organism, and we have
seen that the body-temperatures of many homeotherms are maintained
within fairly narrow limits as a result of the interplay of these two
parameters. Thus the response to cold may involve an increased heat
production—*chemical thermoregulation*—together with physiological reactions that reduce the loss of heat from the surface of the body—
physical thermoregulation. The increased heat production is typically
brought about by shivering, but "non-shivering thermogenesis" also
contributes, and this is especially manifest in the consumption of
"brown fat" during cold-stress. The reflex physical thermoregulation,
in man, consists in a constriction of the blood vessels of the skin that
reduces surface cooling of the blood; in hairy animals and birds, the
erection of hairs, or fluffing of feathers, reduces heat losses by increasing
the thickness of the layer of still air on the surface. More complex
behavioural responses are the huddling of animals and the putting on
of warm clothes by man.

Heat Dissipation

The response to an increased environmental temperature, or an
increased heat-load through exercise, is a peripheral vasodilatation
that increases the cooling of the blood, but the most significant response
in man, so far as its effectiveness is concerned, is the secretion of sweat
by the sweat glands; the evaporative heat loss may amount to some
800 kcal per hr in a nude human subject exposed to a high ambient
temperature, i.e. it may be equivalent to some eight times the basal
heat production. In many animals an increase in the respiratory rate

1

—typically seen in the panting dog—is an important mechanism for increasing evaporative heat-loss; and in experimental studies the respiratory rate of, say, a rabbit is a good index to its response to a heat-stimulus.

Homeostasis

In the present chapter we shall consider the basic mechanisms through which this homeostasis of body temperature is brought about. Before describing some responses of man to changed thermal demands brought about experimentally, it will be convenient to suggest a sketch of the basic control mechanism, and to say a few words on the mechanism of chemical thermoregulation, which in man is manifest as shivering, and on the receptors in the skin that provide the signals for change in ambient temperature.

Control System

Figure 1.1 illustrates a simple system through which temperature regulation could be maintained. Information regarding the body temperature is provided from two main sources, namely from the skin

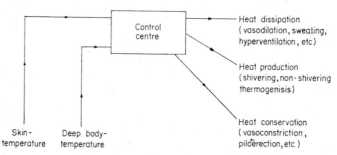

Fig. 1.1. An illustration of a simple control mechanism by which temperature could be regulated.

and from the blood flowing in the deep parts of the body—the *skin-* and *core-temperatures* respectively. This information is passed to a central control zone, and after being sorted out, a thermoregulatory response is induced. This response can be brought about by exciting or inhibiting heat-dissipation, heat-producing, or heat-conserving centres.

Core-Temperature

Of overriding importance will be the core-sensitive neurones, since the essence of the control mechanism is the maintenance of a steady core-temperature; we may expect the thermoregulatory responses to a given change in core-temperature to be far stronger than those to the same change in skin-temperature, and, when these occur in opposite directions, we may expect the information from the core-temperature sensors to be dominant. The site of the neurones sensitive to deep body-temperature has been established by a variety of experiments to be in the anterior hypothalamus, a strategic location that permits a ready activation of the vasomotor and other reactions required to make the appropriate adaptation. The actual integrating centres, as opposed to the temperature-sensitive neurones, are also in the hypothalamus; in fact, it is not easy to distinguish the effects of stimulating a centre from those of stimulating heat- or cold-sensitive neurones.

Set-Point

We may assume that there is a certain "set-point" on the temperature scale, and that any change in the core-temperature away from this "set-point" will result in thermoregulatory responses leading to a return to the set-point.

At this set-point we may assume that neither heat-productive nor dissipatory processes are dominant; it must be appreciated, however, that the animal's heat regulating mechanisms are not exclusively determined by the core-temperature, so that the concept of a rigid point on the temperature scale, set once and for all, is too great a simplification. Under certain conditions the set-point may change, and this may be physiological, as in the hyperthermia during severe exercise, or pathological, as in the fever induced by bacterial pyrogens.

Variable Set-Point. Hammel *et al.* (1963) have introduced a *variable set-point theory* that allows of modifications in the core-temperature at which no thermoregulatory activities are manifest. Thus, we may use the engineer's concept of the "continuous proportional controller", which depends for its action on the difference between the actual temperature, T_h, and the set-point temperature, T_{ho}. The action depends on the "load error", i.e. the value of $T_h - T_{ho}$, so that the response, $R - R_0$, is given by:

$$R - R_0 = a_R(T_h - T_{ho})$$

where the coefficient, a_R, is constant for a given form of thermoregulatory activity, e.g. sweating. Thus, in dogs, the coefficient was 2·3 for panting and -1 to $-1·5$ for shivering. The essential point to the theory is that the set-point is variable; for example, it was 2°C greater for panting than for shivering in a cold environment, 2–3°C greater than for shivering in a neutral environment, and 4°C greater than for shivering in a hot environment, the shivering being induced by artificially altering the hypothalamic temperature.

Chemical Thermoregulation

The Shivering Mechanism

When an animal is placed in a cold environment we have seen (Vol. 1, Ch. 3) that the metabolic rate increases linearly with the degree of cooling, indicating that chemical thermoregulation is an important mechanism in maintaining homeothermy. This increased metabolic rate occurs in many animals without obvious shivering, a process called *non-shivering thermogenesis*; for example, rats exposed to cold and treated with curare to prevent muscular activity, still show an increased metabolic rate. Davis and Meyer divide the increased response to cold into a *physical thermogenesis*, due to muscular contraction, and a *chemical thermogenesis*, due to a generalized increase in cellular metabolism. Thus normal rats at neutral temperature had a basal O_2-consumption of 1·7 ml/min/100 g; at 5°C this rose to 3·8 ml/min, and in curarized animals it only rose to 2·54 ml/min, so that the extra metabolism of the curarized animals was some 40 per cent of the normal extra metabolism. At first the muscular activity is of an unco-ordinated nature and only detectable by placing recording electrodes in the muscles; later it develops into the rhythmic involuntary co-ordinated act of shivering. This requires central coordination since Sherrington found that, when the spine is transected, the animal does not shiver below the level of transection.

Shivering Centre. Experiments on stimulation and ablation of various parts of the brain suggest that there is a region in the dorso-medial caudal hypothalamus, near the wall of the IIIrd ventricle, that may be described as a chemical regulation, or *shivering*, centre, corres-ponding with that marked P in Fig. 1.5 (p. 9); this part of the brain must remain intact if the animal is to be able to respond to lowered ambient temperature by an increased metabolic rate. This was first described by Isenschmid and Schnitzler in 1914 when they made rabbits poikilothermic by puncturing the brain in this region. As we shall see, however, this is not the main thermoregulatory centre, which is in the more rostral part of the hypothalamus, so that the shivering centre is under control from this rostral centre as well as from other parts of the brain (Hemingway, 1963).

Energy Production. Shivering is an effective manner of increasing heat production, the O_2-consumption being as much as 2–5 times the resting value; this increase is small, however, by comparison with the 10–20-fold increase of exercise.

The Peripheral Sensors

The detailed aspects of cutaneous sensation will be discussed later (Vol. 5); here we need only consider the responses of the cold- and warm-receptors of the skin. The skin is provided with numerous types of nerve ending, some of which are naked and come into relation with no organized receptor structure, whilst others end in relation to organized structures that have been given various names; thus the Meissner corpuscle is a receptor that mediates touch sensation, and it has been suggested that the Ruffini and Krause endings are concerned with thermal sensation, but this is by no means essential since thermal sensations can be evoked from areas of skin devoid of such nerve-endings, and it is likely that the naked ending, free in the tissue, subserves the function of temperature reception.

Cold- and Warm-Fibres

Electrophysiological studies have shown that there are sensory nerve fibres from the skin that respond in a characteristic fashion to cooling and others, the "warm-fibres", to warming. Fig. 1.2 shows the steady discharges of a cold- and warm-fibre innervating the tongue when subjected to steady temperatures.

The cold-fibre, whose responses are shown in open circles, is silent at temperatures of 37–45°; on cooling below 37°C (about the normal tongue-temperature) the discharge increases, to give a maximum at

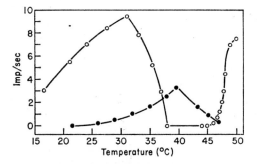

Fig. 1.2. The rate of discharge of three single fibres from the tongue as a function of temperature. Left open circles, cold-fibre; filled circles, warm fibre; right open circles, "paradoxical cold-fibre" which discharges at high temperatures as well as in the usual cold-fibre range. (Dodt and Zotterman, *Acta physiol. scand.*)

about 30°C; at lower temperatures the discharge-rate falls. The warm-fibres are characteristically different, being differentiated from cold-fibres by the fact that their steady discharge increases on warming the tongue from 30° to 40°C whilst on cooling from 40° to about 30°C the firing ceases. Thus, when the tongue is cooled to, say, 22°C only the cold-fibres are responding; as the tongue is warmed, the responses of cold- and warm-fibres increase, and it is only when the temperature is above 32·5°C that the cold-fibres show diminished discharges with further rises in temperature, whilst the warm-fibres continue to increase their discharges.

The Composite Message

The temperature of the skin is indicated to the central nervous system by the combined messages in warm- and cold-fibres; if we look at Fig. 1.2 we see that at 20° and 37°C the cold-fibre is giving the same response of about 4 impulses/sec and so the message sent by this fibre is by itself equivocal, it could indicate either a cool temperature of 20°C or a warm one of 37°C. However, at the cool temperature the warm-fibre is not discharging, whilst at the warm temperature it is discharging strongly; and it is the combined message in the two types of fibre that informs the central nervous system of the skin-temperature.

Human Thermal Receptors

The temperature-sensitive units studied by Dodt and Zotterman, and illustrated in Fig. 1.2, were in the tongue, which has normally a temperature of about 37°C; the skin-temperature of man, for example, is considerably lower than this, so that we may expect the cold-sensitive units to operate over a different range, and in fact a maximal discharge was obtained in the region of 20°C in a study of human thermal receptors by Hensel and Boman (1960).

THERMOREGULATORY RESPONSES

Core- versus Skin-Temperature

The most interesting problem in thermoregulation is that concerned with the interplay of peripheral and central stimuli in determining quantitatively the response to any change of the thermal demands on the animal. Modern techniques of calorimetry applied to human subjects have provided the basis for elucidating some of these inter-actions. The temperature of the blood flowing in the hypothalamic region is best indicated, as we have seen (Vol. 1), by the temperature recorded by a thermocouple placed close to the tympanic membrane of the ear, rather than the rectal temperature so often used in the classical studies. By ingestion of large amounts of ice-cream, the tympanic temperature may be reduced quite considerably and in this way the interaction between reduced core-temperature (or rather hypothalamus temperature) and skin-temperature may be studied. Alternatively, the human subject may be cooled in a bath to the point where his core-temperature is reduced by a given amount, and then his skin temperature may be changed by placing him in a bath at a different temperature.

Metabolic Responses to Cooling

In Fig. 1.3, a subject whose central temperature had been reduced to 36·1°C was kept in a warm bath at 37°C and the O_2-consumption measured; this was at a basal level of 360 ml/min suggesting that the lowered core-temperature was not an adequate stimulus to metabolism; on placing the subject in a bath at 28°C, sufficiently cool to activate the cold-receptors of the skin, there was a large rise in O_2-

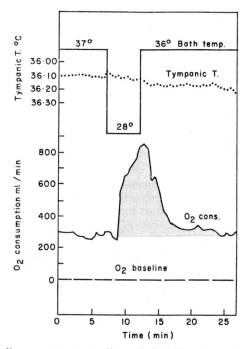

Fig. 1.3. Metabolic response to cooling of the skin. At a constant low central temperature of 36·15°C, transient cooling of the skin to 28°C in a water-bath caused a large increase in oxygen consumption. (Benzinger, *Physiol. Rev.*).

consumption. Thus the lowered core-temperature apparently requires a lowered skin-temperature to exert any effect, and Benzinger suggested that the lowered core-temperature acted on the chemical-regulation (or heat-production) centre by release of inhibition. On this basis, at normal core-temperature or above, the cold-response is held in check by the anterior hypothalamic (or heat-dissipation) centre; cooling the anterior hypothalamic centre removes this inhibition

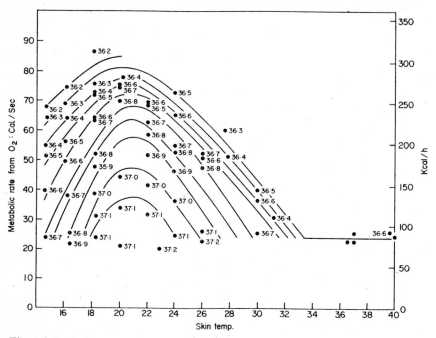

Fig. 1.4. Isotherms of core-temperature showing the variation in oxygen consumption with skin-temperature. Note that the rise in core-temperature apparently inhibits the increase in oxygen consumption that is normally initiated by a fall in skin-temperature. (Benzinger, *Physiol. Rev.*)

but, if the posterior chemical regulation centre is not being activated from the cold-receptors, clearly relief of inhibition will have no effect.

Cooperation between Centres. Hence the two centres cooperate in the response to cold, but not in a simple additive way; this is revealed when the metabolic responses to a variety of experimental conditions, causing altered core- and skin-temperatures, are plotted against skin-temperature. Merely plotting the results gives a confusing array of dots, but if results for the *same core-temperature* are plotted, to give a curve of O_2-consumption against skin-temperature, as in Fig. 1.4, a series of curves are obtained all showing a maximum response at about 20°C. The individual curves are remarkably reminiscent of cold-receptor responses to changed temperature; it is as though the successively higher core-temperatures were inhibiting the effects of the cold-receptor discharges; and we may assume that the meeting place for this inhibition is in the posterior hypothalamus, as indicated in Fig. 1.5. The results emphasize, also, that a lowered skin-temperature, in the absence of a lowered core-temperature, produces little or no

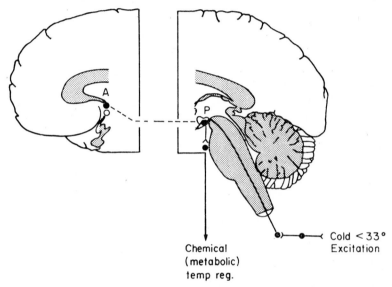

Chemical
(metabolic)
temp reg.

Cold < 33°
Excitation

Fig. 1.5. The integration of cold and warm responses in the hypothalamus. Area P (the Krehl-Isenschmidt centre) in the posterior hypothalamus has been shown, by ablation, to be the area controlling chemical thermoregulation. An area A in the anterior hypothalamus has been shown to contain warm receptors sensitive to core temperature and have an inhibitory influence. Cold receptors in the skin excite area P, but the response to this stimulation can be modified by the core-temperature via impulses travelling from area A to P. (Benzingner, *Physiol. Rev.*)

metabolic response, and it is for this reason that it is often stated that man exhibits little or no chemical thermoregulation when exposed to a low ambient temperature; he must wait till a certain amount of "chilling" has occurred before the metabolic response occurs.

Response to Heat-Loads

Rise in Core-Temperature

The principal mode of acquiring a heat-load, which the organism must dissipate, is through muscular exercise; and we have already seen how the circulatory requirements for cooling compete with the energy requirements of the muscles. In man, the principal mode of dissipation of heat is through sweating, whilst the increased peripheral blood-flow aids in the transport of heat from the core to the surface. The immediate response to bodily exercise is a rise in core-temperature, and as Fig. 1.6 shows, this rise is determined by the work-rate, which is equivalent to the heat-load. It is also interesting that the rise is, over quite a large range—what Lind (1963) calls the *prescriptive range* —independent of the environmental temperature. The important feature to note is that the core-temperature is not as constant as so

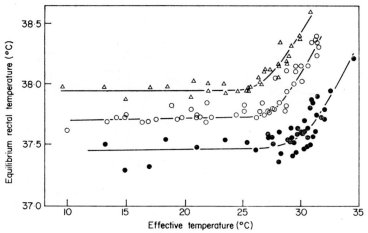

Fig. 1.6. Equilibrium levels of rectal temperature at three work-rates in different environments. Rectal temperature is almost independent of environmental conditions over a wide range—the prescriptive range, but regulation fails when conditions are severe, and the core-temperature begins to rise. Work rates △ 90 w, ○ 64 w ● 38 w. (Lind, "Heat Stress and Heat Disorders", Churchill.)

often stated, so that even when a steady state has been reached, when all the heat produced is dissipated, the organism is content to keep the core-temperature at a higher value than during rest. Furthermore, it seems that the same response is obtained if the heat-load is imposed by diathermy, which heats the deep tissues directly.

Return to Basal Level

With only brief periods of exercise, the body-temperature falls to normal within an hour or so; however, according to Haight and Keatinge (1973a), if heavy exercise is maintained for some 9 hr, there is a sustained rise of some 0·36°C in core-temperature that lasts for some 11 hr in either warm or cool surroundings. During this period the human subject behaved as though his set-point had been raised, since the temperature at which sweating began was correspondingly raised.

Significance of Raised Core-Temperature. There are two ways to regard this change in core-temperature; it may be an adaptive response to the heat-load, in the sense that the set-point of the body thermostat has been raised to permit of a more efficient loss of heat; or it may simply be looked at as an error in the control mechanism. Neither viewpoint is quite satisfactory, however, in view of the independence of the core-temperature with respect to the ambient temperature over the quite wide prescriptive range.

Evaporative Heat-Loss

Under conditions of heat-stress, for example during exercise, the skin-temperature usually rises, so that we may expect to find a relation between sweat-rate and skin-temperature; and this is true as Fig. 1.7 shows. However, as Benzinger has stressed, skin-temperature is a most unsuitable sensor in reflex mechanisms whose end is to maintain the core-temperature within a certain fixed range, since the sweating response to a rise rapidly cools the skin and so removes the stimulus for sweating long before the core-temperature has been reduced

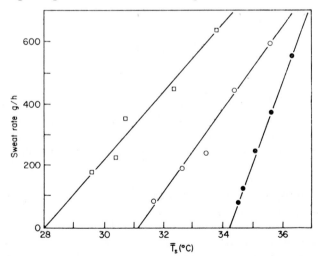

Fig. 1.7. Relation between mean skin-temperature and sweat-rate at three rates of working. Mean values for three subjects whose responses were similar. Work rates □ 490–540 w, ○ 300–350 w, ● 130–170 w (Kerslake, "The Stress of Hot Environments", CUP; from Blockley.)

adequately. Furthermore, it is easily possible to raise core-temperature, and maintain a low skin-temperature, by exercising in a cold environment. Thus we should expect to find far better correlations between core-temperature and sweat-rate than between skin-temperature and sweat-rate. By varying core-temperature and skin-temperature independently in a variety of ways, and measuring sweat-rate, Benzinger was able to produce a wide gamut of sweat-rates, skin-temperatures and core-temperatures.

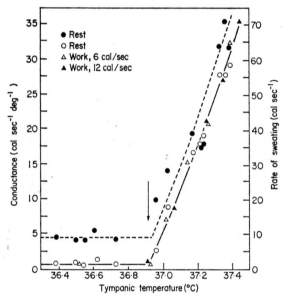

Fig. 1.8. The relationship between conductance and rate of evaporative heat loss to the tympanic temperature.

The subject has a set point of about 37°C and the thermostatic mechanism can be described as a proportional control system since the rate of sweating is proportional to the error, i.e. the difference between the actual core-temperature and the set-point. Circles = conductance; triangles = sweating. (Benzinger, *Physiol. Rev.*)

Relation to Core-Temperature. When the rate of evaporative heat-loss is plotted against skin-temperature, no clear relation emerges. As Fig. 1.8 shows, however, there is a very clear relation between evaporative heat-loss and tympanic temperature, a relation that is independent of the skin- and environmental temperatures. This particular subject has a set-point of about 37°C, and the thermostatic mechanism may be described as a *proportional control system,* since the rate of sweating is proportional to the *error,* i.e. the difference between the actual core-temperature and the set-point. It can be calculated from the curve that, after a deviation of the core-temperature of 1°C from the set-point, the sweating response is adequate to bring a return to the set-point in about 30 min, a fairly rapid approach for a system with such enormous inertia.

Exercise in Cold Environment. An interesting situation arises when exercising in a cold environment; here we may have a rise in

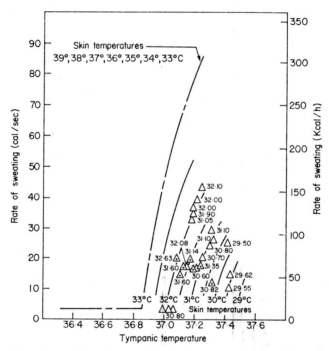

Fig. 1.9. The effect of exercise in a cold environment. The skin cold-receptors inhibit the normal sweating response when the core-temperature begins to rise with exercise, so that as the skin-temperature falls from 33°C to 29°C the threshold at which sweating normally starts is increased from 36·9° to 37·5°C. (Benzinger, *Physiol. Rev.*)

core-temperature with stimulation of cold-receptors in the skin; and the result is a partial inhibition of the sweating response, as shown in Fig. 1.9. Thus the temperature at which sweating begins rises progressively from 36·9°C to 37·5°C as the skin-temperature is reduced from 33°C to 29°C. It might be said that the set-point for temperature regulation was increased in accordance with the peripheral stimuli, and, as we have seen (p. 3), a theoretical basis for thermoregulation based on a variable set-point has been put forward by Hammel and Hardy and their colleagues. According to this, a variety of factors influence the set-point; for example, sleep lowers it giving rise to a fall in core-temperature; stimulation of peripheral cold-receptors raises it. The fever associated with many bacterial infections is due to the production by the bacteria of *pyrogens*—high molecular-weight substances that act directly on the hypothalamic centre, apparently raising the set-point (p. 41).

Vasomotor Reactions

The Skin Blood-Flow

The secretion of sweat is one of two main reactions leading to the dissipation of a heat-load; cooperating with it is the vasodilatation that promotes the transfer of heat from the core to the periphery and also provides the heat required for the evaporation of the sweat. We may measure the change in blood-flow in the skin by inflating a cuff around the proximal end of a limb and estimating the increase in volume over the first few minutes in a suitable plethysmograph. This, of course, gives the flow through the whole limb, but if the finger or hand is chosen, the contribution to the total flow by muscle is very small and can usually be neglected.   Alternatively, we may use, as an index to altered skin blood-flow, the changed conductivity of the body as defined by the ratio of the rate of heat loss (H) to the difference of temperature between core (T_c) and skin (T_s):

$$\text{Conductivity} = \frac{H}{T_c - T_s}$$

Here, of course, the heat-loss is non-evaporative.

The Blood Vessels. The detailed anatomy of the skin, with its sweat glands and hair follicles, will be described in a supplement at the end of this Chapter; here we may note that the papillae of the dermis (Fig. 1.35, p. 59) contain capillaries derived from a richly anastomosing plexus of blood vessels in the deepest part of the corium, single arterioles ascending from this and anastomosing with each other in the upper corium to form the subpapillary arterial plexus (Fig. 1.10); from here smaller arteries give rise to the papillary capillaries, which drain into a subpapillary venous plexus. The vessels in this venous plexus are relatively large and contain, when distended, a large proportion of the total blood in the skin.

Arteriovenous Anastomoses. From the point of view of thermoregulation, an interesting feature of the vascular supply is the large number of arteriovenous anastomoses, permitting a direct shunting of blood from artery to vein without passage through the capillaries. These vessels, particularly frequent at the tips of the fingers and toes, and in the nail-beds and ears, are coiled channels with thick muscular walls, their lumen varying from 20μ to 70μ in diameter according to the degree of vasodilatation. They are innervated by sympathetic fibres. These anastomoses maintain the temperature of the skin, when exposed to cold, through local reflexes, but they also, through central reflex

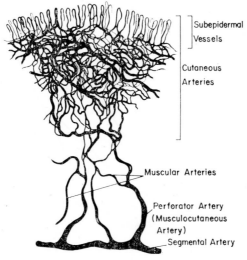

Fig. 1.10. The blood vessels of the skin. Single arterioles arise from the deeper parts of the corium and anastomose to form the subpapillary arterial plexuses. The fine loop vessels of the papillary capillaries branch from this plexus and drain into the subpapillary venous plexus. (Montagna and Parakkal, "Structure and Function of Skin". Academic Press.)

mechanisms, control the dissipation of heat from the surface, since they are capable of increasing skin blood-flow by as much as 200-fold in some parts.

Sweating and Vasodilator Responses

Figure 1.8 shows that, when core-temperature is used as an index to the stimulus for vasodilatation, there is a very striking similarity between the sweating and vasodilator responses; the same type of set-point control being manifest, with gain proportional to the error. Over a range of core-temperature of 0·5°C there was a seven-fold increase in conductivity.

Blood-Flow and Skin-Temperature

Figure 1.11 shows the result of measurements of blood-flow in the hand (skin) by plethysmography; here the blood-flow has been plotted against the skin-temperature brought about by immersing the hand in water at different temperatures. The interplay between the central controlling mechanism and the local skin-temperature is revealed by comparing subjects in warm, comfortable and cold environments. At any given hand-temperature, the blood-flow is

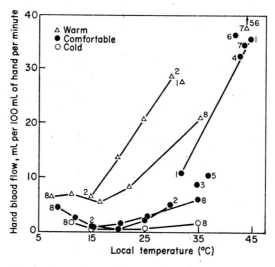

Fig. 1.11. The effects of local temperature on the hand (skin) blood-flow, measured by venous occlusion plethysmography, in warm ($\triangle$), comfortable ($\bullet$) and cold ($\circ$) subjects. Changes in hand-temperature were brought about by immersing it in water at different temperatures (Greenfield, "Handbook of Physiology" Amer. Physiol. Soc.)

greater in warm subjects than those whose environment is "comfortable", and in those who are cold.

Core- and Skin-Temperatures

These experiments illustrate two important principles in thermo-regulation, namely that the response to a change in core-temperature is influenced by the local skin-temperature, and that the local response may be influenced by the core-temperature. That reflex mechanisms are concerned in the local response is shown by the fact that an increase in blood-flow through the hand can be elicited by warming the leg, with its circulation occluded, so that the warm blood does not leave the leg and influence the core-temperature. Even this reflex response is influenced by core-temperature, however; thus Cooper obtained a vasodilatation of the opposite limbs when hand and forearm were immersed in water at 40°C, but this only occurred if the core-temperature was above the set-point of 36·5°–37°C. Thus the reflex is under the permissive control of the core-temperature.* The opposite phenomenon, whereby local cooling may inhibit a generalized vasodilatation, was described by Benzinger when he compared the vasodilator responses to raised core-temperature of resting and working subjects. The working subjects, at the same core-temperature, had the lower skin-temperatures and these were associated with smaller increases in conductivity.

Sweating vs. Vasodilatation

An important point for the experimenter is that the reflex mechanisms through which local temperature influences the whole-body response are different for sweating and for vasodilatation. This may be shown by placing a capsule over a portion of the skin and inducing vasodilatation and sweating by raising the core-temperature. If the skin under the capsule is cooled, the local vasodilatation is inhibited but the secretion of sweat continues.

Bradykinin

The local skin-temperature may not only react reflexly on the general peripheral blood-flow but also directly on the blood-flow in the limb considered, presumably through a direct action of the changed temperature on the blood-vessels of the skin, or through the local liberation of vaso-active substances. For example, the secretion of sweat is accompanied by the liberation of bradykinin, which causes vasodilatation.

Response to Cold

The response to cold is a vasoconstriction, and this acts in support of the chemical thermoregulation that increases the heat-production of the animal. We see from Fig. 1.8 that the body conductance falls to its lowest value when the core-temperature has fallen to the set-point; thus, once central cooling has occurred, there is little else that the vasomotor system can do to restrict the total loss of heat; some

* The rabbit's ear acts as an excellent dissipator of heat; it would seem that a part of the sensory mechanism is also present in the ear since Kluger *et al.* (1970) found that warming a rabbit's ear, when the animal was in a cold environment, gave a decrease in shivering, with a decrease in O_2-consumption and internal body-temperature. Thus the peripheral stimulus was purely the temperature of the ear.

additional local constriction clearly occurs, particularly in fingers and toes when there is severe local cold stress, but this may not be useful biologically if sustained for too long, since it could lead to frostbite.

Local Cooling. The actual local changes in blood-flow when the skin is cooled severely may be measured by placing the hand in water at 0°C. There is an immediate fall in skin-temperature on immersion, due to vasoconstriction, this being accompanied, usually, by pain; following this there is a "cold vasodilatation" with a rise in skin-temperature with a sensation of warmth. This cold vasodilatation occurs only where there are numerous arterio-venous anastomoses, i.e. in the fingers, toes, lobe of the ear and tip of nose. Since it occurs independently of the sympathetic nervous system, we must invoke, perhaps, an axon-reflex type of response, but the exact mechanism has not been elucidated, probably because many factors interact. Thus the vasoconstriction due to cold is due to several factors, such as a direct action of cold on the smooth muscle of the blood vessels as well as a neurogenic response; vasodilatation could be due to the gradual accumulation of vasodilator metabolic products, to the inherent short-lasting nature of the vasoconstriction, and to axon-reflexes in response to the stimulation of pain nerve endings in the skin.

"Hunting". In this connection the "hunting phenomenon" is o some interest; by this is meant the slow oscillations of skin-temperature that occur when the skin is immersed in very cold water. The dilatation of blood vessels due to cold would increase blood-flow, which would warm the skin; the increased flow might also wash away accumulated vasodilator substances so that the vessels would recover their tone. Blood-flow would be reduced and the cycle would begin again.

Brain-Temperature

In man and the monkey there is little doubt that the brain-temperature is governed by that of the arterial blood entering in the carotid and vertebral arteries, so that thermoregulation of the brain is achieved entirely by the various mechanisms that determine the temperature of the blood reaching the heart. In some animals, however, such as the sheep and gazelle, quite large differences in brain-temperature and aortic blood-temperature are encountered when the animal is thermoregulating in response to heat—when the brain-temperature is less than aortic temperature—and in response to cold—when the brain-temperature is warmer than the aortic temperature. Thus in these animals there is a dissociation between brain- and body-temperatures suggesting a separate thermoregulatory control of brain-temperature.

Carotid Rete

The key to this control is in the *carotid rete*, typically seen in the sheep. The blood supply to the circle of Willis (p. 605) is an arterial network, the arrangement being such that the blood supplying the circle, and thus the brain, is exposed to a countercurrent heat-exchange, being exposed to the blood returning from the thermoregulatory cooling surfaces involved in panting, namely the nasal mucosa and

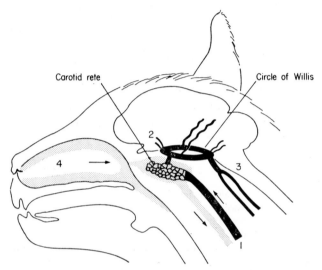

Fig. 1.12. A schematic sagittal section of the cat head. The anterior blood supply to the circle of Willis comes from an arterial network—the carotid rete—which is cooled by blood returning from the evaporative surfaces of the nasal mucosa. In hot conditions thermoregulatory panting cools the nasal passages, which in turn reduces the temperature of the cerebral blood below that of the central arterial temperature. Numbers indicate sites of temperature recording for the results shown in Fig. 1.13.
(Baker, *J. Physiol.*)

other regions of the upper respiratory tract (Fig. 1.12). Thus the ability of the sheep and cat, with carotid retes, to withstand high ambient temperatures in spite of their heavy skin insulation, compared with the lower tolerance of rats and rabbits, without carotid retes, is due to the countercurrent heat-exchange that makes panting an efficient means of cooling the blood passing to the brain, since the rete is surrounded by the venous blood draining the nasal mucosa and superficial cranial regions. When the blood-flow in the mucosa is restricted, as in the cold, the amount of cool blood bathing the rete decreases, and the temperature of cerebral arterial blood tends to

approach that of the aorta; when the mucosa is dilated, the amount
of cool blood increases and the cerebral blood is cooled below central
arterial temperature. An example of this regulation of brain-temperature is shown in Fig. 1.13 where the responses of the aortic, hypothalamic, and cerebral arterial temperatures to warming a cat are
shown.

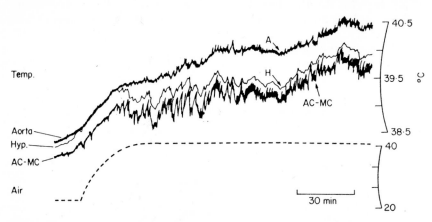

Fig. 1.13. Cooling of the brain during heat exposure in the cat. The records show
the air-temperature increase; the temperature in the carotid rete blood supplying
the brain (AC-MC); the hypothalamic temperature and the aortic temperature. At
room-temperature the animal was active with a respiratory rate of 20/min. As the
air-temperature rose the animal became quiescent, began to pant, with respiration
rising to 260/min. As thermoregulation occurs the brain-temperature (H) can be
seen to fall below that of the aorta (A). (Baker, *J. Physiol.*)

Acclimatization

Non-Shivering Thermogenesis

We may define acclimatization as the adaptation of an animal to
thermal stress, so that its ability to withstand it is improved, as a result
of a continued exposure to either a high or a low ambient temperature.
When rats are placed in a cold environment their metabolic rate
increases—chemical regulation—and it returns to normal on returning
them to a neutral environment. If the rats are maintained for long
periods in the cold, then it is found that, on bringing them back to a
neutral environment, their metabolic rate is some 50 per cent higher
than normal, and remains at this level for several days. These animals
show a greater resistance to cold than non-acclimatized animals. The
increased metabolism of cold-adapted animals is not due to shivering,
and is described as *non-shivering thermogenesis*. As we shall see, the basis

of this increased metabolic rate is largely an increased sensitivity to noradrenaline (p. 56).

Adaptation to Warmth

When rats, normally reared at 30°C, were exposed to an ambient temperature of 38°–39°C they soon died, but if they were maintained first at 35°C they were subsequently able to survive the higher temperature. During the period of acclimatization their basal metabolic rate fell from 697 to 498 kcal/m^3/24 hr (Buzalkov and Andjus, 1960).

Human Adaptation

So far as man is concerned, there is little evidence of any increase in basal metabolic rate during protracted sojourns in a cold environment, nor yet do natives of cold regions, such as Eskimos, have any obvious adaptation to cold; so that man, although a tropical animal originally, has extended his range over practically the whole earth entirely by adjustments in his "microclimate", namely the development of clothes or the lighting of fires.* When exposed to a warm environment, man does show some adaptation, in the sense that he is able to perform work more efficiently, and with less hyperthermia, after a sojourn at high temperatures. Thus Wyndham (1967) found that the sweat-rate of acclimatized subjects, working at a high environmental temperature, was greater than that of unacclimatized subjects, for the same rectal temperatures; thus the set-point for the sweating response is reduced in the acclimatized man.

Controlled Hyperthermia. The adaptation to heat is well illustrated by a study of Henane and Valatx (1973) who used as a test stimulus a period of controlled hyperthermia in a climatic chamber rather than the performance of work, since this latter involves cardiovascular adjustments as well. Subjects were exposed to this controlled hyperthermia over a period of 9 days and their sweat-rates were plotted during each exposure as a function of tympanic temperature. Fig. 1.14 compares the curves for Day 1 and Day 9, and it is seen that, at a given tympanic temperature, the sweat-rate is greater on Day 9; the temperature at which sweat-rate began to rise was lower on Day 9, whilst the time to sweat-onset, after placing in the climatic chamber, decreased after the fourth day. The value of these adjustments was at once manifest when it was found that two subjects were quite unable

---

* Primitive tribes of mankind who go naked and are often exposed to wintry weather, such as the Tierra del Fuegans and Australian aborigines, show some adaptation, in so far as they are able to sleep comfortably when their skin-temperatures have fallen to values that would keep a European awake and restless (Scholander et al., 1958).

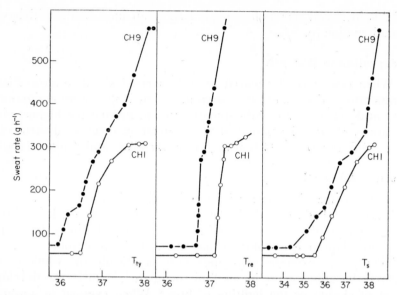

Fig. 1.14. The adaptation to controlled hyperthermia. The records show the response of a subject who has been placed daily in a heated climatic chamber. CH1 indicates the sweat rates at day 1 and CH9 the response after 9 days of acclimatization. Note that the sweat threshold has decreased. The temperatures shown are of the ear (T_{ty}), the rectum (T_{re}) and skin (T_s). (Henane and Valatx, *J. Physiol.*)

to stand the hyperthermia, and this intolerance was related to a failure to show the changes in sweat-rate or time to sweat-onset.

NERVOUS MECHANISMS IN THERMOREGULATION

Peripheral Mechanisms

Inhibition of Vasoconstrictor Tone

So far as the responses to changed core-temperature are concerned, the vasoconstriction due to chilling is sympathetically mediated. The vasodilatation evoked in the interest of heat-dissipation is brought about partly by an inhibition of existing vasoconstrictor tone, but also by active vasodilator impulses. The existence of a normal vaso-constrictor tone is demonstrated by subcutaneous injection of procaine, which causes vasodilatation in the skin of the hands.

Vasodilator Activity

The vasodilatation of the skin vessels concerned in heat-dissipation involves more than inhibition of this pre-existing constrictor tone since it occurs in two phases, the earlier being the result of loss of constrictor tone and the later being due to cholinergic active vasodilator activity (Roddie *et al.*, 1957). It has been argued that this latter cholinergic mechanism is secondary to a primary activation of the sweat glands, which is accompanied by the local release of bradykinin, a vasodilator hormone. Thus the active vasodilatation occurs in the skin of the forearm, calf, upper arm, thigh, trunk and forehead, and these are the areas where thermal sweating occurs (Kuno, 1934). According to Love and Shanks (1962), if the increased blood-flow due to active vasodilator activity is studied, this correlates well with, and precedes, sweat secretion, so that conflicting results, such as those of Hellon and Lind (1956), could have been due to failure to separate the increased blood-flow, due to inhibition of vasoconstrictor tone, from active cholinergic vasodilatation.

Vasoactive Substances

In this connexion we may note that humoral agents causing skin vasoconstriction are adrenaline, noradrenaline, vasopressin and 5-hydroxytryptamine acting directly on the vessels; vasodilatation is produced by acetylcholine, ATP, bradykinin and CO_2; histamine also has a small dilator effect. The nervous supply to the human eccrine sweat glands is sympathetic but the transmitter is acetylcholine, so that an intradermal injection of atropine abolishes sweating locally. In the horse, however, sweating seems to be induced by circulating adrenaline, secreted by the adrenal glands in response to exercise, rather than through nervous mechanisms; thus if an adrenergic mechanism were operating on the horse's sweat glands we should expect noradrenaline, the adrenergic transmitter, to have some action but in fact, when administered intravenously, it does not cause sweating, by contrast with adrenaline.*

The Central Mechanisms

Preoptic Hypothalamic Centre

As we have indicated briefly, changes in the temperature of the hypothalamus, induced, for example, by implanting thermodes in the brain and circulating warm or cold water through them, lead to well defined thermoregulatory responses; thus a rise of 0·5°C may cause panting in the dog and a fall may cause shivering. The best defined

---

* When adrenaline or noradrenaline is given intradermally to man or the cat, sweating from eccrine glands occurs; as there is no evidence for adrenergic transmission, however, the effects must be directly on the tissue of the gland (Collins and Weiner, 1968).

region experimentally is that described by Clark, Magoun and Ranson in 1939 in the rostral hypothalamus, now usually described as the *preoptic region of the anterior hypothalamus (PO/AH)*. Lesions here interfered with homeothermic reactions but did not abolish shivering; in order to do this a more caudal region, corresponding to the Krehl-Isenschmid "shivering centre" had to be damaged. The preoptic region is responsive to local temperature and, as we shall see, contains neurones whose discharges are highly sensitive to this parameter. It is usually described as a centre concerned mainly with promoting heat-dissipation since electrical stimulation, through implanted electrodes in the goat, gave typically a polypnoea and dilatation of the blood vessels in the ears; when the animal was shivering in a cold room, stimulation immediately abolished the shivering and caused polypnoea, but now the strength of the electrical stimulus required to increase the respiratory rate was about twice that required for the animal in a warm environment (Andersson *et al.*, 1956). Discrete lesions in the same region caused the animal to become poikilothermic (Andersson *et al.*, 1965).

Responses to Heat and Cold. However, as we shall see, when the temperature of the actual brain-tissue in this PO/AH region is altered artificially, responses to both cooling and warming are obtained, so that this centre is able to put into effect mechanisms for both heat-production—shivering—and heat-dissipation—vasodilatation and hyperpnoea. As an example we may quote the study of Gale *et al.* (1970) on a conscious monkey with a thermode implanted in the PO/AH region; the animal had been trained to press a bar whenever it felt cold so as to turn on a source of radiant heat. On passing cool water through the thermode the animal pressed the bar, even though the ambient temperature was high. When pyrogen was given intravenously, the monkey pressed the bar during the "chill phase", i.e. when the animal was increasing heat-production by shivering as a result of a raising of the set-point (p. 41).

Shivering Centre

The neurones of the caudal "shivering centre" are not temperature-sensitive, so that activation will be through afferent impulses from the skin, mainly the cold-receptors, but since electrical stimulation of the anterior hypothalamic centre will abolish shivering, and cooling of this centre will initiate it, an input from this centre must be postulated. Fig. 1.5 (p. 9) illustrates the schematic relation between the two centres; the so-called Krehl-Isenschmid centre, P, receives an afferent cold-drive from the skin and an inhibitory warm-drive from the anterior hypothalamic centre. When the cold-drive exceeds the inhibitory warm-

drive, chemical thermoregulation is brought about, e.g. shivering.*
Heat dissipatory mechanisms are brought into play through the
anterior hypothalamic centre.

Temperature-Sensitive Units

By inserting recording electrodes into the hypothalamus and other
regions of the brain we may record the behaviour of individual neurones
or "units", in response to altered temperature; the change in temperature can be confined to the neighbourhood of the recording
electrode by implanting a thermode nearby, through which water at a
given temperature may be circulated. The effects of changed ambient
temperature, acting through the skin-temperature, can be studied by
observing the discharges immediately after changing the ambient
temperature, i.e. before the effects have led to a change in core-
temperature. If a thermode has not been implanted in the brain, then
the effects of changed core-temperature are often revealed by the
changes in discharge rate of a neurone taking place some time after
the change in ambient temperature, i.e. when the blood temperature
has changed.

Types of Response: Cat. In Wit and Wang's (1968a) study,
reliance was placed on this last method, the cat being exposed to a
variable ambient temperature and the discharges in single hypothalamic units recorded; a thermistor in the neighbourhood of the
recording electrode indicated the temperature of the hypothalamic
tissue. Some 85 per cent of the neurones in the PO/AH region were
insensitive to warming the animal. The remainder were temperature-
sensitive and showed three types of response. Type IA (Fig. 1.15) responded with an increased frequency only when the hypothalamic
temperature rose by 0·2° to 0·4°C. Thus, although the animal's skin-
temperature was maintained high, it was only when the hypothalamic
temperature rose that a response was obtained. Type IB showed a
decline in frequency with rising PO/AH temperature and a rise in
frequency on cooling to 36°–37°C. These were thus cold-sensitive
neurones. Type II neurones showed an increased frequency of discharge as soon as the ambient temperature was raised; these clearly
received input from the peripheral temperature-receptors. If the raised

---

* The Krehl-Isenschmid centre may be inhibited by stimulation of several parts of the
brain as well as the anterior hypothalamus, notably the cerebral cortex, and the forebrain
septum; there is also a region quite close to the centre in the caudal hypothalamus that has
an inhibitory action when stimulated (Stuart, Kawamura and Hemingway, 1961). The
possible role of the septum in the higher (cortical) control of thermoregulation has been
discussed by these authors; they point out that it has intimate connexions with neocortical
and rhinencephalic pathways to and from the thalamus, hypothalamus and midbrain.

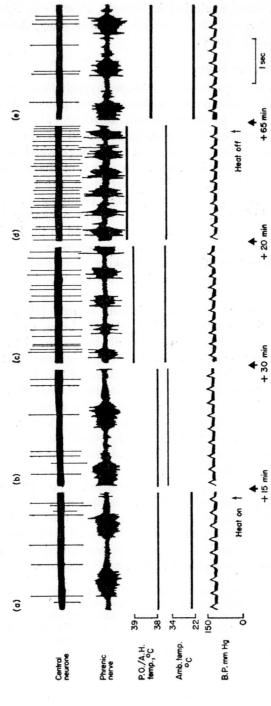

Fig. 1.15. The effects of increased ambient temperature and of increased preoptic/anterior hypothalamic temperature (PO/AH) on a temperature-sensitive Type IA neurone. (a) Control; (b) no change in neuronal activity during increased ambient temperature; (c and d) a progressive increase in activity and respiration with increase in ambient and PO/AH temperature; (e) recovery after return to control temperature. (Wit and Wang, *Amer. J. Physiol.*)

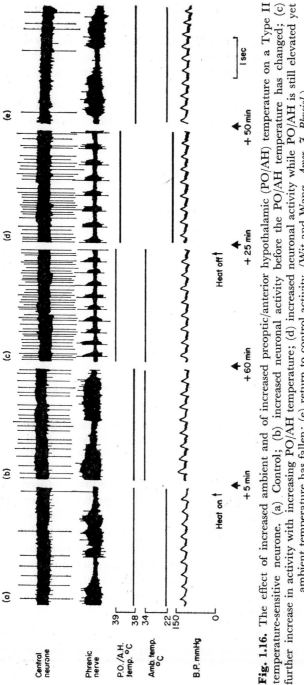

Fig. 1.16. The effect of increased ambient and of increased preoptic/anterior hypothalamic (PO/AH) temperature on a Type II temperature-sensitive neurone. (a). Control; (b) increased neuronal activity before the PO/AH temperature has changed; (c) further increase in activity with increasing PO/AH temperature; (d) increased neuronal activity while PO/AH is still elevated yet ambient temperature has fallen; (e) return to control activity. (Wit and Wang, *Amer. J. Physiol.*)

temperature was sustained until the hypothalamic temperature rose, then there was a further increase in discharge rate (Fig. 1.16).

Rabbit. In Hellon's (1970) study of the rabbit, the hypothalamic and ambient temperatures were varied independently; some units responded rapidly to a change of ambient temperature, and some of these responded only to cooling, others only to warming, and some to both; six of the temperature-sensitive units responded to changes in both ambient and hypothalamic temperature; these were equivalent to Wit and Wang's Type II neurones. Fig. 1.17 shows the records from

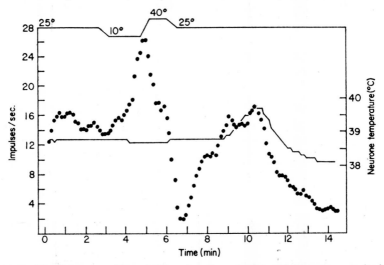

Fig. 1.17. The firing rate (dots, left-hand ordinate) of a rabbit neurone excited by ambient cooling, slowed by ambient heating (upper solid line) and also responding to hypothalamic temperature (solid line, right-hand ordinate.) (Hellon, *Pflüg. Arch.*)

a neurone that was excited by ambient cooling, slowed by ambient warming, and responded to changes in hypothalamic temperature.

Type II Units. The Type II neurone is clearly something more than a temperature-sensor, since it responds not only to the temperature in its neighbourhood but also to the ambient temperature, the effects of which must have been transmitted by nervous impulses arising initially in temperature-receptors of the skin. A collection of such neurones could operate as a "centre", integrating the inputs from both periphery and central nervous system.

Interneurones. More detailed analyses of the responses of individual hypothalamic neurones to locally applied temperature changes indicate a very characteristic difference amongst them suggesting that some are the primary "temperature sensors" and others are interneurones which, although responsive to temperature changes, may actually be responding synaptically to true temperature-sensitive neurones in their immediate neighbourhood. The primary neurones have a high temperature coefficient (Q_{10}) of greater than 2, in the sense that their discharge-rate more than doubles with a rise of 10°C, and they respond linearly with temperature-change. The putative interneurones are sensitive to barbiturate anaesthetics and have a lower Q_{10}; they do not respond linearly to changed temperature but in a more complex fashion, and are not confined to the PO/AH region (Nakayama and Hardy, 1969; Eisenman, 1969). Nakayama and Hardy suggest that the cold-sensitive neurones of the PO/AH region are, in fact, interneurones receiving messages from neurones in a more caudal region; thus the behavioural responses to cooling the PO/AH region would, on this basis, be the result of inhibiting warm-sensitive neurones and releasing their tonic inhibition of the caudal heat-production or shivering centre.

Spinal Temperature-Sensitive Neurones

There is no doubt that in many species there are spinal neurones sensitive to changes in temperature; it must be appreciated that the discharge of any neurone will be affected to some extent by changed temperature, but the effects described in this context reveal a specialized sensitivity that represents an adaptation in the interests of thermoregulation. For example, Guieu and Hardy (1970) passed warm water through a thermode surrounding the spinal cord, as in Fig. 1.18 and observed an increase in breathing rate of some 40–60 breaths/min, the temperature of the spinal canal being some 43°–44°C. When the preoptic region of the hypothalamus was warmed to 40°–40·5°C the rate increased by 120–150 breaths/min and when both regions were warmed the rate was 160–210 breaths/min. That the hypothalamus had an overriding control of the response to warmth was shown by the complete inhibition of the cord response by depressing the preoptic temperature below 37·5°C. Integration of the cord responses probably takes place within the hypothalamus since severing connections between the two abolishes the effect of warming the cord.

Cord vs. Hypothalamus Temperature. The relative unimportance of the cord-temperature, as opposed to that of the hypothalamus, shown by these experiments on the rabbit, may have been due to the depressing effect of anaesthesia that reduced the effects of the discharges from the cord on the thermoregulatory neurones in the hypothalamus. Jessen and Mayer (1971), working on conscious dogs, found that the thermoregulatory responses to warming and cooling, measured by evaporative loss from the mouth, and shivering, respectively, were about equivalent, so that the graphs obtained by plotting these variables against either spinal cord- or hypothalamic temperature were remarkably similar (Fig. 1.19). When the temperatures of the two regions were altered independently, either in the same or in opposite directions, there was a remarkable addition or subtraction; this was especially true of the shivering response to cooling of the two systems, so that warm stimuli applied to the one area, e.g. hypothalamic, immediately inhibited the shivering due to a cold stimulus applied to the other. With the panting response to warming of the areas, the relationship was not so simple, so that intense cooling of the one area could not cancel out the effects of warming the other. In this case, then,

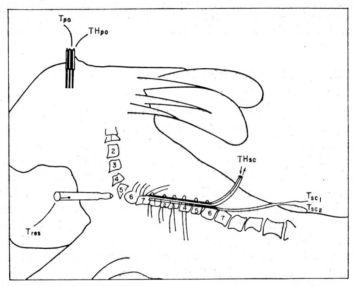

Fig. 1.18. Schematic diagram traced from a lateral X-ray of the rabbit showing preoptic thermodes and re-entrant tube for thermocouple, TH_{po} and T_{po} respectively; tracheal cannula with thermocouple, T_{res}; spinal canal thermode, TH_{sc} and thermocouples Tsc_1 at T_2 and Tsc_2 at T_4 respectively. (Guieu and Hardy, *J. appl. Physiol.*)

it is the warming of the hypothalamus or cord that dominates panting. Thus central warm signals, whether they arise in hypothalamus or cord, have priority over cold signals with respect to panting, and actually prevent the cold signals from causing shivering. This is a reasonable arrangement, since it ensures that the more dangerous condition, overheating of the animal, is not easily brought about.

Single-Unit Responses from Cord. By placing steel electrodes in the cord at levels between C2 and C4, the responses of individual neurones to changes in cord-temperature could be measured. Some showed an increased discharge on warming and others an increase on cooling thereby exhibiting a remarkable similarity with temperature

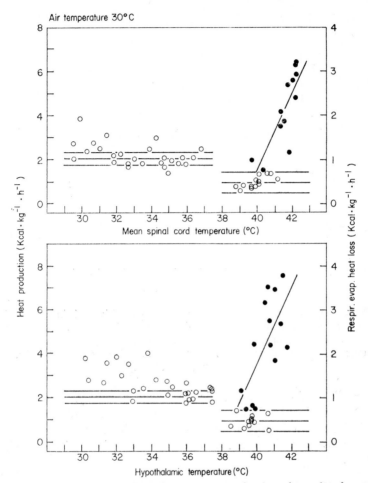

Fig. 1.19. Heat production and respiratory evaporative heat loss related to spinal cord temperature (above) and hypothalamic temperature (below) in the conscious dog at an ambient air temperature of 30°C. (Jessen and Mayer, *Pflüg. Arch.*) Each circle represents one stimulation, oblique lines give the mean squares of filled circles.

receptors of the skin. In Fig. 1.20 the average responses of the two types of neurone at temperatures between 20° and 43°C are shown, and it will be seen that the messages from the two types of sensor would provide the higher hypothalamic centres with a fairly accurate picture of the temperature of the blood flowing through the spinal cord. At normal body temperature there would be low discharges in both types of neurone; as the cord was cooled the "cold-neurones" would increase their discharge steeply, and as the cord was warmed the "warm-

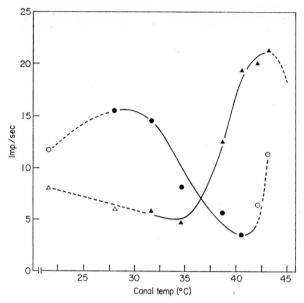

Fig. 1.20. The responses of the two types of thermosensitive unit in the spinal cord. The temperature was varied by a thermode in the vertebral canal. Average responses of cold-sensitive units are shown by the circles and those of heat-sensitive units by the triangles. Open symbols indicate values obtained from less than 6 units. (Simon and Iriki, *Pflüg. Arch.*)

neurones" would increase their discharge abruptly. The responsive units were all located in the region of the spinothalamic tracts, so that their information on cord-temperature is carried by the same ascending pathway as that from the temperature-receptors of the periphery (Vol. 5).

The Medulla Oblongata

There is no doubt that heating the medulla modifies the activities of neurones within it, especially those concerned with respiration, but this has been said to result in a depression of respiration with raised temperature,* i.e. the opposite effect to that of heating the hypo-thalamus, and it has been argued that the temperature-sensitivity of the medullary neurones represents a non-specific response of which there are many examples in the central nervous system, e.g. cortical sensory neurones (Gartside and Lippold, 1967). However, recent

---

* Chai and Lin suggest that the depression of respiration observed in cats by warming the medulla described by Chai *et al.* (1965) and Tabatabai (1972) could have been due to the simultaneous warming of the lateral reticular formation 3–4 mm below the floor of the IVth ventricle, a region that, when electrically stimulated, gives marked respiratory responses.

studies of Chai and Lin on the unanaesthetized monkey (1972) and decerebrate rabbit (1973) do suggest that the medulla contains a centre that responds to blood-temperature. Chai and Lin emphasize that, when the hypothalamus has been separated from the rest of the neuraxis, although thermoregulation is no longer sustained, there are still thermoregulatory responses, such as the vasodilatation and sweating in response to raised ambient temperature found in humans with high spinal transection (Randall *et al.*, 1966).

Normal and Decerebrate Rabbits. In their experiments on decerebrate rabbits, i.e. animals transected below the hypothalamus in the mid-collicular region and therefore without a functional hypothalamic centre, they altered the temperature of the medulla by a coil of tubing inserted into the IVth ventricle, through which they could circulate cold or warm water. In the normal animal the responses to changed ambient temperature were those to be expected; e.g. in the warm, the ear-temperature rose and breathing-rate increased. The effects of decerebration were to reduce the responses, indicating the importance of the hypothalamus, but they were not abolished. Raising the temperature of the medulla from $38 \cdot 2°$ to $42 \cdot 4°C$ produced active thermoregulatory responses; thus, at the end of 5 min of heating, the ear-temperature had risen by $2 \cdot 7°C$ and the respiratory rate had increased by 45 breaths/min. Rectal temperature remained unaltered. After decerebration, exactly the same responses were obtained, indicating that they were not mediated by afferent impulses from the medulla to the hypothalamus, nor yet by passage of warm blood from the medulla. Essentially similar responses to warming and cooling the spinal cord were obtained, so that it would seem that at least three regions of the central nervous system are temperature-sensitive, whilst it is only the hypothalamus that carries out the coordination necessary for homeothermy.

Midbrain Reticular Formation

In the rabbit Nakayama and Hardy (1969) have described both warm- and cold-sensitive neurones in the midbrain reticular formation; here the cold-sensitive neurones were much more frequent than the warm-sensitive, in marked contrast to the hypothalamus; more than half of these responded to changed temperature of the skin, as well as to local temperature change.

Drinking and Eating Centres

The part of the hypothalamus that contains temperature-sensitive neurones which, when their environmental temperature is altered, give rise to thermoregulatory responses, is closely related to centres concerned with food and water intake. Thermoregulation, in so far as it involves losses of water, should logically be related to the animal's intake of this fluid, and it is interesting that when Andersson and Larsson (1961) cooled the preoptic area and rostral hypothalamus of

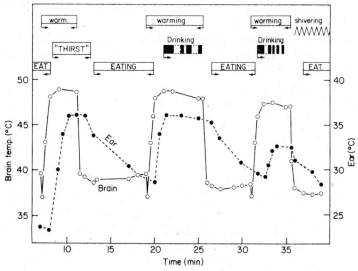

Fig. 1.21. Results of warming the preoptic area and rostral hypothalamus in the previously hungry animal. Brain temperature was recorded close to the surface of the thermode. The goat was fed hay at the beginning of the experiment and had free access to water except during the first period of central warming. During the periods of warming, eating stopped simultaneously with the onset of peripheral vaso-dilatation (rise of ear temperature) and started again when ear surface-temperature had begun to fall after discontinuation of central warming. The perfusion of the thermode with warm water induced a strong urge to drink. During the first period of central warming, when the water container was temporarily removed, it was evidenced by the animal's licking the drops of water coming out of the outlet tubing of the thermode ("thirst") and later on by the repeated drinking of large amounts of water during the periods of central warming. (Andersson and Larsson, *Acta Physiol. Scand.*)

dehydrated goats they were able to inhibit their urge to drink. On warming same area, water-drinking was induced in the normally hydrated animal. Destruction of this zone by proton irradiation caused a permanently raised temperature-threshold for the initiation of heat-dissipation responses, an impaired resistance to cold, and a complete adipsia. As Fig. 1.21 shows, warming this hypothalamic region inhibited eating, presumably by activating neurones either in, or closely related to, the satiety centre, damage to which causes hyperphagia and obeseness in rats (Ch. 4). Whether the eating response to cold, and inhibition with warmth, may likewise be viewed as adaptations to thermal change in the interests of thermoregulation it is not easy to say; it is certainly of survival value if an animal is stimulated to eat in a cold environment.

NEUROHUMORAL ASPECTS OF THERMOREGULATION

Intraventricular Injections

The responses of the animal to thermal demands are mediated largely through the hypothalamus, which lies close to the third ventricle; the neurohumoral agents concerned in these responses, e.g. acetylcholine, noradrenaline, etc. may well "spill over" into the cerebrospinal fluid and be detected here in increased concentration during thermal adaptations. Furthermore, thermoregulatory behaviour may be induced by injections of these neurohumours into the cerebrospinal fluid, or the tissue of the hypothalamus.

5-HT and NA

According to the studies of Feldberg and Myers (1964), 5- hydroxytryptamine (5-HT or serotonin) raised body-temperature of cats when injected into the ventricle, whilst noradrenaline lowered it, when it had been artifically raised by injections of pyrogen* (p. 41). If, as seems likely, these substances are transmitters in the hypothalamus, we may assume that they are mimicking the actions of certain neurones in this part of the brain concerned in thermoregulation; thus if the transmitter of cold-sensitive neurones is 5-HT, we may expect an intraventricular injection to increase thermogenesis; similarly if the warm-sensitive neurones employ noradrenaline as their transmitter, the response will be to promote heat-dissipation.

Carbachol

Cholinomimetic substances, such as carbachol, tended to be hyperthermic in so far as they caused shivering with a rise in rectal temperature in the sheep and goat but, as with the amines, there are species differences so that in the rabbit the effects were opposite. In general, it must be appreciated that there must be several types of

* There are very pronounced species differences in the responses to intraventricular injections. 5-HT is hyperthermic in the cat, dog and monkey, and noradrenaline is hypothermic. In sheep and rabbits the reverse happens, 5-HT being hypothermic and catecholamines hyperthermic; in the goat and ox 5-HT is hypothermic whilst catecholamines have no effect (Feldberg *et al.*, 1967).

excitatory and inhibitory synapses in the centres controlling responses to warm and cold, and these may be activated by one of several transmitters, so that the application of a given transmitter to the brain in this way is very much of a blunderbuss procedure.

Effects of Ambient Temperature. Moreover, as Bligh *et al.* (1971) have pointed out, the responses to a drug may vary with the ambient temperature to which the animal is exposed at the time of

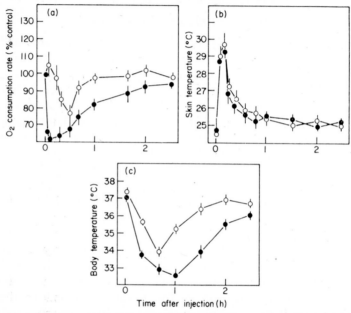

Fig. 1.22. The effect of an intraventricular injection of 5 μg of noradrenaline on oxygen consumption, skin-temperature and body temperature. At 30 minutes before the catecholamine, animals received a subcutaneous injection of saline (open circles) or propanolol 0·5 mg/kg (closed circles). (Handley and Spencer, *J. Physiol.*)

application. For example, when Avery (1972) implanted a cannula in the medial preoptic area of the hypothalamus of rats, injections of the cholinomimetic drug, carbachol, raised core-temperature at an ambient temperature of 24°C, presumably by activating a heat-production centre, but at an ambient temperature of 35°C they had no effect.

Escape into Blood. In this connexion it must be appreciated that substances injected into the cerebrospinal fluid pass quite rapidly into the blood, so that a systemic action, in addition to a central one, may confuse the issue. For example, Handley and Spencer (1972) found, in the mouse, that intraventricular noradrenaline caused hypothermia at an ambient temperature of 15°C and hyperthermia at 36°C; however, when the peripheral effects of any escaping noradrenaline were blocked by intravenous propanolol, a β-blocker, hypothermia was observed at both low and high ambient temperatures, suggesting that a heat-dissipation centre, sensitive to noradrenaline, was active at all ambient temperatures. Thus the hyperthermia at high ambient temperatures was due to the escaped noradrenaline which stimulated metabolic rate, and thus reduced the effective intensity of any centrally induced hypothermia. The striking effects of intraventricular noradrenaline at an ambient temperature of 20°C are shown in Fig. 1.22. O_2-consumption is reduced, skin-temperature rises and core-temperature falls, effects that are sustained in the presence of propanolol.

Intracerebral Injections

A more precise localization of the applied transmitter can be achieved by implanting a cannula with its tip in a specific region of the brain, as in Avery's (1972) studies, or by the use of 5-barrelled electrodes inserted close to single neurones, the transmitter being ejected by micro-iontophoresis into the medium surrounding the neurone from which records are made (Hori and Nakayama, 1973).

Push-Pull Cannula

Finally, the release of transmitter in response to thermal changes may be measured, either by withdrawal of cerebrospinal fluid from the ventricles, or by the push-pull type of concentric cannulae described by Myers (1970) that permit the localized perfusion of a site in the brain with subsequent analysis of the outgoing fluid. As illustrated by Fig. 1.23, flow of fluid passes down the inner cannula and out of the concentric surrounding one; the fluid is pushed in by one syringe and sucked out by another, the syringes being arranged with their plungers back to back, so that a push on the injection syringe causes an equal suction on the withdrawal tube, and thus no changes in pressure are caused by the perfusion.

Biogenic Amines: Monkey

Using the latter method, and connecting push-pull cannulae to a pair of monkeys in such a way that the fluid emerging from the one animal's brain passed into the second animal's brain (Fig. 1.24), Myers and Sharpe (1968) showed that, when one of the animals was cooled, the body-temperature of the recipient rose by 0·7°C within an hour; if the donor animal was warmed, the recipient's temperature fell by 0·4°C. Again, Myers and Chinn (1973) measured a release of noradrenaline from the cat's hypothalamus when the animal was heated, suggesting either the adrenergic activation of a heat-dissipation centre or an adrenergic inhibition of the heat-production centre. On

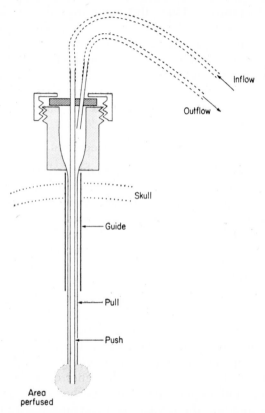

Fig. 1.23. A push-pull cannula for the localized perfusion of areas of the brain. Fluid can be pumped down the central cannula and withdrawn up the outer by a coupled syringe arrangement so that no changes in pressure are caused by the perfusion, and the area perfused is localized to some 1·5 mm in diameter. (Myers, *Physiol. Behav.*)

cooling a monkey, 5-HT was released from the PO/AH region, whilst warming had no effect on the release (Myers and Beleslin, 1971).

Rabbit. In the rabbit, intraventricular injections of 5-HT cause hypothermia, and of noradrenaline hyperthermia (Cooper *et al.*, 1965). If the anterior hypothalamic neurones, responsive to raised blood-temperature, were responsive to 5-HT (or exerted their effects by liberation of 5-HT in their near vicinity) we should expect this biogenic amine to increase the activity of these warm-sensitive neurones. By contrast, noradrenaline might be expected to increase the discharge of cold-sensitive neurones. In fact, Hori and Nakayama (1973), employing a 5-barrelled electrode, found that the discharges of warm-sensitive neurones in the preoptic area of the hypothalamus increased

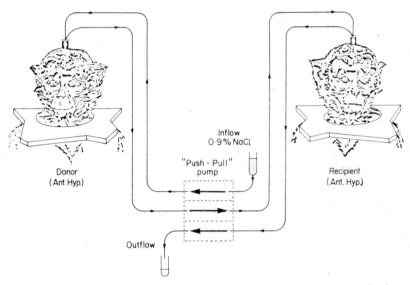

Fig. 1.24. Diagram of a unilateral "push-pull" transfusion between anterior hypothalamic areas of two unanaesthetized monkeys. Sterile saline (inflow) is pumped via the "push" cannula into the donor's anterior hypothalamus (ant. hyp.) and withdrawn at the same flow-rate via the "pull" cannula. This perfusate is then pumped by the withdrawal syringe to a corresponding hypothalamic site (ant. hyp.) in the recipient monkey via its "push" cannula. The perfusate is then drawn off at the same rate via the "pull" cannula to the outflow. The donor is either heated or cooled just before transfusion, and changes in the recipient's temperature are monitored after transfusion. (Myers and Sharpe, *Science*.)

with local application of 5-HT and were depressed by noradrenaline, whilst the discharges of cold-sensitive neurones were affected in the opposite manner. Both types of neurone were unresponsive to acetylcholine.

Amines as Neuronal Modulators

As to whether the thermo-responsive preoptic neurones actually liberate the amines in response to changes in temperature of the blood is by no means certain; the hypothalamus contains the enzymes for synthesis and breakdown of both noradrenaline and 5-HT, but the amines are largely concentrated in the terminals of nerves derived from other parts of the central nervous system, e.g. the mid-brain reticular system (Dahlström and Fuxe, 1964), so that it seems more likely that the activities of the thermosensitive neurones are modulated by these transmitters.

Cholinergic Pathways

By varying the sites of perfusion throughout the hypothalamus and midbrain, and measuring the amounts of acetylcholine released in response to heating or cooling a monkey, Myers and Waller (1973) concluded that there was a cholinergic pathway originating in the anterior preoptic region of the hypothalamus, transmitting signals for heat-production; in the posterior hypothalamic area there appeared to be another cholinergic system responsible for heat-production as well as one for heat-loss. On the basis of experiments involving the precise localization of a micropipette for injection of transmitters or their analogues, carried out by Avery and others, Hall and Myers (1972) have suggested that there are nicotinic (cholinergic) receptors in the posterior hypothalamus which, when activated, cause heat-production and hyperthermia, whilst in the anterior hypothalamus nicotinic receptors subserve heat-loss and hypothermia.

Neuronal Model

It is doubtless futile at present to attempt to develop a consistent scheme of the neuronal arrangements that operate temperature regulation in the hypothalamus, even when a single species is considered. Basically, however, a simple scheme of synapses like that of Fig. 1.25 may be postulated; warm-stimuli converge on synapse A, which causes discharges to synapse C, leading to heat-dissipation; on the basis of reciprocal innervation, the heat-production centre could be inhibited at synapse D. In a similar way a cold-stimulus, acting at synapse B, would activate the heat-production centre and inhibit the heat-dissipation centre. The question would be to decide where the biogenic amines, 5-HT and noradrenaline, exert their opposing influences, and the role of cholinergic transmitters. If any of the proposed schemes may be said to be successful in interpreting many of the experimental findings it seems to be that of Myers and Yaksh (1969) based on their studies on the micro-injection of putative transmitters at some 86 sites in the hypothalamus. According to this, 5-HT-containing cells in the anterior hypothalamus are activated by cold to release 5-HT, which activates a cholinergic pathway to the heat-production centre. When noradrenaline-containing cells are activated by warming, the 5-HT-cholinergic pathway is inhibited, thereby suppressing the heat-production pathway. This suppression permits a second cholinergic pathway to activate an efferent heat-dissipation pathway, which may be tonically active through impulses derived from other parts of the nervous system.*

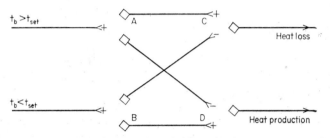

Fig. 1.25. A simple model of temperature regulation by the hypothalamus. When the body temperature (t_b) exceeds the set-point temperature (t_{set}) warm stimuli converge on synapse A, which causes discharges to synapse C and heat-dissipation. At the same time inhibitory influences from A act on D, and heat-production is reduced. When t_b is less than t_{set} the reverse response occurs. (After Cremer and Bligh, *Brit. Med. Bull.*)

Bacterial Pyrogens

The fever caused by bacterial infections is due, as we have seen, to the production of specific compounds by the bacteria, called pyrogens. These may have a direct action, or may stimulate leucocytes to release their own pyrogens. The site of action of pyrogen is the anterior hypothalamus, so that injections of preparations of pyrogen into the hypothalamus tissue, or into the adjacent cerebrospinal fluid, will cause fever.† The effect is apparently to change the set-point of the temperature-control mechanism rather than to excite, directly, the heat-production mechanism, or inhibit the heat-dissipation centre. Thus the effect of the pyrogen depends greatly on the environmental temperature at which it is injected; at neutral temperature there are both increased heat-production and reduced heat-loss, but at high ambient temperature the fever is produced almost entirely by diminished heat-loss, with little increase in heat-production.

* Jell (1974) has discussed the model of Myers and Yaksh and that of Bligh *et al.* (1971) in the light of his own studies on cats, employing a multi-barrelled electrode system that permitted recording from single units under the influence of locally applied drugs.

† *Shigella dysenteriae* pyrogen is effective when given systemically, e.g. intravenously, as well as into the ventricle or hypothalamus (Feldberg *et al.*, 1973).

Site of Action. As to the actual point of attack of the pyrogen, we may envisage an increased sensitivity of the temperature-sensitive primary sensors of the PO/AH; and this view finds support from Wit and Wang's (1968b) studies of single units. They found that pyrogen consistently reduced the thermal responses of Type IA neurones, i.e. those that required a change of hypothalamic temperature to respond; aspirin returned the responses to normal (Fig. 1.26). According to Nakayama and Hori (1973) pyrogen also increased the firing-rate of cold-sensitive units in the mid-brain reticular formation.*

Fever as a Mechanism of Resistance. It has very frequently been claimed that the elevated temperature during many infections is a purposive response, or defence mechanism, to combat the micro-organisms. "Fever is the mighty engine which Nature brings into the world for the conquest of her enemies". As Bennett and Nicastri (1960) have argued, however, to prove this in any instance we must show that the capacity of the organism to multiply is prejudiced by raising the body-temperature from, say, 36° to 42°C, or show that the body's resistance is improved in some way. In fact, critical examination of any given claim leaves little sound evidence in favour except, perhaps, with the beneficial effects of "fever therapy" in gonococcal and some other infections; thus gonococci are certainly sensitive to temperature, one of 41°C being lethal, but here one must be careful since gonococcal urethritis and ophthalmitis are usually non-febrile diseases.

Prostaglandins

The prostaglandins are lipid molecules that may be described as local hormones (Vol. 2). The fever caused by bacterial pyrogen is associated with release of prostaglandin (PGE_1) into the cerebrospinal fluid, having presumably been released from the adjacent hypo-thalamic region in response to the pyrogen (Feldberg and Gupta, 1973). Microinjection of PGE_1 into the anterior hypothalamus caused fever in rabbits and this was brought about, like that of pyrogen, by a change in set-point since, in the cold, the fever was associated with increased heat-production but in the warm by reduction in evaporative and dry heat-losses with no change in heat-production. Stitt (1973) showed, moreover, that the anterior hypothalamic area retained its heat-sensitivity during pyrogen fever, since warming this region attenuated the fever whilst cooling augmented it.

* According to Eisenman (1969) it is the interneurones of the hypothalamus that are affected by pyrogen, which would thus modify the responses of the primary temperature-sensitive units to altered temperature or to synaptic inflow from peripheral receptors.

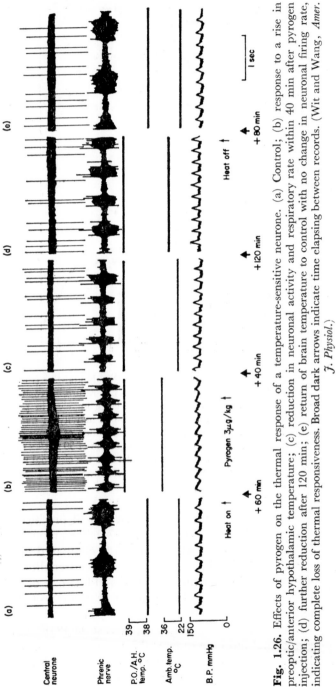

Fig. 1.26. Effects of pyrogen on the thermal response of a temperature-sensitive neurone. (a) Control; (b) response to a rise in preoptic/anterior hypothalamic temperature; (c) reduction in neuronal activity and respiratory rate within 40 min after pyrogen injection; (d) further reduction after 120 min; (e) return of brain temperature to control with no change in neuronal firing rate, indicating complete loss of thermal responsiveness. Broad dark arrows indicate time elapsing between records. (Wit and Wang, *Amer. J. Physiol.*)

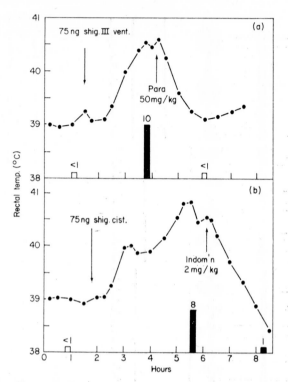

Fig. 1.27. The effects of pyrogen on the release of prostaglandin-like (PGE$_1$) activity into the cerebrospinal fluid of the cat. The rise in temperature in response to intra-ventricular *Shigella* pyrogen is accompanied by a large increase in prostaglandin activity. The heights of the columns are the PGE-like activity in mg/ml of CSF. In the upper diagram, the first arrow indicates the injection of 75 mg pyrogen into the third ventricle, and second an intraperitoneal injection of 50 mg/kg paracetamol. In the lower diagram 75 mg of pyrogen was injected into the cisternal magna at the first arrow and at the second 2 mg/kg indomethacin was given. (Feldberg *et al.*, *J. Physiol.*)

Direct injection of PGE$_1$ into the ventricles will produce a hyper-thermic response (Milton and Wendlandt, 1971); the amounts required are of the order of a few picograms $(10^{-12}$ g) compared with micro-grams required for the amines, such as 5-HT, adrenaline and nor-adrenaline. It is possible that the action of 5-HT is one of promoting synthesis and release of prostaglandin rather than a direct transmitter action in the hypothalamus.

In Fig. 1.27 the effects of pyrogen on release of PGE$_1$-like activity into the cerebrospinal fluid are shown; the curves illustrate the changes in rectal temperature of the cat, and the heights of the columns indicate

PGE_1-like activity in the cerebrospinal fluid. The rise in temperature in response to intraventricular *Shigella* pyrogen is accompanied by a large increase in prostaglandin activity; paracetamol, an inhibitor of prostaglandin synthesis, reduces rectal temperature and brings the PGE_1-like activity back to its original very low amount (Feldberg *et al.*, 1973).

Antipyretics. It has been known for a long time that salicylates, such as aspirin, reduce the body-temperature when this has been raised in fever but that they do not reduce the normal body-temperature The explanation for this contrasting behaviour was provided by Vane (1971) who showed that aspirin and paracetamol inhibited the synthesis of prostaglandins.

BEHAVIOUR

Conscious awareness of cold or heat is clearly man's best aid in adapting to thermal stress; if he feels cold he will put on more clothes, avoid draughts, slap his arms, and so on; in a similar way we may infer that the huddling of domestic animals is a response to an awareness of discomfort presumably involving cortical activity. This awareness of thermal stress is brought about by peripheral temperature-receptors, as well as by the activities of temperature-sensitive neurones in the hypothalamus, but the relative importance of the two sources of information is a matter of dispute. The operation of both factors is easily demonstrated by altering a subject's core-temperature by immersion in a bath for a prolonged period, and determining his sensation when he places his arm in a bath of cool or hot water. If the subject has been made hypothermic, with a low core-temperature, then a low temperature of 17°–30°C is disagreeable and a warm one of 37°–47°C is agreeable; by contrast, if he is hyperthermic, the warm temperature of 37°–47°C becomes disagreeable and the cool one agreeable (Cabanac and Chatonnet, 1968).

EEG-Arousal

When Gale and his colleagues cooled or warmed the baboon's preoptic hypothalamic region they observed typical "arousal" reactions on cooling, and a tendency to lethargy on warming the hypothalamus. The arousal reaction, or its opposite, may be recognized in the electro-encephalogram (EEG), the record of potential changes taking place at the surface of the brain; during sleep or drowsiness the EEG exhibits typical synchronized waves, and local warming of the PO/AH region produces these typical EEG sleep patterns in cats (Roberts and Robinson, 1969).

Poikilothermia

In poikilothermic animals, such as lizards, behavioural responses are the only ones possible; and it is remarkable how, by basking in the sun, and so on, these animals may maintain a steady temperature.

The Set-Point Hypothesis

The idea that the changed body-temperature resulting from pyrogen, exercise, or sleep, can be described in terms of an altered set-point has not been universally accepted. So far as the hyperthermia of exercise is concerned, this was first described by Nielsen (1938) who showed that working human subjects stabilized their core-temperatures at a value that was related to the level of exercise and was largely independent of ambient temperature; and this suggested a raised set-point. However, Hammel (1968) argued that the set-point would, on physiological grounds, be more likely to be lowered, thereby tending to mitigate the hyperthermia of exercise, which might otherwise be fatal. Thus the high temperature of exercise occurs *in spite of* a lowered set-point. Cabanac *et al.* (1971) have made use of their finding that a human subject will select a comfortable temperature for his hand that is strictly governed by his core-temperature. They argued that a change in set-point would be reflected in a change in the relation between core-temperature and comfortable temperature, so that, for example, if the set-point had been lowered by exercise, the subject would choose, at a given core-temperature, a lower hand-temperature as being the more comfortable. In fact, when subjects were asked to adjust the temperature of a water-jacketed glove so as to feel most comfortable under different conditions, exercise exerted no influence except in so far as it altered core-temperature, the relation between core-temperature and comfortable temperature being quite unchanged by exercise. In support of this finding, which suggests that in exercise there is no change in set-point, Cabanac *et al.* quote the work of Chatonnet *et al.* (1965) in which dogs were immersed in water, their core- and skin-temperatures being both controlled. The transition from remaining still in the water to vigorous swimming did not change the threshold temperature for panting.

ADRENAL AND THYROID GLANDS

The circulatory and sweating adjustments to a heat-load are largely mediated by the central nervous system, and the same is true of the shivering in response to cold. In lower animals, where chemical thermogenesis, with and without shivering, constitutes an important

adjustment to a low ambient temperature, the general level of metabolism of the body as a whole can increase in response to cold, and
this level is controlled predominantly by hormonal mechanisms,
notably the thyroid, secreting the hormone thyroxine and its relatives,
and the adrenal gland, the medullary hormones adrenaline and
noradrenaline being definitely involved.

Adrenal Secretions

The structure and main functions of the adrenal gland have already
been described in some detail (Vol. 2) and we have only to recall that
the hormones secreted by the medulla of this organ in response to
immediate stresses are adrenaline and noradrenaline; in man and
many other mammals adrenaline is the principal hormone; noradrenaline is the sympathetic transmitter and since, during stress, the
sympathetic system is activated, this means that the hormones of the
adrenals cooperate with the nervous mechanisms in producing the
appropriate responses.

Thyroid Secretions

The thyroid gland has so far not been described, and this will be
left to a supplement to this chapter; suffice it to say at this point that
its secretion, thyroxine, is an iodine-containing compound, and the
level of this in the blood exerts a powerful influence on the intensity
of metabolism of the cells of the body. As with so many endocrine
glands, the thyroid is activated by the pituitary through a trophic or
stimulating hormone—TSH—whilst the release of this hormone is
determined by a releasing factor, or releasing hormone, TSH-RF or
TSH-RH, liberated by the hypothalamus. Thus the location of the
temperature-regulating centres in the hypothalamus provides an
ideal arrangement both for the nervous activation of thermoregulatory
mechanisms—e.g. vasoconstriction through the vasomotor centre—and
for the hormonal activation of metabolism.

Activation of the Thyroid by Cold

Because of the powerful influence thyroxine exerts over the metabolic
rate, the thyroid gland has for long been considered as an important
gland in the response to cold; it is certainly of interest that it is only
in the homeotherm that injections of thyroxine will increase the
metabolic rate*; also that during hibernation the gland has a characteristically different histological appearance.

* In adult poikilotherms thyroxine has no influence on metabolic rate; in larval forms,
e.g. the tadpole, thyroxine accelerates metamorphosis, and an intact gland is necessary for
this transformation.

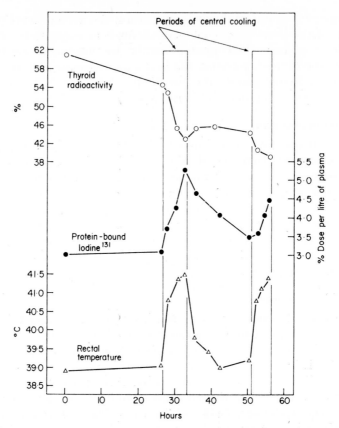

Fig. 1.28. The effect of cooling the preoptic area in a goat. The animal was given radioactive ^{131}I a few days before the experiment, which had become incorporated in its thyroxine. Stimulation of the hypothalamus by cooling causes a fall in the radioactivity of the thyroid gland, as thyroxine is released, and an increase in the plasma protein-bound I^{131} activity. Note that, as the central cooling occurred, the animal began to shiver and the rectal temperature increased. (Andersson *et al.*, *Acta physiol. scand.*)

Hypothalamic Cooling. Support for the importance of thyroxine in mediating thermogenesis was provided by Andersson's experiments on the goat. If an animal is given radioactive iodide—^{131}I—a few days before the experiment, its thyroxine becomes labelled with the isotope, and the radioactivity of the gland is a measure of the amount of thyroxine in it, whilst the radioactivity of the circulating blood is a measure of the concentration in this fluid, especially if only the protein-bound ^{131}I is measured, i.e. by dialysing the blood against a saline medium and analysing the blood, any free iodide and the small amount of free thyroxines being carried away in the dialysate. Fig. 1.28 shows the effects of cooling the preoptic region of the hypothalamus; as a result of the lower temperature, shivering ensued and the animal's rectal temperature increased rapidly; at the same time the protein-bound ^{131}I in the plasma rose, and the radioactivity of the thyroid gland, measured with an external counter placed over the gland, showed a corresponding fall. The local cooling was carried out by implanting a "thermode" in the hypothalamus, i.e. a piece of metal through which cold water could be circulated from outside. When the same region was warmed, then it was possible to inhibit the normal shivering-response to exposing the animal to cold and prevent the rise in blood-^{131}I that would have occurred. When the preoptic region was selectively damaged by passing a strong electric current through it, the thyroid responses to cold were abolished. Andersson concluded from his studies that the heat-loss centre exerted a tonic inhibition of the thyroid, an inhibition that was released by cooling of the blood flowing through the centre, or by nervous afferent discharges from the cooled skin. Since the thyroid is not activated directly, we may assume that the neurones that secrete the TSH releasing factor are maintained in a state of tonic inhibition, and that this is released by cold. As we have seen, it is possible to record from cold-sensitive neurones in the hypothalamus; some of these show a tonic discharge at normal temperature.

Working on conscious baboons with thermodes implanted in the PO/AH (Fig. 1.29), Gale et al. provoked a typical response to cooling, namely shivering, peripheral vasoconstriction, and a rapid rise in core-temperature; the protein-bound iodine in the blood, presumably representing thyroid hormone, rose and reached a peak within 3·5 hr of the onset of cooling. The authors noted, however, that increased thyroid activity was not always a result of pre-optic cooling, although the other responses, such as peripheral vasoconstriction, were present.

Man's Response to Cold. In spite of these demonstrations of the activation of the thyroid gland by cold, the role of the gland in the physiological response has been questioned. Thus Wilson et al. (1970) showed that, in man, acute exposure to cold for 3 hr at −5° to +2°C caused no change in the blood thyroxine nor yet in the concentration of TSH, whereas there were increases in plasma cortisol and urinary catecholamines, indicating activation of the adrenal gland.*

* Eastman et al. (1974) exposed human subjects, staying in Antarctica, to a mean air-temperature of 6·6°C in a cold-room for four days. There was a significant rise in blood tri-iodothyronine (T_3, p. 77) by the second day, which returned to pre-exposure level within 2 days of return to a normal environment. The rise in thyroxine (T_4) was slower but returned to normal at the same time.

Altered Thyroxine Metabolism. There is a considerably augmented excretion of thyroxine in the bile and faeces of rats exposed to
cold, but when these losses are compared with the additional secretion
it is found that there is actually a *deficiency* of thyroxine in the circulating
blood in the cold-exposed animal, so that the increased metabolism

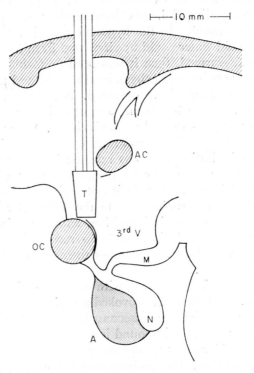

Fig. 1.29. A diagram of the position of the thermode in the mid-sagittal hypothalamus of conscious baboons. AC, anterior commissure; T, thermode; OC, optic
chiasma; M, mammillary body; A, adenohypophysis; N, neurohypophysis; 3rd V,
third ventricle. (Gale *et al., Amer. J. Physiol.*)

must be due to the liberated catecholamines rather than thyroid
activity. We may assume that the increased secretion of the thyroid,
caused by cold, occurs as a result of a positive feedback stimulus
resulting from an increased *elimination* of thyroxine, caused by the cold
(Galton and Nisula, 1969).

In their studies on the pig, when they cooled both the cervical cord
and hypothalamus, Evans and Ingram (1974) concluded that, because
of its transitoriness, the rise in circulating thyroxine following cooling

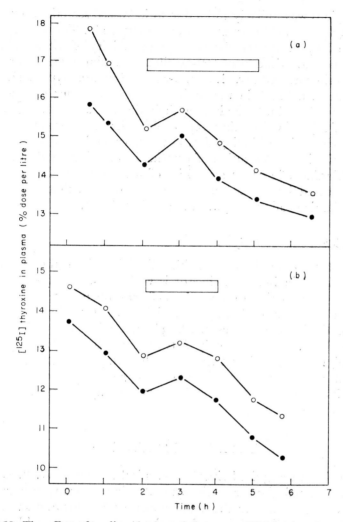

Fig. 1.30. The effect of cooling the hypothalamus to 10°C in the pig on the disappearance of total radioactivity (open circles) and radioactivity after removal of free iodide (closed circles). The ^{125}I thyroxine was injected 15 hr before the start of the experiment. The bars indicate the periods of cooling. (Evans and Ingram, *J. Physiol.*)

these regions was unlikely to be due to increased secretion, but rather to altered metabolism or distribution in the body. This seemed to be confirmed by measuring the fall in radioactivity of the plasma after an intravenous injection of ^{125}I-labelled thyroxine some 15 hr before the experiment. As Fig. 1.30 shows, cooling the hypothalamus to 10°C caused a break in the decline in concentration; such a break would be reflected in a rise in total thyroxine in the blood. The mobilization of thyroxine resulting from cooling the brain or cord could be due to release from binding sites in the liver, or it could be due to a general rise in concentration of proteins in the blood with the consequent binding of greater quantities of the hormone; such a rise in proteins could be the consequence of the diuresis that accompanies hypothalamic cooling (Hayward and Baker, 1968).

Thyroid-Adrenal Relations

It must be emphasized that neither the adrenal nor the thyroid can be considered in isolation, since it is well established that thyroxine sensitizes the organism to the actions of noradrenaline and adrenaline, so that a great deal of the thyroid activity can be blocked by administering anti-adrenergic drugs such as phentolamine. In fact it has been argued that the thyroid only acts through the body's adrenergic mechanisms, but this is not true since, by complete blockage of these, it is not possible to make the animal hypothyroid, i.e. one cannot reduce its metabolic rate below the normal euthyroid level.

The Adrenal Mechanism

It has been recognized since the classical studies of W. B. Cannon that the adrenal gland and the sympathetic nervous system together play a dominant role in the acute responses to cold; and subsequent studies of metabolism of tissues have shown that the adrenal hormones have an excitatory effect on both fat and carbohydrate metabolism. For example, treatment of isolated fat cells with noradrenaline increases the breakdown of fat—lipolysis—providing free fatty acids available for entry into the tricarboxylic acid cycle. In the liver, adrenaline stimulates the breakdown of glycogen—glycogenolysis—an action, like that on lipolysis, which is mediated by the "second messenger", cAMP (Vol. 2). The immediate metabolic response to cold may be regarded, then, as a part of the adrenal-sympathetic "fight or flight" response to an emergency.

Hypothalamic Cooling

Andersson *et al.* (1963) showed that, when they cooled the pre-optic region of the hypothalamus in the goat, there was increased urinary excretion of adrenaline and noradrenaline, that of adrenaline preponderating. More recently, Gale *et al.* (1970) have shown that cooling this region in the baboon produces the expected thermo-regulatory reactions, such as peripheral vasoconstriction and shivering,

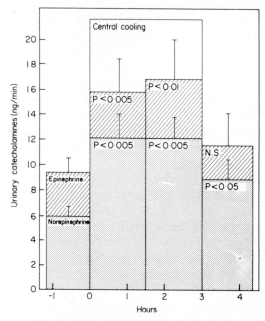

Fig. 1.31. The effect of cooling the preoptic anterior hypothalamus in the conscious baboon on the release of catecholamines in the urine. (Limits indicate the stand and error.) (Gale *et al.*, *Amer. J. Physiol.*)

whilst the urinary excretion of free catecholamines is considerably increased; as Fig. 1.31 shows, the increase occurs in both adrenaline and noradrenaline, suggesting both adrenal secretion and liberation from adrenergic nerve terminals. On warming the same region Proppe and Gale (1970) obtained a 35 per cent decrease in O_2-consumption, cutaneous vasodilatation and lethargy, associated with a fall in core-temperature of as much as 1·9°C, and a diminished urinary excretion of catecholamines. Thus it would seem that raising blood-temperature in hyperthermia activates hypothalamic neurones, causing them to suppress adrenal medullary excretion and thus to act as a brake on metabolic rate.* In essentially similar studies on the pig, Baldwin *et al.* (1969) found that cooling the animal caused increased urinary output of catecholamines, mainly noradrenaline, this time; when they cooled the hypothalamus the effect depended strongly on the ambient temperature, so that at 35°C, for example, there was no increase.

Long-Term Adaptation to Cold-Stress

Of special interest is the involvement of catecholamines, in particular noradrenaline, in the long-term adaptations to cold stress. It has been briefly indicated that in many animals the metabolic response to acute cold may be divided into a shivering and non-shivering thermogenesis, the latter being manifest when an animal is curarized. The metabolic origin of this non-shivering thermogenesis is uncertain; the liver seems to have been excluded and it may well be that fatty tissue provides the greater part. In the animal maintained in its normal environment without severe cold-stress, the non-shivering response is small or in some species non-existent. When a rat is adapted for a long period to cold, then, as indicated earlier, it shows an adaptive increase in metabolic rate, which is not generated by shivering, so that when it is brought from its cold environment into a thermally neutral one its metabolism remains high. It seems that, in this cold-adapted state, it has switched its thermogenic mechanism from the shivering, to the non-shivering, type; and it further appears that this is accompanied by a shift from a predominantly adrenaline-mediated to a noradrenaline-mediated response, i.e. a switch from adrenal medulla to sympathetic nervous system.

Non-shivering thermogenesis may be studied in the newborn and early infantile animal where it occurs without any preliminary cold-adaptation; as the animals get older, the non-shivering thermogenesis gives way to the shivering type. That this non-shivering calorigenesis is mediated by noradrenaline is made probable by Fig. 1.32 which shows the decrease in the calorigenic response of rats to an injection of noradrenaline as they increase in weight. As the animal ages, the sympathetic mechanism is replaced by motor nerve activity.

Multilocular Fat. The involvement of fat in the noradrenaline-sensitive metabolism is suggested by many experiments, in particular the function of the so-called multilocular or brown fat originally described as the "hibernating organ" (Vol. 1). There is little doubt that this fat, which is prominent in the newborn and usually disappears

---

* Cooling the hypothalamus caused a rise in excretion of 17-hydroxycorticosteroids (mainly hydrocortisone) whilst warming caused a decrease.

in the adult, is utilized preferentially in response to cold by the new-born, and it is interesting that the rise in temperature of this fat, normally occurring in response to cold-stress, is abolished if the animal is treated with pronethalol, a β-receptor inhibitor. When the O_2-consumption of the isolated fat cells is measured experimentally, this is increased by treatment with noradrenaline. That cyclic AMP is involved as a second hormone is suggested by the increase in lipolysis of brown fat caused by this or its dibenzoyl derivative, effects that may be mimicked by theophylline.

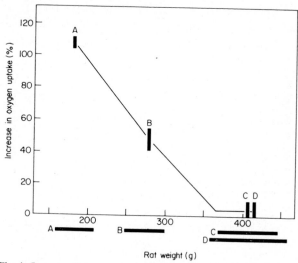

Rat weight (g)

Fig. 1.32. The influence of age on the calorigenic effect of noradrenaline in the rat. The weight of the rats is used as an indication of age. Bar represents S.D. of mean. (Carlson, from Himms-Hagen and Hagen, "Actions of Hormones on Molecular Processes", Wiley.)

Liver and Intestines. In most adult animals the source of the extra heat in non-shivering thermogenesis is not brown fat, and there has been much speculation as to the organ or organs most concerned. The liver has definitely been implicated by the experiments of Stoner (1973), who established, with the aid of implanted thermocouples in cold-acclimatized rats, that the temperature of this organ was always above that of the aortic blood, and nearly always above that in the portal vein, when the animals were maintained at 20°C. Raising the ambient temperature to 30°C, when non-shivering thermogenesis is abolished, led to a fall in liver-temperature, in spite of a fall in liver blood-flow. If the liver had not been active in the non-shivering thermogenesis, its temperature should have risen on raising the ambient temperature since the main loss of heat from this organ is through the body-wall. When the ambient temperature was raised above 37°C, then the liver-temperature did rise, but this was presumably because the heat-production could not be reduced further. The finding that the temperature of the blood passing from the aorta to the portal vein also increased suggests that the intestines are also a source of this extra heat.

Sympathetic and Adrenal Actions

In general, Leduc (1961) concluded that the newborn, or the cold-acclimatized, animal's response to cold-stress was mediated through the sympathetic nervous system, liberating noradrenaline at its nerve

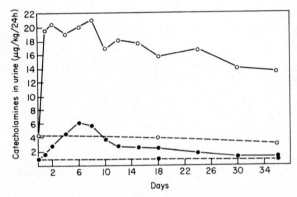

Fig. 1.33. The urinary excretion of catecholamines in rats maintained at 3°C (—) compared with that at 22°C (– –). Adrenaline is shown as filled circles, noradrenaline as open circles. (Leduc, *Acta physiol. scand.*)

terminals; cold-adaptation could be regarded as an increase in sensitivity of the sympathetically innervated target organs to the transmitter. The role of adrenaline, then, would not be great; only when the amounts of noradrenaline liberated began to fall off with continued cold-stress would the adrenal gland be excited to secrete adrenaline. The liberated noradrenaline would presumably exert a direct action on the cell's metabolic apparatus mediated through cyclic AMP. As Fig. 1.33 shows, there is a large increase in urinary excretion of noradrenaline when rats are maintained at 3°C, whilst that of adrenaline is much smaller. The sympathetic action is mediated through β-receptors so that the non-shivering thermogenesis is inhibited by propanolol, a β-blocker (Brück and Wünnenberg, 1965).

Changed Vascular Response

An increased excretion of, and sensitivity of the animal to, nor-adrenaline in cold-adaptation might be expected to result in con-striction of arterioles leading to reduced blood-flow through the tissues; if this reduction occurred in the skin it would serve to preserve heat, but might also permit freezing of the tissue, e.g. of the feet of an

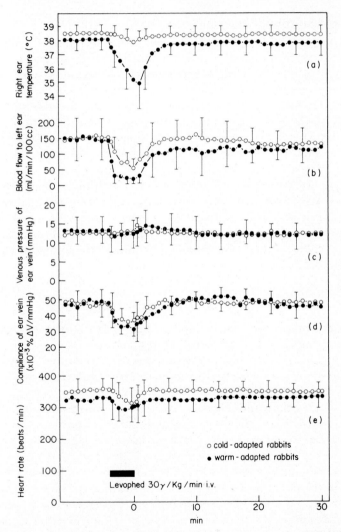

Fig. 1.34. The effects of noradrenaline on circulation parameters in cold- and warm-adapted rabbits. (Honda *et al.*, *J. appl. Physiol.*)

animal standing on ice. Thus we might expect, in the interests of cold-adaptation, a change in the effect of noradrenaline on the peripheral blood circulation. In the warm-adapted rabbit noradrenaline causes a constriction of the blood vessels in the ear with a resultant cooling; when the animal is adapted to cold, however, this cooling of the ear is much reduced even though the test is made at a warm temperature (Fig. 1.34).

Acute and Chronic Responses

To conclude, then, it seems that the acute response to cold in the adult non-adapted animal is predominantly mediated through nervous activation of the muscles; the release of adrenaline by the adrenal medulla promotes the increased energy consumption by the muscles and also favours, to a less significant extent, the metabolism of cells generally. Adrenaline, by increasing the tissues' sensitivity to thyroxine, would be able to exert this latter action. In cold-acclimatized, or infant, animals the response to cold is mediated through noradrenaline, liberated mainly from adrenergic nerve terminals; this neurohumour is able, as we have seen, to accelerate metabolism through activating adenylcyclase. Moreover, like adrenaline, its action is potentiated by thyroxine; and it is interesting that, in the cold-acclimatized rat, the thyroxine requirements are doubled and TSH levels are high, in fact the cold-acclimatized animal has much in common with the hyperthyroid state.

Hypothermia of Physical Exhaustion

Hypothermia is considered to be a cause of death after collapse from physical exhaustion in cold surroundings, and this may well be secondary to a fall in blood-sugar that impairs the operation of the hypothalamic neurones concerned in temperature-regulation; thus insulin-hypoglycaemia abolishes shivering in cold-exposed cats and dogs (Cassidy, Dworkin and Finney, 1925). Experimentally such a condition is, of course, difficult to establish, since severe exercise of itself does not lead to serious hypoglycaemia; however, Haight and Keatinge (1973b) exploited the fact that ethyl alcohol, when combined with heavy exercise, does cause a lowered blood-sugar by impeding gluconeogenesis in the liver (Krebs et al., 1969). When human subjects exercised for 2 hr at about 70 per cent maximum O_2-uptake, and were subsequently exposed to cold, after a dose of 28 ml of ethyl alcohol by mouth, their rectal temperatures fell to a mean of 34·5°C with virtually no increase in metabolic rate or shivering, indicating a failure of the thermoregulating mechanism, a failure that could be rectified by feeding glucose. As the authors point out, "the casual hill walker who stops in the open to drink spirits, without taking carbohydrate as well, runs a serious risk of developing hypoglycaemia which is liable to be followed by death from hypothermia."

Supplement I

THE SKIN

Structure

Heat is lost mainly from the surface of the skin so that the physiology of this portion of the human body is of interest in connexion with thermoregulation.

The generalized structure of skin is illustrated in Fig. 1.35; it may be divided into an outer *epidermis*, consisting of layers of epithelial cells, in various stages of being shed, and melanocytes containing

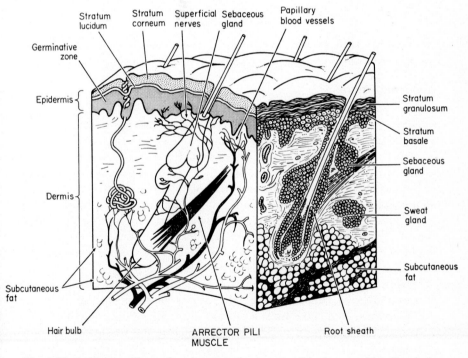

Fig. 1.35. A diagram illustrating the general structure of the human skin. (Lewis, in Davson and Eggleton, "Principles of Human Physiology", Churchill.)

pigment, and the *dermis*, containing the blood vessels, sweat glands, etc. The most superficial layer of the corium, or dermis, is prolonged into minute papillae over which the epidermis is moulded to give the finger-print. These papillae are of interest in regard to cutaneous touch reception since some of the receptors are in close relation with them (Vol. 5); as indicated earlier (p. 14) they also contain capillary blood vessels derived from a richly anastomosing plexus of vessels in the deepest parts of the corium.

Colour

The colour of the skin is determined by the degree of filling of the capillaries and the state of the blood in them; thus it is white when the capillaries have largely closed down through arteriolar constriction; when the capillaries have been filled during arteriolar dilatation, as in exercise, the skin is pink. When the capillaries are filled, but the flow is sluggish, the skin tends to be blue owing to the high proportion of deoxygenated haemoglobin in the blood.

Sweat Glands

These are of two kinds according to their embryological origin and the nature and mode of formation of their secretions.

Apocrine Glands

The *apocrine glands* are derived embryologically from the hair follicles, and are confined to limited regions of the body, e.g. the axilla (Fig. 1.36). As indicated in Fig. 1.37, which shows both types of gland and their relation to a hair follicle, the apocrine gland consists of a coiled tubular system; the duct usually opens into the inside of the pilary canal although some may open directly on to the surface of the epidermis. The coils of the glandular region are made up of single layered epithelial tubes. As their name implies, it has been considered that the mode of secretion is by the elimination of granules into the lumen of the tube by a process of exocytosis similar to the emptying of granules of pancreatic secretion (Vol. 1).

Granules. In the electron microscope, however, the characteristic granules do not concentrate at the apices of the cells, so that the granules may well have only a storage function, emptying their contents into the cytoplasm which then pass across the plasma membrane into the duct. The apocrine glands secrete a scanty creamy material, containing fat and protein; immediately on secretion this is said to be odourless, the characteristic odour developing as a result of bacterial action. The secretion in man results from emotional stress* and is thus not concerned with thermoregulation; as indicated earlier, in the horse, the apocrine secretions are responsible for the profuse sweating during the thermoregulation of exercise.

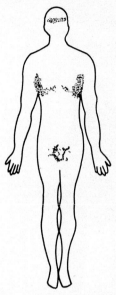

Fig. 1.36. The distribution of apocrine sweat glands in man. (Champion, "An Introduction to Biology of the Skin", Blackwell.)

Eccrine Glands

The *eccrine glands* are the most numerous being distributed over practically the whole skin; they are most numerous on the palms of the hands and soles of the feet, and they secrete in response to both thermal and emotional stresses. Essentially these glands are long unbranched epithelial tubes stretching from the dermis to the epidermis and opening on to the surface through shallow depressions, or pores, in the cristae cutis. The deep, dermal, portion is tightly coiled and enveloped by capillaries from the cutaneous plexus of blood vessels; the epithelium, one layer thick of high cuboidal cells, is invested with myoepithelial cells which may possibly contract and expel the contents of the coiled epithelial tube upwards, but this is not certain. The more superficial

---

* Until recently it has been generally believed that emotional sweating is largely confined to the palms of the hand, soles of the feet and axillae; however, Allen *et al.* (1973) have shown experimentally that the sweat-responses to solving mental arithmetical problems were distributed evenly over the body.

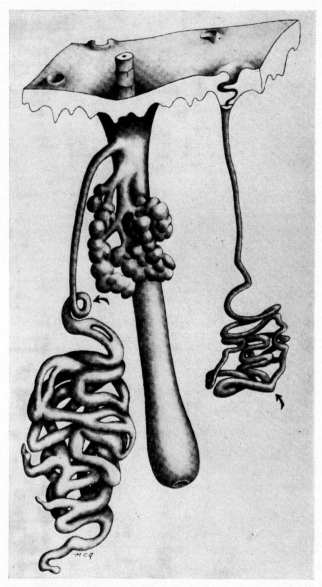

Fig. 1.37. Stereogram of an eccrine sweat gland on the right and an apocrine sweat gland on the left. Note the relation of the apocrine gland to the hair follicle. (Montagna, "Structure and Function of Skin", Academic Press.)

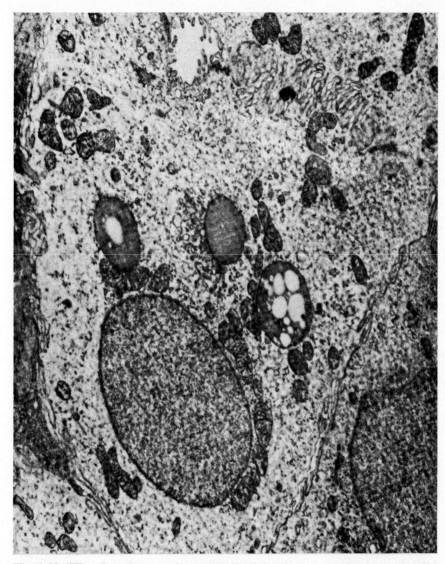

Fig. 1.38. "The ultrastructure of the epithelial lining from an eccrine sweat gland". An intracellular canaliculus can be seen at the top of the photograph with microvilli projecting into the lumen. On the right of the canaliculus can be seen a prominent terminal bar which effectively isolates the canalicular system from the intercellular cleft between the two epithelial cells and the luminal surface of the cells. The cytoplasm of the cell contains numerous mitochondria, lipid droplets and a Golgi zone. The cloudy appearance of the cytoplasm is characteristic of glycogen. (Ellis, in *"Structure and Function of Skin"*, Montagna, Academic Press.)

portion of the tube is distinguished from the deep coiled structure by its epithelial wall, which consists of two layers of low cuboidal cells; and it is considered that this region acts merely as a duct, carrying the fluid secreted by the deeper portion, which constitutes some two-thirds of the whole, up to the surface.

Epithelial Cells. The epithelial cells lining the coiled portion of the gland have typically interdigitated plasma membranes charac-teristic of secretory epithelia (Vol. 1); in certain regions the cell membranes and intercellular clefts come into relation with inter-cellular canaliculi, and it is here, presumably, that the transport of salt and water to form the primary secretion is brought about, the canaliculi emptying into the duct (Fig. 1.38). The cells constituting the inner layer of the duct have microvilli on their luminal surface whilst their lateral plasma membranes show elaborate interdigitations and tight junctions, so that it seems very likely that the duct zone is also capable of secretory activity, perhaps modifying the composition of the primarily secreted fluid as it passes to the surface of the skin (Sato and Dobson, 1970). The relations of the two types of gland to a hair follicle are shown in Fig. 1.37.

Sweat

Salt Concentration

Sweat contains the non-colloidal constituents of blood plasma, but the salt concentration is usually very much lower so that the fluid is hypotonic to the plasma; thus a concentration of sodium of 8 meq/litre is not unusual compared with one of 150 meq/litre in plasma.

Changes with Flow. The salt concentration varies with the rate of secretion, tending to rise with increased rate; and since increased rate is caused by raised body-temperature it has been argued that the composition is influenced by either skin- or core-temperature or by both. It could be argued that the primary secretion in the deep region of the gland is isotonic with plasma, and that reabsorption of salt occurs into the blood as the secretion passes along the gland and duct; increasing the rate of flow might limit the amount of absorption and thus lead to a high salt concentration. In this event, we might expect the salt concentration to extrapolate towards that in plasma at very high rates of sweating; as Fig. 1.39 shows, this does, in fact, occur.

Micropuncture. A more direct proof of the character of the initial secretion was provided by Schulz *et al.* (1965), who punctured the most proximal region of the human sweat gland and compared the fluid withdrawn from here with that emerging from the sweat-pore, and with a sample taken at the transition from the thick to thin sections of the duct. As Fig. 1.40 shows, osmolality and Na^+ and Cl^- concentrations are high proximally and have fallen to the values characteristic of sweat by the transition from the thick to the thin sections. The reabsorptive process was inhibited by strophanthidin, causing concentrations of Na^+ and Cl^- to rise. Since Sato *et al.* (1969) observed, in addition, a diminished rate of secretion of sweat on intradermal injection of ouabain, we may assume that active transport of Na^+ is

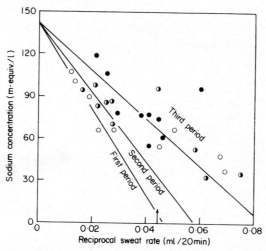

Fig. 1.39. The relationship between the sodium concentration in sweat and the reciprocal of the rate of sweating. Three consecutive periods are shown. Open circles first period, half closed circles second period and closed circles third period. The lines indicate best fit points to the left of the arrow which intercept at a common point supporting the concept of a high sodium primary secretion. (Bulmer and Forwell, *J. Physiol.*)

involved both in the production of the primary fluid and in its subsequent modification.

Relation to Salt-Balance. The concentration of salt in the sweat is closely bound up with the salt-needs of the whole body; under conditions of prolonged sweating the body may well become salt-deficient, and there is no doubt that the composition of the sweat is controlled in accordance with the general salt-retaining mechanisms of the body, i.e. it is controlled through the adrenal cortical hormone and linked to renal and intestinal salt-retaining mechanisms. Thus human subjects, unadapted to a hot climate, show a large increase in salt concentration as their sweat-rate increases; after adaptation, however, their salt concentration remains low. If, however, the adapted subjects are given adequate salt, the concentration at high sweat-rates remains high. Again, if a man is made salt-deficient without sweating, he produces a low-salt sweat immediately at the onset of exercise (Robinson and Robinson, 1954).*

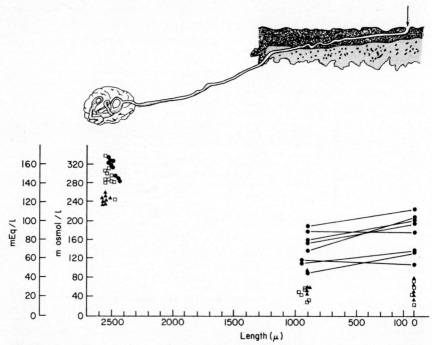

Fig. 1.40. Micropuncture studies of the ionic concentration of fluid from various parts of a human eccrine sweat gland. The osmolarity (circular symbols), the sodium concentration (square symbols) and the chloride concentration (triangles) are all high and similar to plasma values in the coiled portion of the duct, but samples taken from distal regions close to the skin show the characteristic low values associated with sweat. (Shulz *et al.*, *Pflüg. Arch.*)

An interesting feature of the chemical composition is the high concentration of urea, which on average is some 1·8 times that in plasma, and the ratio remains remarkably constant in spite of wide variations in sweat-rate (Schwartz *et al.*, 1953).

* In the cat the concentrations of Na^+ and Cl^- are comparable with those in plasma, and this may be associated with a shorter duct-segment than in humans (Brusilow and Munger, 1962). Treatment with aldosterone causes a decrease in Na^+-concentration and an increase in that of K^+ (Dobson and Slegers, 1971) whilst the sweat-rate is decreased. ADH reduces the sweat-rate induced by pilocarpine in the rat, an effect due to its antidiuretic type of action, rather than vasoconstriction, since octapressin PLV-2, with similar vasoconstrictive action to that of ADH but less antidiuretic activity, is less effective. The decreased secretion is accompanied by increased concentration of Na^+ (Quatrale and Speir, 1970).

Insensible Perspiration

At all temperatures there is a continuous loss of water by evaporation from the skin—the so-called *insensible perspiration*—this being due to the slow diffusion of water from the deeper to the superficial layers of the skin associated with a continuous slow basal secretion of sweat. It has been estimated that the loss due to diffusion of water through the epidermis, under average conditions of temperature and vapour pressure, amounts to some 85–170 ml/day, compared with a loss by insensible perspiration, without visible sweating, of some 33–500 ml/day. Similarly, the air leaving the lungs is saturated with water vapour so that, in all, there is a loss of about 600–700 g of water per day by this route, and this contributes to heat loss so that under basal conditions it amounts to about 25 per cent of the whole.

Anhidrosis

When the hand is immersed in water at 33–35°C for some 45 min, there is an inhibition of the sudomotor response to hyperthermia in the palmar surface, a phenomenon described as *anhidrosis*. This seems to be due to a swelling of the cells, or the protein matrix, of the epidermis surrounding the openings of the sweat ducts; at any rate if strong saline solutions are used the effect does not occur, the effect being inversely proportional to the concentration of salt in the water (Peiss *et al.*, 1956). There is no doubt that, on immersion in water, there is an initial rapid uptake of water by the stratum corneum. The effect is rapidly reversible on exposure of the skin to dry air, and so it is not due to an actual plugging of the ducts by cell debris.

Physiological Significance

As Brebner and Kerslake (1968) have shown, anhidrosis is much more rapid in onset when the subject sweats during submersion than when in thermoneutral water. We may assume that the phenomenon is of physiological importance since it tends to limit the sweat-secretion to those portions of the skin that are not wet, whether this wetness is due to immersion or to actual sweating. Thus Allan (1965) found that the mean sweat-rate of acclimatized human subjects in the last three hours of exposure to humid heat fell from 830 to 600 g/hr, whilst their body-temperatures remained constant, indicating that initially they were wasting some 230 g/hr.

Hair

The Follicle

Hairs are peculiar to mammals; they are dead structures composed of keratinized cells growing out of tubes of epidermis, the *hair follicles*, sunken into the dermis; it is the proliferation of a small mass of cells at the base of the follicle—the *matrix*—that gives rise to the hair, but it must be appreciated that the formation of new hair that accompanies the shedding of the old involves the new formation of a part of the old follicle, which degenerates after completion of the previous hair. The main regions of the active hair follicle are shown in Fig. 1.41. The hair is formed, essentially, by the proliferation of the matrix cells, which are pushed higher and higher. In the *keratogenous zone* the cells keratinize; here the cells become hyalinized, and distinct fibrils can be seen in their cytoplasm with the aid of polarized light. The cells keratinize first in the innermost layer of the follicle—*Henle's layer*—and thus form a sheath that determines the shape of the hair, the rest of which is made by keratinization of cells within this *Henle tube*. Above the keratogenous zone the hair is said to be mature. When the hair is complete, the phase of *anagen* is said to be over and *catagen* begins, the lower portion of the follicle degenerating to leave only a string of cells that constitute the germ for the new phase of anagen (Fig. 1.42). Pigmentation of the hair is brought about by melanocytes situated in relation to the follicle; these give pigment to the presumptive cells of the cortex and medulla of the hair.

Sebaceous Glands. Sebaceous glands are part of the hair follicle, and they empty their oily secretions—the sebum—usually into the pilary canal, although in some regions, e.g. in the eye-lids where they are called *Meibomian glands*, they open on to the surface of the skin. The gland is organized on an acinar basis, the acini being attached to a common secretory duct consisting of squamous epithelium continuous with the wall of the pilary canal.

Pilo-Erection

The erection of the hairs that contributes to thermal insulation is made possible by the *arrectores pilorum muscles*, smooth muscle strands that extend at an acute angle from the surface of the dermis to the *bulge*, a swelling on the side of the follicle just below the level of the sebaceous gland. This muscle is activated by the sympathetic division and accounts for the bristling of the hair in acute fear, rage, etc. In pulling the hairs erect they also pull the skin around the follicles giving rise to the elevations of "goose flesh".

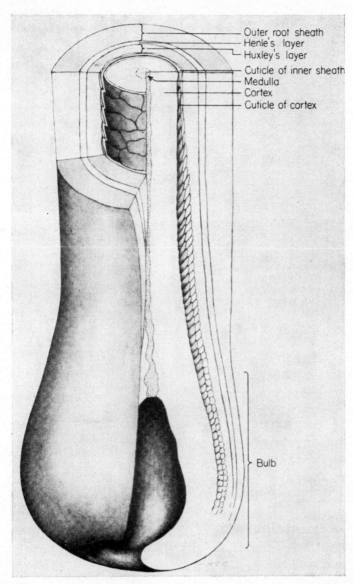

Fig. 1.41. Stereogram of the lower part of a hair follicle of man. The cellular details have been omitted, but the proportions and the relationships of the layers have been maintained. (Montagna, "Structure and Function of Skin", Academic Press.)

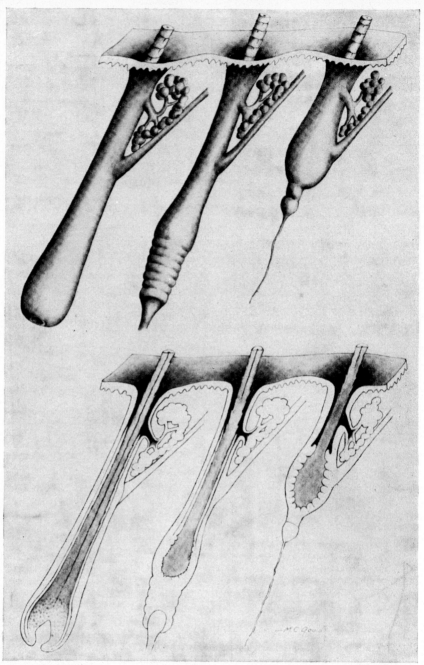

Fig. 1.42. Representation of three stages of the hair growth cycle, each seen in three dimensions, above, and cut longitudinally, below. On the left is an active anagen follicle; in the middle is a follicle in catagen; and on the right is a quiescent, or telogen, follicle. (Montagna, "Structure and Function of Skin", Academic Press.)

The Epidermal Barrier

Loss of water by the transepidermal route is very much less rapid than from an equal area of water, or from the skin denuded of its epidermis; the latter thus constitutes a barrier to the path of water. Such a restraint on water penetration is revealed, too, in the immunity of the deeper layers of the skin to osmotic lysis when the body is submerged for long periods in pure water, whilst the passage of many solutes, such as salts, is likewise restrained so that only under special conditions does the application of a medicament to the skin result in appreciable absorption into the underlying dermis and blood.

Layer of Keratinized Cells

Experiments in which layers of the epidermis have been removed, by applying cellophane tape and stripping away, have shown that the barrier remains until practically the whole of the stratum corneum— i.e. the thin coherent membrane of keratinized epidermal cells comprising the dead surface layer of the epidermis—has been removed; but the idea that there is a thin critical layer, just above the layer of living cells, responsible for the barrier, seems to be erroneous; and modern work implicates the whole of the 40–50 μ-thick layer of keratinized cells as the barrier, the viable layer beneath being highly permeable to solutes. The ultrastructure of the stratum corneum, as revealed by the electron microscope, suggests that it might, indeed, act as a barrier to diffusion; thus the cells, on moving up from the deeper layers, become differentiated, mitosis ceasing and synthesis of keratin filaments and keratohyalin granules taking place. These granules ultimately form a dense matrix for the keratin filaments. The synthetic apparatus of the cell, including the nucleus, ultimately disappears whilst "membrane coating granules" formed within the cell empty their contents by exocytosis on to the surface, forming a thick intercellular cement. Ultimately, then, the layer becomes a laminated structure of tightly packed overlapping cornified cells with a dense intercellular material.

Permeability

The permeability of the epidermis may be studied *in vitro* by excising, for example, the roof of a blister and using this as a membrane to separate two fluid-containing chambers; passage of solute from one chamber to the other, in unit time, allows the computation of a permeability coefficient. *In vivo* measurements may be made of the loss of solute from a reservoir on the surface of the skin, the rate of loss being, in fact, governed by diffusion through the stratum corneum, the remaining pathway to the blood in the dermis being so much less restricted.

Coefficients. In general, the permeability coefficients, whether carried out on dead skin *in vitro*, or living skin *in vivo*, are low and comparable with those encountered in cell exchanges, and suggest that diffusion through the epidermis is reduced in rate by quite a large factor, presumably because of the densely packed structure of the stratum corneum (Bettley, 1970). Thus Scheuplein and Blank (1971) compute that the effective diffusion coefficient for water passing through the stratum corneum is 5.10^{-10} cm^{2}sec^{-1}; this compares with

TABLE I

Permeability coefficients of skin for several solutes

Substance	Permeability (cm hr^{-1})
Water	0·5
Methanol	0·5
Ethanol	0·8
Octanol	52
Ethyl ether	15–17
Progesterone	1·5
Cortisone	0·010
Hydrocortisone	0·003

$2·5.10^{-5}$ cm^{2}sec^{-1} for diffusion of water in water and $6·2.10^{-11}$ cm^{2}sec^{-1} for diffusion of water in teflon. Comparison of the permeabilities of different types of molecule has shown that, within a series, lipid-solubility is important, so that octanol has a permeability coefficient of 52 cm hr^{-1} compared with 0·5 for methanol or H_2O (Table I).

Lipid-Solubility. The fact that lipid-solubility is important in diffusion through a layer that consists of tightly packed dead cells is surprising, since most cells lose their selectivity on death. We may assume, therefore, that the layer of material secreted by the "membrane coating granules", described by Matoltsy and Parakkal (1965), is mainly lipoid in character, thus favouring solubility of the lipid-soluble solutes in the layer and favouring passage. It is unlikely that the stratum corneum will have identical permeability characteristics with those of cell membranes, however, since the layer has a considerable degree of hydration under normal conditions, its water-content being some 0·92 g H_2O per g of dry-matter; and the modern view is that permeability is compounded of two main pathways, the lipid-pathway becoming more and more significant as lipid-solubility increases.

Surface-Active Agents. Surface-active substances increase the permeability of the skin, presumably by disrupting the tight structure; thus when a disc of stratum corneum was soaked in a solution of sodium laurate, there was an obvious expansion of the disc in the plane of the tissue; this could be due to a change from the α- to the β-configuration of the coiled keratin filaments, allowing more water to be taken up; this would both increase the area of the layer and increase its permeability.

Aprotic Solvents. Dimethylsulphoxide (DMSO), a so-called aprotic solvent, is used as a vehicle in which to dissolve a substance when applying it to the skin, with a view to increasing penetration; the increased permeability seems not to be due to damage to the stratum corneum but rather to the replacement of the water by DMSO, the character of the DMSO molecule being such as to leave the structure less compact in molecular terms, thereby favouring diffusion (Sweeney and Downing, 1970).

Penetration through the Appendages

The epidermis is not a uniform layer but is perforated by the hair follicles and sweat ducts (Fig. 1.43), so that some penetration of solute may well occur through these gaps in the stratum corneum; however, their area is small in comparison with the whole, namely about one thousandth, so that unless penetration through these structures is very much more rapid than through the remainder of the stratum corneum we need not expect the appendageal route to be significant. In fact, there was little change in permeability of many substances when the number of hair follicles included in the area of skin to be studied was varied; however, when permeability is highly restricted, as with cortisone and hydrocortisone, it is likely that the appendageal route acquires significance. Moreover, it is easy to show theoretically that the diffusion through the skin, at an early stage after application, can be much more strongly affected by the presence of high permeability shunts, than the steady-state diffusion.

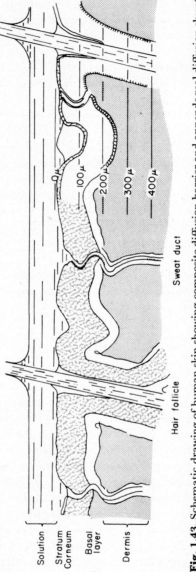

Fig. 1.43. Schematic drawing of human skin showing composite diffusion barrier and appendageal diffusion shunts. (Scheuplein and Blank, *Physiol. Rev.*).

Supplement II

STRUCTURE AND FUNCTION OF THE THYROID GLAND

Structure

In man and other higher vertebrates, the gland consists of two lobes lying on either side of the trachea below the larynx. The basic unit of structure is a single layer of cells—the follicular epithelium—encompassing a central mass of protein—the *colloid*—to form the follicle (Fig. 1.44). The follicles are some 15–100μ in diameter, and their individual epithelial cells rest on a basement membrane which constitutes a continuous investment. The whole gland is invested in a connective-tissue capsule which has extensions plunging into the depth of the tissue to divide it into lobules.

Vascularization. Arteries penetrate and ramify into capillary networks that surround each follicle. The vascularization is great so that the blood-flow is actually twice that of the kidney on a weight-basis. The capillaries belong to the so-called fenestrated type, the endothelial cells having attenuations to give the appearance of large pores some 600 Å across. A lymphatic network is also present but is more distant from the follicle than the blood-capillaries, so that the transport of the thyroid secretion to the tissues doubtless occurs through the blood capillaries.

Innervation

The gland is innervated by both the sympathetic, by way of the superior cervical ganglion, and the parasympathetic through the superior laryngeal nerve, a branch of the vagus (NX). It is generally believed that the innervation is primarily concerned with the control of the blood supply, the release of the hormone being determined by the thyrotrophic hormone, TSH, rather than nervous discharge.

Synthesis of Colloid

The epithelial cells of the follicles synthesize the colloid, which is a glycoprotein, *thyroglobulin*, within their cytoplasm, and eject it into the surrounding follicular space; the cells thus share many of the characteristics of exocrine cells of such tissues as the pancreas, i.e. cells that are primarily concerned with synthesis of enzymes associated with digestion. As we have seen, the enzymes are synthesized within the cells on the endoplasmic reticulum, and they accumulate within the cisternae of the Golgi apparatus where they become vesicles that

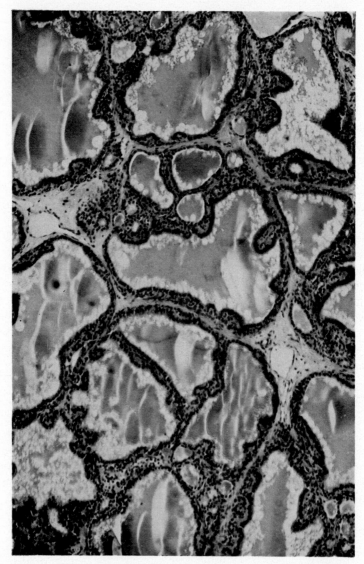

Fig. 1.44. The thyroid follicles of the human thyroid gland. Each follicle is composed of cuboidal epithelium forming a cavity filled with a coagulable fluid, the colloid. ×2500. (By courtesy of Anatomy Department, St Thomas's Hospital Medical School.)

finally mature into the microscopically visible secretory granules; in response to an appropriate stimulus the granules are ejected into the acinar space surrounding the exocrine cells by a process of exocytosis (Fig. 1.36, Vol. 1). In a similar way the epithelial cells of the thyroid exhibit the formation of vesicles that represent the synthesized colloid; when synthesis of colloid is provoked, as by giving goitrogenic agents such as propylthiouracil, then the cells become filled with vesicles, apparently taking origin in the Golgi apparatus.

Stimulus to Synthesis. The normal stimulus to liberation of the hormone, thyroxine, is through the thyrotrophic hormone TSH; when this is injected into an animal there is an immediate increase in the number of vesicles crowding the apices of the epithelial cells. It must be appreciated that the formation of colloid is to be regarded as a vegetative process, providing a store of material that is later to be employed by the gland in its endocrine function, i.e. of liberating the hormone, thyroxine, into the blood.

Thyroxine

The main active principle of the thyroid is, as we have said, thyroxine (T_4), an organic iodine-containing compound characterized by Harington as a tetra-iodinated phenolic ether with an alanine side-chain (Fig. 1.45).

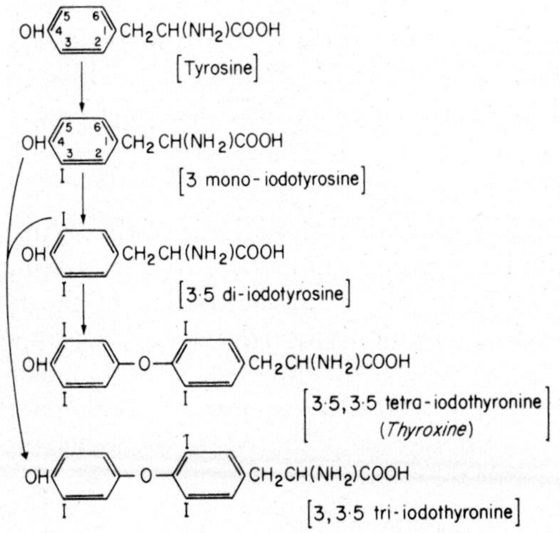

Fig. 1.45. The structures and synthetic pathway of the thyroid hormones. (Clegg and Clegg, "Hormones, Cells and Organisms", Heinemann.)

Other active compounds, present in much smaller amounts, are tri-iodothyronine (T_3),* di-iodothyronine (T_2) and mono-iodothyronine (T_1). In the gland these organic iodine derivatives are associated mainly with the colloid thyroglobulin in the follicles, but when liberated into the blood they are separated from the protein, so that the secretory process, whereby the gland exhibits its endocrine function, as opposed to its exocrine function of synthesis of colloid, involves the splitting off of thyroxine and its liberation into the blood.

Synthesis

The synthesis of thyroxine involves several steps, which have been elucidated by the use of the radioactive isotope of iodine, namely ^{131}I. When the radioactive iodine, Na ^{131}I, is injected into the blood it appears rapidly in the thyroid gland, and by appropriate measures its stages of entry into the precursors of thyroxine may be traced. The first stage consists in an active accumulation of the ion by the cells, the epithelial cells possessing the power of accumulating the ion intra-cellularly to concentrations many times that in the plasma. This process is best demonstrated in an animal treated with a goitrogenic drug that blocks the incorporation of I^- into organic compounds. Under these conditions there is a considerable uptake of I^- that exists as inorganic ion. In the normal animal the iodide taken up by the cells is rapidly incorporated into organic compounds. After oxidation of the iodide ion to iodine, the latter reacts with the tyrosine residues within the thyro-globulin molecules of the colloid, forming first mono-iodotyrosine (MIT) then di-iodotyrosine (DIT); two residues of DIT condense, as illustrated in Fig. 1.45, to form thyroxine (T_4), whilst tri-iodothyronine (T_3) is formed by condensing one MIT and one DIT.

Thyroglobulin

The remarkable feature of the synthesis of thyroxine is that it takes place within the large protein molecule, thyroglobulin, the iodination process consisting essentially of an iodination of the tyrosine residues within the protein molecule. Thyroglobulin is a protein of molecular weight 670,000, as computed from its sedimentation coefficient of 19 Svedberg units; it constitutes some 80 per cent of the gland's protein and the material so prepared is homogeneous, in the sense that it is not possible to separate fractions on the basis of their molecular weight.

---

* Weight-for-weight, T_3 is actually more effective than thyroxine (T_4), and its role is minor only because of the much smaller amounts present in the secretion.

Multiple Degrees of Iodination. When, however, more sensitive methods, based on the ionization properties of the molecule are used, such as gel-filtration on DAE cellulose, then fractions of differing iodine-nitrogen ratio are obtained, and this conforms with what one would expect if the thyroglobulin molecule were acting as the basis for synthesis of thyroid hormones. Thus each molecule of thyroglobulin contains some 16 residues of tyrosine, so that different degrees of iodination of these residues would modify the proportion of iodine to nitrogen in the protein molecule, and since the presence of an iodine atom in the *ortho*-position of the tyrosine molecule makes it much more acid, the degree of ionization of the total protein molecule will be affected by the number of iodine atoms in it. When thyroglobulin, extracted from glands, is treated with iodine, further iodination occurs, the iodine appearing mainly in tyrosine residues as DIT; smaller amounts are found as thyroxine and MIT, however.

Site of Iodination. As to whether the iodination of thyroglobulin takes place within the epithelial cell or within the lumen of the follicle, there is some doubt; the evidence adduced to support one or other contention is based on autoradiography, i.e. the detection of radio-activity in histological sections after injecting $^{131}I^-$ into the blood. In the normal animal this radioactivity seems to occur exclusively in the colloid of the follicle, but in animals where liberation of TSH was blocked, through hypophysectomy, radioactivity was confined to the cells. One thing seems certain, namely that synthesis of thyroglobulin and its subsequent iodination are independent processes, and it is possible that they occur at different sites.

Oxidation of Iodide. As to the mechanism whereby the stable iodide ion is able to react with organic compounds, it is established that the reaction involves the oxidation of I^- with hydrogen peroxide formed by the oxidation of glucose, catalysed by glucose oxidase:

$$Glucose + O_2 + H_2O \longrightarrow H_2O_2 + Glucuronic\ acid$$
$$H_2O_2 + 2I^- + 2H^+ \longrightarrow 2I + 2H_2O$$

the iodine liberated in the second reaction being in a highly reactive state that enables it to combine with tyrosine derivatives.

Splitting Away of Thyroxine

The synthesized thyroxine is a part of the thyroglobulin molecule and, as indicated earlier, it is stored extracellularly as the colloid in the thyroid vesicle. To be liberated from the gland the thyroxine molecules must be separated from thyroglobulin, and this involves the activity of protein-splitting enzymes, proteases. Experimentally this splitting has been achieved by a variety of protein-splitting enzymes, for instance those of the pancreas, or by proteases, extracted from the thyroid gland itself. In general, several proteases, as well as peptidases, have been extracted, and it is interesting that, when the thyroid was stimulated with TSH or methyluracil, the concentration of the peptidase, cysteinyl-tyrosinase, was diminished, as would be expected were thyroid activity accompanied by enzymatic splitting off of thyroxine and a concomitant loss of some of the enzyme during the process. Again, the proteolytic activity of thyroid slices *in vitro* was increased if, before removing the gland, thyroid-stimulating hormone had been injected into the animal.

Endocytosis of Colloid

When secretion of the thyroid gland is provoked by administering TSH, the liberation of thyroxine into the blood is accompanied by the appearance of large numbers of vesicles crowding the apical regions of the epithelial cells; this accumulation was, at one time, thought to

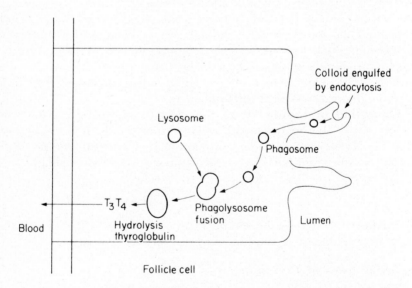

Fig. 1.46. Endocytosis of colloid. Colloid is engulfed by endocytosis and the droplets —phagosomes—appear at the apical zone of the cell. Pre-existing granules— lysosomes—containing proteolytic enzymes unite with the phagosomes to form phagolysosomes, and as a result of this, thyroxine is liberated. (Modified from Stanbury, *Erg. der Physiol.*).

represent synthesis of colloid within the cells, but it seems more likely that it represents the *absorption of colloid*, by endocytosis, into the epithelial cells. Within the cells the colloid could then be split by a protease to give free thyroxine, which would then diffuse into the extracellular space surrounding the follicle, where it would be taken up by the capillaries and transported to its target sites. Thus we may label the existing colloid in an animal's thyroid gland by feeding it with inorganic radioactive iodide, ^{131}I, and then block further synthesis by administering, say, thiouracil. Secretion of thyroxine is now provoked by injecting TSH, and it is found that the droplets appearing in the epithelial cells are radioactive, as indicated by radioautography. Thus the droplets are derived from the colloid and not synthesized *de novo* within the cell.

Phagolysosomes. We have earlier seen how many cells contain an intracellular digestive apparatus constituted by lysosomes, etc. (Vol. 1). The breakdown of ingested colloid to give free thyroxine is essentially an example of this. The colloid is engulfed, by endocytosis, and the consequent droplets—*phagosomes*—appear at the apical zone of the cell. Pre-existing granules—*lysosomes*—containing the proteolytic enzymes, move from the base towards the apex of the cell, and we may presume that they unite with the droplets—*phagosomes*—to form *phagolysosomes*; as a result of the interaction, the thyroxine is liberated and diffuses out of the cell (Fig. 1.46).

General Scheme

The basic process of incorporation of iodine into thyroglobulin is illustrated in Fig. 1.47; here the accumulation of inorganic I^-, and its conversion to organic I, are considered to take place within the lumen of the follicle, in close association with epithelial cells; liberation of thyroxine is represented as a hydrolysis, taking place within the lumen of the follicle rather than intracellularly, when T_4 and T_3 pass into the blood together with some inorganic I^- which may enter the blood or remain within the gland.

Iodide Pools

In this connexion we may note that biochemists speak of a "second iodide pool", meaning thereby a portion of the iodine in the gland that is apparently iodide, but differs from another pool of iodide in that it exchanges with ^{131}I injected into the blood much more slowly. It is considered that the first pool, exchanging rapidly with ^{131}I, is that brought into the cell and follicle by active transport, a process that can be blocked by competitive inhibitors, such as perchlorate, which have a high affinity for the postulated carrier in the active transport process. The second pool may well be the iodide liberated by the gland from its own organic compounds, as illustrated in Fig. 1.47; but it remains to be seen why it should differ from the first pool in its accessibility to blood-[131]I. It seems reasonable to suppose that the two pools occupy different sites within the gland.

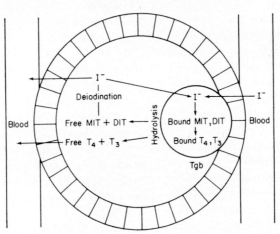

Fig. 1.47. A schematic outline of thyroid hormone biosynthesis. Iodide from the plasma is actively accumulated by the cells of the thyroid and oxidized to iodine, which then reacts with tyrosine residues to form mono-iodotyrosine (MIT) then di-iodotyrosine (DIT); two residues of DIT condense to form thyroxine (T_4) whilst tri-iodothyronine forms from one MIT condensed with one DIT. Tgb, thyroid-binding globulin. (Pitt-Rivers and Cavalierii, *In* "The Thyroid Gland", Vol. 1, Butterworth.

Carrier Proteins

We have seen that very few hormones are carried in a free condition in the blood; the nature of their molecules is such as to attract them strongly to protein molecules of the plasma, and it is in this "bound" condition that they are transported, sometimes on a special protein that has a specifically high affinity for the hormone and sometimes on a protein, such as serum albumin, whose main function is other than that of a carrier. Experimentally we may add thyroxine and other iodinated compounds, such as T_3, to a preparation of plasma and separate the constituent plasma proteins by such techniques as electrophoresis or ion-exchange chromatography; if the iodinated compounds have been labelled with radioactive ^{131}I, then it is easy to follow the fractions containing them. The major proteins of plasma capable of acting as carriers are three, namely an α-globulin called "thyroxine-binding globulin" (TBG); a rapidly migrating "pre-albumin" called thyroxine-binding prealbumin (TBPA); and serum albumin (HSA). Of these, TBG has a high affinity for T_4 and T_3, but its capacity, i.e. the number of moles taken up per unit weight of protein, is small compared with that of TBPA with, however, a lower affinity. Serum albumin has a low affinity but high capacity. Because of these differences, at normal levels of thyroid hormones in serum, TBG binds most of the circulating hormone, with TBPA coming next.

Binding. The binding is reversible, obeying the classical equilibrium conditions; so that it may be defined in terms of an affinity constant:

$$T + Carrier \rightleftharpoons T. Carrier$$
$$\frac{[T] \times [Carrier]}{[T. Carrier]} = K$$

As the equation shows, the level of free hormone in the blood will be governed by the affinity constant and the relative concentrations of hormone and carrier; addition of hormone to the blood will push the equilibrium over to the right, causing more binding; at the point where thyroid hormone is being utilized the concentration of free hormone will fall and the equilibrium will shift in favour of dissociation from the carrier. Since thyroid hormone must detach itself from its carrier to be able to reach its site of action, the binding is of the greatest importance from the point of view of thyroid function, so that pathological increases in, say, carrier protein might well reduce the availability of the circulating hormone, and *vice versa*.

That the binding to TBG and TBPA is a specific process is revealed by the remarkable changes in binding capacity when the structure of the iodinated compound is altered; thus TBPA, binding T_4 firmly, does not bind T_3 at all. Again, the types of binding show different susceptibilities to drugs; thus the binding of thyroid hormones to TBPA is inhibited by veronal but not that to TBG and HSA.

Mechanism of Action

Throxine, when added to an isolated tissue maintained in a nutrient medium, will stimulate its oxygen consumption; in fact there is quite a strict parallelism between the changed activity in the tissue and in the intact animal.

Thus Table II shows the changes in tissue O_2-consumption, measured *in vitro*, after either thyroidectomy of the animals or after previous administration of thyroxine for several days. It is interesting, however, that certain tissues seem to be uninfluenced by the thyroid, notably the brain, the gonads and accessory sexual organs, as well as the spleen. The exclusion of the brain from acting in the thermoregulatory mechanism is understandable, since homeostasis of the central neurones' environment is so important; large fluctuations in metabolic rate of the neurones would doubtless produce considerable disturbances not only in their own basic activities, but also in their environment, since the concentrations of glucose, amino acids and so on would be greatly altered by fluctuations in utilization.

Activation of Enzymes. The analysis of the particular links in the metabolic chains that are affected by thyroxine is by no means complete, and a description of the work would carry us too far into the

TABLE II

Summary of oxygen consumption changes produced in rat
tissue by thyroidectomy or thyroxine injection.
(Barker, "The Thyroid Gland", Ed. Pitt-Rivers and Trotter)

Tissue	Per cent change produced by	
	Thyroidectomy	Thyroxine
Liver	−20	+62
Diaphragm	−31	+73
Kidney	−15	+48
Salivary gland	−22	+34
Pancreas	−20	+51
Heart	−38	+132
Epidermis	−71	*
Lung	+2	
Brain	−2	+7
Spleen	−5	+3
Testis	+2	+13
Seminal vesicle	−3	0
Prostate	−1	+4
Ovary	−1	−2
Uterus	−0	−3
Thymus	−9	+8
Lymph node	−2	+4
Gastric smooth muscle	+4	+3
Dermis	0	*
Adenohypophysis	+49	−36

* Not tested on thyroidectomized animals; neither epidermis nor dermis from injected
intact animals showed a greater than normal oxygen uptake.

intricacies of intermediate metabolism. Suffice it to say that the activities of certain intracellular enzymes, such as diglycerophosphate dehydrogenase in mitochondria of liver and kidney, are greatly increased, an increase that does not extend to the brain enzymes.

Cyclic AMP. As with the influence of so many hormones, cyclic AMP seems to be a second messenger in at least some of the activities of the thyroid; for example, thyroxine induces an increased lipolysis in fatty tissues, giving rise to elevated plasma fatty acids, which become available for metabolism. If excised fat-tissue was treated with thyroxine (T_3), its normal lipolytic response to treatment with norepinephrine and dibutyryl cAMP was increased. Furthermore, thyroxine actually caused an increase in cAMP accumulation in the fat-cells (Caldwell and Fain, 1971).

Control

Hypothalamus

We have seen (Vol. 2) that the liberation of hormones from many glands occurs in response to a primary excitation of the hypothalamus; this causes liberation of releasing factors carried to the anterior pituitary gland, which then secretes trophic hormones that activate glands in many parts of the body. The thyroid is activated in this way, the specific releasing factor being a simple tripeptide, which causes the release of thyrotrophin (TSH), which is a glycoprotein, i.e. a protein with a carbohydrate residue linked to it covalently. Thus the primary response to altered temperature is excitation of the hypothalamus, and so far as the thyroid is concerned it excites the liberation of thyroxine through first exciting the anterior pituitary through its TSH releasing factor (TRF).

Response to Cold. We have seen that Andersson showed that cooling the pre-optic region of the hypothalamus in conscious goats caused a rise in thyroxine production; this was abolished by a lesion in the median eminence that presumably prevented the transport of releasing factor to the anterior pituitary. Although removing the thyroid, or the anterior pituitary, reduces very considerably the responses of animals to cold, it must be emphasized that it does not completely block the metabolic response, as judged, say, by the ability of an animal to withstand cooling, so that there is little doubt that the adrenal medullary mechanism is of significance, especially, as we have seen, in the immediate response, since the liberation of TSH is a sluggish process.

Feedback Loops. The basic level of metabolism is maintained at a steady level presumably by the interplay of many factors, chief of which may well be the level of circulating thyroid hormones in the blood; and this level is maintained steady primarily by a simple negative feedback between the level of thyroxine in the blood and the anterior pituitary, so that raising the level diminishes the secretion of TSH. As Fig. 1.48 indicates, there are other subsidiary feedback loops; for example on the hypothalamic cells secreting releasing factor; on to the thyroid gland itself through the blood-level of thyroxine, and so on. The interaction of these loops gives rise to a steady state with the level of thyroid hormones at a given level, and it is customary to refer to this level, and the corresponding level of metabolic activity, as the "set-point". It must be emphasized that the TSH response of the pituitary is a sluggish one and is turned on much more slowly than it is turned off; thus injection of thyroxine causes an immediate fall in

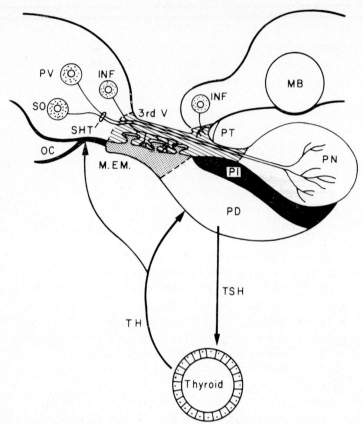

Fig. 1.48. The interacting components of the neuroendocrine mechanism controlling thyroid function. Thyroid stimulating hormone (TSH) released from the anterior pituitary (PD) causes the release of thyroid hormones (TH) which feed back directly on to the anterior pituitary (heavy arrows) inhibiting TSH release. Feedback also occurs into the hypothalamus (thin arrow), and the release of thyrotropin releasing hormone (TRH) is also inhibited.) TRH passes by neurosecretion from a diffuse area of the hypothalamus into the hypophyseal portal system and acts on the anterior pituitary to release TSH. PV, paraventricular nucleus. SO, supra optic nucleus. INF, parvicellular nuclei. MB, mamillary body. 3rd V, 3rd ventricle. MEM, median eminence. PN, pars nervosa. PI, pars intermedia. PT, pars tuberalis. OC, optic chiasma. (D'Angelo *in* "Advances in Neuroendocrinology", University of Illinois Press.)

the TSH in the blood, but if the level of thyroxine in the blood is lowered experimentally, then it takes days to return to normal.

Actions of TSH

The effect of TSH on the thyroid gland is obvious histologically; the large numbers of droplets in the apical regions of the epithelial cells indicate rapid absorption of colloid, preliminary to its breakdown to thyroxine and liberation into the blood. TSH does more than activate liberation of the thyroid hormones, since it also increases the rate of uptake of iodide and its conversion to organic compounds, increases rates of protein and carbohydrate metabolism, and so on. It could well be, however, that the multifarious responses are, indeed, the consequence of a primary stimulus to the cell, and this may be through cyclic AMP produced in response to the hormone. i.e. cAMP is the "second messenger".

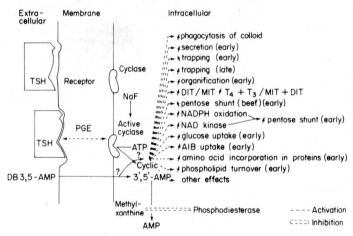

Fig. 1.49. The multiple effects of thyrotrophic hormone on the thyroid cell. (Schell-Frederick and Dumont in Stanbury, *Erg. der. Physiol.*)

Cyclic AMP. Thus the release of thyroxine from mouse thyroid is increased by administration of cAMP, an influence that may be augmented by simultaneous administration of theophylline, which inhibits the enzymic breakdown of cAMP by phosphodiesterase. As we have indicated earlier, the mechanism by which the hormone, TSH, increases the cellular production of cAMP is probably through an activation of the enzyme adenylcyclase, which catalyses the formation of cAMP from ATP. This presumably happens at the cell membrane, where the enzyme is apparently fixed; once the adenylcyclase has been activated, the increased concentration of cAMP stimulates a variety of metabolic reactions, as illustrated in Fig. 1.49; included in this series is an activation of the apical cell membrane to cause endocytosis and subsequent formation of phagolysosomes, as illustrated in Fig. 1.50.

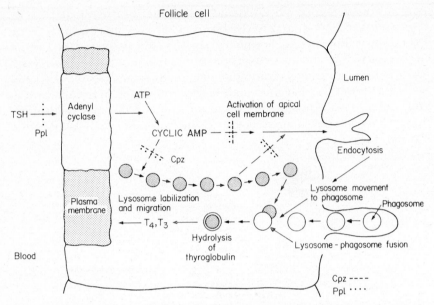

Fig. 1.50. Steps in the secretion of thyroid hormones. Two alternate pathways are shown between cyclic AMP and the activation of endocytosis. Possible sites of inhibition by chlorpromazine (Cpz) and propranolol (Ppl) are indicated by the dashed and dotted lines respectively. (From Onaya and Solomon, in Stanbury, *Erg. der. Physiol.*)

Pathological Conditions

Goitre

By goitre is meant an abnormally large thyroid gland; this can result from iodine deficiency, the gland responding to lowered blood-iodide by multiplication of its cells; in a similar way the goitrogenic agents, such as thiouracil, which block the incorporation of iodine into organic compounds, stimulate production of cells. It is essentially the low blood-thyroxine levels, causing increased liberation of TSH by the anterior pituitary, that stimulate the hyperplasia of the gland. The goitre of iodide deficiency is associated with the condition of *myxoedema*, consisting of an overgrowth of subcutaneous tissue associated with a general slowing of body functions, the subject appearing slow and stupid in his reactions. The cause of these symptoms is not easy to assess; the basal metabolic rate is low, as we should expect, but whether the changes are secondary to this cannot be stated. An enlarged gland is also associated with the *excessive* thyroid activity in Graves disease, or *exophthalmic goitre*; here the gland is pathologically enlarged and the concentration of thyroxine in the blood is raised; the subject is highly irritable with a basal metabolic rate some 60 per cent above normal. Histologically the gland exhibits numerous small vesicles with very little colloid, presumably because it is being liberated so rapidly into the blood. The relation of the exophthalmos—i.e. a protrusion of the eyes from their orbits due to the accumulation of mucoid material behind the globes—to the increased thyroid activity is not clear, nor yet is the causative factor in the hyperthyroidism understood.

LATS. In many patients a substance that stimulates the thyroid to secrete, called *long-acting thyroid stimulator* (*LATS*), is found in the blood (Adams, 1958); it is similar in many ways to TSH but takes much longer to cause a maximum release of thyroxine; recent work casts doubts on its role in the cause of the disease, however (Stanbury, 1972).

Cretinism

This is a congenital defect, manifesting itself in defective growth with mental retardation, and is due to either an absent, or defectively functioning, thyroid in the infant. As we should expect, the condition can be prevented by early treatment with thyroxine.

REFERENCES

Adams, D. A. (1958). The presence of an abnormal thyroid-stimulating hormone in serum of some thyrotoxic patients. *J. clin. Endocrinol*, **18**, 699–712.

Allan, J. R. (1965). The effects of physical training in a temperate and hot climate on the physiological responses to heat stress. *Ergonomics*, **8**, 445–453.

Allen, J. A., Armstrong, J. E. and Roddie, I. C. (1973). The regional distribution of emotional sweating in man. *J. Physiol.*, **235**, 749–759.

Andersson, B., Ekman, L., Gale, C. C. and Sundsten, J. W. (1963). Control of thyrotrophic hormone (TSH) secretion by the "heat loss centre". *Acta physiol. scand.*, **59**, 12–33.

Andersson, B., Gale, C. C., Hökfelt, B. and Ohga, A. (1963). Relation of preoptic temperature to the function of the sympathetico–adrenomedullary system and the adrenal cortex. *Acta physiol. scand.*, **61**, 182–191.

Andersson, B., Gale, C. C., Hökfelt, B. & Larsson, B. (1965). Acute and chronic effects of preoptic lesions. *Acta physiol. scand.*, **65**, 45–60.

Andersson, B., Grant, R. and Larsson, S. (1956). Central control of heat loss mechanisms in the goat. *Acta physiol. scand.*, **37**, 261–280.

Andersson, B. and Larsson, B. (1961). Influence of local temperature changes in the preoptic area and rostral hypothalamus on the regulation of food and water intake. *Acta physiol. scand.*, **52**, 75–89.

Arnold, K., Grusnick, D. and Ulmer, F. (1964). Zentrale und periphere Faktoren bei der Auslösung von Kreislaufveränderungen in Hyperthermie. *Pflüg. Arch. ges. Physiol.*, **278**, 487–499.

Avery, D. D. (1972). Thermoregulatory effects of intrahypothalamic injections of adrenergic and cholinergic substances at different environmental temperatures. *J. Physiol.*, **220**, 257–266.

Baker, M. A. (1972). Influence of the carotid rete on brain temperature in cats exposed to hot environments. *J. Physiol.*, **220**, 711–728.

Baldwin, B. A., Ingram, D. L. and LeBlanc, J. (1969). The effects of environmental temperature and hypothalamic temperature on the excretion of catecholamines in the urine of the pig. *Brain Res.* **16**, 511–515.

Barker, S. B. (1964). Physiological activity of thyroid hormone and analogues. In *The Thyroid Gland* (Ed. Pitt-Rivers, R. and Trotter, W. R.), Vol. I, pp. 199–256. Butterworth, London.

Bennett, I. L. and Nicastri, A. (1960). Fever as a mechansim of resistance. *Bact. Rev.*, **24**, 16–34.

Benzinger, T. H. (1969). Heat regulation: homeostasis of central temperature in man. *Physiol. Rev.*, **49**, 671–759.

Bettley, F. R. (1970). The epidermal barrier and percutaneous absorption. In *An Introduction to the Biology of Skin* (Ed. R. H. Champion *et al.*). Blackwell.

Bligh, J. (1966). The thermosensitivity of the hypothalamus and thermoregulation in mammals. *Biol. Rev.*, **41**, 317–367.

Bligh, J., Cottle, W. H. and Maskrey, M. (1971). Influence of ambient temperature on the thermoregulatory responses to 5-hydroxytryptamine, noradrenaline and acetylcholine injected into the lateral cerebral ventricles of sheep, goats and rabbits. *J. Physiol.*, **212**, 377–392.

Brebner, D. F. and Kerslake, D. McK. (1968). The effects of soaking the skin in water at various temperatures on the subsequent ability to sweat. *J. Physiol.*, **194**, 1–11.

Brück, K. and Wünnenberg, B. (1965). Blockade der chemischen Thermogenese und Auslösung von Muskelzittern durch Adrenolytica und Ganglionblockade beim neugeborenen Meerschweinchen. *Pflüg. Arch. ges. Physiol.*, **282**, 376–389.

Brusilow, S. W. and Munger, B. (1962). Comparative physiology of sweat. *Proc. Soc. exp. Biol. N.Y.*, **110**, 317–319.

Bulmer, M. G. and Forwell, G. D. (1956). The concentration of sodium in thermal sweat. *J. Physiol.* **132**, 115–122.

Buzalkov, R. and Andjus, R. K. (1960). Aspect bioénergétique de l'adaptation du rat aux températures élevées. *J. de Physiol.*, **52**, 40–41.

Cabanac, M., Stolwijk, J. A. A. and Hardy, J. D. (1968). Effect of temperature and pyrogens on single-unit activity in the rabbit's brain stem. *J. appl. Physiol.*, **24**, 645–652.

Cabanac, M. and Chatonnet, J. (1968). Influence de la température intime sur le caractère affectif d'une sensation thermique cutanée. *J. de Physiol. Paris*, **56**, 540–541.

Cabanac, M., Cunningham, D. J. and Stolwijk, J. A. J. (1971). Thermoregulatory set point during exercise. *J. comp. physiol. Psychol.*, **76**, 94–102.

Caldwell, A. and Fain, J. N. (1971). Triiodothyronine stimulation of cyclic adenosine 3', 5'-monophosphate accumulation in fat cells. *Endocrinology*, **89**, 1195–1204.

Carlson, L. D. (1966). The role of catecholamines in cold adaptation. *Pharmacol. Rev.*, **18**, 291–301.

Cassidy, G. J., Dworkin, S. and Finney, W. H. (1925). Insulin and the mechanism of hibernation. *Amer. J. Physiol.*, **73**, 417–428.

Chai, C. Y. and Lin, M. T. (1972). Effect of heating and cooling the spinal cord and medulla oblongata on thermoregulation in monkeys. *J. Physiol.*, **225**, 292–308.

Chai, C. Y. and Lin, M. T. (1973). Effects of thermal stimulation of medulla oblongata and spinal cord on decerebrate rabbits. *J. Physiol.*, **234**, 409–419.

Chai, C. Y., Mu, J. Y. and Brobeck, J. R. (1965). Cardiovascular and respiratory responses from local heating of medulla oblongata. *Amer. J. Physiol.*, **209**, 301–306.

Chatonnet, J., Cabanac, M. and Jeddi, E. (1965). Le niveau de réglage de la témp-
erature interne. Est-il modifié par le travail musculaire? *C.r. Soc. Biol.*, **159**,
1576-1578.

Clark, G., Magoun, H. W. and Ranson, S. W. (1939). Hypothalamic regulation
of body temperature. *J. Neurophysiol.*, **2**, 61–80.

Collins, K. J. and Weiner, J. S. (1968). Endocrinological aspects of exposure to high
environmental temperatures. *Physiol. Rev.*, **48**, 785–839.

Cooper, K. E., Cranston, I. and Honour, A. J. (1965). Effects of intraventricular and
intrahypothalamic injection of noradrenaline and 5-HT on body temperature in
conscious rabbits. *J. Physiol.*, **181**, 852–864.

Cooper, K. E., Johnson, R. H. and Spalding, J. M. K. (1964). The effects of central
body and trunk skin temperatures on reflex vasodilation in the hand. *J. Physiol.*
(London), **174**, 46–54.

Cremer, J. F. and Bligh, J. (1969). Body-temperature and responses to drugs. *Brit.*
med. Bull., **25**, 299–306.

Dahlström, A. and Fuxe, K. (1964). Evidence for the existence of monoamine-con-
taining neurons in the central nervous system. *Acta physiol. scand.*, Supp. 232,pp. 1–55.

Davis, T. R. A. and Mayer, J. (1955). Nature of the physiological stimulus for
shivering. *Amer. J. Physiol.*, **181**, 669–674.

Davis, T. R. A. and Mayer, J. (1955). Demonstration and quantitative determination
of the contributions of physical and chemical thermogenesis on acute exposure to
cold. *Amer. J. Physiol.*, **181**, 675–678.

Dobson, R. L. and Slegers, J. F. G. (1971). The effect of aldosterone on sweating in
the cat. *J. Invest. Derm.*, **56**, 337–339.

Dodt, E. and Zotterman, Y. (1952). Mode of action of warm receptors. *Acta. physiol.*
scand., **26**, 345–357.

Dodt, E. and Zotterman, Y. (1952). The discharge of specific cold fibres at high
temperatures. (The paradoxical cold.) *Acta. physiol. scand.*, **26**, 358–365.

Eastman, C. J., Ekins, R. P., Leith, I. M. and Williams, E. S. (1974). Thyroid
hormone response to prolonged cold exposure in man. *J. Physiol.*, **241**, 175–181.

Eisenman, J. S. (1969). Pyrogen-induced changes in the thermosensitivity of septal
and preoptic neurones. *Amer. J. Physiol.*, **216**, 330–336.

Evans, S. E. and Ingram, D. L. (1974). The significance of deep body temperature
in regulating the concentration of thyroxine in the plasma of the pig. *J. Physiol.*,
236, 159–170.

Feldberg, W. (1965). Changes in temperature produced by micro-injections of
amines into the anterior hypothalamus of cats. *J. Physiol.*, **177**, 239–245.

Feldberg, W. and Gupta, K. P. (1973), Pyrogen fever and prostaglandin-like
activity in cerebrospinal fluid. *J. Physiol.*, **228**, 41–53.

Feldberg, W., Gupta, K. P., Milton, A. S. and Wendlandt, S. (1973). Effect of
pyrogen and antipyretics on prostaglandin activity in cisternal c.s.f. of unanaesthetized cats. *J. Physiol.*, **234**, 279–303.

Feldberg, W., Hellon, R. F. and Lotti, V. J. (1967). Temperature effects produced
in dogs and monkeys by injections of monoamines and related substances into the
third ventricle. *J. Physiol.*, **191**, 501–515.

Feldberg, W. and Myers, R. D. (1964). Temperature changes by amines injected
into the cerebral ventricles. *J. Physiol.*, **175**, 464–478.

Feldberg, W. and Myers, R. D. (1964). Effects on temperature of amines injected
into the cerebral ventricle. *J. Physiol.*, **173**, 226–237.

Gale, C. C., Jobin, M., Proppe, D. W., Notter, D. and Fox, H. (1970). Endocrine
thermoregulatory response to local hypothalamic cooling in unanesthetized
baboons. *Amer. J. Physiol.*, **219**, 193–201.

Gale, C. C., Mathews, M. and Young, J. (1970). Behavioural thermoregulatory responses to hypothalamic cooling and warming in baboons. *Physiol. Behav.*, **5**, 1–6.

Galton, V. A. and Nisula, B. C. (1969). Thyroxine metabolism and thyroid function in the cold-adapted rat. *Endocrinology*, **85**, 79–86.

Gartside, I. B. and Lippold, O. C. J. (1967). The production of persistent changes in the level of neuronal activity by brief cooling of the cerebral cortex of the rat. *J. Physiol.*, **189**, 475–487.

Guieu, J. D. and Hardy, J. D. (1970). Effects of preoptic and spinal cord temperature in control of thermal polypnea. *J. appl. Physiol.*, **28**, 540–542.

Haight, J. S. J. and Keatinge, W. R. (1973(a)). Elevation in set point for body temperature regulation after prolonged exercise. *J. Physiol.*, **229**, 77–85.

Haight, J. S. J. and Keatinge, W. R. (1973(b)). Failure of thermoregulation in the cold during hypoglycaemia induced by exercise and ethanol. *J. Physiol.*, **229**, 87–97.

Hall, G. H. and Myers, R. D. (1972). Temperature changes produced by nicotine injected into the hypothalamus of the conscious monkey. *Brain Rec.*, **37**, 241–251.

Hammel, H. T. (1968). Regulation of internal body temperature. *Ann. Rev. Physiol.*, **30**, 641–670.

Hammel, H. T., Jackson, D. C., Stolwijk, J. A. J., Hardy, J. D. and Stromme, S. B. (1963). Temperature regulation by hypothalamic proportional control with an adjustable set point. *J. appl. Physiol.*, **18**, 1146–1154.

Handley, S. L. and Spencer, P. S. J. (1972). Thermoregulatory effects of intraventricular injection of noradrenaline in the mouse and the influence of ambient temperature. *J. Physiol.*, **223**, 619–631.

Hardy, J. D. (1961). Physiology of temperature regulation. *Physiol. Rev.*, **41**, 521–606.

Hayward, J. N. and Baker, M. A. (1968). Diuretic and thermoregulatory responses to preoptic cooling in the monkey. *Amer. J. Physiol.*, **214**, 843–850.

Hellon, R. F. (1970) The stimulation of hypothalamic neurones by changes in ambient temperature. *Pflüg. Arch. ges. Physiol.*, **321**, 56–66.

Hemingway, A. (1963). Shivering. *Physiol. Rev.*, **43**, 397–422.

Henane, R. and Valatx, J. L. (1973). Thermoregulatory changes induced during heat acclimatization by controlled hyperthermia in man. *J. Physiol.*, **239**, 255–271.

Hensel, H. and Boman, K. K. A. (1960). Afferent impulses in cutaneous sensory nerves in human subjects. *J. Neurophysiol.*, **23**, 564–578.

Honda, N. *et al.* (1962). Effects of adrenaline and noradrenaline on ear vessels in cold- and warm-adapted rabbits. *J. appl. Physiol.*, **17**, 754–758.

Hori, T. and Nakayama, T. (1973). Effects of biogenic amines on central thermoresponsive neurones in the rabbit. *J. Physiol.*, **232**, 71–85.

Isenschmid, R. and Schnitzler, W. (1914). Beitrag zur Lokalization des der Wärmeregulation vorstehenden zentral Apparatus in Zwischenhirn. *Arch. exp. Path. Pharmacol.*, **76**, 202–223.

Jell, R. M. (1974). Responses of rostral hypothalamic neurones to peripheral temperature and to amines. *J. Physiol.*, **240**, 295–307.

Jessen, C. and Ludwig. (1971). Spinal cord and hypothalamus as core sensors of temperature in the conscious dog. II. *Pflüg. Arch. ges. Physiol.*, **324**, 205–216.

Jessen, C. and Mayer, E. T. (1971). Spinal cord and hypothalamus as core sensors of temperature in the conscious dog. I. *Pflüg. Arch. ges. Physiol.*, **324**, 189–204.

Jessen, C., McLean, J. A., Calvert, D. T. and Finlay, J. D. (1972). Balanced and unbalanced temperature signals generated in spinal cord of the ox. *Amer. J. Physiol.*, **222**, 1342–1347.

Jessen, C. and Simon, E. (1971). Spinal cord and hypothalamus as core sensors of temperature in the conscious dog. III. *Pflüg. Arch. ges. Physiol.*, **324**, 217–226.

Kerslake, D. McK. (1972). *The Stress of Hot Environments.* C.U.P.

Kluger, M. J., Gonzalez, R. R. and Hardy, J. D. (1972). Peripheral thermal sensitivity in the rabbit. *Amer. J. Physiol.*, **222**, 1031–1034.

Kluger, M. J., Gonzalez, R. R., Mitchell, J. W. and Hardy, J. D. (1971). The rabbit ear as a temperature sensor. *Life Science*, **10**, (pt. 1) 895–899.

Krebs, H. A., Freedland, R. A., Hems, R. and Stubbs, M. (1969). Inhibition of hepatic gluconeogenesis by ethanol. *Biochem. J.*, **112**, 117–124.

Kuno, Y. (1934). *The Physiology of Human Perspiration.* Churchill, London.

Leduc, J. (1961). Catecholamine production and release in exposure and acclimation to cold. *Acta physiol. scand.*, **53**, Suppl. 183.

Lind, A. R. (1963). A physiological criterion for setting thermal environmental limits for everyday work. *J. appl. Physiol.*, **18**, 51–56.

Love, A. H. G. and Shanks, R. G. (1962). The relationship between the onset of sweating and vasodilatation in the forearm during body heating. *J. Physiol.*, **162**,121–128.

Matoltsy, A. G. and Parakkal, P. F. (1965). Membrane-coating granules of keratinizing epithelia. *J. Cell Biol.*, **24**, 297–337.

Milton, A. S. and Wendlandt, S. (1971). Effects on body temperature of prostaglandins of the A, E and F series on injection into the third ventricle of unanaesthetized cats and rabbits. *J. Physiol.*, **218**, 325–336.

Montagna, W. (1962). *The Pilary System. Ch. 4. Structure and Function of Skin.* Academic Press, New York.

Myers, R. D. (1970). An improved push-pull cannula system for perfusing an isolated region of the brain. *Physiol. Behav.*, **5**, 243–246.

Myers, R. D. and Beleslin, D. B. (1971). Changes in serotonin release in hypothalamus during cooling or warming of the monkey. *Amer. J. Physiol.*, **220**, 1746–1754

Myers, R. D. and Chinn, C. (1973). Evoked release of hypothalamic norepinephrine during thermoregulation in the cat. *Amer. J. Physiol.*, **224**, 230–236.

Myers, R. D. and Sharpe, L. G. (1968). Temperature in the monkey: transmitter factors released from the brain during thermoregulation. *Science*, **161**, 372–373.

Myers, R. D. and Waller, M. B. (1973). Differential release of acetylcholine from the hypothalamus and mesencephalon of the monkey during thermoregulation. *J. Physiol.*, **230**, 273–293.

Myers, R. D. and Yaksh, T. L. (1969). Control of body temperature in the unanaesthetized monkey by cholinergic and aminergic systems in the hypothalamus. *J. Physiol.*, **202**, 483–500.

Nakayama, T. and Hardy, J. D. (1969). Unit responses in the rabbit's brain stem to changes in brain and cutaneous temperature. *J. appl. Physiol.*, **27**, 848–857.

Nakayama, T. and Hori, T. (1973). Effects of anesthetic and pyrogen on thermally sensitive neurons in the brainstem. *J. appl. Physiol.*, **34**, 351–355.

Nielsen, M. (1938). Die Regulation der Körpertemperatur bei Muskelarbeit. *Skand. Arch. Physiol.*, **79**, 193–330.

Peiss, C. N., Randall, W. C. and Hertzman, A. B. (1956). Hydration of the skin and its effect on sweating and evaporative water loss. *J. invest. Dermatol.*, **26**, 459–470.

Pitt-Rivers, R. and Trotter, W. R. (Eds.) (1964). *The Thyroid Gland*, Vols. 1 and 2 Butterworth, London.

Proppe, D. W. and Gale, C. C. (1970). Endocrine thermoregulatory responses to local hypothalamic warming in unanesthetized baboons. *Amer. J. Physiol.*, **219**, 202–207.

Purves, H. D. (1964). Control of thyroid function. In *The Thyroid Gland.* (Ed. Pitt-Rivers, R. and Trotter, W. R.), Vol. 2, pp. 1–38. Butterworth, London.

Quatrale, R. P. and Spier, E. H. (1970). The effect of ADH on eccrine sweating in the rat. *J. Invest. Derm.*, **55**, 344–349.

Randall, W. C., Wurster, R. D. and Lewin, R. J. (1966). Responses of patients with high spinal transection to high ambient temperatures. *J. appl. Physiol.*, **31**, 955–993.

Roberts, W. W. and Robinson, T. C. L. (1969). Relaxation and sleep induced by warming of preoptic region and anterior hypothalamus in cats. *Exp. Neurol.*, **25**, 282–294.

Robinson, S. and Robinson, A. H. (1954). Chemical composition of sweat. *Physiol. Rev.*, **34**, 202–220.

Roddie, I. C., Shepherd, J. T. and Whelan, R. F. (1967). The contribution of constrictor and dilator nerves to the skin vasodilatation during body heating. *J. Physiol.*, **136**, 489–497.

Sato, K. and Dobson, R. L. (1970). Enzymatic basis for the active transport of sodium in the duct and secretory portion of the eccrine sweat gland. *J. Invest. Derm.*, **55**, 53–56.

Sato, K., Taylor, J. R. and Dobson, R. L. (1969). The effect of ouabain on eccrine sweat gland function. *J. Invest. Derm.*, **53**, 275–282.

Scheuplin, R. J. and Blank, I. H. (1971). Permeability of the skin. *Physiol. Rev.*, **51**, 702–747.

Sholander, P. F., Hammel, H. T., Hart, J. S., Le Mesurier, D. H. and Steen, J. (1958). Cold adaptation in Australian aborigines. *J. appl. Physiol.*, **13**, 211–218.

Schulz, I. *et al.* (1965). Mikropunktion und elektrische Potentialmessung an Schweissdrüsen des Menschen. I. *Pflüg. Arch. ges. Physiol.*, **284**, 360–372.

Schwartz, I. L., Thaysen, J. H. and Dole, V. I. (1953). Urea excretion in human sweat as a tracer for movement of water within the secreting gland. *J. exp. Med.*, **97**, 429–437.

Simon, E. and Iriki, M. (1971). Sensory transmission of spinal heat and cold sensitivity in ascending spinal neurons. *Pflüg. Arch. ges. Physiol.*, **328**, 103–120.

Stanbury, J. B. (1972). Some recent developments in the physiology of the thyroid gland. *Ergeb. Physiol.*, **65**, 94–125.

Stitt, J. T. (1973). Prostaglandin E_1 fever induced in rabbits. *J. Physiol.*, **232**, 163–179.

Stoner, H. B. (1973). The role of the liver in non-shivering thermogenesis in the rat. *J. Physiol.*, **232**, 285–296.

Stuart, D. G., Kawamura, Y. and Hemingway, A. (1961). Activation and suppression of shivering during septal and hypothalamic stimulation. *Exp. Neurol.*, **4**, 485–506.

Sweeney, T. M. and Downing, D. T. (1970). The role of lipids in the epidermal barrier to water diffusion. *J. Invest. Derm.*, **55**, 135–140.

Tabatabai, M. (1972). Respiratory and cardiovascular responses resulting from heating the medulla oblongata in cats. *Amer. J. Physiol.*, **222**, 1558–1564.

Tata, J. R. (1964). Distribution and metabolism of thyroid hormone. In *The Thyroid Gland* (Ed. Pitt-Rivers, R. and Trotter, W. R.), Vol. 1, pp. 163–186. Butterworth, London.

Vane, J. R. (1971). Inhibition of prostaglandin synthesis as a mechanism of action of aspirin-like drugs. *Nature*, **231**, 232–235.

Wilson, O., *et al.* (1970). Thyroid and adrenal response to acute cold exposure in man. *J. appl. Physiol.*, **28**, 543–548.

Wit, A. and Wang, S. C. (1967). Effects of increasing ambient temperature on unit activity in the preoptic anterior hypothalamus (PO/AH) region. *Fed. Proc.* **26**, 555.

Wit, A. and Wang, S. C. (1968a). Temperature-sensitive neurons in preoptic-anterior hypothalamic region: effects of increasing ambient temperature. *Amer. J. Physiol.*, **215**, 1151–1161.

Wit, A. and Wang. S. C. (1968b). Temperature-sensitive neurons in preoptic-anterior hypothalamic region: actions of pyrogen and acetylsalicylate. *Amer. J. Physiol.*, **215**, 1160–1169.

Wyndham, C. H. (1967). Effect of acclimatization on the sweat-rate/rectal temperature relationship. *J. appl. Physiol.*, **22**, 27–30.

CHAPTER 2

The Control of the Vascular Circulation

General Principles

The flow of blood through the vascular system, which we measure as the cardiac output, is remarkably constant in a subject at rest, and this is reflected in the effective constancy of the pressure in the large arteries; hence, in examining the control mechanisms, we are concerned with the manner in which this homeostasis is achieved. Furthermore, we have seen that the cardiac output is well adjusted to changes in the demands of the body for oxygen; so well indeed that, even when an athlete is working at his maximum capacity, requiring a ten-to-twelve fold increase in oxygen consumption, it is found that the blood leaving his left ventricle is just as fully oxygenated as it was at rest. Thus, not only has the cardiac output been adjusted to the requirements, but the ventilation of the blood in the lungs has been adjusted adequately too.

Supply to the Brain

Besides the control over the total circulation, we shall find mechanisms that divert blood from "reservoir regions" to the active muscles when this is necessary, but this diversion, although it may involve an enormous increase in flow through the exercising muscles, is not allowed to impair the blood-supply to the brain; furthermore, mechanisms are present to prevent any serious *increase* in blood-flow through the brain under these conditions. Thus an increased flow of blood through the working limbs could be achieved by an increase in the level of central arterial pressure caused, say, by more powerful and rapid beating of the heart. This increased aortic pressure would cause an increased flow of blood through the brain, as well, unless compensatory mechanisms were brought into play.

Autoregulation. In fact, as we shall see, negative feedback mechanisms come into operation tending to return the aortic pressure to its previous level. We shall see, furthermore, that because a constant blood-flow through the brain is physiologically essential, this flow is, in fact, maintained remarkably constant even when the aortic pressure is allowed to vary over a large range, a phenomenon that is usually described as autoregulation and observed also to a marked degree in the kidney and to a lesser extent in other tissues.*

Homeostasis of Arterial Pressure

The general cardiovascular and respiratory changes taking place during exercise have been described briefly in Vol. 1 (Fig. 8.4, p. 356), and will be discussed more extensively later in this chapter. Cardiac output may, in trained athletes, reach as high as 42·3 litres/min. This could be achieved either by developing a higher arterial pressure or a decreased resistance to flow, or both. In fact the mean arterial pressure in the athletes studied by Ekblom and Hermansen was only 107 ± 9 mm Hg, not very different from their resting values. Thus, not only does the mean arterial pressure remain constant in a given individual over long periods of rest or quiet activity, but also when extreme demands are made on the cardiovascular system, so that our consideration of the control over the blood circulation demands a careful examination of the mechanism of this *homeostasis of the arterial pressure.* We shall see that the level is determined by the interplay of many factors, prominent among which are some well defined reflexes, but in general we may say that no single factor determines a change in pressure. Thus, an increased force and frequency of heart-beat induced by the hormone adrenaline will tend to raise the arterial pressure, but a negative-feedback mechanism comes into play tending to bring the arterial pressure back to its original value.

Resistance Control

Homeostasis of the arterial pressure is one aspect of cardiovascular control, but the more fundamental one is, of course, the adaptation of the cardiac output to the oxygen requirements of the individual. Clearly if the arterial pressure is held fairly constant, changed demands

---

* Strictly speaking, autoregulation refers to the ability of an isolated organ, such as a limb, or the kidney, to maintain a constant blood-flow in the face of a variable perfusion-pressure (arterial minus venous), and is a feature of the vascular system *per se* rather than any reflex control over it, since it occurs in the denervated organ. As we shall see (Chapter 5), to apply this term to the constancy of blood-flow through the brain over a wide range of perfusion-pressures is hardly justifiable, especially since an important factor in maintaining this constancy is reflex control through the carotid sinus (Ponte and Purves, 1974).

for O_2 will be met by altered resistance to flow. Thus the control over the "resistance vessels" and pre-capillary sphincters that enables flow through an organ to be modified in accordance with its O_2-requirements is another aspect that we must consider. This control over resistance can be exerted in two manners, namely by vasodilatation to increase the blood-flow to working muscles or other organs requiring extra O_2, and by vasoconstriction in other, non-working, regions, such as the splanchnic, thereby diverting blood that would have been circulating through these regions to others where it is required more urgently.

Haematocrit and Viscosity

Control over the heart and blood vessels is the main basis of the homeostasis of the arterial pressure, but it must not be forgotten that other factors can be important, especially in the long term. Thus the viscosity of the blood plays an important role in determining the rate of flow under given conditions of pressure and vascular diameter; we have seen that the haematocrit, i.e. the percentage of cells in the blood, is important in determining the viscosity, and it has been concluded that there is an optimal haematocrit value for blood of 40 per cent when its viscosity and its O_2-carrying capacity are both taken into account. Thus a diminished haematocrit would increase blood-flow

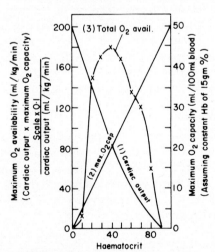

Fig. 2.1. Cardiac output, oxygen capacity and total oxygen available are plotted as functions of the haematocrit. The cardiac output falls with increasing haematocrit, but the oxygen capacity increases as the number of erythrocytes increases. The result of these two opposing factors is that the total oxygen available to the tissues passes through a maximum at a haematocrit of 40 per cent. (Smith and Crowell, *Amer. J. Physiol*).

owing to lowered viscosity, but the O_2-carrying capacity would be reduced proportionately, and it requires a knowledge of the way viscosity varies with haematocrit to determine the "optimum". Guyton and Richardson showed that the venous return in the dog, in the absence of reflexes due to raised atrial pressure, mean arterial pressure and nervous reflexes to the systemic circulation, was inversely proportional to the haematocrit; this meant that the minute-volume of erythrocytes travelling through the circulation passed through a maximum at haematocrits of 30–50 per cent. Thus, increasing the haematocrit beyond, say, 50 per cent would increase the volume of erythrocytes carried by unit volume of blood, but the increased viscosity arising from this increase in haematocrit would decrease the flow, and the net result would be a decrease in the minute-volume of erythrocytes. This point is well illustrated by Fig. 2.1 from Smith and Crowell (1963), where cardiac output, oxygen capacity and total oxygen available are plotted as functions of the haematocrit. Thus cardiac output falls with increasing haematocrit but the oxygen carrying capacity of the blood increases because of the greater concentration of erythrocytes. As a result of the interplay of these opposing factors, the *total oxygen available* to the tissues passes through a maximum at a haematocrit of about 40 per cent.

Haemorrhage. This consideration is of interest mainly in the long term, but during haemorrhage, because of the rapid mobilization of extracellular fluid into the blood (Vol. 1), there is, indeed, a considerable reduction in haematocrit, and it is not surprising to find that haemorrhage is accompanied by reflex effects on the heart and blood vessels, whilst the function of the kidney is modified by a reflex liberation of antidiuretic hormone that prevents undue loss of water.

Relation to Respiration

Finally, we must note that control over the cardiovascular system has meaning largely in relation to the supply of O_2 to, and removal of CO_2 from, the parts of the body; and this means that the mechanisms controlling blood-flow must be intimately linked with those controlling aeration of the blood, i.e. that respiratory and cardiovascular reflexes must be considered together.

THE SENSORY MECHANISMS

Arterial Baroreceptors

If the pressure in the large arteries is to be controlled, information regarding their diameters must be transmitted to the central co-ordinating centres, since a change in pressure of an elastic tube is reflected in a change in diameter. The sensors able to respond to changes in diameter, with the consequent stretch of elastic elements in the wall, belong to the class of *mechanoreceptors*, and are called more specifically *baroreceptors*. They are located at certain critical places in the arterial tree, notably close to the bifurcation of the common carotid artery—the *carotid sinus*—and in the arch of the aorta.

Carotid Sinus and Aortic Arch

The location of the mammalian carotid sinus is illustrated in Fig. 2.2; at the bifurcation of the artery the internal carotid artery shows a characteristic and localized change, acquiring a thinner and more elastic tunica media. This part is called the *elastic segment*, and here the

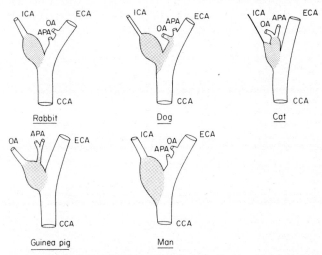

Fig. 2.2. The extent of the "elastic segment" of the carotid bifurcation (stippled) in different mammals (not to scale). CCA, common; ECA, external; ICA, internal carotid; OA, APA, occipital and ascending pharyngeal arteries. (Rees, *J. comp. Neurol.*)

density of innervation is increased. The baroreceptors are not encapsulated organs like those responsible for sensing alterations in pressure on the skin (Vol. 5), but are simply naked nerve endings lying in close relation to connective-tissue elements of the arterial wall. The nerve fibres are both myelinated and non-myelinated, and it has been suggested that the unmyelinated fibres represent the sympathetic innervation to the smooth muscle elements. We shall see that sympathetic stimulation tends to increase the sensitivity of the carotid sinus and aortic arch to altered pressure, and it is conceivable that contraction of smooth muscle elements in the adventitia of the sinus wall might increase sensitivity (Sampson and Mills, 1970).

Innervation. The carotid sinus is innervated by the carotid sinus-nerve, which is a branch of the glossopharyngeal (N IX); the sensory fibres have their cell-bodies in the petrosal ganglion and run centrally in the tractus solitarius. The aortic arch is innervated by the aortic nerve, a branch of the vagus (N X), with cell-bodies in the nodose ganglion.

Effects of Altered Arterial Pressure

Mechanical stimulation of the baroreceptive regions causes enhanced discharge in these nerves, whilst lowering the arterial pressure, e.g. in the carotid sinus by clamping the common carotid artery, causes a reduction in the tonic discharge. This is most clearly revealed in the oscillation of the discharge in phase with the heart beat.

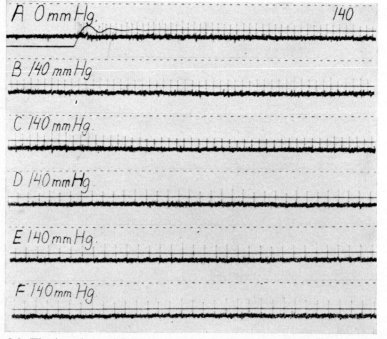

Fig. 2.3. The impulse activity from a single baroreceptor fibre in the cat carotid sinus nerve. Trace A shows the response to suddenly increasing the pressure in the carotid sinus from 0 to 120 mm Hg. Traces B and C are continuous with A; D, 15 sec after C; E, 1 minute after C; and F, 5 minutes after C. Note that there is some adaptation of the response. (Landgren, *Acta physiol. scand.*)

Single-Fibre Responses: Carotid Sinus

The classical studies of single-fibre discharges during mechanical stimulation of the sinus were carried out by Landgren, and Fig. 2.3 shows the increase in discharge taking place on rapidly raising the

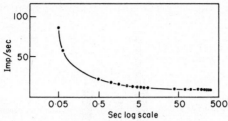

Fig. 2.4. The response of a carotid sinus baroreceptor unit to a continuous pressure of 120 mm Hg as a function of time following the rapid increase in pressure from 0 mm Hg. (Landgren, *Acta physiol. scand.*)

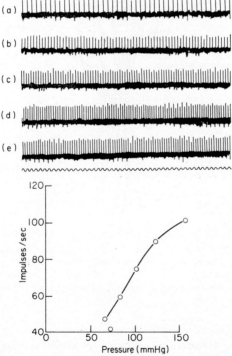

Fig. 2.5. The response of a single aortic arch baroreceptor fibre, from the isolated aortic arch of the rabbit, to variation in aortic pressure. a, 65 mm Hg; b, 82 mm Hg; c, 100 mm Hg; d, 122 mm Hg; e, 155 mm Hg. As can be seen in the graph the impulse-frequency varies almost linearly with the aortic pressure once the threshold pressure of 65 mm Hg has been exceeded. Time marker, 50 c/s. (Angell James, *J. Physiol.*)

pressure within the sinus to 140 mm Hg. The discharge shows some adaptation, in the sense that the frequency tends to fall after the initial increase, so that we may speak of a *phasic* increase, leading to a *tonic*, or maintained, increase (Fig. 2.4). An interesting feature of the discharge is that a given fibre remains silent until a threshold

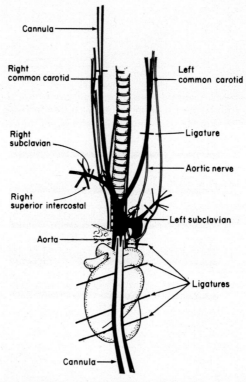

Fig. 2.6. Diagram showing the isolated perfused aortic arch and right subclavian regions of the rabbit, and indicating the site of the ligatures and cannulae. The architecture of the main branches of the aortic arch is variable but that depicted here is the commonest variant. (Angell James, *J. Physiol.*)

pressure, in the region of 100 mm Hg is reached; as the pressure is raised the steady frequency increases to attain a maximum at about 100–200 mm Hg when further increases are without effect. Frequently on lowering the pressure the fibre would remain silent at pressures, say, between 100 mm Hg and 50 mm Hg but at this point there might be a burst of action potentials; this shows that the receptors are "distortion receptors" responsive to a change in the arrangement of elastic elements in the wall of the sinus; usually the distortion that provokes a discharge is one involved in stretch, i.e. a rise in pressure, but at very low pressures a distortion of the opposite kind can also arouse a discharge. This distortion is produced not so much by a change in arterial pressure, *per se*, but of the transmural pressure, so that if the pressure outside the artery (extramural pressure) is increased in parallel with the intramural pressure, no activity should be recorded, and this was in fact shown by Angell James (1971).

Aortic Arch. Fig. 2.5 shows single-fibre responses arising in the aortic arch and recorded in the aortic nerve, when the rabbit's aorta was perfused at varying pressures. As indicated by Fig. 2.6, the perfusion fluid was passed into the ventricle close to the aorta and carried away in the right common carotid artery. It will be seen from Fig. 2.5 that the impulse-frequency varies almost linearly with the aortic pressure, from the threshold pressure of 65 mm Hg.

Pulsatile Pressure

The responses shown in Figs. 2.3 and 2.5 were responses to changes in steady pressure in the carotid sinus or aortic arch; under natural conditions, of course, the pressure is pulsatile, and there is no doubt from the study of Ead, Green and Neil (1952) that the pulsatile stimulus is more effective than the steady pressure, the effectiveness being measured by the frequency of discharge in a few-fibre preparation of the carotid sinus-nerve; in fact it could be found that a preparation would show no discharge at a steady pressure, but a discharge when a pulsatile pressure—with the same mean value—was substituted.

Reflex Responses to Raised Pressure

The reflex effects of a rise in carotid sinus- or aortic arch-pressures are a dilatation of the resistance vessels and slowing of the heart that tend to counteract the rise in arterial pressure. Angell, James and Daly (1970) perfused both the carotid sinus and arch of the aorta separately, as illustrated in Fig. 2.7; in this way they were able to measure the effects of changed pressure in these regions on the systemic resistance of the dog, and also the effects of switching from a steady to a pulsatile pressure. The reflex effects were measured as a percentage decrease in flow-resistance, as calculated from the perfusion-pressure and the blood-flow. As Fig. 2.8 shows, the reflex effects of a pulsatile pressure are considerably greater than those of a steady pressure, the carotid sinus being much the more sensitive in this respect.

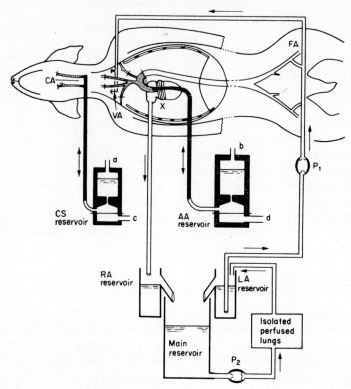

Fig. 2.7. Diagram showing the methods of separate perfusion of the isolated carotid sinuses, the isolated aortic arch, the systemic circulation and the isolated perfused lungs of a donor animal. The filled tubes are the perfusion circuits for the isolated carotid sinuses and aortic arch; the open tubes are the perfusion circuits for the systemic circulation and isolated lungs. The stippled blood vessels are those included in the carotid sinus and aortic arch perfusions. By means of the reservoirs CS and AA, which contain blood, the mean pressure, pulse-pressure and pulse-frequency are controlled independently in the carotid sinuses and aortic arch.

The systemic circulation is perfused by pump P_1 with blood from the left atrial reservoir. Blood from the systemic circulation drains through a cannula in the right atrium into the right atrial reservoir and thence into the main reservoir. The lungs (not shown) of the recipient animal are not perfused, but the left atrium is cannulated to drain broncho-pulmonary blood into the main reservoir. The isolated lungs of a donor dog are perfused through the pulmonary artery by pump P_2 with blood from the main reservoir; blood from the left atrium drains into the left atrial reservoir.

a, b, connexions to compressed air air-leak by-pass systems for controlling mean pressures in the two reservoirs; c, d, connexions to spaces above diaphragms of Dale-Schuster pumps (water-filled systems) for controlling pulse pressure and pulse frequency in the reservoirs. AA, aortic arch; CA, carotid arteries; CS, carotid sinus; FA, femoral arteries; LA, left atrium; RA, right atrium; VA, vertebral arteries; X, tape tied round ventricles below atrio-ventricular groove and embracing the aortic arch cannula. (Angell James and Daly, *J. Physiol.*)

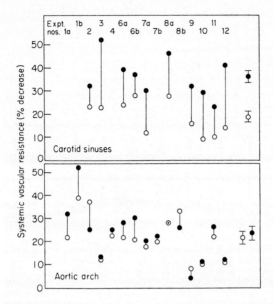

Fig. 2.8. A comparison of the effect of pulsatile perfusion-pressure (open circles) with that of non-pulsatile perfusion-pressure (closed circles) on the carotid sinuses and aortic arch. A much greater fall in vascular resistance is seen when the arterial baroreceptors are stimulated by pulsatile pressure than with non-pulsatile pressure. Bars join responses in individual animals to the changed pressure-pattern. Mean values and SE are given on the right. (Angell James and Daly, *J. Physiol.*)

Cardiac Receptors

Atrial Receptors

It is important that the central coordinating centre should have information relating to the filling of the heart, and this is provided by mechanoreceptors situated in the great veins at their junctions with the atria—these *atrial receptors* consist in ramifications of the nerve endings of relatively large (rapidly conducting), myelinated fibres derived from the vagus nerve. Fig. 2.9 shows the electrocardiogram of a dog, above, and the discharges in a single fibre; the discharges are synchronous with the so-called *a*-wave. In the lower record the effects of an infusion of saline intravenously are shown, the discharge now taking place throughout most of the cardiac cycle.

Ventricular Receptors

Not only are mechanoreceptors concentrated in the atria and their junctions with the great veins, but also the ventricles provide information; in fact when the character of the afferent fibres derived from the dog's heart in the thoracic autonomic nerves was analysed, 26 per cent of these were ventricular compared with only 14 per cent atrial, the remaining 50 per cent being aortic (Armour, 1973). Fig. 2.10 shows records from a receptor localized, by probing, in the right ventricular mass. Activity is clustered round the QRS-complex of the ECG and is

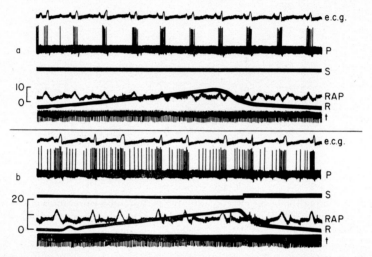

Fig. 2.9. (a) Discharge in fibre from right atrio-venous system with a pattern of discharge synchronous with the "a-wave" in the atrial pressure record. (b) The same preparation after a late systolic volley had been brought about by an infusion of 200 ml of isotonic saline into the femoral vein. The signal-marker, S, indicates the end of the infusion. e.c.g., electrocardiogram; P, action potentials in vagal slip; RAP, right atrial pressure; R, tracheal pressure, upstroke = inflation; t, time (1/50 sec.). (Coleridge *et al.*, *J. Physiol.*)

greatly increased when intraventricular pressure is increased by partial occlusion of the pulmonary artery. The distribution of mechano-receptors is illustrated in Fig. 2.11.

Skeletal Muscle Receptors

Information indicating the need of a working muscle to receive more blood is required; we shall see that local mechanisms, not involv-ing afferent impulses, undoubtedly operate, but also there is no doubt that afferent impulses from the muscles can bring about cardiovascular adjustments leading to increased blood-flow in the working muscle. This reflex is more evident in the respiratory response to exercise

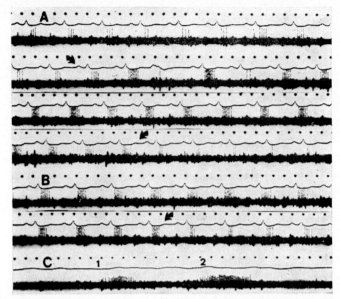

Fig. 2.10. Mechanoreceptors in the ventricles. Records obtained from receptors in the ventricular wall. In each trace the upper record is ECG and the lower record is the ventricular receptor discharge in the recurrent cardiac nerve. In trace A the control record shows the activity clustered around the QRS complex of the ECG. Between the arrows or Section A the aorta was occluded and released. In B the receptor is responding to pulmonary occlusion and the frequency of discharge decreased at the arrow when the occlusion was released. In C the ventricles were fibrillating and at (1) and (2) the septum was gently touched. (Armour, *Amer. J. Physiol.*)

(Ch. 3), and it seems that it is not the muscle spindles that provide the sensory response but other receptors in the muscle and probably in the joints.

Mesenteric Vascular Bed

The need for O_2 by the working muscle is met by an increased blood-flow, mediated by reduced resistance; shunting of blood from the abdominal viscera plays a part, so that information from the veins in the splanchnic area might well be required to assist in this type of adjustment. According to Andrews, Andrews and Orbach (1972), a rise in mesenteric venous pressure by mechanical obstruction of the portal vein caused discharges in afferent nerves from the intestine, the increase in frequency being proportional to the rise in venous pressure. Associated with this afferent discharge, there was an efferent discharge in the intestinal nerves, unaffected by section of the vagi in the neck,

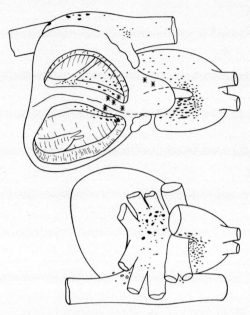

Fig. 2.11. A diagram of the distribution of cardiovascular mechanoreceptors in the heart. Each dot represents the area of sensitivity covered by the receptor. Stars are chemoreceptors, which were confined to the intraventricular septum and medial aspect of aortic root. (Armour, *Amer. J. Physiol.*)

and probably mediated by the sympathetic. This efferent discharge probably led to a constriction of the vascular bed, since Gammon and Bronk had shown that such a congestion of the mesenteric blood vessels caused an increase in resistance in the mesenteric arterial bed. It is possible, then, that this reflexogenic area is of importance in the distribution of blood to the different parts of the body according to its needs.

Carotid and Aortic Bodies

As emphasized earlier, the circulation must be regulated in close relation to the ventilation of the blood, so that sensors responding to the PCO_2 and PO_2 of arterial blood are necessary if cardiovascular adjustments are to be made in accordance with the gaseous requirements of this fluid. The sensors in this respect are located strategically in the carotid sinus and arch of the aorta, being described as the *carotid* and *aortic bodies*. They are activated by a fall in PO_2 or a rise in PCO_2 of the arterial blood, their messages being carried in the same nerves as those from the baroreceptors of the same regions, namely the carotid sinus and aortic nerves.

Blood Supply

The bodies are highly vascularized groups of what are often called *glomus cells*; the cells rest on fenestrated capillaries. They receive an arterial supply of blood from a branch of the neighbouring main artery; e.g. the occipital artery, a branch of the carotid, supplies the carotid body. The artery gives rise to a complex system of fenestrated capillaries on which rest the epithelioid "glomus cells", which come into relation with sensory nerve fibres, with their cell-bodies in the petrosal ganglion of the glossopharyngeal nerve. The blood supply to the carotid body, expressed in terms of the weight of the organ, is enormous, namely 2000 ml/min per 100 g tissue, and this allows the glomus cells to act as samplers of the chemical state of the arterial blood. Furthermore, there is a very prominent arrangement of arteriovenous shunts that serve, when open, to divert blood away from the complex series of sinusoidal vessels, and thus to deprive the glomus cells of oxygen.

Glomus Cells

In the electron microscope the glomus cells of the carotid body are distinguishable into Types I and II; the Type I cells occur in groups and are surrounded by the thin protoplasmic processes of Type II or sustentacular cells, as illustrated in Fig. 2.12; nerve fibres come into relation with these cells in several ways, of special interest being the synaptic bag (nf_2) where the fibre makes an indentation into the surface of the Type I cell; the cytoplasm of the nerve fibre contains vesicles of several sizes. An interesting feature is the interdigitation of cell membranes of adjacent Type II cells (mf), containing nerve fibres; on cutting the carotid sinus nerve these membranes show rapid degenerative changes. Also, after carotid body denervation, the nerve endings forming synaptic bags show changes indicating that these belong to the carotid sinus nerve.

Functions of Glomus Cells

As to the functions of the two types of cell, and the mechanism of activation of the afferent nerve supply, little is known definitely. The Type I cells contain, within their cytoplasm, typical dense-cored vesicles similar to the catecholamine-containing vesicles of adrenergic nerves, and have been shown to contain dopamine.

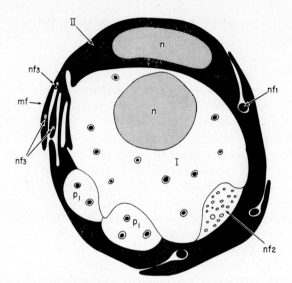

Fig. 2.12. A diagram of the electron microscopic appearance of the glomus cells of the carotid body. Layout of Type I and Type II cells and their nerve supply. p_1, finger-like projection of a neighbouring Type I cell; nf_1, small nerve fibre carried by Type II cell; nf_2, a synaptic bag on the surface of Type I cell; nf_3, small nerve fibres carried in a folded membrane system, mf. (Kock and Dunn, *Arterial Chemoreceptors*, Blackwell.)

According to Møllgård and Sørensen (1974) there is a large increase in the number of these dense-cored vesicles, with a corresponding increase in the amount of dopamine in the cells, when rabbits are maintained chronically hypoxic. It has been suggested that the Type I cells are the sensors, or receptor cells, responding to altered gas-tensions of the blood, and subsequently activating the sensory nerve endings lying in close relation to them. However, there are strong reasons to support Biscoe's contention that the nerve fibres coming into close relation with Type I cells are *efferent*, subserving a central control over the responses of the carotid sinus.

Efferent Discharge to Glomus Cells. Thus stimulation of the sinus nerve reduces the response of the carotid or aortic bodies to anoxia or hypercapnia, and it could be that efferent fibres in the nerve acted on the glomus cells, causing them to release catecholamines, which reacted on the true sensory elements which might be the nerve endings that apparently wrap themselves around the Type I cells.

The nerve endings that are closely related to the Type I cells contain microvesicles, similar to the synaptic vesicles of the central nervous system, and so appear to be efferent. Furthermore, Biscoe, Lall and Sampson (1970) cut the glossopharyngeal nerve centrally to the petrosal ganglion, and found degeneration of nerve endings related to Type I cells. Since the sensory fibres have their cell-bodies in the petrosal ganglion, these would be unaffected by the section whereas efferent fibres, derived from the nucleus of the glossopharyngeal nerve in the medulla, would be cut off from their cell-bodies and show degeneration.

Nerve Endings as Sensors. If the Type I cells are not sensory, what, then, are the elements sensitive to altered gas-tension? According to Mitchell *et al.* (1972) the nerve endings themselves are sensitive. They cut the carotid sinus nerve and inserted its distal end in the adjacent tissue where it developed a neuroma. The nerve subsequently was shown to be responsive to altered P_aCO_2 and P_aO_2 and cyanide, and on examination histologically the neuroma showed no sign of Type I cells.

Efferent Inhibition. If the nerve-endings are, indeed, the sensitive elements, we can picture the efferent impulses reaching the Type I cells causing a discharge of dopamine in their neighbourhood and decreasing the sensitivity of the nerve endings, and in this way we have a central control over the sensitivity of the carotid body. This *efferent inhibition* of the carotid body response can certainly be mimicked by catecholamines; thus Sampson (1971) found that intra-carotid injections of adrenaline, noradrenaline and dopamine depressed the spontaneous discharge in the carotid-sinus nerve, whilst an α-blocking agent, dibenzyline, caused an increase in the baseline discharge and reduced the effects of catecholamines and of stimulation of the carotid sinus nerve.*

Type II Cells. The Type II cells are reminiscent of glial or Schwann cells in so far as they ensheathe the nerve fibres, and it may be that they have a corresponding function in the carotid and aortic bodies, surrounding the true chemosensitive nerves and providing a "micro-environment" for these. In some way O_2-lack might alter the resting potential at the endings and eventually lead to the generation of spike potentials. We may assume that the high rate of metabolism of the

---

* According to Pearse (1969), the Type I cells are histologically similar to a group of cells in different tissues classed as *APUD cells*. They typically produce polypeptide hormones, such as the C-cells of the thyroid, the ACTH- and MSH-secreting cells of the pituitary, β-cells of the pancreas, and so on. He suggests that the Type I cells produce a hormone, *glomin*. In this connexion we may note that an erythropoietin-secretory function has been attributed to the carotid body (Tramezzani *et al.* 1971), but histochemical tests have failed to reveal the presence in it of a glycoprotein, thus excluding erythropoietin which belongs to this class of substances (Hansen *et al.*, 1973).

nerve endings and glomus cells makes them very sensitive to alterations in PO_2.

A-V-Shunts

Thus *tissue hypoxia* could be determined both by a low blood PO_2 but also by a diminished blood-flow through the capillaries of the carotid body, so that if the carotid body is to sense the PO_2 of the blood its blood-flow should either be constant or it, too, should be dependent on PO_2. De Castro drew attention to the arteriovenous shunts in the carotid body, and observed that when the animal was made to breathe a low-O_2 gas mixture the shunts opened so that blood was diverted from the glomus cells. The opposite effect was observed with an oxygen-rich gas mixture. It seems, therefore, that the effects of lowered blood-PO_2 are amplified in the carotid body, the low PO_2 *per se* presumably having an effect on the glomus cells, whilst the operation of the a-v-shunt increases this effect still further. De Castro assumed that the oxygen-lack activated the smooth muscle of the artery at the a-v-shunt directly.

Effects of Blood Pressure

We must note that if the carotid body is to act as a sensor for the gas composition of the blood it would be desirable if it did *not* respond to blood pressure, leaving this to the carotid sinus; in fact, the flow of blood through the carotid body is reflexly controlled by pressure-receptors in the main artery supplying it, so that it is, in effect, independent of the central arterial pressure.

Role of Acetylcholine

It has been suggested that the glomus cells are activated by the chemical stimuli that lead to discharge in the carotid sinus nerve, and it is postulated that they transmit their influence by the liberation of a chemical mediator; specifically it has been argued that acetylcholine is the liberated transmitter activating the generator region of the nerve ending. Certainly the carotid body contains this neurotransmitter in concentrations as high as in the superior cervical ganglion. It must be emphasized, however, that it is not sufficient to demonstrate that the carotid body may be activated by acetylcholine since this transmitter will initiate action potentials in unmedullated nerve fibres; only if this type of fibre can be excluded from the response could we begin to argue in favour of this substance as a transmitter. Moreover, we know that acetylcholine does excite the Pacinian corpuscle but it is also known that the sensory nerve of this mechanoreceptor is not excited naturally by this substance, but by the mechanical deformation of the generator region of the fibre.

Loewi-Type Experiments. The strongest evidence favouring release of acetylcholine is based on Eyzaguirre and Koyano's "Loewi-type" experiments in which two isolated carotid bodies are placed in a current of fluid; stimulation of the "upstream" carotid body causes discharge in the sensory nerve of the "downstream" one if it is appropriately eserinized, but the interpretation of even this experiment has been called into question.

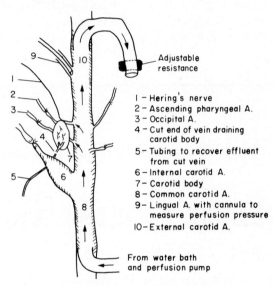

Adjustable resistance

1 – Hering's nerve
2 – Ascending pharyngeal A.
3 – Occipital A.
4 – Cut end of vein draining carotid body
5 – Tubing to recover effluent from cut vein
6 – Internal carotid A.
7 – Carotid body
8 – Common carotid A.
9 – Lingual A. with cannula to measure perfusion pressure
10 – External carotid A.

From water bath and perfusion pump

Fig. 2.13. Illustrating the method by which the carotid body can be isolated and perfused. (Metz, *Resp. Physiol.*)

Perfusion Experiments. Again, by tying off the appropriate arteries in the carotid sinus region, as in Fig. 2.13, the dog's carotid artery could be perfused with fluid independently of the general circulation whilst the effluent blood could be collected from a cut vein (5). When blood with normal PCO_2 and PO_2 was perfused there was no release of acetylcholine into the venous effluent, but when blood that had been made hypercapnic and hypoxic was perfused the large increase in ventilation was accompanied by considerable efflux of acetylcholine. The compound HC3, which inhibits synthesis of acetylcholine, reduced the effects of hypercapnia and hypoxia and also reduced the amount of acetylcholine in the effluent.

Deformation of Nerve Ending

Paintal has suggested that deformation of the sensory nerve ending is the common feature of both mechanical and chemical stimuli; thus O_2-lack would cause certain O_2-sensitive cells to change shape and that would be sufficient to deform the nerve ending.

Sinus-Nerve Discharge

Isolated Carotid Body

The reflexes mediated by the carotid and aortic bodies will be discussed later; here we may consider experiments on the isolated system that reveal the mode of response of the bodies to change in the blood

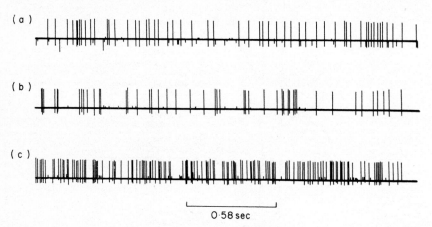

0·58 sec

Fig. 2.14. The response of a single chemosensory fibre from the isolated carotid body of the cat to variations in the gas tensions of the bathing medium. (a) 50 per cent O_2 in N_2, pH 7·32, impulse-frequency 2·1/sec. (b) 5 per cent CO_2 in O_2, pH 7·34, impulse-frequency 1·71/sec. (c) air, pH 7·32 impulse-frequency 7·06/sec. Eyzaguirre and Koyano, *J. Physiol.*)

passing through them. Thus Eyzaguirre and Koyano removed the carotid body, with its nerve, from cats and maintained this in functional condition in an oxygenated Locke's solution. Action potentials from small filaments of the nerve were recorded, often from single fibres. Fig. 2.14 shows the effects of changes in the O_2 or CO_2 tension in the fluid bathing the preparation. This receptor was silent in 100 per cent O_2. In (a) it was exposed to 50 per cent O_2 in N_2 giving a discharge of 2·1/sec; in (b) the medium was 5 per cent CO_2 in O_2 and the discharge was 1·7/sec. In (c) the saline was equilibrated with air and the discharge-frequency was some 7/sec. Under these experimental conditions saline exposed to air (20 per cent O_2) provided inadequate oxygen so that the response was to anoxia. Most single fibres responded to both hypercapnia and hypoxia, but a few responded to only one type of stimulus.

Intact Animal

In the intact animal the carotid sinus may be perfused with blood independently of the general circulation, as indicated earlier, and

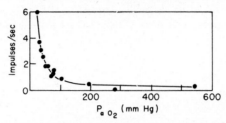

Fig. 2.15. The rate of chemoreceptor afferent discharge as a function of arterial oxygen tension. Impulses from a single fibre in the sinus nerve of a cat with a mean arterial blood pressure of 95 mm Hg and an arterial PCO_2 of 30 mm Hg. (Biscoe, Purves and Sampson, *J. Physiol.*)

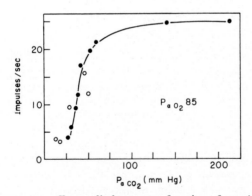

Fig. 2.16. Chemoreceptor afferent discharge as a function of arterial carbon dioxide tension. The response is of a single chemoreceptor fibre in the sinus nerve of cat. The rate and volume of artificial ventilation were varied to change the $P_a CO_2$. The P_aO_2 was 85 mm throughout. Filled circles indicate the response as the CO_2 tension was increased; open circles as it was decreased. Mean arterial blood pressure 115 mm Hg. (Biscoe, Purves and Sampson, *J. Physiol.*)

single chemoreceptor fibres in the sinus nerve may be identified by their rapid responses to changes in the PO_2 or PCO_2 of the blood passing through the sinus. The steady tonic discharge falls as PO_2 is raised and increases when PO_2 is lowered or PCO_2 is increased.

Baroreceptor fibres, by contrast, showed discharges that were synchronized with the heart-beat, and their discharge-rate fell on clamping the carotid, whereas those of chemoreceptor fibres increased, due to the asphyxia. Fig. 2.15 from a systematic study of Biscoe, Purves and Sampson (1970) shows the effects of PO_2 on discharge in single fibres of the cat; Fig. 2.16 shows the effects of increased arterial PCO_2.

PCO_2 and pH. Alterations in PCO_2 are usually accompanied by changes in pH, so that the receptor may be described as a H^+-ion receptor. However, it is possible, by using different concentrations of bicarbonate in the perfusion fluid, to establish the same pH with

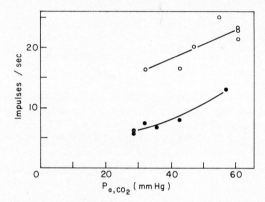

Fig. 2.17. The discharge in impulses per second recorded from a single chemoreceptor afferent fibre as a function of P_aCO_2. For each curve the pH was kept constant. Open circles, pH 7·25, mean arterial pressure 91 mm Hg. Filled circles pH 7·45, mean arterial pressure 0·85 mm Hg. P_aO_2 80 mm. (Biscoe, Purves and Sampson, *J. Physiol.*)

different PCO_2, and in this case it is found that the higher PCO_2 gives the stronger discharge; this is demonstrated by Fig. 2.17 where the intensity of discharge of a single fibre is plotted against P_aCO_2; in each curve the pH was maintained constant, at 7·25 for the upper curve and 7·45 for the lower curve. Thus, when pH is held constant, the discharge-rate rises almost linearly with P_aCO_2, whilst for a given P_aCO_2 the discharge is greater at the more acid pH.

EFFECTOR MECHANISMS AND EFFERENT PATHWAYS

Control over the cardiovascular system is exerted on the muscle of the heart, varying its contractility and altering the frequency of spontaneous discharge of the pace-maker zones. Control over the diameter of the blood vessels is exerted through the smooth muscle of the vessel; this muscle is especially effective in the "resistance vessels" whereas we have seen that in large vessels the force exerted is usually ineffective in reducing the diameter. Contraction of the smooth muscle of veins takes place, and is undoubtedly employed in reflex adaptations requiring a reduction in the capacity of the vascular system.

Nervous Control of the Heart

Vagus

The frequency of the heart beat may be slowed by stimulation of the vagus nerve, the parasympathetic supply; this is the so-called *negative chronotropic effect*; in addition, the force of contraction may be reduced— the *negative inotropic effect*, but this is not so easily demonstrated. The action of the vagus may be blocked by atropine and mimicked by acetylcholine or muscarine. It will be recalled that the parasympathetic nerve supply to an organ relays in ganglia close to the innervated organ; so with the vagus, the preganglionic axons relay in numerous ganglia scattered in both atria and in the A.V. groove; postganglionic fibres run to the atria, the bundle of His and to the base of the ventricles. The right vagus tends to arborize in the S.A. node and the left in the A.V. node (Fig. 2.18 summarizes roughly the complex innervation). The nervous control seems to be exerted, as we might expect, largely through the pacemaker zones, and it is here that nerve terminals, coming into close relation with the cells, are frequent.

Sympathetic

The reverse actions, positive chronotropic and inotropic effects, are brought about by stimulating the sympathetic supply to the heart; the effect is inhibited by propanolol so that the action involves the β-receptor, which is in contrast to the sympathetic activation of the smooth muscles of the blood vessels, which involves the α-receptor. The sympathetic supply to the heart leaves through the second to fourth thoracic nerves, relaying mainly in the stellate ganglion; postganglionic fibres are distributed in the cardiac plexuses, intricate masses of nerve fibres that supply the nodes and muscle fibres with both sympathetic and parasympathetic outflow from the central nervous system. Stimulation of the right stellate ganglion produces nearly three times greater increase in heart-rate than stimulation of the left, whereas the strength of ventricular contraction is influenced in the reverse manner, the left stellate ganglion causing the larger increase in contractility.

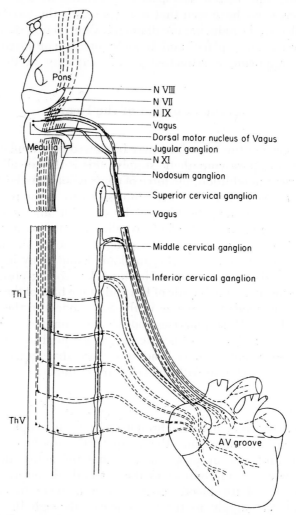

Fig. 2.18. A diagram of the innervation of the mammalian heart. The continuous lines, running down the spinal cord, represent sympathetic accelerator fibres which are preganglionic and synapse in the sympathetic chain before innervating the atria and the ventricles. Ascending along the same nerve supply are sensory pain fibres. The parasympathetic supply, slowing the heart, passes as preganglionic fibres via the vagus nerve and these synapse in the heart, primarily the pacemaker region and the atrioventricular node. Sensory fibres also ascend in the vagal pathways. (Bard Macleod's *Physiology in Modern Medicine*, Kimpton.)

Reciprocal Innervation

As with so many systems, reflex control over activity of the heart is exerted by reciprocal activation and inhibition; thus the reflex response to baroreceptor stimulation is brought about by activation of the vagus and inhibition of the sympathetic supply; this is demonstrated by the reflex slowing of the heart and fall in blood pressure that can take place even when the vagi are cut. Thus the sympathetic exerts a tonic action on the heart both in respect to rate and force of contraction.

The mechanisms through which the neurotransmitters, acetylcholine and noradrenaline, influence the heart have been discussed earlier (Vol. 2); the strong effect of adrenergic substances on the strength of the heart-beat is presumably related to increased entry of Ca^{++} into the muscle fibres.

Vasomotor Apparatus

The sympathetic supply causes constriction of arterioles by activating the circularly orientated smooth muscle; there is normally a vasoconstrictor tone, in the sense that the smooth muscle is maintained at a definite tension through sympathetic discharge, so that cutting the sympathetic supply to a limb causes dilatation of the blood vessels to the skin. Thus vasodilatation is most often an essentially negative phenomenon, the inhibition of sympathetic vasomotor tone; however, there are definite vasodilator nerves running to the blood vessels of the muscles, as opposed to the skin, so that stimulation of these causes the blood vessels to expand. Since it is difficult to conceive of an active expansion of the blood vessels, this dilatation must be attributed to an inhibition of an inherent tonus in the smooth muscle of the vessels.

This *myogenic tone* is probably important in the phenomenon of autoregulation, the name given to the tendency for the blood-flow through an organ to be independent of the perfusion pressure in spite of denervation; it seems that a rise in pressure enhances the myogenic tone of the arterioles, thereby increasing the resistance and stabilizing the flow-rate (Bayliss, 1902). Thus there are two mechanisms of vasodilatation; inhibition of sympathetic activity and inhibition of the inherent muscular tone.

Cholinergic Vasodilator

The sympathetic vasodilator fibres to skeletal and cardiac muscle are cholinergic, a logical arrangement, since exercise of the skeletal muscles is usually accompanied by discharge of the adrenal hormones into the blood; if these exerted the same vasoconstrictor action on the skeletal muscle arterioles as they did in the skin and viscera, they would seriously hamper the supply of blood to the exercising muscles.

Histaminergic Vasodilators

According to Brody (1966) there is a group of vasodilators brought into play during reflex vasodilatation and operating through the carotid sinus and aortic arch baroreceptors, that release histamine at their nerve endings, the amount of ^{3}H-labelled histamine passing into the blood perfusing a limb being increased during sympathetic stimulation. This histaminergic type of dilatation was sustained for longer than the more transient cholinergic type, and it was considered by Beck *et al.* (1966) that this might be important in the vasodilatation of muscle during exercise.

Antidromic Response

In addition to these vasodilator responses there is the so-called *antidromic response*, the vasodilatation described by Bayliss on stimulating the posterior roots of a nerve; the impulses run down the sensory fibres to their terminations in the periphery and thus are antidromic. It is certainly unlikely that vasodilator impulses would originate in the cell bodies of the sensory neurones and run down to the periphery, since they would be blocked by the normal traffic of sensory impulses running centrally. Certainly, in any depressor response, involving dilatation of peripheral blood vessels, antidromic impulses are not involved, and it is considered that this antidromic response reveals a branching of the sensory axon, so that an action potential, initiated at its terminal in the skin or other tissue, passes up to the cord but of course also passes down the branch; if this branch were connected to a blood vessel, the action potential might cause dilatation. Essentially, then, the antidromic response is the basis of the axon-reflex described by Lewis, the dilatation of skin blood vessels that occurs on stroking the skin when the connexion of the sensory nerve with the central nervous system has been cut (Fig. 4.12, Vol. 2).

Local Activation

We shall see that exercising a limb causes an immediate dilatation of the blood vessels in its muscles, and this is considered to be due largely to the liberation of some agent by the exercising muscle that acts either directly on the vessels or indirectly through local axon reflexes.

Veins

The veins, large and small, are also susceptible to nervous control; thus sympathetic stimulation decreases their distensibility and permits the more efficient transmission of blood required when cardiac output is increased in exercise. This is especially manifest in the lungs (p. 188), and ensures that the large amounts of blood pumped into the pulmonary system during exercise do not remain in large pools, as would occur if the blood-vessels were too distensible. Certainly the amount of blood in the lungs, which amounts to some 10 per cent of the whole, is remarkably constant in the face of large variations in cardiac output, so that the concept of the lungs acting as a reservoir of blood that ensures adequate filling of the heart, is probably too simple.

CENTRAL MECHANISMS

Bulbar Centres

Ablations of certain regions of the medulla cause serious cardiovascular defects, and these regions are called *cardiac* and *vasomotor centres*; they are collections of neurones that receive impulses from all parts of the body, and other parts of the brain, and send motor discharges to the heart and muscle walls of the blood vessels. There is normally a tonic discharge from the centres, so that destruction of these causes a fall in blood pressure in consequence of the dilatation of the "resistance vessels". Since cutting the vagus nerves of the animal usually causes an acceleration of the heart, it would seem that the heart-rate is tonically inhibited by the bulbar centre.

Cardiac and Vasomotor Centres

Cardiac centres are differentiated from the vasomotor centres, and these are divided, in turn, into cardio-inhibitory, cardio-acceleratory, vasoconstrictor and vasodepressor portions; it must be appreciated that the reticular formation of the medulla, in which these regions are located, is a highly complex network of neurones and fibres, so that it is not easy to characterize the centres morphologically. In general, as we should expect, the cardio-inhibitory and vasodepressor centres are closely related, as are the cardio-acceleratory and vasoconstrictor centres. The centres show some tonic activity, so that cutting off the influence of the vasoconstrictor centre from the periphery, by section of the medulla, causes a profound lowering of blood pressure due to loss of tone of the muscles of the arterioles. In general, the centres interact with each other, so that a pressor response, i.e. a physiological adjustment leading to raised arterial pressure, is mediated not only by the cardio-acceleratory and vasoconstrictor centres but by reciprocal inhibition of the opposing centres.

Cholinergic Vasodilator Response

A further point to note is that a depressor response, i.e. a reflex leading to lowering of blood pressure, does not involve activation of the cholinergic vasodilator fibres of the sympathetic; these are activated independently from brain sites other than the vasomotor centres of the medulla; the pathway includes the hypothalamus as a relay station, whence the messages are eventually carried to the ventrolateral region of the spinal cord containing the sympathetic preganglionic neurones.

Hypothalamic Centres

The hypothalamus is concerned in the integration of so many visceral functions that its involvement in the integration of vascular reflexes would not be surprising. One such involvement has already been described when considering the role of the hypothalamus in thermoregulation; if this region of the brain is to control the blood-flow to the skin in accordance with the thermal demands, we must expect a close cooperation between the bulbar vasomotor centres and the thermoregulatory centre. Hilton has emphasized the role of the hypothalamus, generally, in the integration of cardiovascular reflexes with the other visceral reflexes.

Defence Reaction

This is especially evident in the *defence reaction*, or *sham rage*, seen in the cat either by stimulating a specific area in the hypothalamus—the defence reaction centre—or by removing higher parts of the brain thereby releasing this reaction from inhibition by higher centres. The reaction involves snarling and hissing, dilatation of the pupils and piloerection, and is accompanied by a vasodilatation of the blood vessels to the muscles by contrast with the constriction of the skin vessels. Recent studies from Hilton's laboratory have supported the contention that the hypothalamus is closely involved in the carotid sinus baroreceptor reflex. Stimulation of localized regions brought about depressor responses involving sympathetic inhibition and vagal activation.

Carotid Sinus Reflex. The similarity between the response to hypothalamic stimulation and the response to raising the pressure in the isolated carotid sinus to 160 mm Hg is illustrated in Fig. 2.19. Lesions in this area can lead to abolition of the carotid sinus depressor

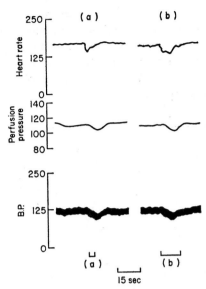

Fig. 2.19. A comparison of the effect of raised pressure in an isolated perfused carotid sinus with stimulation of the depressor area of the hypothalamus on blood pressure (bottom trace), heart rate (top trace), and on hind limb perfusion pressure (middle trace) in the cat. At (a) the carotid sinus pressure was raised to 160 mm Hg (static) and at (b) the hypothalamus was stimulated with a current of 140 μ A. (Hilton and Spyer, *J. Physiol.*)

response, so that Hilton and Spyer (1971) conclude that its integrity is essential for this reflex, in fact that the region is the place where the primary afferent impulses from the carotid sinus-nerve relay in the brain, running in the tractus solitarius of the medulla.

Vasodilator Region in Brain-Stem

The parts of the brain-stem, stimulation of which leads to vaso-dilatation in the muscles, have been accurately plotted by a stereotactic manoeuvre by Coote, Hilton and Zbrozyna (1973); the region extends caudally from the hypothalamus as far down as the pons and medulla and, in fact, in the medulla it coincides with the classical vasomotor pressor centre (Fig. 2.20). When implanted electrodes were stimulated in the waking animal, responses were obtained similar in many ways to the defence reaction characteristically seen when stimulating the hypothalamus, namely flattening of the ears, pupillary dilatation and piloerection of the tail; accompanying this was a reduction in the vascular resistance in the hind limb, unaffected by atropine and presumably due to inhibition of adrenergic vasoconstriction. These authors concluded that, in the true defence reaction in the intact animal, the whole region stretching from medulla to hypothalamus would be activated; in this case vasodilatation due to both cholinergic fibres activated by the hypothalamus, and inhibition of adrenergic tone, would combine to produce the large increase in limb blood-flow necessary for the emergency.

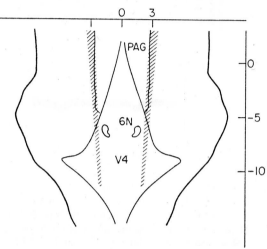

Fig. 2.20. Diagrammatic dorsal view of floor of fourth ventricle showing area (shaded) in the lower brain-stem from which muscle vasodilatation is obtained. PAG, periaqueductal grey matter; 6N, nucleus of the abducens; V4, fourth ventricle. (Coote *et al.*, *J. Physiol.*)

Relation to Baroreceptor Reflex. A further interesting point brought out by these workers is the apparent failure of the baroreceptor reflex to influence the vasodilatation accompanying the defence reaction. Thus, normally, a rise in arterial pressure, such as that occurring during the defence reaction, is opposed by a baroreceptor reflex that slows the heart and causes peripheral vasodilatation, two responses that tend to bring the arterial pressure back towards its original level. Several studies have shown that the cardiac inhibition is suppressed during the defence reaction. The reaction of the blood vessels is not suppressed, however, so that the reflex dilatation of the blood vessels to the muscles that accompanies the baroreceptor reflex remains. Thus the high blood-flow to the limbs, necessary in the defence reaction, is assured; the cholinergic vasodilatation, initiated in the hypothalamus, being reinforced by the reflex inhibition of sympathetic tone (Djojosugito *et al.*, 1970). The fact that the arterial pressure remains high in the face of the vasodilatation is due to the increase in cardiac output permitted by the suppression of vagal inhibition. In this connexion it must be pointed out that not all species have the cholinergic vasodilator mechanism, many species, including monkeys, relying on inhibition of vasomotor tone for increasing blood-flow to the limbs. Thus in these species, the defence reaction would require release of adrenergic vasoconstriction, i.e. the cooperation of the baroreceptor reflex.

Stimulation of Defence Area

The experiments of Djojosugito *et al.* are instructive and are typified by Fig. 2.21, which shows the arterial blood pressure, heart-rate,

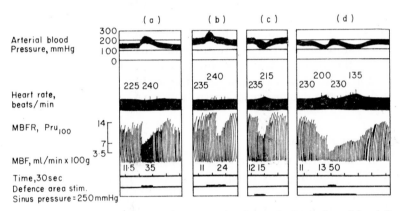

Fig. 2.21. The effect of carotid baroreceptor activation and stimulation of the defence area (DA), either alone or combined, on the cardiovascular responses in the cat. The cat was immobilized with Flaxedil, ventilated, vagal nerves and the left carotid sinus nerve cut. MBFR, muscle blood flow resistance; MBF, muscle blood flow. (a) Defence area stimulation with right carotid sinus in circuit and exposed to the BP rise. (b) As (a) but carotid sinus excluded from the circulation and kept at a constant pressure of 40 mm Hg. (c) Elevation of the carotid baroreceptors to 250 mm Hg pressure in an external circuit. (d) As (c) but when the fall in pressure was maximal the defence area was stimulated as in (b). Note the large increase in MBF compared with (b) while the same heart-rate is reached. (Djojosugito *et al.*, *Acta physiol. scand.*)

muscle blood-flow resistance (MBFR) and muscle blood-flow (MBF) in a cat under different conditions. The vagi had been cut, in order to remove any possible baroreceptor activity from the aorta, and one carotid sinus-nerve had been cut; thus baroreceptor activity was confined to a single carotid sinus. In (*a*) the defence area was stimulated with the one intact carotid sinus baroreceptor; blood pressure rises and also heart rate; there is a fall in muscle resistance indicating dilatation of the resistance vessels, and the muscle blood-flow (MBF) increases from 11·5 to 35 ml/min. In (b) the same defence area stimulation was repeated; but baroreceptor reflexes were excluded by excluding the left carotid sinus from the circulation and perfusing it with a low pressure. Now the muscle blood-flow increases only moderately. (c) Shows the effect of activating the carotid baroreceptors by exposing them to 250 mm Hg sinus-pressure; arterial pressure and heart-rate fall together with the resistance in the muscle blood-vessels, but, because of the fall in arterial pressure, blood-flow in the muscles only increases a little. In (d) the same rise in sinus-pressure is brought about but superimposed on this is stimulation of the defence area; the fall in arterial pressure is reversed, heart-rate increases, and the blood-flow through the muscles attains a very large value, namely 50 ml/min. If we compare this with 35 ml/min when the defence area was stimulated without carotid sinus stimulation, the cooperation between the two reactions becomes evident. Thus, as in the vaso-dilatation of sustained exercise, the baroreceptor reflex as a whole is reset during the defence reaction (p. 155).

Single Unit Responses

Neurones in the medial region of the caudal hypothalamus could be found responding, by changed frequency of discharge, to changes in arterial pressure or to hypoxia induced by cyanide; some units showed an increased discharge and these were probably activated by the chemoreceptors by contrast with those that showed a diminished discharge, which were thought to be activated by baroreceptors (Thomas and Calaresu, 1972).

The "Vasomotor Centres" of the Medulla

As indicated earlier, the classical workers, basing themselves on changes in arterial pressure taking place on stimulation or destruction of various medullary regions, defined several vasomotor centres, and it was considered that vasomotor responses, integrated at higher levels of the brain, e.g. the cortex or hypothalamus, would be mediated by activating these centres, each of which had a "ready-made" type of response; e.g. vasoconstriction with increased heart-rate. More recent work, for example that of Manning, requires a modification of this viewpoint. He found that, even when very large lesions were made in the medulla involving these classical "centres", complex reflex adjustments, such as the pressor responses to occlusion of the carotid arteries or stimulation of the sciatic nerve, were still possible, whilst stimulation of the defence area of the hypothalamus gave the typical defence vascular reactions. It would seem that the integration of cardiovascular responses to meet any situation relies primarily on a relatively limited portion of the brain-stem, confined to the midline structures stretching from the hypothalamus to the medulla. These regions obviously come into relation with the other medullary areas and cooperate with them in producing the final response to a given situation, so that lesions in the "classical centres" must produce some impairment, but the ability to execute the complex vascular and other visceral reactions involved in the defence reaction is by no means abolished by destroying these centres, so long as the thin midline region is spared.

Chemical Influences on the Vasomotor Centres

Sensory information regarding the chemical composition of the blood may be conveyed to the cardiovascular and vasomotor centres through the carotid and aortic body afferent nerves; however, the neurones of the vasomotor centre are themselves highly sensitive to the PCO_2 and PO_2 of the blood, so that an increase in PCO_2 or decrease in PO_2 of the arterial blood causes an increase in discharge from the centre, leading to raised blood pressure; on the other hand, hyperventilation, leading to a reduction in blood PCO_2, causes a profound lowering of the blood pressure due to paralysis of the vasomotor centre.

Raised Intracranial Pressure

Perhaps the most interesting demonstration of the activity of the vasomotor centre is when the pressure in the hollow cavities of the brain, the intracranial pressure (Ch. 6), is raised by forcibly injecting fluid into them; if the increase of pressure is such as to cause the cerebral arteries to collapse, the resulting asphyxia of the vasomotor centre causes the arterial pressure to rise to the point that the cerebral arteries open up. The renewed flow of blood through the vasomotor centre causes cessation of its discharge, so that the blood pressure falls, but this now allows the arteries to collapse again, giving rise to asphyxia of the vasomotor centres, and so on. Thus the arterial pressure rises and falls rhythmically so long as the increased intracranial pressure is maintained.

SOME CARDIOVASCULAR REFLEXES

Baroreceptor Reflexes

We have seen how the discharge in the afferent nerve fibres from the carotid sinus and aortic arch waxes and wanes with each pulsatile increase in systolic pressure; when the average pressure increases, the average frequency of discharge increases. If we record the *efferent* discharge *to* the heart from a sympathetic cardiac fibre, we observe a rhythmic, rather than continuous, discharge, due to a periodic inhibition of tonic sympathetic activity as the arterial pressure rises; there is a greater inhibition during inflation of the lungs—the *inflation reflex* (p. 129). Fig. 2.22 illustrates this inhibition in the normal animal, (a), and its absence in the animal with its sinus nerve and vagus cut, (b).

Effects of Stimulation of Sinus and Aortic Nerves

In the intact animal, electrical stimulation of, say, the aortic nerve causes slowing of the heart (bradycardia) and a fall in blood pressure; the bradycardia is due to the inhibitory impulses in the vagi and the

(a)

(b)

Fig. 2.22. The effect of lung inflation on sympathetic discharge to the heart. In each record the upper trace is endotracheal pressure; middle trace, femoral arterial pressure; lower trace, electroneurogram from the inferior cardiac nerve. In (a) the carotid sinus and vagi are intact and inhibition of sympathetic discharge is seen with each heart beat and with lung inflation. In (b) the sinus nerve and vagi are cut and no inhibition of the sympathetic discharge is seen. Time marks, 0·1 sec. (Downing & Siegal, *Amer. J. Physiol.*)

inhibition of tonic sympathetic impulses, whereas the fall in blood-pressure is due to inhibition of sympathetic tone. Electrical stimulation will, of course, excite both the baroreceptor and chemoreceptor fibres of the aortic and carotid sinus nerve, and since their reflex responses can be antagonistic—the chemoreceptors produce a rise in vascular resistance whereas the baroreceptors produce a lowering—it is not surprising that the effects of stimulation of the nerves are variable and depend on the frequency of excitation, a given frequency tending to excite one form of nerve fibre in preference to the other.

Perfused Sinus or Aorta

To separate the effects, and study each reflex in isolation, a variety of experimental manoeuvres have been employed. In general, it is possible to perfuse the carotid sinus and aortic regions with a separate circulation, so that alterations in the pressure in the carotid sinus, and/or the aortic arch may be studied, or alternatively the pressure may be maintained constant and the gas-content of the perfusing blood altered. An experimental arrangement permitting the study of both the carotid sinus and aortic arch, employed by Angell James and Daly is illustrated in Fig. 2.7, p. 104. Under these conditions raising the pressure in the carotid sinus reduces the heart-rate and arterial pressure—the *depressor response*—the fall in arterial pressure being accompanied by a reflex vasodilatation. Conversely, lowering the pressure in the sinus increases heart-rate and arterial pressure—the *pressor response*. In a similar way it can be shown that stimulation of the carotid bodies by high PCO_2 (hypercapnia) or low PO_2 (hypoxia) causes slowing of the heart and systemic vasoconstriction, leading to increased arterial pressure. Stimulation of the aortic bodies also causes vasoconstriction but the action on the heart may be slowing (*bradycardia*) or acceleration (*tachycardia*). These reflexes have been demonstrated in animals whose respiration was controlled artificially, but Daly has shown that they may be obscured in the intact, spontaneously breathing, animal through reflexes initiated elsewhere, particularly in the lungs. Thus in the spontaneously breathing animal the responses to carotid body stimulation are *tachycardia* and *vasodilatation*, due to competition of the primary reflex bradycardia and vasoconstriction with secondary mechanisms evoked by the concomitant increase in breathing, by the altered blood pressure, and by the secretion of catecholamines.

Inflation-Reflexes

Inflation of the lungs activates stretch receptors in these organs to bring about a reflex tachycardia and vasodilatation, so that stimulation of the carotid bodies by hypoxia, by increasing inflation of the lungs, will evoke this inflation-reflex which, in fact, overrides the cardiovascular reflex from the carotid body. It might appear, then, that the primary vascular reflex is unimportant physiologically, but this is not true since there are situations in which the animal may become hypoxic and hypercapnic without increased ventilation of the lungs, namely when submerged in water, when respiration is inhibited. The physiological response to diving in such typical diving animals as the duck or seal consists in an immediate slowing of the heart, *bradycardia*, and an increased peripheral resistance that virtually closes down the circulation to "less essential organs", thereby permitting an economy in the use of oxygen whilst permitting adequate blood-flow through the brain and those muscles that are necessary for underwater activity. This reflex is initiated by sensory stimulation of the nose or beak by immersion, and so disappears if the trigeminal nerve (NV) is not intact; it is reinforced by the developing asphyxia, whereas lung movements oppose it, through the inflation-reflex.

Apnoeic Asphyxia. The demonstration of this inflation-reflex, initiated by apnoeic asphyxia, was carried out by perfusing the systemic circulation of a spontaneously breathing dog, avoiding circulation of blood through the pulmonary circulation. Thus the lungs operated only to draw air in and out but were without effect on the state of aeration of the systemic blood, this being controlled by an oxygenator in the perfusion circuit. The carotid bifurcation and aortic arch regions were separated from the main circulation, and perfused separately; in this way the composition of the blood flowing through the chemoreceptors could be altered without affecting the blood passing through the brain. To simulate apnoeic asphyxia, movements of the lungs were prevented, and the PO_2 and PCO_2 of the blood perfusing the carotid bodies were decreased and increased respectively. The result was a general vasoconstriction revealed by an increase in resistance to blood-flow (Fig. 2.23(a)). If the blood perfusing the carotid body was made normal, the vasoconstriction was largely abolished, showing that the carotid and aortic bodies were responsible. Re-establishing the lung movements during asphyxia of the carotid and aortic bodies gave rise to a fall in systemic vascular resistance and abolition of the tachycardia (Fig. 2.23(b)). However, if the lungs were denervated by section of the vagi, spontaneous lung movements no longer prevented the increase in resistance (Fig. 2.23(c)).

Significance of Inflation-Reflex. Expansion of the lungs brings about a vasodilatation proportional to the degree of expansion; it is unaffected by atropine and so not due to activation of sympathetic cholinergic vasodilators, but it is inhibited by a-sympathetic blockers, such as bretylium tosylate, under which condition tonic vasoconstriction is abolished so that further dilatation by inhibition of sympathetic impulses is not possible. Although the resistance to flow in skin, splanchnic area and muscles is decreased, that in the muscles is decreased much more, so that there is a preferential shunting of blood to the

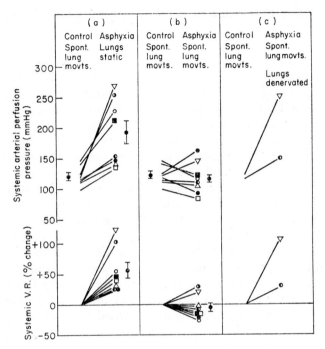

Fig. 2.23. The effects of apnoeic asphyxia on the cardiovascular system of the dog. The carotid bodies and the aortic arch were perfused in a separate circuit and the lungs bypassed. The control levels are shown on the left hand side of each trace and the effect of hypoxic hypercapnia on the right. In (a) the lungs were static and the fall in PO_2 and increase in PCO_2 caused a rise in systemic pressure and vascular resistance. In (b) the lungs were allowed to move, and the effect abolished. In (c) the vagi were cut to denervate the lungs and the effect is again seen. The mean values ($\pm$SE) are shown in (a) and (b) for eight observations in five experiments. In (c) two observations in two experiments. (Angell James and Daly, *J. Physiol.*)

limbs. Thus the expansion of the lungs during exercise contributes reflexly to the redistribution of blood-flow necessary for the nutrition of the exercising limbs.

Interaction of Baroreceptor and Chemoreceptor Activities

The reflex responses brought about, say, by changed PO_2 or PCO_2 of the blood result in an alteration of arterial pressure and consequently they are modified by baroreceptor reflexes tending to bring the arterial pressure back to its original value; thus raised PCO_2 increases arterial pressure and heart-rate, but these increases are modified by the baroreceptor reflex that tends to decrease arterial pressure and slow the heart.

Hypoxia

The complexities arising from this interaction are well illustrated by the effects of hypoxia. Inhalation of air with a low PO_2, thereby reducing the P_aO_2 of the arterial blood, has a reflex action on the cardiovascular system, operating through the carotid and aortic bodies. The reflex tends to raise the blood-flow through the brain by causing a raised arterial pressure through peripheral vasoconstriction combined with cardio-acceleration. The raised arterial pressure, of course, brings into play the baroreceptor response, and the net effect in the intact animal is a slowing of the heart with maintained vasoconstriction.

Asphyxia. The high P_aCO_2 that accompanies hypoxia during asphyxia has similar actions, operating through the chemoreceptors of the carotid and aortic bodies, but these are augmented by a direct action on the neurones of the vasomotor centre, promoting peripheral vasoconstriction and cardio-acceleration. The high P_aCO_2 also has a direct vasodilator action on the arteries of the brain (Chapter 6), so that asphyxia is accompanied by an increased blood-flow through the brain.

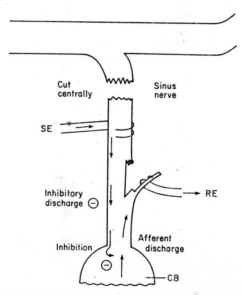

Fig. 2.24. Illustrating the inhibitory effect of stimulation of fibres in the carotid sinus nerve; afferent discharge is recorded in part of the nerve (RE) whilst stimulating electrodes (SE) are applied to another part. CB, carotid body.

Arterial Pressure and Chemoreceptors

A further point concerns the manner in which the chemoreceptors themselves are influenced by arterial pressure, since this could influence the availability of O_2 to the rapidly metabolizing glomus cells. In fact, the responses of chemoreceptors are not greatly modified by changes in arterial pressure, a valuable feature permitting the independent sensoring of chemical and pressure changes.

Efferent Influences on Carotid and Aortic Reflexes

Stimulation of the sympathetic supply to the sinus and aorta, through the cervical sympathetic trunk, causes an increased sensitivity of the baroreceptors, possibly through activation of smooth muscle fibres in the adventitia and thus altering the setting of the receptors (Sampson and Mills, 1970). In a similar way, stimulation of the sympathetic facilitates the chemoreceptor responses of the carotid and aortic bodies,* an action that may well be mediated through constriction of the blood vessels since, in vitro, adrenergic drugs had no effect (Eyzaguirre and Lewin, 1961). An opposite effect, namely the inhibition of carotid body afferent activity, was described by Neil and O'Regan, who separated a branch of the sinus nerve from the remainder and cut it centrally, as in Fig. 2.24; stimulation of this branch caused a diminution of the afferent discharge in the remainder of the nerve in response to hypoxia. The normal efferent activity was recorded from a branch separated from the carotid body with its central connexions intact, as in Fig. 2.25(a), whilst afferent activity could be recorded in another branch, similarly separated, but with its peripheral termination intact and cut centrally as Fig. 2.25(b). Under these conditions the response of the animal to breathing hypoxic air consisted of both afferent and efferent discharges; the efferent discharge was abolished by cutting the connexion of the sinus nerve with the glossopharyngeal nerve; it was also very considerably reduced if the afferent activity in the remainder of the sinus-nerve was abolished by cutting it peripherally, so that the inhibition appears to be a negative feedback from the chemoreceptors themselves, similar to that seen in other sensory systems, e.g. the ear

---

* Biscoe and Purves (1967) activated the sympathetic in a natural way, as opposed to electrical stimulation, and obtained increased chemoreceptor discharges; this was not confirmed by Davies and Lahiri (1973), nor yet by Majcherczyk et al. (1974) who made use of the increased sympathetic activity that is observed when the chemoreceptors are stimulated naturally; this did not facilitate activity in the contralateral chemoreceptors. We must note that when Biscoe and Stehbens (1967) cut the sympathetic supply to the carotid body they observed no degeneration of fibres in relation to the Type I glomus cells.

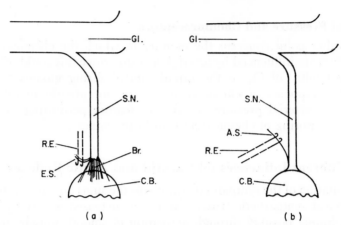

Fig. 2.25. Diagrammatic representation of the methods used to record sinus nerve activity. A fine slip of fibres is teased from the main sinus nerve to record either efferent activity to the carotid body as in (a) or afferent activity as in (b). A.S., afferent slip; S.N., sinus nerve; E.S., efferent slip; G.L., glossopharyngeal nerve; R.E., recording electrodes. C.B. carotid body. (Neil and O'Regan, *J. Physiol.*)

(Vol. 5). Removal of the cervical sympathetic supply did not affect the responses, so that the efferent activity is presumably due to neurones of N IX passing through the petrosal ganglion in the sinus nerve.

Vasomotor Reaction

Neil and O'Regan excluded a vasomotor effect, e.g. a vasodilatation, as the cause of the inhibition, but a critical analysis of their experimental technique by Goodman suggests that the effects of electrical stimulation of the sinus-nerve could, indeed, have been due to stimulation of the vasodilator fibres running in it. In addition he showed that, when a branch of the sinus-nerve is stimulated, it is easy for the fibres in another branch, from which the recording is taken, to be excited; the antidromically conducted effects of this stimulation would depress the sensitivity of the nerve endings—antidromic depression—and so give rise to an apparent, but factitious, inhibition. When this stimulation is prevented, true efferent activity in the sinus-nerve does, indeed, influence the response to hypoxia, but not in the regular manner described by Neil and O'Regan. This would be consistent with an effect of the stimulation on vasomotor fibres in the sinus-nerve; these are both sympathetic (constrictor) and parasympathetic (glossopharyngeal vasodilator), so that the effects of electrical stimulation would vary according to the existing state of vasomotor tone and the relative degrees to which the two types of fibre were stimulated by the electrical pulses.

If Goodman's interpretation is correct, we do not have to invoke any specific action of efferent fibres on the glomus cells, or their related sensory fibres; instead, we must ask how a change in blood-flow through the carotid bodies, normally very high, can influence the response to hypoxia.

Reflexes Initiated in the Atria and Great Veins

Bainbridge Reflex

Bainbridge described a reflex increase in heart-rate in consequence of a rise in pressure in the great veins produced by intravenous infusions—the *Bainbridge reflex*—a response that would be valuable in adjusting cardiac output to any increase in venous return. Although this reflex has fallen into disrepute, work from Linden's laboratory has firmly established the existence of a reflex increase in heart-rate when a small bladder, placed in the junction between the pulmonary vein and the left atrium, is inflated (Fig. 2.26). The increased heart-rate, mediated by the sympathetic outflow to the heart, was unaccompanied by an increased force of contraction, so that the S.A.-node is

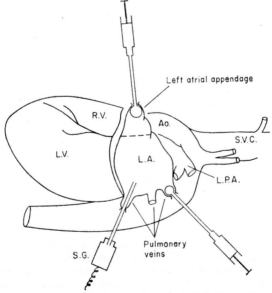

Fig. 2.26. The preparation used to demonstrate the Bainbridge reflex. Latex balloons are placed in the left atrium at the junction with the pulmonary veins and can be inflated with saline at 38°C to distend this region. Left atrial pressure is recorded by the transducer S.G. R.V. and L.V., left and right ventricles; L.A., left atrium; S.V.C., superior vena cava; L.P.A., left pulmonary artery. (Kappagoda *et al.*, *J. Physiol.*)

specifically affected. The increased frequency of action potentials in the vagus in the neck suggested that the receptors were the characteristic nerve endings in the subendocardial tissue described by Coleridge *et al.* (p. 105). A similar increase in heart-rate was found on stretching the junction of the right atrium with the vena cava; and, by applying local pressure with probes, definite areas could be identified, stimulation of which produced responses in a single vagal fibre (Kappagoda *et al.*, 1972).*

Diuresis. A chronic distension of the great veins is indicative of too great a circulating blood-volume, in so far as the heart is unable

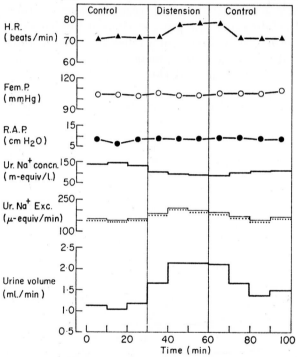

Fig. 2.27. The effect of distension of a segment of the right atrium on the cardio-vascular system and the kidney. Distension causes an increase in heart-rate (H.R.), no change in femoral arterial pressure (Fem.P.) and right atrial pressure (R.A.P.). Urine sodium (Ur. Na+) level fell. Urine sodium excreted increased, as did the urine volume, which doubled. (Kappagoda *et al.*, *J. Physiol.*)

* Earlier workers obtained conflicting results when distending the atrium by various means, e.g. infusion of saline, expanding a balloon, etc., and it is clear that the well-defined increase in heart-rate is achieved only if the receptors at the junction of the atrium and vein are excited. More diffuse stimulation, as with a large balloon in the atrium, probably results in other responses leading to slowing of the heart.

to deal adequately with the venous input. An adaptation to this condition is a diuresis, i.e. increased output of urine (Ch. 5). Thus Fig. 2.27 shows the increased urinary volume when a balloon in the junction between the right atrium and vena cava was inflated. The diuresis is apparently not achieved by a reduced secretion of anti-diuretic hormone (ADH), although such a reflex mechanism has been postulated repeatedly as a factor in the control of blood-volume; nevertheless, the agent is blood-borne, since the reflex remains in the denervated kidney (Ledsome et al., 1961).

Cardiac Chemoreceptors

In his analysis of the afferent fibres from the heart, Armour found some that did not discharge phasically with the beat, but did do so when the ventricles fibrillated; and these turned out to be chemo-sensitive fibres presumably derived from chemoreceptors within the ventricular wall and aortic root. These may well play a role during ischaemic states caused by coronary failure. As to the type of receptor cells that initiate the response, we may presume that they are similar to those in the more organized carotid and aortic bodies, perhaps like the "miniglomera" found in the adventitia of the carotid and occipital arteries at some distance from the principal carotid body (Matsura, 1973). These have a similar electron-microscopical appearance to that of the glomus tissue of the carotid body, but they are small, in the region of 30 to 500 μ in diameter.

EFFECTS OF HUMORAL AGENTS

The hormones most obviously related to cardiovascular changes are those of the adrenal gland, some 85 per cent (in man) being adrenaline and the remainder noradrenaline. Noradrenaline, it will be recalled, is the adrenergic transmitter whilst in many of its actions adrenaline mimics the action of noradrenaline and thus mimics the actions of the adrenergic nerves, which are mainly sympathetic.

Alpha- and Beta-Receptors

It will also be recalled that effectors influenced by the adrenergic autonomic system, e.g. the smooth muscle of the gut, myometrium, cardiac muscle, and so on, may be characterized as having "receptors" of two main kinds according to their sensitivity to certain adrenergic-type drugs, and according as their activities may be blocked by specific inhibitors. The α-receptor is usually highly responsive to the natural transmitter, noradrenaline, so that where the α-receptor is concerned, such as action on the smooth muscle of arterioles, the nictitating membrane of the eye, and the pilo-erector muscles of the skin, the contraction brought about by noradrenaline is equivalent to that obtained by sympathetic stimulation. The α-receptor is specifically blocked by phenoxybenzamine. The β-receptor is recognized by its sensitivity to the artificial derivative of noradrenaline, isoproterenol (Fig. 2.28)

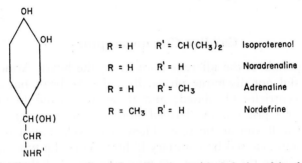

Fig. 2.28. The structure of noradrenaline (norepinephrine) and its derivatives.

whilst its action is typically blocked by propanolol. Usually, when both receptors are present on a given effector, the α-receptor is excitatory and the β-inhibitory, but this is not always true. Certain tissues are predominantly activated by the β-receptors, and in the present context the cardiac muscle and S.A.-node are typical examples, so that isoproterenol will mimic the effects of sympathetic stimulation. Since noradrenaline is liberated by the sympathetic nerves to the heart, this means that noradrenaline can excite both α- and β-receptors; where both are present in the same tissue, as in the smooth muscle of many organs, the α-effect predominates.

Adrenaline

In general, adrenaline, the dominant adrenal hormone, influences both the α- and β-receptors, so that its influence on effectors such as the smooth muscle of arteries, which has both types of receptor, is often complex. The dominant effect is on the α-vasoconstrictors bringing about a generalized vasoconstriction with a rise in blood-pressure assisted by its positive inotropic and chronotropic effects on the heart, this time operating through β-receptors. We have seen that skeletal muscle of many species has a cholinergic vasodilator mechanism that comes into play when activated through the hypothalamus;

however, intra-arterial injection of low concentrations of adrenaline causes dilatation of the blood vessels in skeletal muscle, and this suggests that their smooth muscle also carries β-receptors which, when activated, cause dilatation, i.e. inhibition of tonic myogenic tension. Thus, under conditions of stress, when the animal needs a good supply of blood to its skeletal muscles, the adrenaline liberated from the adrenal gland could, through its β-action, contribute to this flow, whilst its strong vasoconstrictive α-action on the vasculature of the

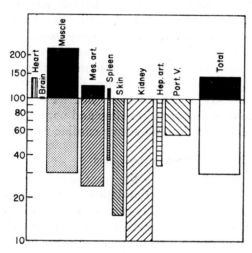

Fig. 2.29. The initial and secondary responses of various vascular beds to intra-arterial injection of 1 to 10 μg adrenaline. The light coloured blocks represent the initial response; dark coloured blocks, secondary response. (Green *et al.*, *Handbook of Physiology*.)

splanchnic area would tend to divert blood from this region. The blood vessels of the heart—coronary circulation—and brain are also caused to dilate through the β-action of adrenaline, a vasoconstriction, either through hormone action or sympathetic stimulation, not being observed (pp. 171 and Ch. 6).

Variety of Effects. The variety of responses to an intra-arterial injection of adrenaline according to the vascular bed stimulated is well illustrated by Fig. 2.29; here the initial effect—due to α-stimulation—is indicated by the light bars and is vasoconstrictor, causing a decrease in flow, indicated on the ordinates. The secondary response, which emerges after the α-effect has worn off and is due to β-action, since essentially similar effects are obtained after α-blockade with phenoxy-benzamine (Dibenzyline), is indicated by the black bars. The brain shows no appreciable response to adrenaline whilst skeletal muscle, mesenteric vessels and spleen show secondary dilator responses. The only effect on the heart is one of vasodilatation.

Subdivision of the β-Receptors

Lands *et al.* (1967) noted that when they studied the effects of a series of related derivatives of noradrenaline on four typical β-reactions, namely lipolysis, cardiac acceleration, bronchodilatation, and dilatation of peripheral blood vessels (after a-blockade), the order of effectiveness was very similar for lipolysis and cardiac acceleration, on the one hand, and for bronchodilatation and vasodepression on the other, but there was little correlation between the two pairs of effectors. Consequently, they suggested that the β-receptors be divided into two subclasses, β_1 and β_2. This means, of course, that it is practicable to find drugs that affect, say, cardiac action but have little influence on bronchodilatation; in fact noradrenaline and nordefrine (Fig. 2.28) do have little bronchodilatation but strong cardiac stimulation.

Acetylcholine and the Parasympathetic

Parasympathetic influences on the vasculature are not so important as those of the sympathetic; stimulation of the chorda tympani (a branch of the facial nerve, NVII) causes secretion of the submaxillary salivary gland and a strong vasodilatation, but since this latter effect is not blocked by atropine it seems that the nerve has no direct action on the vascular musculature; instead it has been shown that bradykinin (Vol. 2) is liberated, and this may well have the vasodilator effect (Hilton and Lewis, 1955). Stimulation of the vagus causes an increase in splanchnic blood-flow under experimental conditions of perfusion, but it has been argued by Grim (1963) that this could be an artefact, and Kewenter (1965) could find no evidence for this so far as the small intestine was concerned. In the intact animal it causes dilatation of both the bronchial and pulmonary circulations, effects that are blocked by atropine.

Cardiac Effects. Stimulation of the vagus causes slowing of the heart, as we have seen; it is unlikely to have much effect on the force of contraction of the ventricular myocardium, owing to the paucity of innervation of this tissue; and in fact, when the chronotropic (rate) effects were discounted, by using a heart beating with an artificial pacemaker, Schreiner *et al.* (1957) found no significant change in aortic and left atrial pressures, or cardiac output; when the pacemaker was turned off, and the heart beat with its own rhythm, the heart-rate decreased, but arterial pressure remained the same. The authors concluded that vagal stimulation had no effect on "left ventricular function", i.e. the stroke-work as a function of mean left atrial pressure.

Angiotensin

This is the most strongly vasoconstrictor hormone known; it is formed by an enzymatic reaction with renin, secreted by the cells of the juxtaglomerular apparatus of the kidney, and "renin substrate", which is an α_2-globulin of plasma or lymph (*angiotensinogen*); the reaction leads to the splitting off of a decapeptide—*Angiotensin I*—and

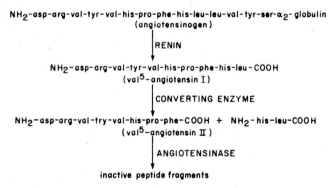

NH_2-asp-arg-val-tyr-val-his-pro-phe-his-leu-leu-val-tyr-ser-α_2- globulin
(angiotensinogen)

RENIN

NH_2-asp-arg-val-tyr-val-his-pro-phe-his-leu-COOH
(val^5-angiotensin I)

CONVERTING ENZYME

NH_2-asp-arg-val-try-val-his-pro-phe-COOH + NH_2-his-leu-COOH
(val^5-angiotensin II)

ANGIOTENSINASE

inactive peptide fragments

Fig. 2.30. Stages in the metabolism of angiotensin. (Sander and Huggins, *Ann. Rev. Pharmacol.*)

this is converted to the octapeptide—*Angiotensin II*—through a converting enzyme (Fig. 2.30). It is Angiotensin II that is the active vasoconstrictor substance. It may be regarded as a "local hormone" intimately concerned in renal mechanisms, and it is questionable whether it has any great significance, normally, in maintenance of arterial pressure, although there is little doubt that it is involved in pathological conditions of high blood-pressure associated with renal pathology, and in the vascular adaptation to severe haemorrhage (p. 160).

Bradykinin

This is another peptide "local hormone" (Vol. 2) with vasodilator activity concerned in local reactions to injury.

5-Hydroxytryptamine

As indicated in Vol. 2, 5-hydroxytryptamine is liberated from blood platelets when blood clots; it is an active vasoconstrictor and obviously contributes to local haemostasis.

Autoregulation in Skeletal Muscle

We have indicated earlier that in certain organs, especially the brain, the flow of blood tends to remain constant in the face of quite large variations in perfusion-pressure, where this is defined as the difference between arterial and venous pressures. In the case of the kidney, this definitely occurs in the denervated organ, and so non-neural mechanisms must be sought, but of course in the intact system neural mechanisms will have some effect and may in fact dominate the situation.

Rigid Tubes

It will be clear that if the total vascular bed of the organ behaved like a set of rigid tubes, and flow was laminar with viscosity unaffected by flow-rate, the pressure-flow relationship would be linear, as in Fig. 2.31(a), and there would be no evidence of autoregulation.

Passively Expansible Tubes

If the vascular bed were expansible, so that the diameters of the conducting tubes increased with increasing pressure, we should find flow increasing to a greater extent for a given increment of pressure,

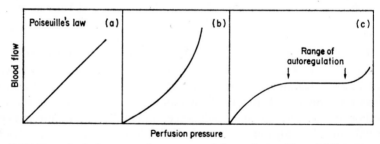

Fig. 2.31. Hypothetical curves of pressure and flow relationships: (a) Laminar flow in rigid tubes; (b) Flow in tubes with expansible walls; (c) A system exhibiting autoregulation.

and the pressure-flow relationship would give a curve convex towards the pressure-axis as in Fig. 2.31(b). Once again there would be no sign of autoregulation, a change in pressure giving a greater change of flow than expected of a rigid system of tubes. If autoregulation is to occur, the pressure-flow curve must be as in Fig. 2.31(c), concave to the pressure-axis, and, if autoregulation is perfect over a certain pressure-range, the curve should straighten out to a line parallel with the pressure-axis.

Possible Mechanisms

Bayliss (1902) first described the phenomenon of autoregulation*
in muscle, finding that a fall in the central arterial pressure caused an
expansion of a denervated limb due to vasodilatation, and he suggested the so-called *myogenic theory*, namely that when pressure rose
the tone in the smooth muscle of the resistance-vessels increased, and
vice versa. It could be argued that the extravascular pressure rose, due
to increased capillary filtration, and this tended to compress the
vessels. Or, again, it might be argued that changes in pressure altered
the degree to which vaso-active metabolites could accumulate; thus a
fall in pressure would decrease flow initially, and this would cause
accumulation of a vasodilator metabolite; resistance would fall and
flow would return to its normal value.

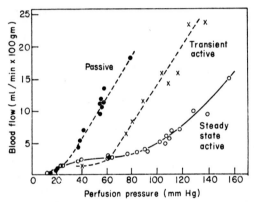

Fig. 2.32. The pressure-flow curves of a denervated, artificially perfused muscle
showing the transient response (crossed) and the steady-state response (open circles)
to changes in perfusion-pressure. The passive response of the muscle, fully dilated
with chloral hydrate, is shown on the left (filled circles). (Stainsby and Renkin,
Amer. J. Physiol.)

Muscle. It is generally agreed that, where autoregulation really
occurs, i.e. independently of nervous activity, no single explanation is
adequate. According to Stainsby and Renkin's (1961) study the
immediate effect of a rise in perfusion-pressure, applied to a denervated
muscle, is an increase in flow, followed by a slower fall; similarly, if

* The three main hypotheses put forward to explain autoregulation have been discussed
by Johnson (1964). Green and Rapela (1964) have discussed flow in a passive circulation
bed. The autoregulation of skeletal muscle, according to Folkow (1964), is the integrated
result of several interacting factors; thus there is no doubt that in some way the metabolic
requirements of the working muscle bring about dilatation of the arterioles and precapillary
sphincters; opposing this would be the myogenic autoregulation that would restrict blood-
flow if arterial pressure rose.

the pressure falls the flow slows and later returns to near its original value. The steady-state pressure-flow curve is indicated by Fig. 2.32, where it is seen that autoregulation is by no means perfect. In the Figure there is a pressure-flow curve for the same muscle when treated with chloral hydrate, a treatment that apparently destroys the muscle's capacity to autoregulate; now the relation between the two parameters is nearly linear.

Local Metabolite. Stainsby (1962) found that autoregulation was just as efficient when the muscle was active as when it was resting, so that the level of blood-flow was governed by the oxygen requirements of the tissue rather than by the perfusion-pressure. He considered, in the light of this finding, that the vascular bed had a basic constrictor tone, which might be governed by a humoral agent or by an innate tendency for the smooth muscle to contract in opposition to any expansive force. The local accumulation of a vasodilator metabolite would oppose this tone, and it would be the interplay of these two tendencies, with the local concentration of metabolite varying inversely with flow-rate, that would lead to autoregulation.

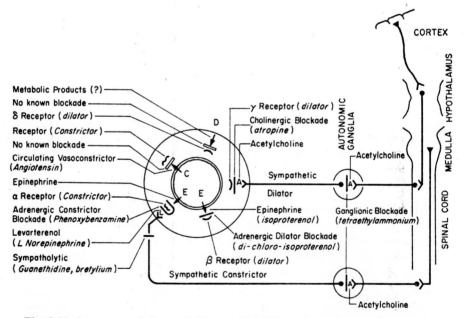

Fig. 2.33. A summary diagram of the neural and other mechanisms operating on the smooth muscles of the arterioles of skeletal muscle. The acetylcholine-sensitive sympathetic vasodilator has been indicated by a β-receptor. (Green *et al.*, *Handbook of Physiology*.)

Response to Standing

The importance of myogenic contraction is illustrated in the body's defence against loss of fluid from the capillaries of the lower limbs during standing; according to Mellander *et al.* (1964), a rise in trans-mural pressure, due to venous stasis, causes increased tone in the precapillary sphincters, thereby reducing capillary pressure and filtration.

Summary Diagram

Figure 2.33 is a summary diagram of the neural and other mechanisms operating on the smooth muscle of the arterioles of skeletal muscle; here the acetylcholine-sensitive sympathetic vasodilator mechanism has been indicated by a β-receptor.

CARDIOVASCULAR ADJUSTMENTS IN EXERCISE

Oxygen Utilization and Cardiac Output

The transition from basal metabolism to that required for maximal exercise in man requires an increase in O_2-consumption from a basic 250 ml/min to some 5500 ml/min or more (Ekblom and Hermansen, 1968); this is achieved partly by an increased utilization of the oxygen carried in the blood, and partly by an increased cardiac output. The former factor is revealed by the change in the arterio-venous difference

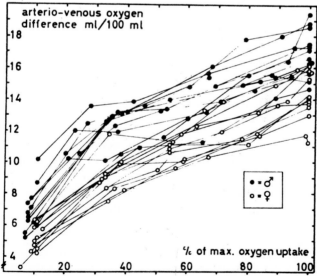

Fig. 2.34. The increase in arteriovenous oxygen difference with exercise in 23 subjects. Oxygen uptake during exercise increases from resting values to the individual's maximum (100 per cent). (Åstrand *et al.*, *J. appl. Physiol.*)

of oxygen-content of the circulating blood, illustrated by Fig. 2.34 which shows that, in a subject with a resting difference of about 6 ml/100 ml this rises to about 14 ml/100 ml at maximum work-load and thus accounts for an increased O_2-carriage by a factor of about two-and-a-half.

Cardiac Output

As Fig. 2.35 shows, the bigger factor is the increased cardiac output, which increases linearly with increasing oxygen consumption during exercise. To a relatively small extent, this is achieved through an

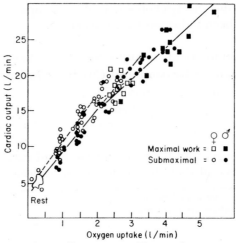

Fig. 2.35. The increase in cardiac output with exercise as represented by oxygen uptake. Exercise was taken on a bicycle ergometer, at rest, during submaximal and maximal exercise. Regression lines drawn through the points: continuous lines, males; broken lines, females. (Åstrand *et al.*, *J. appl. Physiol.*)

increased stroke-volume, consequently the main increase results from a progressively increasing pulse-rate with increasing work-load so that, at maximum rate of work, this is of the order of 200 strokes/min.

Stroke-Volume. The increase in stroke-volume found by Åstrand, for example, was from 68 ml to 100 ml in women and from 88 ml to 134 ml in men,* and this seems to be the result of more efficient

---

* An important point to bear in mind, as Bevegård *et al.* have emphasized, is that cardiac output and stroke-volume are quite different in the supine and erect positions at rest; thus when the subject is supine, because of the better filling of the heart, the cardiac output is some 2 l/min better than when erect, and the stroke-volume is some 40 per cent greater. During maximum exercise, whether erect or supine, the stroke-volume is the same, and this means that the increase in stroke-volume caused by maximum exercise is smaller when the comparison is made in the supine position than in the erect; thus the increase in the supine position is only some 10–20 per cent compared with some 50 per cent in the erect position.

emptying rather than enlargement during diastole, since X-ray measurements of the heart during severe exercise failed to indicate any appreciable increase in size.

Arterial Pressure. Other things being equal, to pump blood several times faster than at rest requires a corresponding increase in the mean arterial pressure; in fact, however, the arterial pressure, measured for example in the brachial artery, increases only by about 20 per cent, so that the extra output is associated with a great diminution in resistance.

Vasodilatation

This decrease is due entirely to the dilatation of vessels in the exercising limbs, since the main requirements of the vascular system are not only an increased cardiac output but also a diversion of the blood to the exercising limbs, and this is achieved by *increasing* the resistance in the splanchnic and skin regions.

Body-Temperature

A further factor that has to be taken care of is the body-temperature, since cooling is dependent on diversion of blood to the skin; hence, as exercise is increased in intensity, or is prolonged, blood required for the working muscles must be more and more diverted to the skin in the interests of temperature-regulation.

Diversion of Blood

That diversion of blood occurs, is easily shown by measuring blood-flow through a viscus such as the liver or kidney. For example, the blood-flow through the liver may be estimated by the efficiency with which a dyestuff, such as indigocyanine green, is cleared from the blood since this dye is excreted in the bile, the rate of excretion being dependent on the rate of blood-flow through the liver. In fact Fig. 2.36 shows in human subjects a linear relation between clearance and O_2-intake during exercise, so that at maximum exercise the clearance is only some 20 per cent of that at rest.* In a similar way the blood-flow through the arms, during running, can be shown to be decreased, although the eventual diversion of blood to the skin may reverse this adaptation.

---

* This diversion is not always evident; Van Citters and Franklin (1969) found no change in mesenteric blood-flow in Alaskan dogs when working at full capacity, although there was a 12-fold increase in total blood-flow.

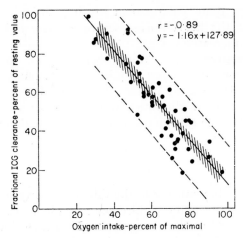

Fig. 2.36. The relation between liver blood-flow, indicated by clearance of indigo-cyanine green (ICG), and the oxygen-intake, during exercise. As exercise increases the clearance falls. About the least-squares regression line are (a) the 95 per cent confidence interval (shaded area) for the true mean value of y (ICG clearance) for a given value of x (oxygen intake) from the regression equation; and (b) the wider 95 per cent confidence interval for the true y-value of an individual having the x-value, indicated by the dashed lines. (Rowell *et al. J. clin. Invest.*)

Brain Blood-Flow

We need not expect the flow of blood through the brain to be affected; exercise probably involves little increase in oxygen requirements by the brain; the rise in aortic pressure that accompanies severe exercise, although not very large, would cause an increased cerebral blood-flow, but this may well be antagonized by the tendency for the PCO_2 of arterial blood to fall under these conditions, a change that would cause constriction of the cerebral arteries (Ch. 6). At any rate, it is interesting that the baroreceptors of the carotid sinus and aortic arch still maintain their homeostatic influence on the arterial pressure when cardiac output is at its maximum, tending to hold the aortic and carotid arterial pressures *down,* and thus to prevent the increased cerebral blood-flow that would ensue were the arterial pressure to be allowed to rise to heights that would favour increased flow through the working muscles.

Constancy of Brain Environment. In this connexion we may ask why the brain "objects" to an increased blood-flow, stabilizing the arterial pressure so that it neither rises nor falls beyond strict limits. The answer is doubtless that the central neurones require a constant chemical environment, and this means not only constant levels of ions such as K^+, Na^+, Cl^-, Ca^{++}, but also of such metabolites as glucose, lactic acid, bicarbonate and so on. Clearly the best way of maintaining these is with a constant rate of flow of blood; thus lactic acid is continually being formed by the central neurones and this diffuses away into the blood to give a steady level determined by rates of production and clearance; increasing the clearance causes the level to fall, and thus to disturb the homeostasis. The same may well apply to many compounds involved in nervous transmission, such as acetylcholine, noradrenaline, dopamine, and so on (Chapter 6).

Local Response

The unsolved problem regarding the response to exercise is the manner in which the increased cardiac output is initiated. It is agreed that the first vascular change is a dilatation of the arterioles supplying the exercising muscles; the response to muscular contraction is rapid

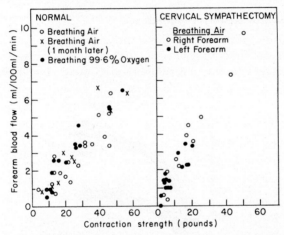

Fig. 2.37. Increase in flow in forearm immediately after single brief contraction of forearm muscles in a normal subject and in a subject who had had cervical sympathectomy 3 years previously. The increase in forearm flow was obtained by subtracting the resting flow before each contraction from the flow measured just after contraction. O_2 capacity of radial artery blood was 19.4 vol. per cent, breathing air, and 20·8 vol. per cent while breathing O_2. (Corcondiles *et al.*, *J. appl. Physiol.*)

so that within 0·3 sec after a brief contraction of the forearm muscles an increase in blood-flow in the arm can be measured (Fig. 2.37). The magnitude, and time of onset, are the same in the sympathectomized arm, so that the motor mechanism does not involve sympathetic vasodilators, and is apparently mediated through local mechanisms, e.g. the liberation of some metabolite that acts directly on the blood vessels or on sensory nerves in an axon reflex; such an increase in blood-flow would cause an increased venous return and thus initiate reflexes that augmented heart-rate and force of contraction.

Exercise Pressor Reflex

The local increase in blood-flow is accompanied by cardiovascular changes that must, however, be reflex in nature, derived from a primary stimulus in the working limbs rather than secondarily to the increased blood-flow to the heart, since they occur too rapidly to result from blood-borne substances from the limbs. Thus, at the onset of exercise, there occur an increase in heart-rate and a rise in arterial pressure; this effect is *augmented* by occlusion of the circulation through the working limbs, and is thus not due to changes in the composition of blood flowing through the brain.

Accumulation of Reactive Substance

The occlusion presumably allows the accumulation of some reactive substance in the limb that acts on the endings of sensory nerves that conduct messages to the central nervous system. Fig. 2.38 shows the

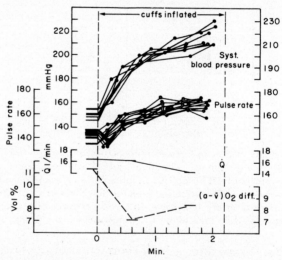

Fig. 2.38. The reflex nature of exercise hyperaemia. The subjects were performing steady-state exercise when cuffs were inflated around the thighs, occluding the venous return. Rapid rises in blood-pressure and heart-rate were seen almost immediately, which were reflexly mediated. Cardiac output $(\dot{Q})$; arteriovenous oxygen-difference, $(a-v)O_2$ diff. Work intensity, 760 kpm/min. (Asmussen and Nielsen, *Acta physiol. scand.*)

large rise in arterial pressure, from 150 to 220 mm Hg, in human subjects working on a bicycle ergometer when a cuff was inflated over the thigh occluding the venous return; the pulse-rate rose from 140 to 170 per min whilst cardiac output fell slightly, so that the reflex changes must have involved a considerable rise in peripheral resistance. That the adjustment is not due to cortical influences, but is reflex in

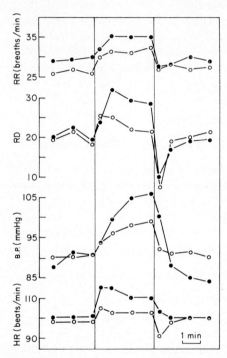

Fig. 2.39. The cardiovascular response of a cat whose motor denervated limbs were moved passively. Records from above RR respiratory rate, RD respiratory depth, BP blood pressure, HR heart rate. Open circles show the changes caused by moving one hind limb. Filled circles reciprocal movements of both hind limbs. (Barron and Coote, *J. Physiol.*)

nature, is further shown by the effects of electrical stimulation of the anterior roots of the nerves supplying a limb. In this case an increase in arterial pressure was obtained proportional to the tension developed in the muscles, an effect that was abolished by section of the posterior roots. Again, we may attach the foot of a cat to a device that causes rapid walking movements in the limbs without any motor innervation; as Fig. 2.39 shows, the heart-rate and blood-pressure rise rapidly and fall abruptly on cessation. The effect was abolished by section of the ipsilateral sciatic femoral and obturator nerves.

Afferent Pathway

Hodgson and Matthews (1968) established that the large Group I nerve fibres, concerned in the afferent responses from muscle spindles and Golgi tendon organs, werê not involved in this reflex, but rather the smaller Group III and IV fibres that come into relation with the blood vessels, and Barron and Coote concluded that the most likely source of the afferent impulses in the reflex was the joint itself, fibres conducting at less than 18 m/sec being concerned; these might be those that have free endings in the intra- and extra-articular fat-pads and in the fibrous capsule.

The Local Vasodilatation

The exercise-reflex causes an immediate increase in heart-rate, and a rise in arterial pressure through generalized vasoconstriction, but the local dilatation of the blood vessels is not a part of this reflex, and is due to the production of some vasoactive material, or may be simply due to O_2-lack resulting from the muscular work. The vasoactive material could act directly on the blood vessels or less directly through an axon-reflex.

Reactive Hyperaemia

Simple O_2-lack as a cause seems to have been excluded on the grounds that breathing pure O_2 does not affect the response; however, Barcroft (1972) has emphasized the strong analogy between the hyperaemia of exercise and the hyperaemia following occlusion of a limb. Thus the circulation to a limb may be occluded for a period of minutes, and on releasing the occlusion the blood-flow through the limb is found to be some four-to-five times the pre-occlusion rate. If anoxia is, indeed, the cause of the reaction, then the hyperaemia, i.e. increased blood-flow, should be sustained if, instead of allowing fully oxygenated blood to enter after the occlusion, deoxygenated blood is allowed to flow, and this was, indeed found by Fairchild, Ross and Guyton (1966) as illustrated by Fig. 2.40. Other evidence strongly supports the idea that the degree of hypoxia in the limb determines the magnitude of the reactive hyperaemia. Hypoxia, of course, can mean the accumulation of products of anoxia, e.g. lactate, K^+, inorganic phosphate, hyperosmolarity, and so on; and claims for all of these have

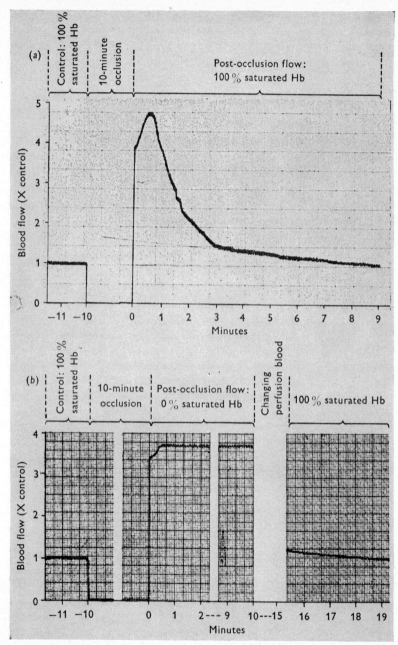

Fig. 2.40. Record (a) shows control blood-flow followed by a period of occlusion, then the rapid increase in blood-flow following the occlusion (reactive hyperaemia) which gradually returns to control values. In record (b) there is a failure of recovery from reactive hyperaemia when the perfusing blood contains no oxygen, but as the last part of the record shows, normal recovery can occur when the blood is again saturated with oxygen. (Barcroft, *J. Physiol.* after Fairchild *et al.*, *Amer. J. Physiol.*)

been put forward, but so far as the reactive hyperaemia is concerned Barcroft points out that, when long periods of occlusion are carried out, the degree of reactive hyperaemia does not increase, although the concentration of metabolites must have risen.

Hypoxia of Exercising Muscle

Although the arterial blood during severe exercise is just as fully oxygenated as at rest, this does not mean that the blood in the exercising muscle has the same average degree of oxygenation; far from it, since, as we have seen, the degree of utilization increases greatly; this is well illustrated by Fig. 2.41 which shows the fall in O_2-saturation of the venous effluent from the dog's gastrocnemius muscle when it is

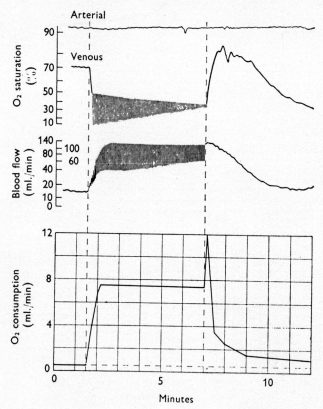

Fig. 2.41. Showing the effect of rhythmic stimulation of the isolated perfused dog gastrocnemius muscle. The upper records show the oxygen-saturation of arterial and venous bloods, and the increase in blood-flow. Note that the venous oxygen-saturation returns to control value more rapidly than does the blood-flow. (Barcroft, *J. Physiol.*, after Kramer. *Pflüg. Arch.*)

rhythmically stimulated; as blood-flow increases, the saturation decreases from 70 per cent to about 30 per cent. Thus Barcroft's suggestion is that the defective supply of oxygen to the smooth muscle of the arterioles and precapillary sphincters causes these to relax, a relaxation that is maintained during exercise or during occlusion of the limb. However, because in severe exercise muscle blood-flow may be more than double that during reactive hyperaemia, it is likely that metabolites have an influence; and this is especially true of the hyperaemia that persists after exercise, since O_2-lack in the resting limb is not a factor. This is shown by Fig. 2.41 where it is seen that, after the rhythmic stimulation, the venous O_2-saturation returns to above 70 per cent rapidly, whilst the blood-flow tapers off only slowly. An obvious candidate for this vasodilator action is histamine, since it certainly has a strong local action on blood vessels; however, there is no evidence supporting this.

Cholinergic Vasodilatation

As to whether central mechanisms contribute to the local vaso-dilatation, little definite can be said; there is some evidence that, at the very beginning of exercise, cholinergic vasodilators cause a dilatation of the vessels supplying the muscles in the whole body when exercise is confined to a single limb; this is sufficient to cause a transient fall in arterial pressure. It is thought that this reflex dilatation, at the start of exercise, could aid the local metabolites in causing dilatation of the active muscles, although, as Bevegård argues, the rapid local response makes a more generalized response unnecessary.

Re-setting the Baroreceptor Reflex

Severe exercise usually involves some increase in arterial pressure, and the question is whether the baroreceptor reflex, that would tend to slow the heart-rate under these conditions, is abolished, or whether the increased heart-rate, required for exercise, is permitted by a re-setting of the reflex mechanism, so that cardiac slowing only comes into play at higher arterial pressures. There is no doubt that the reflex is not abolished, and can be effective in exercise (Bevegård and Shepherd, 1966) so the re-setting hypothesis seems the correct one. Bristow et al. (1971) measured the reflex sensitivity by the effect of arterial pressure on the interval between heart-beats. As Fig. 2.42 shows, a straight line may be obtained describing the relation between pulse-interval (i.e. the reciprocal of the heart-rate) and the systolic pressure; the slope of this line gives the sensitivity, and it will

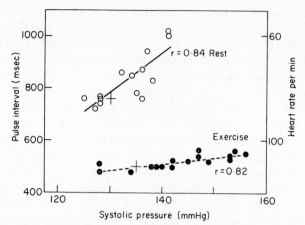

Fig. 2.42. The effect of phenylephrine on the relation between arterial pressure and the interval between heart-beats (the reciprocal of heart-rate) at rest and during exercise. During exercise the slope of the line has reduced, indicating a re-setting of the reflex mechanism so that a higher pressure is associated with a shorter pulse-interval. The lines are the calculated regression lines of pulse-interval on systolic pressure; r = correlation coefficient; + = pre-injection values of pulse-interval and systolic pressure, averaged for 10 beats. (Bristow *et al.*, *Circ. Res.*).

be seen that, during exercise, the slope becomes much flatter, indicating a resetting of the reflex mechanism so that a higher pressure is associated with a shorter pulse-interval during exercise. In other words, a faster heart-rate is permitted for a given level of arterial pressure.*

The Basic Mechanisms

To summarize, then, the two prime vascular events during exercise are the immediate pressor response and a dilatation of blood vessels in the exercising muscles; the latter, on purely hydrodynamic grounds, causes an increased blood-flow and lowered total peripheral resistance. The consequent lowering of the arterial pressure causes a reflex augmentation of cardiac activity, through the baroreceptors; and cardiac output increases by virtue of cardio-acceleration associated with increased filling pressure in the left atrium, due to the augmented venous return accomplished by the muscular exercise. At the same time,

---

* A re-setting in the opposite direction occurs during sleep; here the arterial pressure falls together with the pulse-rate, yet we would expect the pulse-rate to rise in response to the lowered arterial pressure. Smyth, Sleight and Pickering (1969) have shown that the slope of pulse-interval versus arterial pressure increases during sleep, indicating an increased reflex sensitivity; thus during sleep a given arterial pressure will be associated with a slower heart-rate.

blood is diverted from the reservoirs by vasoconstriction, including the skin, but, as body-temperature rises, the vasoconstriction here relaxes. So effective is the increased cardiac and vasomotor activity that aortic pressure rises, but this is held in check by baroreceptor mechanisms in the interests of a constant cerebral circulation.

Starling's Law

Another factor, of course, is the inherent tendency of the heart to increase its output as input increases—Starling's Law of the Heart; thus in the dog whose heart has been denervated there is an increase in cardiac output with exercise, but this time without cardio-acceleration, so that increased output is the result of greater stroke-volume— i.e. greater initial stretch of the cardiac muscle. In the intact animal, changes in stroke-volume are not large during maximal cardiac output, and this means that the Starling mechanism is not a prime factor increasing output; nevertheless it must be operating, and it tends to ensure that the two ventricles adjust their outputs to each other leading to a constancy of distribution of blood between the pulmonary and systemic circulations.

Venous Reflexes

Quite clearly, additional factors contribute to the smooth increase in cardiac output as exercise increases in intensity; thus reflexes mediated through distension of the great veins and both atria apparently favour emptying (p. 136).

Chemoreceptor Activity

So far as altered PCO_2 and PO_2 of the blood are concerned in actuating carotid body and aortic body reflexes, it would seem that these influences, if they occur, are minor, except in so far as the respiratory reflex responses react back on the cardiovascular system; e.g. the increased expansion of the lungs reflexly increases the heart-rate—the inflation reflex (p. 129).

Capacitance Vessels

The large veins play a minor role in vascular adjustments; in so far as they must carry a greatly increased flow of blood efficiently we would expect that an increase in muscular tone would help, otherwise blood would tend to pool in these easily distensible vessels. In fact, if a piece of a large vein is exposed and tied off from the general circulation, a decrease in its extensibility, measured by the expansion brought about by an artificially imposed pressure-increment, occurs during exercise. In a similar way the large pulmonary vessels show an increased tone during exercise, thereby permitting a more efficient throughway and reducing the tendency for blood to be stored in the lungs. In general, the volume of blood in the lungs is remarkably constant, about 10 per cent of the whole; and this is in spite of large variations in cardiac output, so that the concept of the lungs acting as a store for blood, which is called upon during exercise, is probably incorrect. Consequently, changes in supply to the left ventricle are achieved by changes in tone of the pulmonary vascular tree, acting in conjunction with changing output from the right ventricle to ensure adequate delivery to the left ventricle (p. 188).

CARDIOVASCULAR ADAPTATION TO HAEMORRHAGE

Increased Vascular Tone

The immediate reflex response to loss of blood is an increased vasomotor tone, manifest as an increased peripheral resistance. The vasoconstriction is selective, being largely confined to the mesenteric, renal, cutaneous and muscular vascular beds, so that when Neutze *et al.* (1968) measured the proportions of the total blood-flow represented by different organs and tissues, by injecting microspheres (p. 421), they found that the proportions taken up by the cerebral, coronary and hepatic circulations were increased at the expense of the remainder. At the same time, there was a widespread constriction of the veins in all vascular territories.

Chemo- and Baro-Receptors

The response is probably mediated by the stagnant anoxia of the chemoreceptor tissues, so that denervation of the carotid bodies causes a further fall in arterial pressure (Heymans and Neil, 1958). The pulsatile stimulus to the baroreceptors of the carotid sinus and aortic arch becomes feebler, and this tends to reduce the effectiveness of the baroreceptor reflexes, which tend to cause vasodilatation and slow the heart-rate. In this way heart-rate increases and the vasoconstriction brought about by the chemoreceptor reflex is maintained (Folkow *et al.*, 1965). The reflex nervous effects are reinforced by the secretion of catecholamines by the adrenal gland (see, for example, Regoli and Vane, 1966).

High and Low Pressure Systems. We shall see that the anti-diuretic response to loss of blood, exhibited as an increase in secretion of the antidiuretic hormone—ADH or vasopressin—by the posterior pituitary, takes place before there is any significant change in mean arterial pressure, and it has been concluded that changes in the low pressure system, e.g. in the filling of the atria, are responsible for the first responses, at any rate in so far as the secretion of this hormone is concerned. When haemorrhage is more serious, leading to loss of arterial pressure, the carotid sinus and aortic arch buffer systems come into play, causing the increased tone in the splanchnic and other vascular beds that divert blood to the brain.

Vasopressin and Angiotensin

Vasopressin

The homeostatic mechanisms that tend to ameliorate the consequences of lost blood-volume have been largely indicated in Vol. 1, and the point we may emphasize here is the role of vasopressin and angiotensin. It has been pointed out by Rocha e Silva and Rosenberg (1969) that the amounts of the antidiuretic hormone, or vasopressin, released during haemorrhage are some hundred times greater than the amount required to produce maximum antidiuresis, so that the action of the hormone on the vascular resistance must clearly be taken into account when considering the total response to loss of blood. The release occurs through a vagal reflex since it is abolished by section of this nerve (Clark and Rocha e Silva, 1967). Vasopressin, like angiotensin II, has a powerful vasoconstrictor action so that it tends to raise arterial pressure.

Potentiation of Catecholamines. It does this by a direct action on the smooth muscle of the vasculature but also, according to Bartelstone and Nasmyth (1965), by potentiating the action of catecholamines; thus the contractions of strips of aortic smooth muscle in response to adrenaline and noradrenaline were increased by concentrations of vasopressin that were of themselves inadequate to produce effects. In intact dogs, too, Traber et al. (1967) showed that the reflex pressor responses were larger if the animals were given physiological doses of vasopressin; and they suggested that the hormone increased permeability of the muscle cells permitting readier access of the catecholamines to receptor sites.

Pressor Effect. Rocha e Silva and Rosenberg showed that the amounts of vasopressin released into the blood during haemorrhage were adequate to have significant effects in restoring blood-pressure to normal; thus a fall in pressure of 25 mm Hg gave a concentration of 65 μg/ml whilst infusion of the hormone into the blood to give this concentration caused a rise in arterial pressure of 20 mm Hg. It would seem that the high degree of vasomotor tone during haemorrhage, mediated through the vagus and carotid sinus-nerves, is due partly to release of vasopressin by the hypophysis, since hypophysectomy gives a fall in blood-pressure with a time-course similar to that obtained by cessation of an infusion of the hormone. Again, it was observed by Frieden and Keller (1954) that hypophysectomized dogs had a lowered resistance to haemorrhage; thus it required the removal of 35–50 ml/kg of blood to cause a fall in mean arterial pressure below 70 mm Hg in normal dogs whereas in hypophysectomized animals only 20–35 ml/kg had to be withdrawn; infusions of pitressin intra-arterially during the haemorrhage increased the amount of blood that had to be withdrawn to produce the fall in arterial pressure.

Angiotensin

Another potent vasoconstrictor, whose concentration rises in the blood during haemorrhage, is angiotensin II, formed through the kidney hormone renin, whose secretion parallels closely that of aldo-sterone, the other hormone concerned in regulation of the water and salt balance of the animal.

Scornik and Paladini (1964) measured the changes in angiotensin concentration in the blood of dogs during haemorrhage; a typical experiment gave the following:

Loss of blood (ml per kg)	Mean B.P. (mm Hg)	Angiotensin (μg/litre)
0	150	0·55
20	50	1·02
45	10	3·08

Two minutes later the animal died.

Haemorrhagic Shock

In a recent study Errington and Rocha e Silva (1974) have revealed the important roles that the two hormones, vasopressin and angio-tensin, may play in *increasing* mortality from excessive haemorrhage. When haemorrhage leads to a large and sustained fall in arterial pres-sure, a condition of irreversible shock may ensue, the characteristic feature of which is the low arterial pressure in the presence of a high degree of splanchnic vasoconstriction, a rapid heart-rate (tachycardia) and low stroke-volume. When the irreversible condition is reached, re-infusion of the lost blood, although it may restore blood pressure and consciousness, fails to prevent subsequent death within 24 hours.

Inhibited Hormone Secretion

Errington and Rocha e Silva (1974) compared the effects of sustained haemorrhage in normal dogs and in animals whose synthesis of angiotensin II had been blocked by the bradykinin-potentiating nonapeptide (BPP$_{9a}$); in another series, normal dogs were compared with

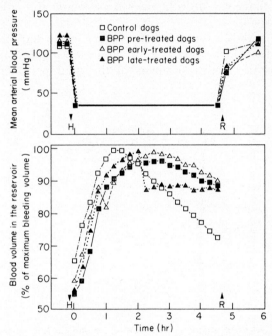

Fig. 2.43. The effect of inhibition of angiotensin production on the ability to withstand haemorrhage in dogs. Dogs were bled into a reservoir held at a constant pressure of 35 mm Hg at H and retransfused at R. Upper panel is a record of mean arterial blood pressure. Lower panel, blood volume in reservoir as a percentage of maximum bleeding volume. The bradykinin-potentiating nonapeptide (BPP$_{9a}$) was given at 10 min before the start of the experiment, 45 min and 2 hours after the start. Note that in the control dogs blood pressure was not maintained as well as in the BPP-treated dogs since the reservoir-volume began to fall after an hour.
(Errington and Rocha e Silva, *J. Physiol.*)

animals whose secretion of vasopressin was abolished by surgical damage to the median eminence (diabetes insipidus dogs). Loss of blood was caused by connecting the dog's femoral artery to a reservoir such that a pressure of 35 mm Hg was reached and maintained; the volume of blood in the reservoir during the next four hours was measured, and this increased with time to a maximum as bleeding continued. In control dogs, as Fig. 2.43 shows, the volume in the reservoir began to fall after about 1 hr, and this meant that the animal's arterial pressure was falling, so that the blood from the reservoir, held at a height equivalent to a pressure of 35 mm Hg, passed into the artery. As Fig. 2.43 shows, animals pre-treated with BPP and therefore not producing angiotensin II, were able to sustain a higher arterial pressure, so that very little blood ran back into the circulation after the initial loss.

Figure 24.4 shows the parallel changes in cardiac output, and it will be seen that the treated dogs maintained a higher output than the untreated controls; measurements of the total peripheral resistance

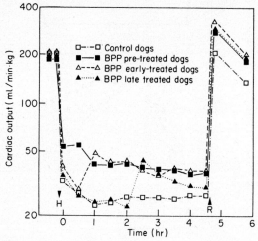

Fig. 2.44. The effect of angiotensin inhibition on the cardiac output of dogs after haemorrhage. Dogs were bled into a reservoir held at a constant pressure of 35 mm Hg. H indicates beginning of bleeding. R indicates beginning of retransfusion. Angiotensin production was inhibited by the administration of bradykinin potentiating nonapeptide (BPP$_{9a}$) at 10 mins. before the start, 45 min and 2 hours after the start of the experiment. The BPP-treated dogs had a significantly higher cardiac output than the control dogs during the haemorrhage period. (Errington and Rocha e Silva, *J. Physiol.*)

showed that the higher cardiac output was made possible by a reduced resistance. Rather similar results were obtained when diabetes insipidus dogs were compared with the normal controls.

Post-Mortem Evidence. The important finding of Errington and Rocha e Silva was that the control dogs failed to survive retransfusion of their lost blood, dying within 24 hr, whilst the BPP-treated and diabetes insipidus dogs all recovered. Post-mortem studies indicated that the animals dying of this irreversible haemorrhagic shock had haemorrhagic lesions in their stomachs and intestines that could be attributed to a sustained hypoxia due to the primary vasoconstriction; these lesions were negligible or absent in the animals that survived, i.e. those treated with BPP or previously made diabetic by median eminence lesions: these last-mentioned animals were, however, not completely free of haemorrhagic lesions.

Ischaemic Hypoxia. These results are of considerable interest since they not only demonstrate the important role of the vasopressin and renin-angiotensin secretory mechanisms in the adaptation to lowered blood-volume and arterial pressure, but also they show that such compensatory mechanisms, whilst fulfilling the function of maintaining adequate brain circulation, defeat their own ends in so far as the ischaemia in the splanchnic region leads, ultimately, to so great a degree of hypoxia that finally the capillaries become more and more permeable, ultimately allowing escape of blood. Thus the "ischaemic hypoxia" leads to a "stagnant hypoxia" with blood pooling in the dilated capillaries; and it is considered that it is at this stage that the reflux of blood back into the animal, shown in Fig. 2.43, takes place.

Catecholamines

Adrenaline and noradrenaline are released from the adrenal gland during haemorrhage; the effect could be secondary to the release of angiotensin, since Feldberg and Lewis (1965) have shown that this peptide hormone, as well as bradykinin, has a direct action on the medullary cells, activating them independently of the cholinergic splanchnic release-mechanism. According to Regoli and Vane (1966), however, the release of catecholamine in the dog during haemorrhage is a primary response, since adrenaline, and later noradrenaline, appear in the blood well before the concentration of angiotensin is adequate to be effective on the adrenal gland.*

CORONARY BLOOD FLOW

Perfusion Pressure

The heart supplies itself with blood through the coronary arteries, derived directly from the aorta, the venous blood being emptied into the right side of the heart through the coronary sinus, the anterior

* The chromaffine cells of the adrenal medulla are analogous with postganglionic sympathetic neurones, being activated by the cholinergic terminals of sympathetic fibres derived directly from the cord (Vol. 2); it is of interest, therefore, that angiotensin and bradykinin stimulate the cells of the superior cervical ganglion, causing contraction of the nictitating membrane. Thus the vasoconstrictor action of angiotensin could be due, not only to a primary action on the blood vessels, but to an action on the adrenal gland, causing release of catecholamines; and finally it could be due to a stimulation of the postsynaptic neurones of sympathetic ganglia (Lewis and Reit, 1965).

coronary veins and the Thebesian vessels (Vol. 1). Thus the pressure driving the coronary flow—the perfusion pressure—is governed by the difference between the aortic pressure and that in the right atrium, and effectively it is the aortic pressure that dominates this factor.

High O_2-Extraction

The striking feature of the coronary circulation is the extremely high extraction of O_2 leading to a high a-v difference of PO_2, or O_2-content, the difference being of the order of 11–14 $mlO_2/100$ ml compared with about half this for other organs. The consequence of this is that the extra amounts of O_2 required during the large variations in work performed by the heart must be obtained by variations in blood-flow rather than extraction. Hence the factors affecting blood-flow are of great interest.

Systolic Stasis

A further point is the fact that the heart impedes its own blood-flow through the force of contraction of the myocardium, so that during systole it is possible for the pressure within the left ventricular myocardium to be greater than that in the coronary artery and for blood-flow to cease. In fact, for a brief period during systole there is a phase of backward flow (Eckstein *et al.*, 1963). Fortunately the period during which this stasis occurs is short, so that flow certainly takes place during systole and, in general, at normal rates of heart-beating the percentage of flow during systole is some 20 per cent; as heart-rate increases, of course, the duration of diastole falls and so to some extent we might expect coronary flow to be reduced as heart-rate increased, due to this mechanical factor. In fact, however, compensatory effects come into play so that blood-flow may be adequately maintained to meet the increasing metabolic demands of the heart when the rate is altered artificially from 50 to 70/min to as high as 250 to 300/min (Fig. 2.45). Since, under these conditions, arterial pressure and cardiac output tend to fall, owing to the diminished filling of the heart, the increased blood-flow that takes place is achieved by a pronounced fall in vascular resistance, i.e. a dilatation of the resistance vessels. This does not mean, of course, that the mechanical factor of compression is unimportant; clearly it must be, and it is demonstrated by measuring the change in blood-flow induced by temporary heart-block, as by vagal stimulation; in this event Sabiston and Gregg (1957) found an increase of 59 per cent in flow. In studying the effects of various influences on coronary blood-flow, it is helpful if this mechanical factor can be allowed for; this can be achieved by

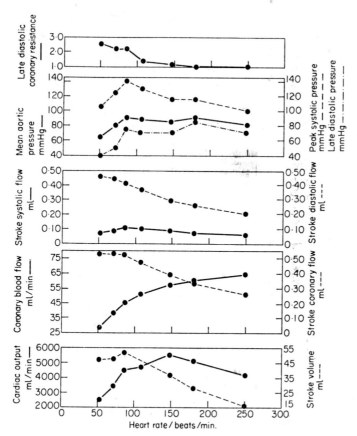

Fig. 2.45. The effect of increasing the rate of beat on the haemodynamics of the heart in the conscious dog. (Pitt and Gregg, *Circ. Res.*).

establishing an artificial block of the AV-node (Pitt *et al.*, 1967) and controlling heart-rate with an artificial pace-maker.

Blood O₂

The factor that emerges as of primary importance is, in fact, the O_2-content of the blood, which itself is determined normally by the degree of hypoxia of the working muscle; as work increases, the O_2-supply becomes inadequate and blood-flow increases, probably by a local action of some metabolite.

Perfusion-Pressure. Another factor is the perfusion—or aortic—pressure, but this of very little significance, partly because of the homeostatic mechanisms that maintain this constant in the face of very large increases in cardiac output, and partly because of the phenomenon of autoregulation, the tendency for the resistance of the blood vessels to rise as perfusion-pressure rises and *vice versa*, a phenomenon that is manifest also in the skeletal muscle (p. 142), in the brain (Ch. 6), and kidney (Ch. 5).

Denervated Heart. Nervous and hormonal influences can be demonstrated experimentally, but as Donald and Shepherd (1963) have shown, the completely denervated dog's heart can work quite efficiently in so far as its performance is adapted to the increased metabolic needs of the animal during exercise, so that it would seem that the dominant control is brought about through the relation between O_2-content of the blood and vascular resistance. This does not mean, of course, that all parameters of cardiac function are not affected by nervous and hormonal influences.

The well-established inotropic and chronotropic influence of the sympathetic nerves and of adrenaline bear witness to this. In Donald and Shepherd's study of dogs with denervated hearts, exercise resulted in an increased cardiac output, but this was achieved by increased stroke-volume, by contrast with the normal response where increased heart-rate is the main factor (p. 146). The important fact for the present argument is that the altered coronary flow in response to exercise can be achieved without nervous or adrenal hormonal influences.

Autoregulation

Strictly speaking an autoregulation of blood-flow in an organ implies the absence of neural reflex mechanisms; as such it applies

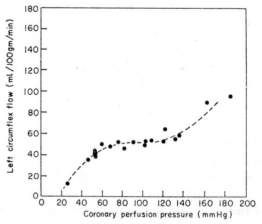

Fig. 2.46. The relation between coronary blood-flow (right circumflex flow) and the coronary perfusion-pressure in the dog. Over the range of 50 to 140 mm Hg, blood-flow is nearly independent of perfusion-pressure. (Mosher *et al.*, *Circ. Res.*).

to the kidney, but where it has been demonstrated in the heart and the brain, reflex mechanisms have by no means been excluded (Ch. 6). If we use the term more loosely, then, we may say that, over a fair range of arterial pressure, the coronary blood-flow is constant; this is illustrated by the study of Mosher *et al.* (1964), who perfused the dog's coronary system with blood independently of the aorta. Beginning with the pressure the same as that in the femoral artery, the coronary artery pressure was suddenly raised or lowered in steps, and the change in blood-flow recorded; there was always a transient rise or fall in flow, according as the pressure rose or fell, but this was soon compensated. In Fig. 2.46 the curve represents the relation between coronary flow and coronary perfusion-pressure at the steady state, i.e. after the transient change had adjusted; over the range of 50 to 140 mm Hg, flow is nearly constant.

Relation of Flow to O_2 Demand

The classical study of Eckenhoff *et al.* (1947), in which the work of the heart was made to vary by adjusting various parameters, such as arterial pressure, cardiac output, or altered O_2-content of the blood, revealed a linear relation between the coronary blood-flow and the O_2-consumption of the heart (Fig. 2.47), and they concluded that the

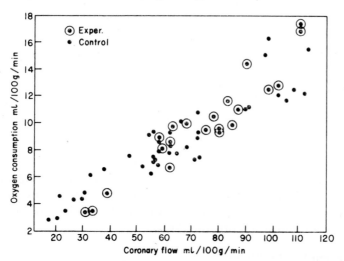

Fig. 2.47. The relationship between coronary blood-flow and cardiac oxygen-consumption. Dots indicate control observations, ringed dots observations during experimental procedures. Flow appears to be adjusted to the demands of the heart. (Eckenhoff *et al.*, *Amer. J. Physiol.*).

flow was, indeed, adjusted to the demands of the heart on the oxygen supply of the blood. Since, as we have seen, extraction is very high indeed, this means that increased requirements are met by increased rates of flow; and experimentally it was shown by Feinberg *et al.* (1962) that when the effort of the heart, measured by the product: Rate × Arterial pressure, was plotted against various parameters, as in Fig. 2.48, there was no significant change in O_2-extraction with

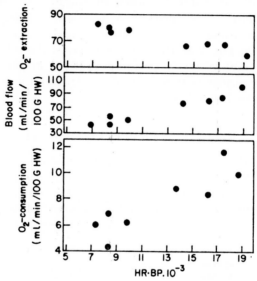

Fig. 2.48. The relationship between cardiac effort, as represented by Heart Rate (HR) × Arterial Pressure (BP), and oxygen-extraction, coronary blood-flow, and oxygen-consumption. (Feinberg *et al.*, *Amer. J. Physiol.*)

altered effort, whereas coronary flow and cardiac O_2-consumption varied almost linearly with effort.

Effects of Breathing O_2

As a corollary to this, it was found by Sobol *et al.* (1962) that increasing the degree of saturation of the blood with O_2, by breathing the pure gas, caused a decrease in flow from 42 ml/min, when breathing air, to 34 ml/min when breathing O_2.

O_2 Carried by the Blood

The important feature is the amount of O_2 carried by the blood to the respiring tissue; thus Guz *et al.* (1960), studying the isolated perfused rabbit's heart, found that altering the blood-O_2-content, by

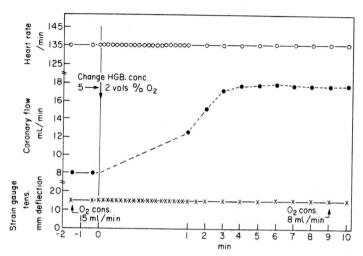

Fig. 2.49. The effect of reducing the haemoglobin concentration in the perfusion-fluid on the coronary blood-flow in the isolated rabbit heart. Oxygen carrying capacity was reduced from 5 to 2 vols. per cent at t= 0. (*Guz et al. J. Physiol.*)

changing the concentration of haemoglobin in it, had parallel effects on the blood-flow. This is shown by Fig. 2.49, where it will be seen that reducing the O_2-content of blood from 5 to 2 vols/per cent caused an increase in blood-flow without, however, affecting the tension developed or the O_2-consumption. Again, we may study the effect of reducing the PO_2 of the blood at a high and low perfusion-pressure, and find that, if the pressure is high, a low PO_2 need not necessarily increase coronary flow, the flow being adequate to provide the hear

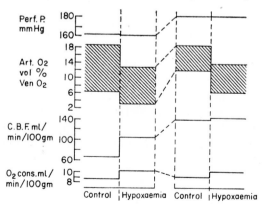

Fig. 2.50. The interaction between perfusion-pressure, oxygen-tension and coronary blood-flow. For explanation, see text. (Berne *et al., J. clin. Invest.*)

with adequate oxygen even at the low PO_2. This is illustrated by Fig. 2.50. The left-hand part shows the effects of reduced blood PO_2 when the perfusion-pressure was high, namely 160 mm Hg. In the control situation, the arterial O_2-content was 18·5 volumes per cent, the coronary venous O_2-content was 6·3 volumes per cent, and the coronary blood-flow was 70 ml/min per 100 g muscle. On reducing the arterial O_2-content to 12·6 volumes per cent, blood-flow increased to 105 ml/min. The right-hand part shows the effects of reduced blood PO_2 when the perfusion-pressure was high, namely 180 mm Hg. In the control situation, the arterial O_2-content was once again 18·5 volumes per cent and blood-flow was higher at 136 ml/min; on reducing the O_2-content of the blood to 11·7 volumes per cent we see that there was no increase in blood-flow because the amount of O_2 available was adequate without this, being provided by the increased flow resulting from the higher perfusion-pressure.

Nervous and Humoral Influences

The sympathetic innervation of the ventricles is unmistakable, whereas that of the parasympathetic is doubtful (Berne, 1964), so that we must expect the dominant influence on the vascular resistance to be exerted through the sympathetic.

Vagus

When summarizing the situation in 1958, Denison and Green stated that the consensus of opinion was that, if the vagus had any effect, it was to *constrict* the coronary arteries, after making allowance for any effects of vagal stimulation on heart-rate. In their own study, they controlled heart-rate with a pacemaker and were unable to find any effect of vagal stimulation on the coronary circulation; acetylcholine had a slight vasodilator effect. Essentially similar conclusions were arrived at by Wang *et al.* (1960); usually there was no effect of vagal stimulation on coronary flow, but if there was a negative inotropic effect, leading to a fall in arterial pressure and cardiac output, then there was a decrease in flow, which was probably causally related. They were doubtful whether this was the consequence of a vaso-constriction, since it could have been due to the fall in arterial pressure alone.

Sympathetic

It has not been easy to establish the effects of sympathetic stimulation on coronary vascular resistance because of the powerful inotropic and chronotropic influences of this branch of the autonomic system. The increase in force of contraction and in rate will exert mechanical influences and also affect the O_2-consumption, so that it is difficult to identify the effect, if any, on the blood vessels.

Perfused Heart. Most of the earlier workers concluded that the main effect of sympathetic stimulation was vascular constriction,

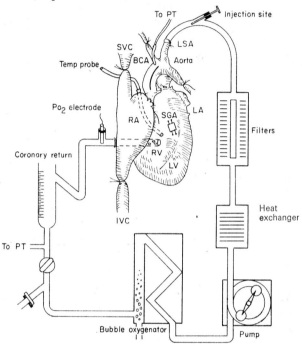

Fig. 2.51. Preparation for studying the isolated perfused dog heart. SVC, superior vena cava; IVC, inferior vena cava; RA, right atrium; RV, right ventricle; LA, left atrium; LV, left ventricle; BCA, brachiocephalic artery; LSA, left subclavian artery; SGA, Walton-Brodie strain-gauge arch; PT, pressure transducer. (Klocke *et al., Circ. Res.*)

decreasing blood-flow (see, for example, Berne, 1964), but more modern work tends to emphasize the vasodilator influence, operating through β-receptors. Thus Klocke *et al.* (1965), employing the isolated dog's heart illustrated by Fig. 2.51, blocked by KCl, found a marked fall in perfusion-pressure when injecting isoproterenol into the perfusing blood; this was accompanied by a transient increase in blood-flow, which returned to its original value in spite of the maintained fall in perfusion-pressure (Fig. 2.52). The effects were blocked by nethalide. Clearly, there was a decrease in vascular resistance; and since this was accompanied by a rise in PO_2 of the outflowing blood, the dilatation of the blood-vessels was not secondary to tissue hypoxia.

Waking Animal. In their study on the waking dog Pitt *et al.* (1967) inserted, in a preliminary operation, thermodilution blood-flow meters in the coronary artery and aorta, and implanted cannulae in the large vessels, so as to monitor pressures. An artificial block of the AV node was established, and the heart was caused to beat at any desired rate. At a fixed heart-rate, an injection of isoproterenol into

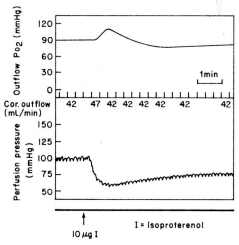

Fig. 2.52. The effect of isoprenaline (isoproterenol) on coronary blood-flow and perfusion-pressure in the isolated arrested dog heart. The isoprenaline caused a profound fall in perfusion-pressure, accompanied by a transient rise in coronary blood-flow, which returned to its original value in spite of the maintained fall in perfusion-pressure. (Klocke *et al.*, *Circ. Res.*)

the jugular vein caused a 46 per cent increase in coronary blood-flow; this was accompanied by a fall in mean aortic pressure by 32 per cent, so that the fall in vascular resistance was in the region of 58 per cent. This was accompanied by a rise in cardiac output of 22 per cent due to a decrease in the systolic ejection period. The effect was blocked by propanolol, so that it appears that there is a β-adrenergic vasodilator mechanism in the coronary vasculature. Adrenaline has both α- and β-actions; under these conditions it increased blood-flow by 194 per cent, and this was accompanied by a rise of 27 per cent in aortic pressure, so that the computed fall in resistance was 52 per cent. When β-blockade was established with propanolol, adrenaline had a variable effect on flow, but it consistently increased the resistance, suggesting an α-constrictor mechanism. Noradrenaline was similar to adrenaline qualitatively. It was observed with adrenaline that the change in coronary resistance occurred long before any effect on systemic haemodynamics, so that it is unlikely that the effect was indirect.

The finding of both a- and β-actions on the resistance doubtless accounts for many conflicting claims in the earlier literature with respect to the effects of sympathetic stimulation or of infused catecholamines.

Responses of Isolated Vascular Smooth Muscle

Studies on isolated arteries are of some interest in connexion with the possible actions of catecholamines, and thus of adrenergic stimulation. As with so many studies on adrenergic influences, care must be taken to isolate a- and β-mediated actions, since most, if not all, tissues influenced by catecholamines contain both types of receptor, usually responding in an opposite manner. Early results suggested that the

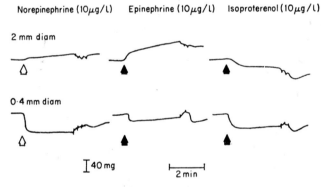

Fig. 2.53. Comparison of responses of strips from large and small coronary arteries, mounted in 15 mM KCl in an organ bath. The large coronary artery is contracted by adrenaline and noradrenaline, while the small one is relaxed. Adrenaline was a more potent constrictor than noradrenaline. Isoproterenol caused relaxation of both large and small vessels. (Zuberbuhler and Bohr, *Circ. Res.*)

predominant effect of catecholamines was to cause contraction, but Zuberbuhler and Bohr (1965) showed that the effect depended on whether smooth muscle was taken from a large—1·5 to 2·4 mm diameter—or small—250–500 μm diameter—artery. With small arteries, whether a strip of muscle was studied or the whole artery was perfused, the catecholamines, noradrenaline and adrenaline, caused relaxation; noradrenaline was effective in a concentration of 0·08 μg/litre, which is less than the normal blood concentration of 1 μg/litre. Adrenaline required some 10 times the concentration.* The effects were blocked by nethalide (α-isopropylamino-1-(2-naphthyl) ethanol) a specific β-blocker, whilst isoproterenol, the synthetic β-mimicker, was most effective. With vessels of 100 μm diameter, the sole effect was relaxation, but with bigger arteries in the small class, there was some evidence for a contractile response in the presence of nethalide, indicating some α-contraction. In large arteries, the effects of α-contraction were more obvious, but the presence of a β-relaxation was manifest by the relaxation caused by isoproterenol. Fig. 2.53 shows the responses of strips from small and large arteries; the small-artery strips show relaxation with all three catecholamines; the large respond by contraction with adrenaline and noradrenaline, but by relaxation with isoproterenol.

Possible Cholinergic Dilator Mechanism

It will be recalled that the vasculature of skeletal muscle has a triple control, an α-adrenergic vasoconstrictor, a β-adrenergic vaso-

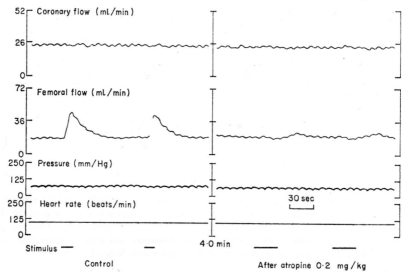

Fig. 2.54. The possible cholinergic vasodilator mechanism in skeletal muscle. The dog was given reserpine for 2 days prior to the experiment to remove catecholamines. Stimulation of the stellate ganglion had no effect on coronary blood-flow, but stimulation of the lumbar sympathetics produced a marked increase in femoral blood flow, which was cholinergic in nature, since it could be blocked by atropine. (Feigl, *Circ. Res.*)

---

* Zuberbuhler and Bohr point out that the classical order of effectiveness of the catecholamines on a β-receptor is: Isoproterenol > Adrenaline > Noradrenaline, whereas with the coronary smooth muscle the order is: Isoproterenol > Noradrenaline > Adrenaline.

dilator, and a sympathetic *cholinergic* vasodilator mechanism. Feigl (1967) attempted to demonstrate a cholinergic dilator mechanism in the coronary system. By treatment of the animal with reserpine, catecholaminergic mechanisms were blocked, and stimulation of the stellate ganglion, or activation of the defence reaction by stimulation of the hypothalamus, failed to influence coronary flow although, as

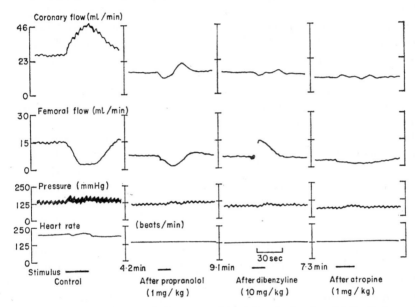

Fig. 2.55. Sympathetic control of coronary blood-flow in the dog. In the first panel, stimulation of the stellate ganglion caused an increase in coronary blood-flow, which was converted into a vasoconstrictor response by β blockade (propanolol, second panel). This vasoconstriction can be abolished by α blockade (dibenzyline, third panel) which also reveals the sympathetic dilator effect shown by the increase in femoral blood-flow when the lumbar sympathetics are stimulated at the same time. Atropine abolishes this last response, which must have therefore been cholinergic in nature. (Feigl, *Circ. Res.*)

Fig. 2.54 shows, there was an increase in flow through the femoral vasculature when the lumbar sympathetic was stimulated simultaneously. The latter effect was blocked by atropine. In the normal animal, stimulation of the stellate ganglion caused an increase in coronary flow, which was converted into a decrease, with a subsequent rebound, after β-blockade; and finally all effects were eliminated by combined α- and β-blockade (Fig. 2.55).

Adrenergic Activity at High Heart-Rates

The question arises as to whether these adrenergic mechanisms play a role in normal vascular adjustments, and the answer seems to be No, except at very high rates of heart-beat. Pitt and Gregg (1968), studying the waking animal with implanted blood-flow meters and a pacemaker, found that increasing heart-rate from 50–70/min to 80–100/min caused a rapid rise in arterial pressure, coronary blood-flow, and cardiac output; when the rate was increased to 130–180/min there was a more gradual rise in blood-flow, whilst arterial pressure and cardiac output remained about the same. These rises in blood-flow were accompanied by a reduction in resistance. When heart-rate was increased still further, cardiac output tended to fall off, due to inadequate diastolic filling, but blood-flow continued to increase up to rates of 250–300/min. When the heart was beating at an optimal rate, of the order of 120/min, infusion of propanolol failed to influence blood-flow, indicating that this was being maintained independently of the adrenergic vasodilator mechanism. In a similar study, Cobb *et al.* (1969) found that when propanolol was administered it did, indeed, reduce coronary blood-flow, but only at the very highest rates, so that it was suggested that sympathetic vasodilatation comes into play only under extreme conditions. In a later study, however, they showed (Cobb *et al.*, 1973) that, in the sympathetically denervated heart, propanol had no effect at very high heart-rates, so that it seemed that circulating catecholamines were not important in regulating blood-flow under these conditions. Hence the depressing effects of propanolol, found with the innervation intact, might be due to an unmasking of an α-constrictor action normally held in check by the β-receptors.

The Vasoactive Metabolite

As with the changed blood-flow of skeletal muscle during exercise, so with coronary blood-flow, it has been postulated that one or more metabolites released during exercise, or increased cardiac effort, have a direct action on the blood-vessels. So far as the heart is concerned, adenosine has been favoured by Berne; thus Rubio *et al.* (1969) occluded the left coronary artery of the anaesthetized open-chest dog and sampled arterial and carotid-sinus blood before and after the occlusion. Adenosine was present after the occlusion, equivalent to an estimated 75 mμmoles/100 ml of extracellular fluid. Infusion of adenosine at a concentration of 56 mμmoles/100 ml is enough to cause maximal coronary vasodilatation. On this basis the hyperaemia of coronary occlusion would be due to the accumulation of adenosine, and if experiments from occlusion can be extrapolated to the situation of O_2-lack through increased cardiac effort, this finding lends support to Berne's hypothesis. However, more recently, Afonso (1969) found that, although lidoflazine increased the response of a dog's coronary blood-flow to adenosine some 25 to 100-fold, it did not potentiate the responses to hypoxia or induced tachycardia, so that the hypothesis appears shaky. Similarly, aminophylline, which also potentiates the action of adenosine, failed to potentiate the response of coronary blood-flow to hypoxia (Afonso *et al.*, 1972).

Role of Prostaglandins

Kraemer and Folts (1973) have described a release of prostaglandins from the heart following occlusion of the coronary artery, the prostaglandins being apparently synthesized from arachidonic acid. According to Afonso *et al.* (1974), the inhibitor of prostaglandin synthesis, indomethacin, reduces the increased coronary blood-flow evoked by anoxia in the dog. The effects are not striking, so that if adenosine is definitely involved, at best the prostaglandins probably exert a minor role. Direct injection of PGE_1 and PGE_2 into the coronary artery increased blood-flow.

Nitroglycerine and Angiotensin

Nitroglycerine is administered during heart failure owing to its beneficial effects on coronary circulation; according to Cohen and Kirk (1973), its main and prolonged effects are on the large arteries, causing dilatation, any effects on small arteries being transient. Angiotensin, the powerful vasoconstrictor released during haemorrhage, likewise makes a preferential attack on the large coronary arteries, constricting these; the constrictor effect on the small vessels is not sustained.

PULMONARY BLOOD-FLOW

Pressures

The basic features of the pulmonary circulation have been briefly described in Vol. 1; the most striking difference from the systemic circulation is in the low pressures throughout the pulmonary vascular system, the mean arterial pressure in man being only 11–15 mm Hg, with systolic values between 20 and 23 mm Hg and diastolic values between 5 and 9 mm Hg. The low pressures are doubtless related to the necessity to avoid filtration through the capillaries; when this occurs pathologically, as in phosgene poisoning, access of air to the alveoli is restricted and leads to asphyxia.

Resistance at Rest

The flows through the pulmonary and systemic circulations are, during any steady state, equal; and this equality, in the presence of such a large difference in perfusion-pressure, is achieved by the absence of a high-resistance system of arterioles; because of this absence, the flow through the pulmonary capillary bed is pulsatile. We may note that the fall in pressure from the capillaries to the pulmonary veins is some 3·6 mm Hg; this, although small, constitutes one third of the total pressure-drop, so that a corresponding fraction of the total resistance is located here.

Resistance in Exercise

The main problem presented to the pulmonary circulation is to keep pace with the systemic output; so far as cardiac adjustments are concerned, we have seen that Starling's Law, according to which the output of a ventricle increases with the degree of filling, ensures that the outputs of both ventricles tend to equalize (Vol. 1); we have seen, however, that the increased cardiac output during exercise is achieved largely by a decrease in total resistance, rather than an increase in arterial pressure, this latter parameter being stabilized by the buffer reflexes.

Pulmonary Arterial Pressure

Early studies on catheterized human hearts during exercise suggested that there was also very little change in right-sided arterial pressure during exercise, so that it was concluded that the increased output here, too, was achieved by a lowered resistance (Riley et al., 1948). More recent work has shown that the pulmonary arterial pressure does, indeed, rise during exercise; thus Elkins and Milner (1971), in their study of the dog, found that, when cardiac output rose from 2·6 to 5·3 litres/min, the mean arterial pressure rose from 18 to 28 mm Hg with no consistent change in the left atrial pressure.* The rise in pressure was not adequate to account for the increased flow, and the resistance in the circuit fell from 480 to 370 dynes sec cm^{-5}. The question that has agitated the minds of investigators in this field (see, for example, Daly, 1958) is the extent to which this adjustment of resistance is achieved by reflex activity, and the extent to which merely passive mechanical adaptations contribute.

---

* Yu et al. (1967) found only small rises in pulmonary arterial pressure in human subjects during exercise, from about 14 mm Hg to about 17 mm Hg.

Mechanical Factors

Thus we may imagine that an increased ejection of blood into the pulmonary artery would increase the arterial pressure and thus the transmural pressure, and if this caused expansion of the blood vessels, the extra flow would take place with only a small increase in arterial pressure. In other words, we are asking the pulmonary vascular bed to reverse the autoregulatory response postulated by Bayliss, so that it expands passively in response to a raised transmural pressure instead of actively constricting. Secondly, the increased ventilation of the lungs, associated with exercise, will tend to alter the average intrapulmonary pressure, leading to a mechanical force that might well favour vascular dilatation. Again, the increased force of contraction of the left ventricle will react on the pressure in the left atrium.

Left Atrial Pressure. This seems to have two effects; clearly it tends to lower the total pressure-drop thus prejudicing flow, but it also favours expansion of the venous bed, so that the net effect may

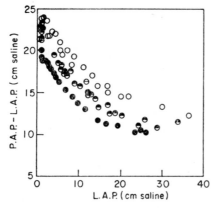

Fig. 2.56. The relationship of the left atrial pressure to the pulmonary vascular resistance. One pair of isolated lungs perfused at three different rates of blood-flow. Positive pressure ventilation. Ordinate: Pulmonary arterial pressure—left atrial pressure (P.A.P.—L.A.P.); Abscissa: Left atrial pressure (L.A.P.). Blood flow (ml/kg/min): ●, 46; ◕, 55; ○, 63. (Carlill and Duke, *J. Physiol.*)

well favour flow. For example, Carlill and Duke (1956, 1957) studied the effects of changing the left atrial pressure in the cat's isolated perfused lung. When blood-flow was maintained constant, and left atrial pressure was altered, the pulmonary arterial pressure altered too, but the change was such that an increase in left atrial pressure was associated with a decrease in resistance. Thus, under conditions of constant flow-rate, the difference, *PAP–LAP*, is a measure of the resistance, and as Fig. 2.56 shows, the difference decreases with increasing left atrial pressure (*LAP*).

Tracheal Pressure. In a more systematic study, Banister and Torrance (1960) showed that the conductance of the vascular system, i.e. the reciprocal of the resistance, varied with both arterial and venous pressures, and could be expressed as a linear function of the mean of these:

$$(P_A + P_V)/2.$$

When the tracheal pressure of the artificially perfused lung was altered, then the slope of the line relating conductance to mean pressure altered, as in Fig. 2.57 indicating that, for a given value of the

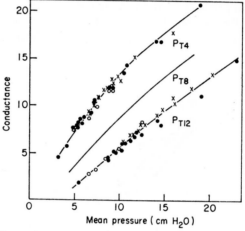

Fig. 2.57. The effects of tracheal pressure (P_T) on the relation between conductance and mean pressure. Points were obtained at P_T-values of 4 and 12 cm H_2O, whilst the P_{T8}-curve was obtained by interpolation using the linear relation between P_A and P_T. (Banister and Torrance, *Quart. J. exp. Physiol.*)

mean pressure, the conductance decreased as tracheal pressure increased; this is to be expected since, if a change in conductance resulted from a passive expansion or contraction of the vessels, an increase in tracheal pressure would tend to resist the expansive tendency of the intravascular pressure, i.e. it would reduce the *transmural pressure*.

Changes in Capillary Bed. A further factor leading to expansion of the vascular bed is an increased number of open capillaries; thus it has been estimated that the capillary volume during exercise increases by some 50 per cent (Johnson *et al.* 1960) and such an opening up could considerably decrease total pulmonary resistance. We may envisage that the increased pulmonary arterial pressure associated with the increase in volume-flow would itself open up the capillary bed, but increased metabolism associated with the increased pulmonary activity might well provide local chemical vaso-active stimulants.

Effects of Lung Inflation

The effects of altered inflation of the lungs will obviously vary according to the manner in which the inflation has been carried out, i.e. whether, in an experiment, inflation was brought about by positive pressure exerted into the trachea, or a negative pressure applied to the surface of the lung. They have been lucidly discussed by Burton and Patel (1958), who have analysed the conflicting claims of earlier authors; as they, and later Howell *et al.* (1961) and Permutt *et al.* (1961) pointed out, the surprising feature of this work was the agreement on facts and the disagreement on their interpretation.

Transmural Pressure

Burton and Patel emphasized that the important influence of inflation was on the *transmural pressure* across the blood-vessels, i.e. the difference between the pressure within and that in the adjacent tissue. This would not affect the *driving pressure*, or *perfusion-pressure*, unless the atrial pressure was altered, so that to utilize an "effective pressure", defined as the pulmonary arterial pressure minus the intrathoracic pressure, as the pressure driving blood through the system is incorrect; this was often done when computing the resistance to flow: Resistance = Flow/Effective pressure, and thus gave erroneous results. The effective pressure would, in fact, be a measure of the transmural pressure, and would govern the tendency of the vessels to expand passively. When this approach was made, it appeared that most of the effects of inflation became intelligible in terms of altered passive expansion of the blood-vessels in response to altered transmural pressure. Thus high positive-pressure inflation should theoretically, and does indeed, cause increased resistance to blood-flow, and all degrees of negative-pressure inflation should decrease resistance, as in fact happens. In general, their own experiments confirmed that negative intrathoracic pressures, induced by inspiration, resulted in a decrease in pulmonary vascular resistance.

Positive-Pressure Inflation   The effects of positive-pressure inflation were more complex, to give U-shaped curves, as in Fig. 2.58, the actual shape depending on the pressure employed to perfuse the lungs. The basic feature of the U-shape is that, with moderate positive inflation pressures, there is a decrease in resistance; and it seemed that this was correlated with a "gnarliness" of the small pulmonary vessels suggestive of an active constriction or of some mechanical kinking, taking place at moderate positive intrapulmonary pressures. Thus experimentally we find that, at moderate degrees of inflation,

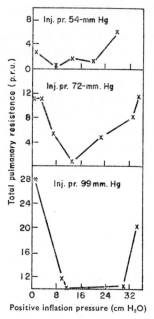

Fig. 2.58. Positive-pressure lung inflation versus pulmonary vascular resistance in the rabbit. As the pressure of inflation is increased the pulmonary vascular resistance decreases at moderate values, but as the pressure values increase the relationship becomes more complex. (Burton and Patel, *J. appl. Physiol.*)

the effects of negative and positive pressure become the same, namely they produce a fall in vascular resistance.

Volume of Blood in Lungs

Permutt *et al.* (1961) examined the volume of blood within the vascular system at different degrees of inflation of the lungs, and they concluded that high positive-pressure inflation tended to drive blood out of the lungs but, as with Burton and Patel's analysis, the situation was complex, and they suggested that there were two compartments of blood, affected differently by lung-volume, the one being compressed and the other expanded when pressure across the lung was altered. They suggested, furthermore, that the compartment responding by dilatation with lung-inflation consisted of the large vessels, whereas the other consisted of the smaller vessels. This conclusion was derived on the basis of changes in fluid-content of the vascular system when this contained saline or paraffin; in the latter instance the small vessels were not filled, due to failure to wet, so that changes in vascular volume reflected changes in the large vessels only. The final effect of a given degree of inflation will thus depend on the balance of opposing changes, and it is doubtless for this reason that there is so much conflict in the literature relating to the effects of lung-inflation on vascular resistance.*

Nervous Stimulation

The pulmonary arteries are innervated by the sympathetic outflow from the cord, passing mainly through the stellate ganglia, so that experimentally the effects of sympathetic stimulation have been usually studied by application of electrodes to these ganglia. Stimulation of the thoracic vago-sympathetic trunk usually has the same effects, although there is no doubt a risk that parasympathetic fibres to the blood vessels will also be stimulated (Daly, 1958), so that atropinization is necessary to separate the effects. With the isolated perfused lung, it has been abundantly shown that stimulation of the sympathetic causes an increase in resistance, manifest as a rise in the pulmonary arterial pressure when the perfusion is carried out at constant volume-flow (see, for example, Daly et al., 1948). A depressor response, i.e. a decrease in arterial pressure due to a fall in vascular resistance, may also be obtained; thus Daly and Daly (1958) often observed a fall in pulmonary arterial pressure when stimulating the left vagosympathetic trunk in the dog, and this occurred in the atropinized animal, suggesting a non-cholinergic pathway.

Parasympathetic

A true parasympathetic vasodilator response was observed by Daly and Hebb (1952) on stimulation of atropine-sensitive vagal fibres. When parasympathetic activity was potentiated with inhibitors of acetylcholinesterase, the net effect was an *increase* in pulmonary vascular resistance (Daly and Wright, 1957); if the parasympathetic innervation to the vasculature is dilator, we must look for secondary causes for this, perhaps the hypoxia and hypercapnia that occurred, which are apparently of themselves vasoconstrictor (p. 193).

* For further hypotheses to account for the effects of positive-pressure inflation of the lung, the interested reader must consult the discussion by Banister and Torrance (1960) of their results. They instance several possible effects of increased intrathoracic pressure, e.g. collapse of capillaries and lengthening and changes in height of vessels, due to lung expansion.

Isolated Artery. Bevan and Su (1964) found that the isolated pulmonary artery constricted in response to acetylcholine, an effect that was blocked by atropine. It is unlikely that this is of physiological significance, however, since the effects of nervous stimulation in the same preparation were completely blocked by the adrenergic inhibitor bretylium. It has been argued by Burn and Rand that acetylcholine might exert its influence by releasing noradrenaline and adrenaline from local chromaffine cells, but this could not be true in this situation since the contraction due to acetylcholine was unaffected by bretylium which inhibits release of catecholamines.

Possible Secondary Effects

The problems confronting investigators have been to ascertain whether the effects of nerve stimulation are genuine consequences of

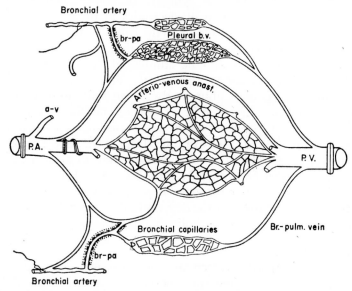

Fig. 2.59. Architecture of the smaller lung vessels showing probable communicating vessels between the bronchial and pulmonary circulations. br–pa = bronchial artery–pulmonary artery anastomoses. (Daly, *Quart. J. exp. Physiol.*)

changes in the state of the pulmonary vessels, be they arteries, capillaries or veins, or whether they may be attributed to a primary influence on some other parameter. Thus the bronchial circulation is not completely separate from the pulmonary, and, as indicated by Fig. 2.59, the connexions might well be such that blood could be diverted from the bronchial to the pulmonary. Such a diversion might, moreover, be of functional importance since it could provide a mechanism for diverting fully oxygenated arterial blood from the bronchial vessels to poorly oxygenated regions of the pulmonary circulation. This difficulty can be avoided in the artificially perfused lung by employing separate pumps for the pulmonary and bronchial circulations, and at the critical point of nerve stimulation the bronchial circulation can be stopped temporarily (Daly *et al.*, 1948). When they used this as a criterion, the various pulmonary responses were shown to be uncomplicated by changes in the bronchial circulation.

Bronchomotor Tone. Another factor that must be controlled, or at least allowed for, is alteration in bronchomotor tone, i.e. the tone of the smooth muscle of the air-conducting system. Thus, when the lungs are being pumped at constant volume, constriction of the bronchioles raises the inspiratory tracheal pressure and air is retained in the alveoli, since it cannot escape easily in expiration. The consequent rise in alveolar pressure would compress the capillaries and increase resistance. Under other conditions the effects of bronchomotor activity may be different and often hard to predict. In general, sympathetic fibres are bronchoconstrictor and parasympathetic are bronchodilator; and experimentally it is not easy to avoid stimulation of bronchomotor fibres at the same time as the vasomotor fibres. The predominant effect of vagosympathetic stimulation is bronchoconstriction, and this can be eliminated by atropinization, so that the vasoconstrictor action of the sympathetic can be demonstrated under these conditions with little fear of interference from bronchomotor activity; the demonstration of parasympathetic vasodilatation, however, is complicated by the parasympathetic bronchodilatation. Alternatively, the effects of nerve stimulation on the collapsed lung have been studied, in the hope that any bronchomotor effects will be without influence on the blood vascular system (Daly *et al.*, 1948, 1954).

The Nature of the Pressor Response

The meticulous studies of Daly (see, for example, Daly and Hebb, 1966) leave little doubt that sympathetic stimulation causes an increase in resistance so that, at constant output, the pulmonary arterial pressure rises. The site at which resistance to flow is increased is by no means clear, but some studies of Ingram *et al.* (1968), and Pace (1971), suggest that the main effect is on the large arteries,* increasing their

* The concentrations of adrenaline and noradrenaline in the walls of the pulmonary arteries and veins are high, and comparable with those in the splenic vessels (Euler and Lishajko, 1958).

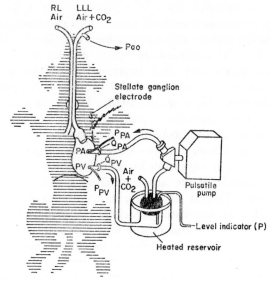

Fig. 2.60. Schematic representation of the isolated perfused lobe preparation. P_{PA} = pulmonary arterial pressure. Q_{PA} = pulmonary arterial flow. P_{PV} = pulmonary venous pressure. Q_{PV} = pulmonary venous flow. P_{ao} = airway opening pressure. RL = right lung. LLL = left lung lobe. PA = pulmonary artery. PV = pulmonary vein. (Ingram *et al., Circ. Res.*)

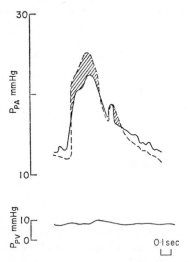

Fig. 2.61. Superimposed pulmonary arterial pressure (P_{PA}) tracings from the control (solid line) period and during sympathetic nerve stimulation (broken line). The higher peak systolic pressure in the record during sympathetic nerve stimulation is offset in its effect on mean pressure by a slightly lower diastolic pressure and a more rapid fall after the dicrotic notch. The arterial flow pulses were identical in the two states and the mean pulmonary venous pressure (P_{PV}) remained unchanged. (Ingram *et al., Circ. Res.*)

tone and decreasing their distensibility. They emphasized the difference between the static resistance to flow—measured by dividing the mean perfusion pressure by the mean rate of volume-flow—and the dynamic *input-impedance* of a pulsatile system. Thus the pump employed in the usual circuit is non-pulsatile and a steady pressure is maintained; alternatively in the intact animal, where pulsatile pressures are present, the resistance is calculated from the mean pressure over a complete cycle. Thus in both situations a static resistance is calculated, and dynamic parameters are ignored.

Dynamic Input-Impedance. When Ingram *et al.* employed a pulsatile perfusion system (Fig. 2.60), they found that the effect of sympathetic stimulation was to increase systolic pressure, and the pulse-pressure, but the *mean pressure* was little altered (Fig. 2.61); the effects were abolished by phenoxybenzamine, and thus represented α-activity. If we consider only the static resistance, the absence of an increase in mean pressure means that no change in this took place, since flow was maintained constant. The increase in pulse-pressure, however, indicates a change in the dynamic input-impedance, resulting from a decrease in the compliance, or distensibility, of the large arteries. Thus the pulmonary input-impedance, Z_0, is calculated from:

$$Z_0 = \sqrt{\rho/AC}$$

where ρ is the density of the blood, A the area of cross-section of the arterial circuit, and C the compliance.

Pace (1971) applied a similar type of analysis to the pulsatile aspects of flow and he, too, concluded that the predominant effect of sympathetic stimulation was the increase in input-impedance, due to a decrease in distensibility (or an increase in elastic modulus). He emphasized that a great deal of the energy developed by the right heart is expended in developing the pulse-pressure; normally this is some 30 per cent of the whole (Milnor *et al.*, 1966), the rest being the kinetic energy of flow; after sympathetic stimulation, because of the greater input-impedance, this rises to 50 per cent of the total.

Exercise

Rise in Impedance

As indicated earlier, exercise is accompanied by an increase in pulmonary arterial pressure, with a fall in resistance, i.e. the resistance to a constant pressure. According to Elkins and Milnor (1971), however, the *impedance* actually rises, due to a decrease in distensibility of the large arteries. This apparent anomaly is explained if we assume that the arteries have dilated in response to the increased arterial pressure; the resulting distension would cause a decrease in their distensibility, i.e. the stretch already imposed reduces their power to stretch further. Thus this particular change in the characteristics of the pulmonary circulation during exercise could be the passive consequence of the increased output from the heart, although the fall in resistance to a steady pressure might well be the consequence of nervous or humoral activity leading to an opening up of new capillaries.

Timing of Flow-Pulse. Severe exercise is accompanied by sympathetic activity and the liberation of adrenaline, and if this leads to vasoconstriction one is inclined to question its teleological significance. As Ingram *et al.* point out, an important aspect in cardiac physiology is the time-relations between right- and left-sided events; in the resting condition the flow-pulse generated by the right ventricle is transmitted to the left atrium in approximately 0·1 sec and propelled into the left atrium at the precise moment of rapid filling of the left ventricle. With the increased heart-rate associated with exercise, this synchrony might well be upset unless the pulse-velocity of the pulmonary system was increased, and this is precisely the consequence of both sympathetic stimulation and of the passive effects of stretching the artery, the pulse-velocity being inversely related to the distensibility, or directly related to the elastic modulus.

The Venous Resistance

We have indicated earlier (Vol. 1) that changes in tone of the pulmonary veins may well be of importance in regulating blood-flow on the right side of the heart. According to Kuramoto and Rodbard (1962), the pressure-drop along the large veins is by no means insignificant; thus, when the pulmonary artery of a dog was 18·4 mm Hg, the pressure in a small vein was 9·1 mm Hg and that in the left atrium was 4·2 mm Hg. Constriction of the veins resulted from stimulation of the aortic body with nicotine (Stern and Braun, 1966). The effect was blocked by guanethidine but not by atropine, and so was presumably mediated by the sympathetic. When animals or men are made hypothermic, e.g. by whole-body cooling, the large veins constrict; according to Stern and Braun (1970), the pulmonary veins share in this reaction, the venous resistance increasing from 0·072 mm Hg/ml/min at normal body-temperature to 0·186 mm Hg/ml/min at 33°C. The effect was blocked by phenoxybenzamine but not by propanolol, and so was due to excitation of α-receptors. Other naturally occurring venoconstrictor substances are histamine and 5-hydroxytryptamine or serotonin (Gilbert *et al.*, 1958)

Reflex Control

Vasosensory Controlled Preparation

As I. Daly (1958) has emphasized, the demonstration of reflex alterations in pulmonary vascular resistance, comparable with those taking place in the systemic circuit, demands an experimental method that allows the elimination of effects that may influence the lungs secondarily, e.g. altered intratracheal pressure, altered left atrial pressure, and so on. Daly and Daly (1959) considered that they had achieved this requirement when they employed the set-up illustrated by Fig. 2.62, described as the "vasosensory controlled perfused living animal preparation". Here the dog's carotid sinus is perfused separately; in addition, the aortic arch is isolated from the general circulation and perfused by a separate pump at controlled pressure. The brain receives its blood through Pump 3 via cannulae inserted into the common carotid arteries but pointing caudally; the lungs are perfused with a separate circuit, Pump 4, whilst aeration of the blood in the whole perfusion system is achieved by pumping blood with Pump 5 through the isolated lungs of another dog (Donor No. 2) maintained in a moist chamber. With this preparation, it is possible to alter the composition of the blood perfusing the carotid sinus and aortic arch without affecting the systemic pressure, and so influences on the bronchial circulation, which might have complicated interpretation of earlier studies (Daly and Daly, 1957), were avoided.

Chemoreceptor Stimulation. Fig. 2.63 shows the responses of some vascular parameters to increasing the PCO_2 and decreasing the PO_2 of blood perfusing the carotid sinus region; in A the bronchial circulation was intact, and there was a fall in pulmonary arterial pressure (PAP); when the bronchial circulation was temporarily cut out, by reducing bronchial arterial pressure to zero, the effect was now a rise in PAP, indicating an increase in vascular resistance. Thus carotid body stimulation of itself apparently causes reflex vasoconstriction in the pulmonary vascular bed, but this effect can be more than compensated by reflex effects on the bronchial circulation, which participates in the generalized reflex vasoconstriction of the systemic circulation, leading to a rise in bronchial arterial pressure. According to Berry and Daly (1931), this rise in bronchial arterial pressure causes a passive rise in pulmonary vascular resistance. Destruction of the stellate ganglia abolished the effects of altered PCO_2 and

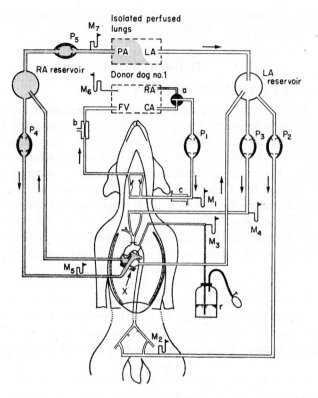

Fig. 2.62. The "vasosensory controlled perfused living animal preparation". Diagram showing the methods of perfusion of the vasosensory areas of the carotip bifurcations and aortic arch, of the brain, the remaining parts of the systemic circulation, and lungs; the lungs are not shown. The isolated carotid sinuses and bodies are perfused by pump P_1 via tap (a) with either oxygenated blood from the carotid artery (CA) or venous blood from the right atrium (RA) of donor dog No. 1. Blood from the cannulated external carotid arteries is returned to the donor animal via a femoral vein. The pressure in the carotid sinuses is controlled by the Starling-type resistance (b). The aortic arch is isolated from the circulation by tying the ascending aorta, the brachiocephalic and left subclavian arteries and the aorta immediately beyond the origin of the left subclavian artery. The pressure in the aortic arch is controlled by means of a pressure-bottle (r) filled with blood and connected to a cannula inserted into the left subclavian artery. The brain is perfused by pump P_3 with blood from the left atrium reservoir (LA) via cannulae inserted into the common carotid arteries, pointing caudally. The vascular bed of the aorta beyond the origin of the left subclavian artery is perfused by pump P_2 via T-cannulae inserted into the femoral arteries. Blood from the systemic circulation drains via a cannula in the right atrium into the right atrial reservoir (RA). The lungs of the recipient animal are perfused through the pulmonary artery with venous blood from the right atrial reservoir by means of pump P_4. Blood from the cannulated left atrium drains into the left atrial reservoir. Connected in parallel with the lungs of the recipient

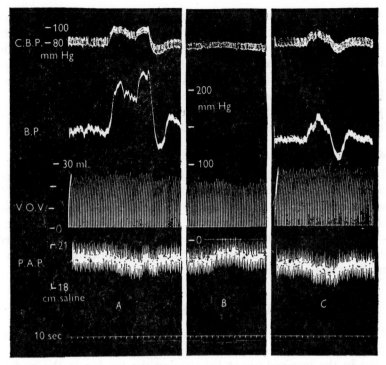

Fig. 2.63. Dog, 11·6 kg. "Vasosensory controlled perfused living animal" preparation. The aortic arch was separately perfused as shown in Fig. 2.62 and the pressure
was maintained at 60 mm Hg. The mean carotid sinus pressure was maintained
constant at 100 mm Hg. In A, B and C the carotid body chemoreceptors were
stimulated temporarily by venous blood from the right atrium of donor dog No. 1.
In B, the test was made at zero bronchial arterial pressure, the pump perfusing the
vascular bed of the aorta beyond the origin of the left subclavian artery being turned
off. The cerebral perfusion pressure was maintained constant. Note reversal of the
response of the pulmonary arterial pressure in B. B.P., femoral arterial blood
pressure; C.B.P., cerebral blood pressure; P.A.P., pulmonary arterial pressure;
V.O.V., ventilation overflow volume. (Daly and Daly, *J. Physiol.*)

---

animal are the isolated lungs of donor dog No. 2. These lungs are perfused through
the pulmonary artery by pump P_5 with blood from the right atrial reservoir; blood
from the left atrium drains into the left atrial reservoir. M_1, M_2, M_3, M_4, M_5, M_6 and
M_7 are connexions to manometers measuring pressures in the different vascular
territories. CA, carotid artery; FV, femoral vein; LA, left atrium; RA, right atrium;
PA, pulmonary artery; a, three-way tap; b, Starling type of resistance; c, warming
coil; X, tape tied round ventricles below auriculo-ventricular groove and embracing
the pulmonary arterial cannula. The stippling represents venous blood. (Daly and
Daly, *J. Physiol.*)

PO_2. As to why, and in what manner, alterations in the bronchial circulation affect the pulmonary resistance, is not easy to decide; Daly and Daly suggest a redistribution of blood in the two circulations.

Baroreceptor Stimulation. When the pressure in the carotid sinus was increased the effect was a decrease in resistance in the pulmonary circulation, which was abolished by stellectomy; the response was obtained when bronchial arterial pressure was zero and so represents a true reflex effect on the pulmonary vessels.

Defence Reaction

It will be recalled that a feature of the integrated defence reaction evoked by hypothalamic stimulation in cats is a dilatation of the vascular bed in skeletal muscle due to excitation of cholinergic sympathetic vasodilators. Stimulation of the same region (near the fornix) in cats caused a rise in pulmonary vascular resistance, of the order of 6–8 per cent, which was abolished by stellectomy or hexamethonium (Anderson *et al.*, 1967).

Direct Effect of the Respiratory Gases

The effects of the respiratory gas tensions on pulmonary circulation in the isolated lung can be studied in two ways; either by altering the tension in the inspired air or by altering the tension in the perfusing blood. In the first case we might expect to be influencing mainly the capillary and post-capillary circulation, whereas when the change has been made in the blood passing through the pulmonary vessels the effects will be predominantly on the precapillary circulation, i.e on the arteries, since by the time the blood reaches the capillaries it will be ventilated by alveolar air and the experimental changes in tension will be largely nullified.

Changes in Inspired Air

Euler and Liljestrand (1946) found that a high P_ACO_2 or low P_AO_2 in the inspired air increased pulmonary arterial pressure in the intact cat, so that resistance was raised, and similar results were obtained by Duke (1951) on the perfused lung. That the effects of changed composition of the inspired air had a direct influence, rather than through altered gas tensions in the general circulation, was demonstrated by Borst *et al.* (1957), who inflated the left and right lungs of a dog separately, and compared the blood-flows in the individual lungs when only one was exposed to a changed gas-content of the inspired air. Increased P_ACO_2 was always vasoconstrictive, whereas the vasoconstriction of hypoxia usually only occurred after the preparation had been running for several hours.

Changes in Blood Composition

Nisell (1951) found that hypoxic or hypercapnic blood, perfusing the cat lung, reduced the pulmonary vascular resistance, i.e. these blood changes had opposite effects to those produced by changes in the inspired air. However, Nisell's results have not been confirmed by other workers; for example, Daly and Wright (1957) found a rise in resistance with hypercapnic and hypoxic blood, and similar effects were obtained by Barer (1963a, b) who concluded that, since the effects were abolished by dibenamine, the blood-changes led to liberation of catecholamines locally.

Physiological Significance

Physiologically, the effects of hypoxia and hypercapnia on blood-flow are of some interest; thus it would be desirable, in the interest of adequate ventilation, if pulmonary blood were diverted away from regions of hypercapnia and hypoxia to regions where the blood would be able to lose CO_2 and gain O_2 more effectively, so that it may be that the effects described above are of some physiological importance.

Effects of Catecholamines

The evidence from sympathetic stimulation, employing artificially perfused lungs, suggests that adrenergic mechanisms cause, if anything, an increase in resistance to flow in the pulmonary circulation. In experiments on the intact animal, either with open-chest and positive pressure respiration or with closed-chest and normal respiration, the effects of infusions of catecholamines are conflicting, in so far as unequivocal influences on vascular resistance are concerned; and this is doubtless because of the complicating effects of alterations in the systemic parameters. It will be sufficient to describe just two experimental studies.

Experiments on Dogs

For example, Feeley et al. (1963) compared the effects of adrenaline and noradrenaline on the systemic and pulmonary circulations in dogs. They found that, with adrenaline, the pulmonary resistance actually fell (Fig. 2.64) and this seemed to be due to a passive dilatation resulting from a rise in left atrial pressure; this was accompanied by a rise in pulmonary arterial and venous pressures, and the net effect was an increased blood-flow. Since it seems well established that the effects of noradrenaline and adrenaline, per se, are to constrict the pulmonary vasculature, the passive effects of the raised pressures counteract the constricting effect. The rise in left atrial pressure is due to effects on the systemic side, namely the more powerful contraction of the left ventricle; this tends to lower the perfusion-pressure (which, it will be recalled, is defined as the difference between the pulmonary arterial and left atrial pressures), but the reduction in perfusion-pressure is insufficient to reduce blood-flow.

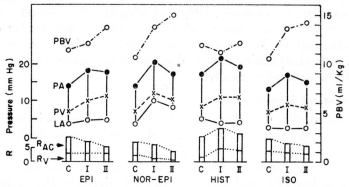

Fig. 2.64. The effects of adrenaline (EPI), noradrenaline (NOR-EPI), histamine (HIST) and isoprenaline (ISO) on pulmonary blood volume (PBV) and mean pressures in pulmonary artery (PA), pulmonary vein (PV) and left atrium (LA). The lowest traces show resistance in pulmonary vein, R_V, and in "arterio-capillary region" (R_{AC} = resistance between pulmonary artery and catheter in small vein). C in each block is the control period; I the response 2–3 min, and II 10–20 min after the intravenous infusion of the drug. Open-chest experiments. With adrenaline and noradrenaline the resistance fell, indicating that their constrictor actions had been overcome by the dilatation resulting from the raised perfusion-pressure. (Feeley *et al., Amer. J. Physiol.*)

Stuhlinger *et al.* (1970) studied the effects of infusing noradrenaline on systemic and pulmonary circulation parameters, and the effects of the β-blocker, propanolol, to ascertain the relative effects of α- and β-activity. Noradrenaline caused a rise in systemic arterial pressure accompanied by a decrease in blood-flow, due to the strong peripheral vasoconstriction; and the effects were modified by propanolol as might be predicted. Thus the rise in arterial pressure was reduced, due to blocking the β-action on the heart, and blood-flow was reduced to much lower values owing to the uncomplicated vasoconstrictor action. In the pulmonary circuit, arterial pressure rose from 18·1 to 21·3 mm Hg, and this was not affected by propanolol. The calculated resistance in the pulmonary circuit rose by some 28 per cent, but this was not statistically significant. Stuhlinger *et al.* concluded that the final effect of the hormone resulted from an interaction between the constrictive

action, *per se*, tending to increase resistance, and the indirect effects of
the cardiac and systemic influences, which tended to increase transmural pressure and thus antagonize the vascular contraction mechanically. We have already alluded to the effects of the β-mimicker,
isoproterenol; the predominant effect of this catecholamine is due to
the increased output by the right ventricle; this raises pulmonary
arterial pressure, and the increased flow is due entirely to this, there
being no evidence for any change in resistance.

Work of Right Heart

Turnheim *et al.* point out that the work of the right ventricle is very
much increased under these conditions (Fig. 2.65), a factor to be taken
into account when treating patients with chronic pulmonary disease in
order to reduce pulmonary arterial pressure; this reduction is effected
by dilatation of the bronchial tubes, which lowers pulmonary arterial
pressure (Rodbard, 1953); if this bronchial dilatation failed, the
effect of isoproterenol would be to raise pulmonary pressure and place
too great a strain on the right side of the heart (Turnheim *et al.*, 1971).

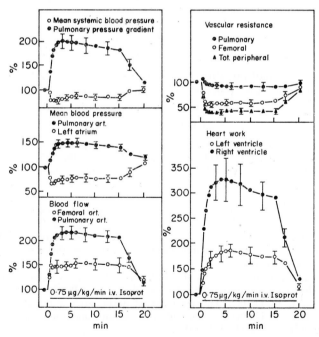

Fig. 2.65. The effects of infusion of 0·75 μg/kg/min of isoproterenol into the open-
chested dog on pulmonary and systemic haemodynamics. Notice the large effect on
the work performed by the right heart. (Turnheim *et al., Pflüg. Arch.*)

Intrinsic and Extrinsic Factors

Where alterations in pulmonary vascular resistance are concerned the experimenter's primary concern has been to separate the extrinsic or secondary influences from the operation of any intrinsic mechanisms.

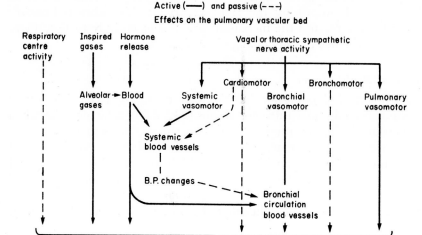

Fig. 2.66. Chains of biological events leading to active and passive effects on the pulmonary vascular bed. (Daly, *Quart. J. exp. Physiol.*)

The large number of possibilities are illustrated by Fig. 2.66, where the dashed lines indicate passive consequences, and the full lines the results of a direct action on the pulmonary vascular bed.

REFERENCES

Afonso, S. (1969). Coronary vasodilator responses to hypoxia and induced tachy-cardia before and after lidoflazine. *Amer. J. Physiol.*, **216**, 297–300.

Afonso, S., Ansfield, T. J., Berndt, T. B. and Rowe, G. G. (1972). Coronary vaso-dilator responses to hypoxia before and after aminophylline. *J. Physiol.*, **221**, 589–599.

Afonso, S., Bandow, G. T. and Rowe, G. G. (1974). Indomethacin and prostaglandin hypotheses of coronary blood flow regulation. *J. Physiol.*, **241**, 299–308.

Anderson, F. L. and Brown, A. M. (1967). Pulmonary vasoconstriction elicited by stimulation of the hypothalamic intigrative area for the defence reaction. *Circ. Res.*, **21**, 747–756.

Andrews, C. J. H., Andrews, W. H. H. and Orbach, J. (1972). A sympathetic reflex elicited by distension of the mesenteric venous bed. *J. Physiol.*, **226**, 119–131.

Angell James, J. E. (1971). The responses of aortic arch and right subclavian baroreceptors to changes of non-pulsatile pressure and their modification by hypothermia. *J. Physiol.*, **214**, 201–223.

Angell James, J. E. and Daly, M. de B. (1969). Cardiovascular responses in apnoeic asphyxia: role of arterial chemoreceptors and the modification of their effects by a pulmonary vagal reflex. *J. Physiol.*, **201**, 87–104.

Angell James, J. E. and Daly, M. de B. (1970). Comparison of the reflex vasomotor responses to separate and combined stimulation of the carotid sinus and aortic-arch baroreceptors by pulsatile and non-pulsatile pressures in the dog. *J. Physiol.*, **209**, 257–293.

Armour, J. A. (1973). Physiological behaviour of thoracic cardiovascular receptors. *Amer. J. Physiol.*, **225**, 177–185.

Asmussen, E. and Nielsen (1964). Experiments on nervous factors controlling respiration and circulation during exercise imploying blocking of the blood flow. *Acta Physiol. Scand.*, **60**, 103–111.

Åstrand, P.-O., Cuddy, T. E., Saltin, B. and Stenberg, J. (1964). Cardiac output during submaximal work. *J. app. Physiol.*, **19**, 268–279.

Banister, J. and Torrance, R. W. (1960). The effects of the tracheal pressure upon flow: pressure relations in the vascular bed of isolated lungs. *Quart. J. exp. Physiol.*, **45**, 352–367.

Barcroft, H. (1972). An enquiry into the nature of the mediator of the vasodilatation in skeletal muscle in exercise and during circulatory arrest. *J. Physiol.*, **222**, 99–118 P.

Barer, G. R. (1963a). The circulation through collapsed adult lungs. *J. Physiol.*, **168**, 10–11 P.

Barer, G. R. (1963b). The mechanism of the increased vascular resistance caused by hypoxaemia in both collapsed and ventilated lungs. *J. Physiol.*, **169**, 102 P.

Barron, W. and Coote, J. H. (1973). The contribution of articular receptors to cardiovascular reflexes elicited by passive limb movement. *J. Physiol.*, **235**, 423–436.

Bartelstone, H. J. and Nasmyth, P. A. (1965). Vasopressin potentiation of catechol-amine actions in dog, rat, cat and rat aortic strip. *Amer. J. Physiol.*, **208**, 754–762.

Bayliss, W. M. (1902). On the local reactions of the arterial wall to changes of internal pressure. *J. Physiol.*, **28**, 220–231.

Beck, L. *et al.* (1966). Sustained dilatation elicited by sympathetic nerve stimulation. *Fed. Proc.*, **25**, 1596–1606.

Berne, R. M. *et al.* (1957). Hypoxemia and coronary blood flow. *J. Clin. Invest.*, **36**, 1101–1106.

Berne, R. M. (1964). Regulation of coronary blood flow. *Physiol. Rev.*, **34**, 1–29.

Berry, J. L. and Daly, I. de B. (1931). The relation between the pulmonary and bronchial vascular systems. *Proc. Roy. Soc. B.*, **109**, 319–336.

Bevan, J. A. and Su, C. (1964). The sympathetic mechanism in the isolated pul-monary artery of the rabbit. *Brit. J. Pharmacol.*, **22**, 176–182.

Bevegård, S. Holmgren, A. and Jonsson, B. (1963). Circulatory studies on well trained athletes at rest and during heavy exercise, with special reference to stroke volume and the influence of body position. *Acta physiol. scand.*, **57**, 26–50.

Bevegård, B. S. and Shepherd, J. T. (1966). Circulatory effects of stimulating the carotid arterial stretch receptors in man at rest and during exercise. *J. clin. Invest.*, **45**, 132–142.

Biscoe, T. J. (1971). Carotid body: structure and function. *Physiol. Rev.*, **51**, 437–495.

Biscoe, T. J., Bradley, G. N. and Purves, M. J. (1970). The relation between carotid body chemoreceptor discharge, carotid sinus pressure and carotid body venous flow. *J. Physiol.*, **208**, 99–120.

Biscoe, T. J., Purves, M. J. and Sampson, S. R. (1970). The frequency of nerve impulses in single carotid body chemoreceptor afferent fibres recorded *in vivo* with intact circulation. *J. Physiol.*, **208**, 121–131.

Biscoe, T. J., Lall, A. and Sampson, S. R. (1970). Electron microscopic and electro-physiological studies on the carotid body following intracranial section of the glossopharyngeal nerve. *J. Physiol.*, **208**, 133–152.

Biscoe, T. J. and Purves, M. J. (1967). Factors affecting the cat carotid chemoreceptor and cervical sympathetic activity with special reference to passive hind-limb movements. *J. Physiol.*, **190**, 425–441.

Biscoe, T. J. and Stehbens, W. E. (1967). Ultrastructure of the denervated carotid body. *Quart. J. exp. Physiol.*, **52**, 31–36.

Borst, H. G., Whittenberger, J. L., Berglund, E. and McGregor, M. (1957). Effects of unilateral hypoxia and hypercapnia on pulmonary blood flow distribution in the dog. *Amer. J. Physiol.*, **191**, 446–452.

Braun, K. and Stern, S. (1966). Functional significance of the pulmonary venous system. *Amer. J. Cardiol.*, **20**, 56–65.

Bristow, J. D. *et al.* (1971). Effect of bicycling on the baroreflex regulation of pulse interval. *Circulation Res.*, **28**, 582–592.

Brody, M. J. (1966). Neurohumoral mediation of active reflex vasodilatation. *Fed. Proc.*, **25**, 1583–1592.

Burn, J. H. and Rand, M. J. (1959). Sympathetic postganglionic mechanism. *Nature (Lond.)*, **184**, 163–165.

Burton, A. C. and Patel, D. J. (1958). Effect on pulmonary vascular resistance of inflation of the rabbit lungs. *J. appl. Physiol.*, **12**, 239–246.

Carlill, S. D. and Duke, H. N. (1956). Pulmonary vascular changes in response to variations in left auricular pressure. *J. Physiol.*, **133**, 275–286.

Carlill, S. D., Duke, H. N. and Jones, M. (1957). Some observations on pulmonary haemodynamics in the cat. *J. Physiol.*, **136**, 112–121.

Clark, B. J. and Rocha e Silva, M. (1967). An afferent path-way for the selective release of vasopressin in response to carotid occlusion and haemorrhage. *J. Physiol.*, **191**, 529–542.

Cobb, F. R. *et al.* (1969). Effects of beta-receptor blockade in the systemic and coronary hemodynamic response to an increasing ventricular rate in the unanesthetized dog. *Circulation Res.*, **25**, 331–341.

Cobb, F. R. *et al.* (1973). Sympathetic influences on coronary and aortic flow responses to increasing heart rate. *Amer. J. Physiol.*, **225**, 538–545.

Cohen, M. V. and Kirk, E. S. (1973). Differential response of large and small coronary arteries to nitroglycerin and angiotensin. *Circulation Res.*, **33**, 445–453.

Coleridge, J. C. G., Hemingway, A., Holmes, R. L. and Linden, R. J. (1957). The location of atrial receptors in the dog: a physiological and histological study. *J. Physiol.*, **136**, 174–197.

Coote, J. H., Hilton, S. M. and Perez-Gonzalez, J. F. (1971). The reflex nature of the pressor response to muscular exercise. *J. Physiol.*, **215**, 789–804.

Coote, J. H., Hilton, S. M. and Zbrozyna, A. W. (1973). The pontomedullary area integrating the defence reaction in the cat and its influence on muscle blood flow. *J. Physiol.*, **229**, 257–274.

Corcondiles, A. (1966). Effect of a brief contraction of forearm muscles on forearm blood flow. *J. appl. Physiol.*, **19**, 142–146.

Daly, I. de B. (1958). Intrinsic mechanisms of the lung. *Quart. J. exp. Physiol.*, **43**, 2–26.

Daly, I. de B. and Daly, M. de B. (1958). Pulmonary vasodilator fibres. *J. Physiol.*, **142**, 19–20 P.

Daly, I. de B. and Daly, M. de B. (1959). The effects of stimulation of the carotid sinus baroreceptors on the pulmonary vascular bed in the dog. *J. Physiol.*, **148**, 220–226.

Daly, I. de B. and Daly, M. de B. (1957). Observations on the changes in resistance of the pulmonary vascular bed in response to stimulation of the carotid sinus baroreceptors in the dog. *J. Physiol.*, **137**, 427–435.

Daly, I. de B. and Daly, M. de B. (1957). The effects of stimulation of the carotid body chemoreceptors on pulmonary vascular resistance in the dog. *J. Physiol.*, **137**, 436–446.

Daly, I. de B., and Daly, M. de B. (1959). The effects of stimulation of the carotid body chemoreceptors on the pulmonary vascular bed in the dog: the "vasosensory controlled perfused living animal". *J. Physiol.*, **148**, 201–219.

Daly, I. de B. and Hebb, C. (1952). Pulmonary vasomotor fibres in the cervical vagosympathetic nerve of the dog. *Quart. J. exp. Physiol.*, **37**, 19–43.

Daly, I. de B. and Hebb, C. (1966). *Pulmonary and Bronchial Vascular Systems*. Arnold London.

Daly, I. de B., Duke, H., Hebb, C. O. and Weatherall, J. (1948). Pulmonary vasomotor fibres in the sympathetic chain and its associated ganglia in the dog. *Quart. J. exp. Physiol.*, **34**, 285–313.

Daly, M. de B., and Wright, P. G. (1957). The effect of anticholinesterases upon pulmonary vascular resistance in the dog. *J. Physiol.*, **139**, 273–293.

Davies, R. O. and Lahiri, S. (1973). Absence of carotid chemoreceptor response during hypoxic exercise in the cat. *Resp. Physiol.*, **18**, 92–100.

De Castro, F. and Rubio, M. (1968). The anatomy and innervation of the blood vessels of the carotid body and the role of chemoreceptive reactions in the autoregulation of blood flow. In *Arterial Chemoreceptors*. (Ed R. W. Torrance). Blackwell, Oxford.

Denison, A. B. and Green, H. D. (1958). Effects of autonomic nerves and their mediators on the coronary circulation and myocardial contraction. *Circulation Res.*, **6**, 633–643.

Djojosugito, A. M. *et al.* (1970). Differentiated interaction between the hypothalamic defence reaction and baroreceptor reflexes. I. *Acta physiol. scand.*, **78**, 376–385.

Donald, D. E. and Shepherd, J. T. (1963). Response to exercise in dogs with cardiac denervation. *Amer. J. Physiol.*, **205**, 393–400.

Downing, S. and Siegiel, J. H. (1963). Baroreceptor and chemoreceptor influences on sympathetic discharge to the heart. *Amer. J. Physiol.*, **204**, 471–482.

Duke, H. N. (1951). Pulmonary vasomotor responses of isolated perfused cat lungs to anoxia and hypercapnia. *Quart. J. exp. Physiol.*, **36**, 75–88.

Duke, H. N. and Lee, G. de J. (1963). The regulation of blood flow through the lungs. *Brit. med. Bull.*, **19**, 71–75.

Ead, H. W., Green, J. H. and Neil, E. (1952). A comparison of the effects of pulsatile and non-pulsatile blood flow through the carotid sinus on the reflexogenic activity of the sinus baroreceptors in the cat. *J. Physiol.*, **118**, 509–519.

Eckenhoff, J. E., Hafkenschiel, J. H., Landmesser, C. M. and Harmel, M. (1947). Cardiac oxygen metabolism and control of the coronary circulation. *Amer. J. Physiol.*, **149**, 634–649.

Eckstein, R. W., Moir, T. W. and Driscol, T. E. (1963). Phasic and mean blood flow in the canine septal artery and an estimate of systolic resistance in deep myocardial vessels. *Circulation Res.*, **12**, 203–211.

Ekblom, B. and Hermansen, L. (1968). Cardiac output in athletes. *J. appl. Physiol.*, **25**, 619–625.

Elkins, R. C. and Milnor, W. R. (1971). Pulmonary vascular response to exercise in the dog. *Circulation Res.*, **29**, 591–599.

Errington, M. L. and Rocha e Silva, M. (1974). On the role of vasopressin and angiotensin in the development of irreversible haemorrhagic shock. *J. Physiol.*, **242**, 119–141.

Euler, U. S. v. and Liljestrand, G. (1946). Observations on the pulmonary arterial blood pressure in the cat. *Acta physiol. scand.*, **12**, 301–320.

Euler, U. S. v. and Lishajko, F. (1958). Catecholamines in the vascular wall. *Acta physiol. scand.*, **42**, 333–341.

Eyzaguirre, C. and Koyano, H. (1965). Effects of hypoxia, hypercapnia, and pH on the chemoreceptor activity of the carotid body *in vitro*. *J. Physiol.*, **178**, 385–409.

Eyzaguirre, C. and Lewin, J. (1961). The effect of sympathetic stimulation on carotid nerve activity. *J. Physiol.*, **159**, 251–267.

Fairchild, H. M., Ross, J. and Guyton, A. C. (1966). Failure of recovery from reactive hyperaemia in the absence of oxygen. *Am. J. Physiol.*, **210**, 490–492.

Feeley, J. W., Lee, T. D. and Milnor, R. (1963). Active and passive components of pulmonary vascular response to vasoactive drugs in the dog. *Amer. J. Physiol.*, **205**, 1193–1199.

Feigl, E. O. (1967). Sympathetic control of coronary circulation. *Circulation Res.*, **20**, 262–271.

Feigl, E. O. (1968). Carotid sinus reflex control of coronary blood flow. *Circulation Res.*, **23**, 223–237.

Feinberg, H., Katz, L. N. and Boyd, E. (1962). Determinants of coronary flow and myocardial oxygen consumption. *Amer. J. Physiol.*, **202**, 45–52.

Feldberg, W. and Lewis, G. P. (1965). Further studies on the effects of peptides on the suprarenal medulla of cats. *J. Physiol.*, **178**, 239–251.

Folkow, B. (1964). Autoregulation in muscle and skin. *Circulation Res.*, **14–15**, Suppl. 1, pp. 19–24.

Folkow, B., Heymans, C. and Neil, E. (1965). Integrated aspects of cardiovascular regulation. *Hdb. Physiol.*, Sect. 2, Vol. III, pp. 1787–1823.

Frieden, J. and Keller, A. D. (1954). Decreased resistance to haemorrhage in neuro-hypophysectomized dogs. *Circulation Res.*, **2**, 214–220.

Gammon, G. D. and Bronk, D. W. (1935). Discharge of impulses from pacinian corpuscles and in the mesentery and its relation to vascular changes. *Amer. J. Physiol.*, **114**, 77–84.

Gilbert, R. P., Hinshaw, L. B., Kuida, H. and Visscher, M. B. (1958). Effects of histamine, 5-HT and epinephrine on pulmonary hemodynamics. *Amer. J. Physiol.*, **194**, 165–170.

Goodman, N. W. (1973). Efferent control of arterial chemoreceptors mediated by glossopharyngeal fibres and artifacts introduced by stimulation techniques. *J. Physiol.*, **230**, 295–311.

Green, H. D. and Rapela, C. E. (1964). Blood flow in passive vascular beds. *Circulation Res.*, **14-15**, Suppl. 1, pp. 11–16.

Green, H. D., Rapela, C. E. and Conrad, M. C. (1965). Resistance (conductance) and capacitance phenomena in terminal vascular beds. *Hdb. Physiol.*, Sect. 2, Vol. II, pp. 935–960.

Grim, E. (1963). The flow of blood in the mesenteric vessels. *Hdb. Physiol.*, Sect. 2, Vol. II, pp. 1439–1456.

Guyton, A. C. and Richardson, T. Q. (1961). Effect of hematocrit on venous return. *Circulation Res.*, **9**, 157–164.

Guz, A. (1960). Relation of coronary flow to oxygen supply. *Amer. J. Physiol.*, **199**, 179–189.

Hansen, A. J., Fogh, J., Møllgård, K. and Sørensen, S. C. (1973). Evidence against erythropoietin production by the carotid body. *Resp. Physiol.*, **18**, 101–106.

Heymans, C. and Neil, E. (1958). *Reflexogenic Areas of the Cardiovascular System*. Churchill, London.

Hilton, S. M. (1966). Hypothalamic regulation of the cardiovascular system. *Brit. Med. Bull.*, **22**, 243–248.

Hilton, S. M. and Lewis, G. P. (1955). The mechanism of the functional hyperaemia in the submandibular salivary gland. *J. Physiol.*, **129**, 253–271.

Hilton, S. M. and Spyer, K. M. (1971). Participation of the anterior hypothalamus in the baroreceptor reflex. *J. Physiol.*, **218**, 271–293.

Hodgson, H. J. F. and Matthews, P. B. C. (1968). The ineffectiveness of excitation of the primary endings of the muscle spindle by vibration as a respiratory stimulant in the decerebrate cat. *J. Physiol.*, **194**, 555–563.

Howell, J. B. L., Permutt, S., Proctor, D. F. and Riley, R. L. (1961). Effect of inflation of the lung on different parts of pulmonary vascular bed. *J. appl. Physiol.*, **16**, 71–76.

Ingram, R. H. *et al.* (1968). Effects of sympathetic nerve stimulation on the pulmonary tree of the isolated lobe perfused *in situ. Circulation Res.*, **22**, 801–815.

Johnson, P. C. (1964). Review of previous studies and current theories of autoregulation. *Circulation Res.*, **14-15**, Suppl. 1, pp. 1–9.

Johnson, R. L., Spicer, W. S., Bishop, J. M. and Forster, R. E. (1960). Pulmonary capillary blood volume, flow and diffusing capacity during exercise. *J. appl. Physiol.*, **15**, 893–902.

Kappagoda, C. T., Linden, R. J. and Snow, H. M. (1972). The effect of stretching the superior vena caval-right atrial junction on right atrial receptors in the dog. *J. Physiol.*, **227**, 875–887.

Kewenter, J. (1965). The vagal control of the jejunal and ileal motility and blood flow. *Acta physiol. scand.*, **65**, Suppl. 251, pp. 1–68.

Klocke, F. J. *et al.* (1965). An intrinsic adrenergic vasodilator mechanism in the coronary vascular bed of the dog. *Circulation Res.*, **16**, 376–382.

Kraemer, R. J. and Folts, J. D. (1973). Release of prostaglandins following occlusion of the coronary artery. *Fed. Proc.*, **32**, 454.

Kuramoto, K. and Rodbard, S. (1962). Effects of blood flow and left atrial pressure on pulmonary venous resistance. *Circulation Res.*, **11**, 240–246.

Landgren, S. (1952). The baroceptor activity in the carotid sinus nerve and the distensibility of the sinus wall. *Acta physiol. scand.*, **26**, 35–56.

Lands, A. M. *et al.* (1967). Differentiation of receptor systems activated by sympathomimetic amines. *Nature*, **214**, 597–598.

Ledsome, J. R., Linden, R. J. and O'Connor, W. J. (1961). The mechanism by which distension of the left atrium produces diuresis in the anaesthetized dog. *J. Physiol.*, **159**, 87–100.

Lewis, G. P. and Reit, E. (1965). The action of angiotensin and bradykinin on the superior cervical ganglion of the cat. *J. Physiol.*, **179**, 538–553.

Lewis, T. (1927). *The Blood Vessels of the Human Skin and Their Responses*. Shaw and Son, London.

Majcherczyk, S., Chruscielewski, L. and Trzebski, A. (1974). Effect of stimulation of carotid body chemoreceptors upon ganglioglomerular nerve activity and on chemoreceptor discharges in contralateral sinus nerve. *Brain Res.*, **76**, 167–170.

Manning, J. W. (1965). Cardiovascular reflexes following lesions in medullary reticular formation. *Amer. J. Physiol.*, **208**, 283–288.

Matsura, S. (1973). Chemoreceptor properties of glomus tissue found in the carotid region of the cat. *J. Physiol.*, **235**, 57–73.

Mellander, S. (1968). Exercise hyperaemia. *Pharmacol. Rev.*, **20**, 117–196.

Mellander, S. (1970). Systemic circulation: local control. *Ann. Rev. Physiol.*, **32**, 313–344.

Mellander, S., Öberg, B. and Odelram, H. (1964). Vascular adjustments to increased transmural pressure in cat and man with special reference to shifts in capillary fluid transfer. *Acta physiol. scand.*, **61**, 34–48.

Milnor, W. R., Bergel, D. H. and Bargainer, J. D. (1966). Hydraulic power associated with pulmonary blood flow and its relation to heart rate. *Circulation Res.*, **19**, 467–480.

Mitchell, R. A., Sinha, A. K. and McDonald, D. M. (1972). Chemoreceptive properties of regenerated endings of the carotid sinus nerve. *Brain Res.*, **43**, 681–685.

Møller, M., Møllgård, K. and Sørensen, S. C. (1974). The ultrastructure of the carotid body in chronically hypoxic rabbits. *J. Physiol.*, **238**, 447–453.

Mosher, P. *et al.* (1964). Control of coronary blood flow by an autoregulatory mechanism. *Circulation Res.*, **14**, 250–259.

Neil, E. and O'Regan, R. G. (1969). Efferent and afferent impulse activity in the "intact" sinus nerve. *J. Physiol.*, **205**, 20–21 P.

Neil, E. and O'Regan, R. G. (1971). The effects of electrical stimulation of the distal end of the cut sinus and aortic nerves on peripheral arterial chemoreceptor activity in the cat. *J. Physiol.*, **215**, 15–32.

Neil, E. and O'Regan, R. G. (1971). Efferent and afferent impulse activity recorded from few-fibre preparations of otherwise intact sinus and aortic nerves. *J. Physiol.*, **215**, 33–47.

Neutze, J. M., Wyler, F. and Rudolph, A. M. (1968). Changes in distribution of cardiac output after hemorrhage in rabbits. *Amer. J. Physiol.*, **215**, 857–864.

Nisell, O. (1948). Effects of oxygen and carbon dioxide on the circulation of isolated and perfused lungs of the cat. *Acta physiol. scand.*, **16**, 121–127.

Nisell, O. (1951). The influence of blood gases on the pulmonary vessels of the cat. *Acta physiol. scand.*, **23**, 85–90.

Pace, J. B. (1971). Sympathetic control of pulmonary vascular impedance in anesthetized dogs. *Circulation Res.*, **29**, 555–568.

Paintal, A. S. (1973). Vagal sensory receptors and their reflex effects. *Physiol. Rev.*, **53**, 159–227.

Pearse, A. G. E. (1969). The cytochemistry and ultrastructure of polypeptide hormone-producing cells of the APUD series . . . *J. Histochem. Cytochem.*, **17**, 303–313.

Permutt, S., Howell, J. B. L., Proctor, D. F. and Riley, R. L. (1961). Effect of lung inflation on static pressure-volume characteristics of pulmonary vessels. *J. appl. Physiol.*, **16**, 64–70.

Pitt, B., Elliot, E. C. and Gregg, D. E. (1967). Adrenergic receptor activity in the coronary arteries of the unanesthetized dog. *Circulation Res.*, **21**, 75–84.

Pitt, B. and Gregg, D. E. (1968). Coronary hemodynamic effects of increasing ventricular rate in the unanesthetized dog. *Circulation Res.*, **22**, 753–761.

Ponte, J. and Purves, M. J. (1974). The role of the carotid body chemoreceptors and carotid sinus baroreceptors in the control of cerebral blood vessels. *J. Physiol.*, **237**, 315–340.

Rees, P. M. (1967). Observations on the fine structure and distribution of presumptive baroreceptor nerves at the carotid sinus. *J. comp. Neurol.*, **131**, 517–547.

Regoli, D. and Vane, J. R. (1966). The continuous estimation of angiotensin formed in the circulation of the dog. *J. Physiol.*, **183**, 513–531.

Riley, R. L. *et al.* (1948). Studies of the pulmonary circulation at rest and during exercise in normal individuals and in patients with chronic pulmonary disease. *Amer. J. Physiol.*, **152**, 372–382.

Rocha e Silva, M. and Rosenberg, M. (1968). Efeito da vasopressina sobre a pressão arterial e sua possível significacão fisiológica. *Cienc. Cult. S. Paulo*, **20**, 375–376.

Rocha e Silva, M. and Rosenberg, M. (1969). The release of vasopressin in response to haemorrhage and its role in the mechanism of blood pressure regulation. *J. Physiol.*, **202**, 535–557.

Rowell, L. B., Blackman, J. R. and Bruce, R. A. (1964). Indocyanine green clearance and estimated hepatic blood flow during mild to maximal exercise in upright man. *J. Clin. Invest.*, **43**, 1677–1690.

Rubio, R. and Berne, R. M. (1969). Release of adenosine by the normal myocardium in dogs and its relationship to the regulation of coronary resistance. *Circulation Res.*, **25**, 407–415.

Rubio, R., Berne, R. M. and Katori, M. (1969). Release of adenosine in reactive hyperemia of the dog heart. *Amer J. Physiol.*, **216**, 56–62.

Sabiston, D. C. and Gregg, D. E. (1957). Effect of cardiac contraction on coronary blood flow. *Circulation*, **15**, 14–20.

Sampson, S. R. (1971). Catecholamines as mediators of efferent inhibition of carotid body chemoreceptors in the cat. *Fed. Proc.*, **30**, 551.

Sampson, S. R. and Mills, E. (1970). Effects of sympathetic stimulation on discharges of carotid sinus baroreceptors. *Amer. J. Physiol.*, **218**, 1650–1653.

Schreiner, G. L. *et al.* (1957). Effects of vagus stimulation and of acetylcholine on myocardial contractility, O_2 consumption and coronary flow in dogs. *Circulation Res.*, **5**, 562–567.

Scornik, A. O. and Paladini, A. C. (1964). Angiotensin blood levels in haemorrhagic hypotension and other related conditions. *Amer. J. Physiol.*, **206**, 553–556.

Smith, E. E. and Crowell, J. W. (1963). Influence of hematocrit ratio on survival of unacclimatized dogs at simulated high altitude. *Amer. J. Physiol.*, **205**, 1172–1174.

Smyth, H. S., Sleight, P. and Pickering, G. W. (1969). Reflex regulation of arterial pressure during sleep in man. *Circulation Res.*, **24**, 109–121.

Sobol, B. J. *et al.* (1962). Alteration of coronary blood flow in the dog by inhalation of 100 per cent oxygen. *Circulation Res.*, **11**, 797–802.

Stainsby, W. N. (1962). Autoregulation of blood flow in skeletal muscle during increased metabolic activity. *Amer. J. Physiol.*, **202**, 273–276.

Stainsby, W. N. and Renkin, E. M. (1961). Autoregulation of blood flow in resting skeletal muscle. *Amer. J. Physiol.*, **201**, 117–122.

Stern, S. and Braun, K. (1966). Effect of chemoreceptor stimulation on the pulmonary veins. *Amer. J. Physiol.*, **210**, 535–539.

Stern, S. and Braun, K. (1970). Pulmonary arterial and venous response to cooling: role of alpha-adrenergic receptors. *Amer. J. Physiol.*, **219**, 982–985.

Stühlinger, W., Turnheim, K., Kraupp, O. and Raberger, G. (1970). The effects of an intravenous infusion of norepinephrine on pulmonary and systemic hemodynamics with and without propanolol pretreatment in dogs. *Europ. J. Pharmacol.*, **10**, 34–44.

Thomas, M. R. and Calaresu, F. R. (1972). Responses of single units in the medial hypothalamus to electrical stimulation of the carotid sinus nerve in the cat. *Brain Res.*, **44**, 49–62.

Traber, D. L., Gary, H. H. and Gardier, R. W. (1967). The involvement of the sympathetic nervous system in the pressor response to vasopressin. *Arch. int. Pharmacodyn.*, **168**, 288–295.

Tramezzani, J. H., Morita, E. and Chiocchio, S. R. (1971). The carotid body as a neuroendocrine organ involved in control of erythropoiesis. *Proc. Nat. Acad. Sci. Wash.*, **68**, 52–55.

Turnheim, K., Stühlinger, W. and Kraupp, O. (1971). Hemodynamic effects of isoproterenol on the pulmonary and sytemic circulations in dogs. *Pflüg. Arch. ges. Physiol.*, **322**, 310–322.

Van Citters, R. L. and Franklin, D. L. (1969). Cardiovascular performance of Alaska sled dogs during exercise. *Circulation Res.*, **24**, 33–42.

Wang, H.-H., Blumenthal, M. B. and Wang, S. C. (1960). Effect of efferent vagal stimulation on coronary sinus outflow and cardiac work in the anesthetized dog. *Circulation Res.*, **8**, 271–277.

Yu, P. N., Murphy, G. W., Schreiner, B. F. and James, D. H. (1967). Distensibility characteristics of the human pulmonary vascular bed. *Circulation Res.*, **35**, 710–723.

Zuberbuhler, R. C. and Bohr, D. F. (1965). Response of coronary smooth muscle to catecholamines. *Circulation Res.*, **16**, 431–440.

CHAPTER 3

Control of Respiration

Eupnoea and Hyperpnoea

The rhythmic inspiration and expiration of normal breathing are, unlike the motions of the heart, of neurogenic origin so that spontaneous respiration can be abolished by, for example, cutting across the brain-stem below the medulla to produce the *spinal animal*. Modifications in respiratory rate, such as the increased ventilation in exercise or the inhibition during swallowing or speech, are achieved through influences exerted on the brain-stem neurones rather than directly on the muscles concerned with respiration. These modifications can consist of complete, but temporary, inhibition, as in swallowing, or in modifications in the depth—tidal volume—and frequency of breathing. Thus in breathing at rest—*eupnoea*—the inspiratory and expiratory phases take place slowly and there is a definite pause between the end of expiration and the beginning of the next inspiration. Hyperpnoea of exercise consists of a more rapid execution of the inspiratory and expiratory acts, due to more powerful muscular contractions, and an increased frequency, i.e. in the number of breaths per sec. The increase in depth of breathing, of course, means that more time will be required to fill and empty the lungs, but the greater power of contraction, in effect, permits a shorter cycle than in eupnoea.

Respiratory Muscles

The principal effectors in respiration are the intercostal muscles of inspiration and expiration, and the diaphragm; these are voluntary muscles and are innervated by the spinal somatic motor neurones; those innervating the intercostal muscles emerge in the $T_1 - T_6$ motor roots, and for the diaphragm from C_2 to C_4 as the *phrenic nerves*. Additional muscles involved are those of the abdominal wall $(T_7 - T_{12}$ and $L_1)$, the scalene $(C_4 - C_8)$ and sternomastoid $(C_2$ and spinal accessory nerve).

Larynx

Associated with the movements of inspiration and expiration there are contractions of the intrinsic muscles of the larynx causing abduction and adduction of the arytenoid cartilages, thereby bringing about a widening of the glottis, in inspiration, and a narrowing in expiration (Green and Neil, 1955). These muscles are activated by the recurrent laryngeal nerve, a branch of the vagus. In Fig. 3.1 the discharges in the recurrent laryngeal nerve (R) and phrenic nerve (P) have been

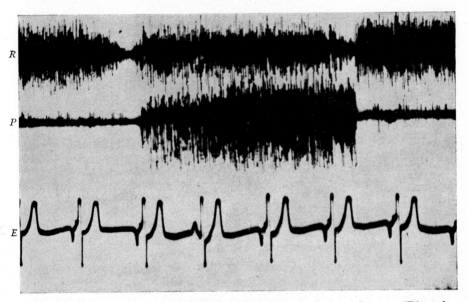

Fig. 3.1. The simultaneous discharge in the recurrent laryngeal nerve (R) and phrenic nerve (P) during breathing. The phrenic nerve only discharges during inspiration while the recurrent laryngeal discharges both in inspiration and expiration, ECG trace E. Dog morphine anaesthetized and curarized. (Rijlant in Wyss, *Erg. de Physiol.*)

recorded simultaneously; the phrenic nerve shows its bursts of activity only during inspiration, whilst activity in the recurrent laryngeal nerve occurs during both inspiration and expiration, with a sharp fall at the end of each phase. In experimental studies on the action of brain-stem neurones it is important to take account of this rhythmic activity in vagal motor fibres, which may well be mistaken for activity in the so-called respiratory neurones whose periodic discharges govern the rhythmicity of breathing (p. 247). Furthermore, it seems that the resistance to passage of air through the larynx materially affects the speed with which expiration can take place, and there is some evidence that this "braking mechanism" on expiration is modified when respiration is increased (Gautier *et al.*, 1973).

BRAIN-STEM NEURONES

The rhythmical contraction and relaxation of the respiratory muscles are determined by rhythmical discharges from the brain-stem, acting on the spinal motor neurones; furthermore, there is no doubt that the main reflex respiratory responses to environmental and other changes are brought about through actions on the brain-stem neurones, rather than more directly on the motor neurones of the cord.

Respiratory Centres

The collections of motor neurones that exert this control have been described as "respiratory centres", and their location has been determined mainly by the rather crude methods of successive removal of parts of the brain, e.g. by transverse section of the brain-stem, until effects on respiration are obtained. Thus in the decerebrate animal, with its brain-stem sectioned at the level of the colliculi, the respiration is intact; section at the caudal end of the medulla, giving the *spinal animal*, abolishes respiration.

Gasping and Apneusis

Sections at intermediate levels do not necessarily give clear-cut answers, in the sense that respiration may still proceed spontaneously, but may not be necessarily normal or *eupnoeic*, i.e. the respiration does not necessarily consist in a rhythmic inspiration and expiration without a perceptible halt in the cycle; instead, respiration may take one of several forms, e.g. *gasping*—initial short spasmodic inspiratory efforts, terminating abruptly—or it may be *apneustic*, consisting of alternating phases of apneusis, i.e. of cessation of breathing, at the maximal inspiratory position, followed by an expiratory spasm; and so on.

Definition of "Centre"

At the outset, then, let us be sure that we know what we mean when we refer to a respiratory centre. As defined by Bard, some time ago, a brain centre is "a circumscribed portion of the brain the functional integrity of which is essential for certain patterned responses, an outstanding feature being its capacity to weld together individual responses to form a complete reaction-pattern. The centre may serve as a focus

3. CONTROL OF RESPIRATION

where afferent impulses, or changes in the blood, act to evoke or repress the total response. Furthermore, with the centre intact it is found that other parts of the central nervous system normally exert modifying influences, either directly upon it or at some point along the pathway over which it controls the peripheral motor neurones."

Multiplicity of "Centres"

The results of ablations indicate unequivocally that there is not just a simple collection of neurones whose activities control the normal pattern of breathing described as eupnoeic; instead, a number of centres have been described, with eupnoeic breathing depending on the harmonious interaction between them all; disturbance of this inter-action, by selective ablations, may bring breathing to a complete halt, or alter its character in a manner suggesting that one or other of the "centres" is now exerting a dominant influence. It would be tedious, and not very instructive, to follow the experiments and arguments that have led to the scheme illustrated by Fig. 3.2, beyond indicating the general reasons for postulating the individual centres.

Afferent Impulses from Lungs

It is first important to establish whether there is, indeed, in the brain, a group of neurones that rhythmically discharge independently of afferent impulses, i.e. if there is a group of neurones in the brain that discharge to the motor apparatus with an inherent rhythm, or does the rhythm depend on afferent impulses from the lungs? Thus we may easily envisage a group of neurones discharging continuously and spontaneously, and which, left to themselves, would cause inspira-tion; if, when the lungs inflated, inhibitory impulses acted on these neurones, inspiration would cease; the lungs would collapse and inspiratory discharge would begin again. Thus such a system would operate without any inherent rhythmicity in the brain neurones. The *Hering-Breuer inflation-reflex*, operating through afferent fibres in the vagus nerves, could fulfil this role; as we shall see, when the lungs inflate, discharges pass to the brain-stem tending to inhibit inspiration. In fact, however, cutting these nerves only modifies the periodicity of breathing, leaving its basic rhythmicity the same.

Rhythmic Centre

Probably the most convincing evidence in favour of an inherent rhythmicity in the brain was provided by Adrian and Buytendijk who measured rhythmic discharges from the brain-stem of the fish after completely removing afferent innervation. In mammals, too, it may be

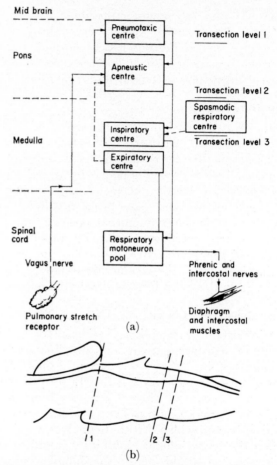

Fig. 3.2. (a) A schematic representation of the organization of the central respiratory mechanisms in the brain-stem of the cat. (b) Mid-sagittal section of the brain-stem indicating critical transection levels in the vagotomized cat. Sections rostral to level 1 produce eupnoea (the breathing pattern is unchanged). Between levels 1 and 2 apneustic breathing occurs (prolonged inspiratory spasms). Between levels 2 and 3 gasping breathing occurs. Caudal to 3, absence of breathing. (Wang *et al.*, *Amer. J. Physiol.*)

shown that rhythmic breathing will persist after separation of the medulla from all afferent input by section of all cervical dorsal roots and transection of the cord at the VIth cervical segment, in addition to dividing all the remaining cranial nerves. Thus it is fair to accept that there is, in the medulla, a group of neurones capable of rhythmic discharge to the motor apparatus of breathing.

Hierarchy of "Centres"

Before discussing the possible mechanism of this rhythmic discharge, let us look at the scheme of respiratory centres illustrated in Fig. 3.2. When the brain-stem was transected in front of the anterior border of the pons, respiration was normal, and the effects of cutting the vagus were similar to those usually observed, i.e. slowing with increased depth. If, now, the transection occurred just a few millimetres below the upper level of the pons, breathing was slowed but remained rhythmic, whilst now cutting off the vagal input caused a cessation of breathing in the inspiratory position—*apneusis* or *respiratory cramp*. It appeared that normal breathing depended on the activity of a *pneumotaxic centre* high up in the pons; this would have an inherent rhythmicity that was only modified by vagal input. When the brain-stem was transected below this pneumotaxic centre, breathing would be controlled by a centre lower down, the *apneustic centre*, whose rhythmicity was critically dependent on the reflex inhibition of inspiration by the vagus; thus cutting the vagus, when breathing is controlled by the apneusis centre, leads to apneusis, i.e. maintained inspiration. If the brain was cut below this apneusis centre, at the level of the striae acousticae, apneusis was replaced by a series of gasps, and breathing was said to be controlled by inspiratory and expiratory centres, which had an inherent rhythmicity, but were not capable of bringing about the smooth cycle described as eupnoea. In this gasping type of respiration, the individual breaths vary in both amplitude and rate, and are usually nearly maximal. The vagus does not influence this respiratory pattern, so that the Hering-Breuer reflexes operate higher up. Whilst there is no doubt that localized lesions in the pons, when combined with vagal section, may bring about a state of apneusis, the function of such a region, or regions, in the control of respiration is by no means clear. One possibility, discussed by Tang (1967), will be considered later.

Localized Stimulation. "Apneusis Centre"

Stimulation of certain regions in the midbrain reticular formation certainly causes apneusis, or respiratory cramp; thus stimulation in the region of the *nucleus reticularis gigantocellularis* causes an inspiratory apneusis, and this is accompanied by powerful discharges in those motor neurones of the thoracic spinal cord that normally discharge during inspiration; as Fig. 3.3 shows, this is accompanied by an inhibition of activity in an expiratory neurone. Again, stimulation of another region of the reticular formation, the *n. reticularis ventralis*, gave rise to an expiratory cramp, with appropriate activation of the thoracic

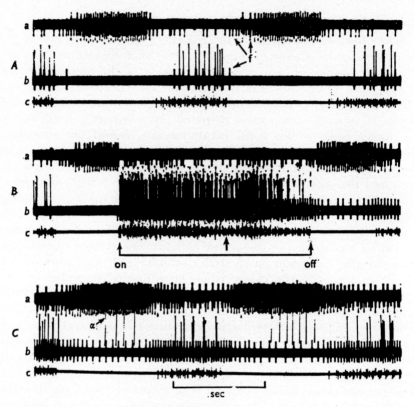

Fig. 3.3. Recordings from efferent filaments of the intercostal nerves in response to stimulation of regions in the midbrain reticular formation. In each record trace (a) is the expiratory discharge, (b) the inspiratory discharge, and (c) the e.m.g. activity of the diaphragm. Record A shows the control trace, B the inspiratory response to stimulation between the arrows. The large arrow shows some breakthrough of spontaneous breathing; C, immediately after B, showing sustained post-stimulation activation of alpha (α) and fusimotor (f) neurones. Stimulus repetitive 300/sec, 8·0 V, 0·1 sec. (Andersen and Sears, *J. Physiol.*)

expiratory motor neurones and inhibition of the inspiratory neurones. These reticular areas give rise to descending long reticulospinal fibres through which the motor neurones at all levels of the cord may be activated; and according to Andersen and Sears, the "apneustic centres" may be regarded as respiratory centres without spontaneous rhythmic capacity, since studies of unit activity in these "centres" fails to reveal units with spontaneously rhythmic discharge like those found in the lateral part of the caudal medulla. Their function is to adjust the "bias" on the respiratory motor neurones, with reciprocal biassing of antagonists; thus, although not having an output with a respiratory rhythm, they could have an important role in the regulation of breathing.

Pneumotaxic Centre. Again, localized stimulations in the pons have not given consistent results, but, of course, if this is a truly rhythmic centre with neurones passing through cycles of discharge and rest, it is not easy to predict the effects of electrical stimulation. Cohen (1970) certainly obtained facilitatory effects on inspiration or expiration according to the regions stimulated in the upper pons, and more recently Bertrand and Hugelin (1971) have shown that localized stimulation of a region in the upper pons in the nucleus parabrachialis medialis gives rise to synchronization of discharge in the phrenic nerve, in the sense that when a stimulus was made at a given phase of inspiration the probability of obtaining spikes in the phrenic nerve was altered. The changes consisted in an advance in the onset of the

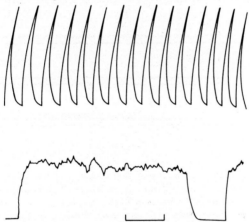

Fig. 3.4. The respiratory apneusis produced by a unilateral lesion in the nucleus parabrachialis medialis. The upper trace is the control integrated phrenic discharge. Lower trace, the apneusis produced by coagulation. Time calibration, 5 sec. (Bertrand and Hugelin. *J. Neurophysiol.*)

phrenic burst, an advance in its cessation, or a delay in the cessation. Bertrand and Hugelin considered that they were, in fact, stimulating the "pneumotaxic centre" which operated through neurones in lower parts of the pons and medulla. Certainly a localized lesion in the same area gave rise to a striking apneusis (Fig. 3.4).

Single-Unit Studies

It must be emphasized that the type of experiment involving gross lesions in the brain, employed to locate the "centres", is rather crude, and that more useful information has been obtained by modern micro-electrode techniques in which the activities of individual neurones in the brain-stem are related to breathing, as manifest, for example, in discharges along the phrenic nerves to the diaphragm. Using this technique, it has been established that neurones in many parts of the brain-stem discharge rhythmically, their discharges being closely related in time (*locked*) to some phase of respiration. These *respiratory neurones* are distributed throughout the reticular formation of the medulla and pons, i.e. they are found in the regions where respiratory centres have been described.

Medullary Reticular Formation

As an example of this type of "probing" we may describe Batsel's study involving introduction of a microelectrode into the medullary

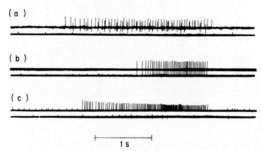

Fig. 3.5. Types of inspiratory units (cat, Nembutal). (a) Early inspiratory unit which began discharge some 140 msec before the diaphragm. The unit of lower amplitude, a late inspiratory, began to discharge with the diaphragm. (b) Late inspiratory unit which began to fire more than a second after the diaphragm had started. (c) An early inspiratory which was located only 100 μ deeper than (b). In all figures the upper channel displays the respiratory unit with negativity upward. The lower channel is the diaphragm EMG. (Batsel, *Exp. Neurol.*)

reticular formation and recording from "units" whose discharges showed an obvious relation to inspiration. Fig. 3.5 shows the responses of typical "inspiratory units", i.e. those that discharged during inspiration, as revealed by the concomitant EMG discharge in the diaphragm.

The discharge occurred during inspiration but in some cases this anteceded diaphragmatic activity (a) and in others (b) occurred more than a second after the diaphragm had started to contract. In a similar way, Batsel found typical expiratory units that discharged at different phases of expiration. Inspiratory and expiratory units

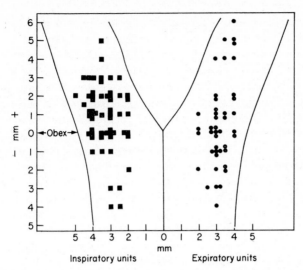

Fig. 3.6. Diagrammatic representation of dorsum of the medulla showing distribution of active respiratory units. Inspiratory units of all types are plotted on the left of the midline and expiratory units of all types are plotted on the right. The ordinate indicates the rostrocaudal position of the units relative to the obex and the abscissa indicates the lateral position. A preponderance of inspiratory units lie rostrally and a preponderance of expiratory units lie caudally. (Batsel, *Exp. Neurol.*)

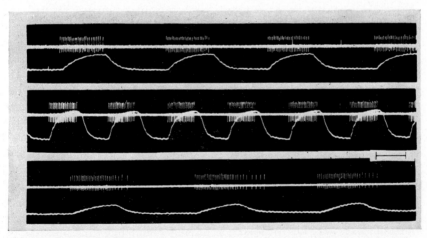

Fig. 3.7. The effects of hypercapnia and hyperoxia on discharge frequency of an inspiratory neurone of the cat. Upper traces, spikes; lower traces pneumograph, upward deflection indicating inspiration. Top record: Resting ventilation, spike frequency 20/sec. Middle record: Inhalation of 4 per cent CO_2, spike frequency 24/sec. Bottom record: Inhalation of 50 per cent O_2, spike frequency 17/sec. Time mark = 1 sec. (Nesland *et al.*, *Exp. Neurol.*)

could be found close to each other, but as Fig. 3.6 shows, there was a preponderance of inspiratory units rostral to the obex and of expiratory units caudal to this point.

Effects of P_ACO_2 and P_AO_2. When the animal was exposed to high CO_2 (hypercapnia) the increased respiratory rate was accompanied by more intense discharges, as illustrated by Fig. 3.7. It was interesting that increased ventilation seemed to be brought about by this increased frequency of discharges in each burst rather than by the recruitment of units that had been silent during eupnoeic breathing, so that it was only by going from the extreme conditions of apnea to hypercapnic ventilation that much evidence of recruitment could be obtained; thus when respiration was strongly depressed by lowered PCO_2, units that had been active fell out; similarly, when respiration was very strongly stimulated by high PCO_2, units that had not been firing started to fire, but, in general, over most of the range of ventilation, the same units seemed to be firing.

Pacemaker Activity

Depolarization of Neurones

Further discussion of the types of respiratory units of the medulla and pons will be deferred till we have discussed some of the reflexes involved in respiratory control; and we may now consider the results of a study on intracellular recording of individual units where the events leading to discharge could be analysed. The discharge in an inspiratory neurone is shown in Fig. 3.8, and it will be seen that, just before the burst began, the membrane potential moved in the direction of depolarization, i.e. it was behaving like a pacemaker cell of the heart; at a certain level of depolarization the spike fired off and the membrane repolarized, so that immediately after the spike the measured membrane potential was high and reached what Salmoiraghi and Baumgarten called the *maximum repolarization level*. The depolarization began again, to give rise to a new spike. Close examination of the records showed that, as the spikes continued, the membrane had to be depolarized more and more in order to fire off a spike, and also the maximum repolarization level became less negative. Thus the burst of spikes may be considered as having a tendency to self-limitation, in that the longer the discharge the less negative becomes the membrane potential between discharges, i.e. the neurone tends to remain depolarized; and we have seen from the study of the excitation of the axon that depolarization, if sustained, tends to inactivate the sodium-permeability mechanism. It is not difficult to envisage, then, a group

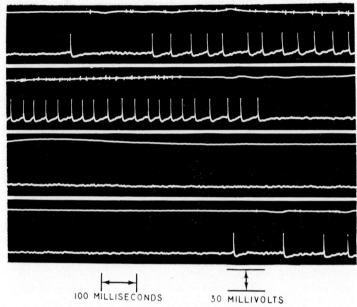

100 MILLISECONDS   30 MILLIVOLTS

Fig. 3.8. Intracellular recording from inspiratory neurone during one respiratory cycle. Continuous record from top to bottom. In each set of records, upper trace: diaphragmatic motor units; lower trace: intracellular potentials. Membrane potential at beginning of record: 49·5 mV. (Salmoiraghi and Baumgarten, *J. Neurophysiol.*)

of neurones with an inherent rhythmicity dependent on a tendency to spontaneous discharge that builds up a residual membrane depolarization between spikes.

Interaction between Neurones

It is likely, as the authors suggested, that the neurones of the inspiratory and expiratory groups react with each other synaptically, the inspiratory neurones sending inhibitory discharges to the expiratory neurones at the same time as they send discharges to the motor neurones of the cord, and *vice versa*. The existence of this sort of reciprocal action was suggested by the presence of hyperpolarizing synaptic potentials on the record when the neurone was silent, e.g. that of the expiratory neurone during inspiration. This reciprocal interaction would enhance the natural rhythmicity of the system; thus, as the discharge of the inspiratory neurone became weaker, its inhibition of the expiratory neurones would be weakened too, so that at the end of inspiration the expiratory neurones would be ready to discharge. Clearly a great deal more work on intracellular recording from respiratory neurones is necessary before we can decide whether individual neurones have, indeed, this assumed spontaneous rhythmicity, and to what extent it is enhanced by reciprocal influences between groups of neurones.

Afferent Input

The study of individual respiratory neurones by intracellular recording showed that, besides discharging regularly, the neurones received a continuous bombardment of afferent impulses, as revealed by the presence of synaptic potentials on the record. Part of these influences are peripheral, as in the Hering-Breuer and chemo-receptor reflexes (p. 219), but also they may be derived from higher parts of the brain including the cortex; of special interest is the relation to the hypothalamus since here we have a centre for temperature control, and an important means of regulating body-temperature in some animals is by variation in respiration. Thus, stimulation of localized regions will cause polypnoea accompanied by cutaneous vasodilatation. Another interesting source of afferent input is from the brain centre concerned with swallowing; this is a complex act involving inhibition of respiration; and records from inspiratory neurones during swallowing, or on stimulation of the "deglutition centre", show an immediate inhibition of discharge. In a similar way the reverse phenomenon, vomiting, is controlled by vomiting centres that activate the complex expiratory movements accompanying this act.

THE RESPIRATORY MOTOR NEURONES

The motor neurones of the spinal cord are the final common path for the centrally determined rhythmic respiratory activities; and their behaviour has been examined in some detail since their activities must reflect to some extent the influences on them from higher centres, as well as those due to feedback from the intercostal muscles.

Central Respiratory Drive

Slow Potentials

The influence of higher centres is revealed by the rhythmic waxing and waning of slow potentials, as illustrated in Fig. 3.9, which shows both an inspiratory and expiratory neurone, identified previously by antidromic stimulation of the nerves from an external or internal intercostal muscle. The lower record is from the diaphragm and shows how the slow potentials are in phase with respiratory activity. The slow potentials consist of summated excitatory and inhibitory synaptic potentials; thus with the inspiratory neurone, the rising phase consists

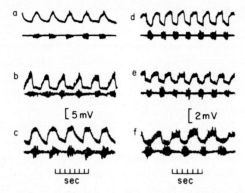

Fig. 3.9. Central respiratory drive potentials (CRDPs) of inspiratory and expiratory motor neurones identified by antidromic invasion from the external and internal intercostal nerves respectively. Upper traces, intracellular d.c. recordings from respiratory motor neurones; lower traces, electromyogram (EMG) of the diaphragm. The slow potentials are in phase with respiratory activity as shown by the diaphragm EMG and are composed of summated excitatory and inhibitory synaptic potentials. (Sears, *Breathlessness.*)

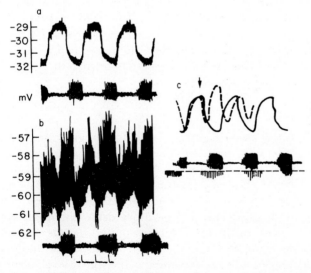

Fig. 3.10. Intracellular recording from an expiratory motor neurone before and after "reversal". Upper traces, intracellular d.c. recording of membrane potential. Lower traces, electromyogram of diaphragm. a, control; note two phases of depolarization with each complete breathing cycle. b, after injection of chloride. c, superimposed tracings of the recordings in a (full line) and b (dotted line). Because the rate of breathing differed the traces have been aligned to give the best fit for the depolarizing phase during expiration of the first complete cycle, as indicated by the arrow. (Sears, *Breathlessness.*)

of excitatory synaptic potentials whilst the waning phase, during expiration, is due to hyperpolarizing inhibitory potentials.

Inhibition. The fact that the waning of the inspiratory potential is accompanied by inhibition, rather than the mere cessation of activation, is proved by injecting chloride into the body of the neurone; this alters the relative concentrations inside and outside, so that an increase in Cl^--permeability, known to be the cause of hyperpolarization in motor neurones, now may be expected to cause depolarization, forcing the membrane to give a potential in conformity with the new ratio of Cl^--concentrations, which is lower than before. In fact, under these conditions, the hyperpolarization of an expiratory neurone during inspiration is converted into a depolarization (Fig. 3.10). This inhibition is probably important for ensuring that, when an inspiratory muscle contracts, it fails to induce a contraction of its antagonistic expiratory muscle that might otherwise have occurred as a stretch-reflex, mediated through muscle receptors (Vol. 4).

Spike Frequency

The slow potentials have been described as *central respiratory drive* potentials; they are recorded by a device that excludes the accompanying spikes (d.c. recording); when these are allowed to appear on the record, however, it is seen that their frequency varies with the level of the membrane potential, so that during the hyperpolarizing phase they are completely silent.

Muscle Spindles

The intercostal muscles, unlike the diaphragm, are well provided with muscle spindles, and this may be recognized by stimulation of Ia sensory fibres from the muscle, when an excitatory synaptic potential is recorded. Sears showed that the input to the motor neurones from the spindles could result in a considerable depolarization, which in its turn would make the central respiratory drive potentials far more or less effective; perhaps the most interesting finding was that the afferent fibres from an expiratory muscle would influence the motor neurones of an inspiratory muscle; in this way, at the spinal level, some degree of interaction between inspiratory and expiratory muscles is possible.

Gamma-Loop. We shall be considering in Vol. 4 the activation of muscle fibres indirectly through what has been called the *gamma-loop*, the muscle spindle being caused to send up an afferent discharge to the motor neurone which then fires impulses into its axon supplying the muscle fibre. It has been suggested that this mode of activation constitutes an important element in the control of intercostal muscle contraction.

Hering-Breuer Reflexes.

The Hering-Breuer inflation-reflex is a progressive inhibition of the inspiratory process as it proceeds; and it may thus be regarded as an important mechanism in the control of the frequency of respiration, bringing the inspiration to a definite halt when the appropriate degree of inflation has been achieved. The afferent pathway is through the vagi, so that, in experimental animals, inspiration is prolonged if these nerves are cut, and the respiration becomes slower and deeper, with the total ventilation, $\dot{V}_E$, virtually unchanged.

Species Variations

Experimentally, the lung may be inflated by positive pressure at given moments in the respiratory cycle, and it can be shown that the

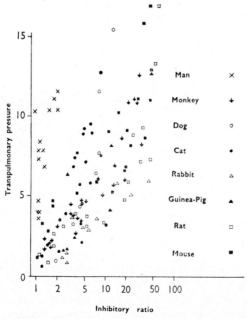

Fig. 3.11. The Hering-Breuer inflation reflex in different species. Ordinate: increase in transpulmonary pressure causing inflation of the lungs. Abscissa: ratio of the apnoea during inflation to the length of the control previous respiratory cycles (logarithmic scale). Results from two individuals of each species are given, with four for men. Note that the values for man show a far weaker, and for rabbits a far stronger, reflex than those for the other species. (Widdicombe, *Clin. Sci.*)

discharge down the phrenic nerve is inhibited, whilst discharge in the vagi increases. In the intact animal the inhibition can be demonstrated by the period of apnoea following the inflation. The strength of the reflex, measured in this way, varies with the species, being greatest in the rabbit and guinea pig (Fig. 3.11), whilst in man it seems that the reflex inhibitory discharge, which can indeed be demonstrated in the vagus (Langrehr, 1964), is not usually sufficiently strong to influence respiratory movements, at any rate those at rest—eupnoea. It is interesting that in newborn babies a definite inflation-reflex can be elicited, but not in adults, so that we may assume that in phylogeny the reflex has become useless.

The Afferent Discharge

Adrian (1933), in his classical study of the afferent discharge in vagal fibres, showed that the discharges that were in phase with inspiration, increasing their frequency as lung-distension increased,

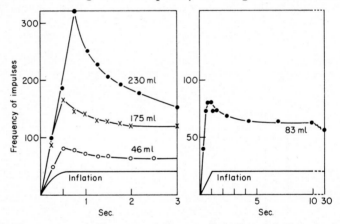

Fig. 3.12. The response of afferent vagal fibres to distension of the lung in the spinal cat. Note the slow rate of adaptation shown by these receptors. (Adrian, *J. Physiol.*)

were carried in large myelinated fibres with high conduction-velocity. A characteristic feature that differentiates them from afferent fibres involved in other types of sensory information is their slow adaptation (Fig. 3.12), in the sense that their discharge is maintained when the lung is held at a constant state of inflation. If the volume of inspired air in a breath is governed by a feedback, conveying information with respect to the state of expansion of the lung at any moment, then it is important that the information be sustained, so that a given frequency of discharge can indicate a given steady state of stretch of the lung.

If the discharge adapted rapidly, as with many touch-receptors, for example, there would be an inadequate feedback of information. This slow adaptation contrasts strongly with the "lung-irritant receptor" which also responds to inflation (and deflation), but which gives a discharge that soon decreases in intensity in spite of the maintained state of the lung (Fig. 3.13).

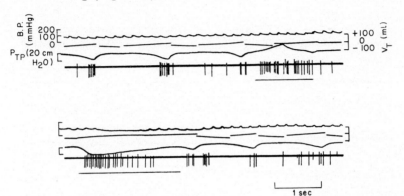

Fig. 3.13. The response of a lung-irritant receptor to deflation (upper record) and inflation (lower record) of the lungs. From above down: systemic arterial blood pressure (B.P.), tidal volume changes (V_T), trace zeroing at points of zero airflow; inflation upwards), transpulmonary pressure (P_{TP}) and action potentials in a single vagal fibre. Deflation and inflation were during the horizontal signal bars. Note the rapidly adapting irregular discharges. (Mills *et al.*, *J. Physiol.*)

Stretch-Receptors

The probable site of the "stretch-receptors" is the smooth muscle of the conducting airway. This location, as opposed to the pleurae, was made probable by Widdicombe's (1954) studies on single vagal fibres responding to inflation of the lung; when broncho-constriction was induced with acetylcholine or histamine, the discharge was increased, presumably because of the greater stretch applied to the stretch-receptors, whilst opposite effects were obtained by broncho-dilators, such as adrenaline. A typical experiment is shown in Fig. 3.14; A represents the discharge in a vagal fibre in response to lung-expansion, as indicated by the rise in the record of intratracheal pressure; the steadily increasing frequency of discharge, with no sign of adaptation, is evident. Between A and B acetylcholine was administered, and the same expansion now caused a more intense discharge; and it will be noted that the intratracheal pressure increased more than in A, presumably owing to the broncho-constriction.

Encapsulated and Free Endings. Many of the sensory endings are encapsulated, and thus bear analogy with cutaneous and sub-cutaneous mechanoreceptors; others are free endings but of a variety of shapes, and they have been identified not only in the larger branches of the bronchial tree but in its utmost ramifications, including the walls of the alveoli (Elftman, 1943). However, the greater concentration is in the large airways (Miserocchi *et al.*, 1973).

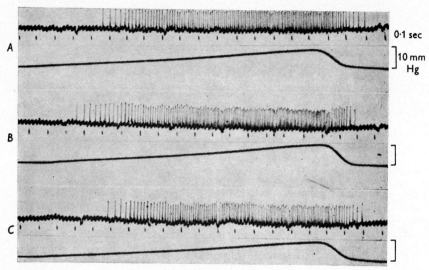

Fig. 3.14. The action of acetylcholine on a pulmonary stretch-receptor. In each record the upper traces are the action potentials from a pulmonary stretch-receptor; the lower traces the intratracheal pressure. A shows the control response, B the response to 200 µg acetylcholine injected intravenously. C, two min later after the drug effect had worn off. The intratrcheal pressure reaches a higher value than in A indicating bronchoconstriction, and the receptor discharges at a higher frequency.
(Widdicombe, *J. Physiol.*)

Epithelial Endings. It is very likely that the sensory endings in the epithelium of the airways are involved in protective reflexes, those in the trachea and extrapulmonary bronchi being concerned with the cough-reflex and those within the lungs being the hypothetical "lung-irritant receptors" (p. 224).

Analogy with Baroreceptors. Although frequently called "smooth muscle spindles", in no way are the sensory organs, responsive to lung inflation, to be considered analogous with muscle spindles or tendon-organs; they are essentially ramifications of a sensory nerve arranged at strategic points in the smooth muscle of the bronchial tree in such a way as to become excited on deformation. They are thus analogous with the baroreceptors of the carotid sinus and other parts of the vascular tree.

Deflation-Reflex

The inflation-reflex leads to inhibition of inspiration; by contrast, the deflation-reflex, brought about by exerting a positive pressure on the thorax or by a pneumothorax, so that the lungs are forcibly deflated, brings about excitation of inspiration through activating different receptors in the lung, the messages being carried in relatively slowly conducting fibres, whilst the receptors may be the same as those concerned in the lung-irritant response (p. 224). As Koller and Ferrer (1970) have emphasized, this reflex is not concerned in the regulation of respiration but is a *nociceptive reflex*, being the response to enforced deflation of the lungs through compression of the thorax.*

Lung-Relaxation Reflex. The lung deflation-reflex must be differentiated from a weak stimulation to inspiration, which occurs at the end of expiration, when the high-frequency discharge in the vagus is subsiding; it has been called a lung-relaxation reflex and is the consequence of a lessening of the tension in the lung stretch-receptors.

Baroreceptors

The carotid sinus and aorta are vascular sites influencing mainly the arterial pressure; changes in pressure may also influence the state of the lungs; thus increased baroreceptor activity in the carotid sinus inhibits respiration. The reflex is of doubtful significance, however.

Protective Responses

Cough-Receptors

An important function of the innervation of the lungs is protective, allowing the animal to respond rapidly to the inhalation of irritant material; the sensory apparatus mediating these responses consists in the terminations of myelinated vagal nerve fibres in the epithelial lining of the respiratory tract, from the trachea and larynx to the bronchi and bronchioles. Mechanical stimulation of the epithelial lining of the larynx and trachea initiates primarily a *cough-reflex*, and the endings here are usually called cough-receptors to distinguish them from the endings in the lungs, which are called *lung-irritant receptors* (Mills *et al.*, 1969).

---

* According to Luck (1970), there are a few afferent vagal fibres in the rabbit that show a rhythmic discharge during *expiration*; these seem to be the same as those involved in the deflation-reflex since they are very sensitive to lung-deflation, but whether they contribute to the regulation of respiration, as claimed by Luck, is an open question.

Lung-Irritant Receptors

As we might expect, such lung receptors respond to altered mechanical conditions within the lung as well as to irritants, such as inhaled particles, or chemicals such as ammonia; they are distinguished electrophysiologically from the stretch-receptors of the bronchial musculature concerned in the Hering-Breuer inflation-reflex by their rapid adaptation and slower conduction-velocity; it is thought, however, that they function in the expiratory Hering-Breuer reflex, since they are stimulated during deflation of the lung and cause a reflex hyperpnoea and hyperventilation. Stimulation of these irritant receptors by chemicals, as well as mechanically, causes hyperpnoea, but not usually coughing. Under appropriate conditions, a reflex bronchoconstriction in response to lung irritants can be demonstrated, the motor pathway being through the vagus, and therefore abolished by subcutaneous atropine (Widdicombe *et al.*, 1962).

J-Receptors

In this connexion we must mention a group of hypothetical receptors connected with unmyelinated vagal C-fibres which have been called by Paintal *juxtapulmonary capillary receptors*, or *J-receptors*, because they must be located very close to the pulmonary capillaries and possibly in the alveolar interstitial space. The endings were recognized through their sensitivity to the drug phenyldiguanide, although this is not completely specific for them since it activates the lung-irritant receptors of Widdicombe. According to Paintal, their normal function is to respond to altered

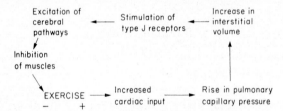

Fig. 3.15. The suggested sequence of events in the J-reflex. (Paintal, *Breathing*, Hering-Breuer Symposium, Ciba.)

pressure within the airways, and thus may contribute to the deflation-reflex, but a far more effective stimulus than lung-deflation is lung-congestion, i.e. the tendency for fluid to exude from the pulmonary capillaries; this may occur during exercise or artificially with the inhalation of chlorine or phosgene; in the latter case the responses can last for many hours and probably for days if the congestion persists. The reflex response involves rapid breathing with a sense of discomfort—dyspnoea—together with an inhibition of skeletal muscle motor neurones, so that if, indeed, they are excited by severe exercise the response, which tends to bring an end to the exercise, may be called protective (Deshpande and Devanandan, 1970). The sequence of events in the J-reflex postulated by Paintal is indicated in Fig. 3.15.

Paradoxical Reflex

Head (1889) described a reflex inspiratory response to large inflations of the lung; and it was considered to be mediated by separate vagal excitatory fibres identified by differential block on cooling the vagus, the inhibitory Hering-Breuer discharge being blocked at a higher temperature (8°–15°C) than the inspiratory discharge (5°–11°C). However, Paintal describes Head's paradoxical reflex as a physiological artefact; under conditions of large expansion of the lungs the frequency of discharge in the sensory fibres mediating the Hering-Breuer reflex will be high, and Paintal showed that block would be more likely during high-frequency discharge than during low-frequency discharge. Thus large distension of the lung plus cooling of the vagus—the conditions required to elicit the "reflex"—lead to inhibition of the Hering-Breuer reflex. In fact it is found that when the nerve is cooled below 18°C the rhythmic pattern of discharge during respiration is reversed, the maximum discharge occurring during expiration.

Chemoreceptor Activity

Since the function of respiration is to ventilate the blood, maintaining the arterial blood at a fixed PCO_2 of 40 mm Hg and a PO_2 of some 100 mm Hg, we may expect the dominant afferent influx to the respiratory centres to be determined by the chemical composition of the blood; and simple experiments demonstrate this unequivocally.

Rebreathing Experiment

Thus, if a subject is caused to rebreathe his own expired air, the ventilation progressively increases—*hyperpnoea*—consisting of both increased rate and depth, until finally a condition is reached where breathing becomes difficult—*dyspnoea*.

Carotid and Aortic Bodies

This increased ventilation is due to both increased P_ACO_2* (hypercapnia) and to decreased P_AO_2 (hypoxia)† and numerous experiments on animals and man have shown that, besides a direct action of the hypercapnia on the central respiratory neurones—or sensitive receptors in the brain in close relation to these—the increased respiration due to hypercapnia and hypoxia is due to a reflex stimulation of the carotid and aortic bodies which, as we have seen, also influence the cardiovascular system. Whereas the effects of altered gas composition on the chemoreceptors have questionable significance in controlling blood-pressure, these effects, especially of hypoxia, exert a dominant role in the adjustment of the respiration to altered blood-gas composition. Thus section of the aortic and carotid sinus nerves in the experimental

---

* It is conventional to symbolize the partial pressure of a gas in the alveolar, or end-tidal, air by P_ACO_2, etc., and the partial pressure in the arterial blood by P_aCO_2, etc.

† As we shall see, the human subject does not respond to an *acute* hypoxia until the PO_2 of the inspired air has been brought down to about 50 mm Hg, so, under the conditions of rebreathing, the hyperventilation is due to the hypercapnia rather than the hypoxia. This does not mean that the chemoreceptors do not respond until the PO_2 of the alveolar air is 50 mm Hg, but simply that the response is counteracted by other changes.

animal, or temporary blockage in humans by application of cold, completely abolishes the hyperventilatory response to hypoxia, in fact, respiration decreases due to a depression of the respiratory neurones.

Effects on Respiratory Neurones. The animal still responds to altered $P_A CO_2$, now through the central action, and at one time it was considered that hypercapnia acted exclusively through this central mechanism, but there is no doubt, from numerous experimental studies, that the chemoreceptors of the carotid and aortic bodies are also responsive to altered $P_A CO_2$, in fact, their strategic positions permit a more rapid and satisfactory sampling of the arterial blood as it emerges from the heart after having been ventilated in the lungs. In consequence of this strategic location, it is possible, in experimental studies on the effects of rapidly induced changes in the PO_2 or PCO_2 of inspired air, to determine whether these effects are mediated reflexly by the short latency (4–5 sec) of the response, the time required for the nerve discharge to be carried to the respiratory neurones being very much less than that required for the altered blood to reach the brain.

Normoxic Drive

A question that has been debated for a long time is the existence, or otherwise, of a normal reflex excitation of respiration when the PO_2 of the blood is in its normal resting range, in the region of 100 mm Hg —i.e. whether there is a "normoxic drive" on the neurones. In man,

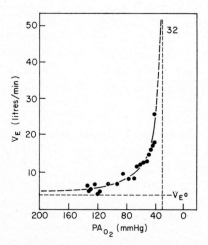

Fig. 3.16. The effect of sudden changes in inspired PO_2 at a constant PCO_2 on the ventilation in man. The parameter $\dot{V}_E^\circ$ is the value for ventilation extrapolated to an infinitely great alveolar oxygen $P_A O_2$. (Weil *et al.*, *J. clin. Invest.*)

the technique pioneered by Dejours (see, for example, Dejours, 1962) consists in suddenly altering the PO_2 of the inspired air for one, two or more breaths and measuring the change in ventilation over the subsequent minute or so. When the subject suddenly breathes pure O_2 there is a decline in respiration of the order of 12–15 per cent, and this is much more dramatic and reproducible if the subject is exercising. In a similar way we may carry out a "hypoxic" test, the subject suddenly breathing air with low PO_2, and there follows a rapid increase in respiration. These experiments show, not only that the human subject responds to alteration in the PO_2 of the inhaled air, but that at the normal resting alveolar PO_2 of about 100 mm Hg the chemoreceptors are above their threshold and exerting a definite drive on the respiratory neurones. Fig. 3.16 shows the results of a study by Weil *et al.* (1970) on human subjects exposed to sudden changes in PO_2 of their inspired air when the PCO_2 was maintained strictly constant. The curve has a characteristic shape and conforms to the equation:

$$\dot{V}_E = \dot{V}_E^\circ + \frac{A}{P_A O_2 - 32}$$

where $\dot{V}_E^\circ$ is the value for the ventilation extrapolated for an infinitely great $P_A O_2$, $P_A O_2$ being the alveolar PO_2.

Influence of $P_A CO_2$

In a similar way, we may examine the influence of sudden changes in PCO_2 of the inspired air; thus Dejours, in the intact dog, maintained a fixed level of PO_2 in the inspired air and suddenly changed the CO_2 concentration to 7 per cent; there always occurred a rise in ventilation within five seconds, and the greater the degree of anoxia of the animal the greater was the response, indicating that the hypercapnic drive depends on a background of anoxia, so that when the animal was hyperoxic, by breathing an O_2-rich mixture, there was little effect. After denervation of the chemoreceptors, the response to hypercapnia was smaller and was delayed to 20–25 sec, suggesting that now it was being mediated by central CO_2-sensitive neurones. The response was now independent of the degree of oxygenation, so that these experiments demonstrate an interaction of PO_2 and PCO_2 at the chemoreceptor level. Such an interaction had been put on a quantitative basis by Hornbein, Griffo and Roos (1961) who studied the discharges in the sinus nerve at different PO_2 and PCO_2. Fig. 3.17 illustrates some results showing the effects of varying PO_2 at two different levels of PCO_2; the curves indicate a marked potentiation of chemoreceptor

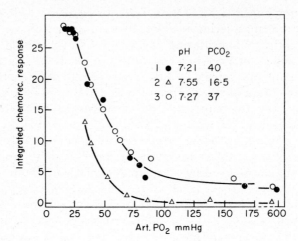

Fig. 3.17. The effect of variation in arterial oxygen tension on the integrated chemo-receptor discharge at different levels of PCO_2. The curves show a marked potentiation of chemoreceptor activity by low PO_2. (Hornbein *et al.*, *J. Neurophysiol.*)

activity by low PO_2; thus at 150 mm Hg PO_2 the response to a rise in 15 mm Hg in PCO_2 in the nerve was 3 units, whilst at a PO_2 of 50 mm Hg the same rise gave 11 units.*

Synergy. An important point made by Joels and Neil (1961) is that the combined effects of raised PCO_2 and lowered PO_2 are greater than the sum of the effects produced separately. Since, in exercise, both these stimuli occur together, this is obviously of significance when assessing the contribution of chemoreceptor drive to the increased ventilation.

Cunningham's Empirical Relationship

Cunningham (1963) has presented the following equation to describe the minute-volume of respiration, $\dot{V}$:

$$\dot{V} = \{1 + A'/(P_AO_2 - C')\}\{a(\log P_ACO_2 + \log [H^+]) + C\}$$

and it will be seen that oxygen tension, carbon dioxide tension and hydrogen ion concentration enter as parameters. The first bracket represents the hypoxic stimulus and the second that of the CO_2-acidity complex.

---

* Similar studies on human subjects by Cunningham *et al.* (1965), in which the immediate changes in ventilation due to sudden breathing of air with high PCO_2 were measured, suggest that the chemoreceptors fail to respond to raised PCO_2 unless there is a mild degree of hypoxia.

Cerebrospinal Fluid

It is one thing to describe the overall effects of altered chemical composition of the blood, but quite another to interpret them in detail, largely because of the uncertainty regarding the relative effects of the CO_2 - H^+ complex on the chemoreceptors and the central respiratory neurones. Thus the central neurones come into close relation with the cerebrospinal fluid (p. 582) in the IVth ventricle (p. 231) and so they will be influenced, not only by the gas tensions and pH

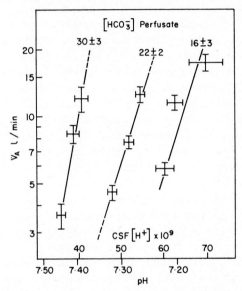

Fig. 3.18. Ventilatory responses of normal goats to inhalation of CO_2 during ventriculo-cisternal perfusions with 30, 22 and 16 mEq/litre HCO_3^-. Crosses represent means and standard errors from 75 steady-state periods in six goats. (Pappenheimer, *Harvey Lectures*.)

of the blood supplying this part of the brain, but also by the corresponding parameters in the cerebrospinal fluid; if these do not vary at the same time and in the same direction, any effects of altered blood composition will be very difficult to predict.

Perfused Ventricles. The respiratory centre is certainly rapidly responsive to alterations in the pH of the cerebrospinal fluid, as Leusen showed when he perfused artificial fluids through the ventricles of anaesthetized dogs; and a more elaborate study carried out by Pappenheimer *et al.* (1965) on conscious goats is illustrated by Fig. 3.18, which shows the effects on ventilation of altered pH of the artificial cerebrospinal fluid perfusing through the ventricles; the alterations in pH were obtained by inhalation of different CO_2-mixtures, and three separate concentrations of bicarbonate were employed. For any given bicarbonate concentration, the ventilation rises linearly with increase in hydrogen-ion concentration, but the same ventilation can be obtained at different pH according to the bicarbonate concentration. This means, of course, that the PCO_2 of the cerebrospinal fluid is more important than the pH, the fluid with the higher concentration of bicarbonate having the higher PCO_2 at any given pH in accordance with the Henderson-Hasselbalch relationship (Vol. 1).

Metabolic Acidosis. Since the cerebrospinal fluid comes into rapid equilibrium with the blood in respect to its CO_2-tension, we may expect the influences exerted through the blood and the cerebrospinal fluid to be in the same direction and of similar magnitude; however, in long-term adaptations, the influence of altered acid-base parameters becomes more complex because of the blood-brain barrier (p. 576), which restricts the rate of exchange of ions, such as bicarbonate, between blood and the cerebrospinal fluid. Thus if the total concentration of bicarbonate is decreased in what is called metabolic acidosis, e.g. after the liberation of lactic acid from exercising muscles, then we know that there is an increased ventilation, and this leads to a lowered blood PCO_2 so that the ratio $[CO_2]/[HCO_3{}^-]$ remains constant to give a virtually completely compensated pH. The effects on the cerebrospinal fluid are delayed, however, because the bicarbonate concentration tends to remains at its original level; furthermore, the cerebrospinal fluid now acquires rapidly the new lowered PCO_2 of the blood, and thus, with its normal bicarbonate level and lowered PCO_2, it actually becomes *more alkaline*, although the blood became more acid. The central respiratory neurones are thus under the influence of the more alkaline cerebrospinal fluid and of the blood, which has reacquired its normal pH through buffering and the increased ventilation that lowered its PCO_2. Thus, if the cerebrospinal fluid can also exert an effect, we may expect the drive to respiration to diminish because of its alkalinity. This is just one example illustrating the complexities of the situation.

The Central Chemosensitive Area. Modifications in composition of the cerebrospinal fluid exert their effects rapidly, so that it has been argued that the sensitive cells are close to the surface of the brain, and that the effects of exciting them are transmitted to the deeper-lying respiratory neurones; it could be argued, on the other hand, that the effects of altered cerebrospinal fluid composition are transmitted directly by diffusion to the respiratory neurones which might, in fact, be the chemosensitive cells. Mitchell *et al.* (1963) described a region on the ventro-lateral surface of the medulla where application of solutions of altered pH produced rapid ventilatory responses (Fig. 3.19), and they concluded that this was the chemosensitive region through which the central effects of altered PCO_2 were mediated. Loeschke *et al.* (1970) have combined localized electrical stimulation of the

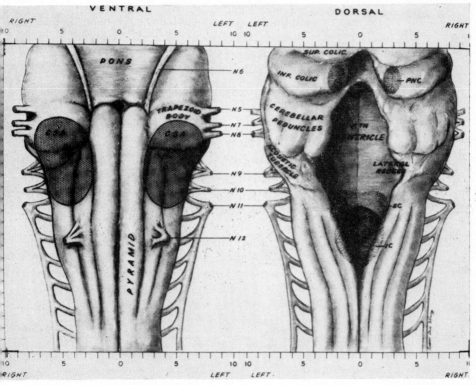

Fig. 3.19. Dorsal and ventral views of the cat medulla and pons. Stippled areas (CSA) represent the superficial regions of respiratory sensitivity to high CO_2 and H^+, nicotine, and acetylcholine. Areas PNC represent the pneumotaxic centres in the region of the locus ceruleus. Areas EC and IC represent the regions of the inspiratory and expiratory centres in the reticular formation. Stereotaxic coordinates are in millimetres. (Mitchell *et al.*, *Cerebrospinal Fluid and the Regulation of Ventilation*, Blackwell Scientific.)

medulla with localized application of acid and have delineated two regions on the surface that respond with increased ventilation to either form of stimulation; one, the more rostral, corresponding with that of Mitchell *et al.*, whilst the more caudal region seems not to have been described before as one from which ventilatory drive could be obtained. Histological examination of the ventral surface of the medulla revealed groups of large multipolar neurones, ventral to the olive and just underneath the glial layer, corresponding in location to the region of maximal sensitivity to electrical stimulation (Trouth and Loeschke, 1969).

Haemorrhage

The cardiovascular responses to haemorrhage have been described earlier (p. 158); it is well established that this causes an increase in ventilation, abolished by carotid sinus denervation; the effect may be mediated by a reduced blood-flow through the carotid body, causing an ischaemic anoxia. As a result of this hyperventilation, the blood during severe haemorrhage becomes alkaline with lowered P_ACO_2 (D'Silva, Gill and Mendel, 1966).

Cheyne-Stokes Breathing

Experimentally a form of breathing, characterized by periods of apnoea, may be induced by a preliminary hyperventilation of the lungs. After a period of apnoea due to the removal of CO_2 from the blood—hypocapnia—a few breaths are taken and then respiration ceases, to begin again for a few breaths, when it ceases again, and so on. The period of no breathing—apnoea—lasts long enough for the PO_2 in the blood to fall, and this is seen by the cyanotic condition that may develop after hyperventilation. The lowered PO_2 now acts as the stimulus for breathing, the PCO_2 of the blood not having risen sufficiently. A few breaths satisfy the oxygen requirements, but now the PCO_2 has been again reduced so that it still does not drive respiration; thus a new period of apnoea intervenes until respiration is initiated by the fall in PO_2. This process continues until eventually the blood PCO_2 builds up to a level to permit it to participate normally in the control of respiration. When breathing at high altitudes, the subject ventilates his lungs to a greater extent than at sea-level because of the low PO_2 in the inspired air; this tends to wash out the CO_2 from his blood, and so the respiratory centre is driven by the PO_2 of the blood rather than the PCO_2, and this can lead to Cheyne-Stokes breathing.

FREQUENCY AND DEPTH OF RESPIRATION

Variations

It is a common observation that, during exercise, the increased ventilation of the lungs required to supply the extra O_2-requirements is met by both a more rapid and a deeper breathing, i.e. both frequency,

f, and tidal volume, V_T, are increased. Moreover, when different individuals are studied, the normal eupnoeic ventilation is achieved by variations on these two themes. When different animals are concerned, some very striking variations are seen, as illustrated by the relation of respiratory frequency to body-size (Fig. 3.20); it will be seen that the respiratory frequency of the masked shrew, weighing

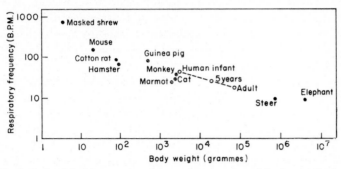

Fig. 3.20. Relationship between respiratory frequency and body-weight in various mammals. All observations were on awake, resting animals at neutral ambient temperatures. (Mead, *J. appl. Physiol.*)

3·5 g, is some 100 times that of the elephant, which weighs some million times more.

Optimal f and V$_T$

The question arises as to why, in a given species, there is a characteristic relation between V_T and f to give the ordinary eupnoeic ventilation, $\dot{V}_E$, and why, when $\dot{V}_E$ is increased, the observed increases in the two variables take place. Otis, Fenn and Rahn (1950) concluded that an optimum frequency and tidal volume would be adopted, governed by the minimum respiratory work, and their calculations indicated that the actual values were in conformity with this requirement in the breathing of resting human subjects.

Minimum Force. On the other hand, Mead's (1960) calculations and experiments indicated that the average minimum force required to be exerted would give a prediction closer to the truth. In general terms we can consider two extremes; at one end the ventilation is achieved with large tidal volume and low frequency, and here the muscle force required to overcome the elastic resistance of the widely expanded lungs will be very large. To produce the same *alveolar* ventilation at very high frequencies and low tidal volume, a large average force will be required and, moreover, the total ventilation must be increased because of the dead space which becomes more important with low tidal volumes. The optimum condition will lie between the two extremes, and will be governed by the ratio of the alveolar ventilation, V_A, and the dead space, V_D and by the mechanical features of the lung represented by the resistance to flow, R, and the compliance, C. Measurement of these parameters in the guinea-pig, on the one hand, where V_A/V_D is large, about 160, and in man where it is small, about 30, allowed the optimum frequencies to be calculated; in guinea-pigs this was 82 BPM corresponding with the actually measured value of 82; in man the calculated value was 19 BPM comparing with measured values of 16 to 18.

Species Variations. The big difference in the optimum frequency between guinea-pig and man is due to the difference in the ratio V_A/V_D, and when animals of different size are concerned this would be expected to vary as the cube root of the weight, and since the optimum frequency is governed by the cube root of V_A/V_D, we may expect a ninth root relation between optimum frequency of breathing and body-weight, which is in fact found. The question as to how this optimum is maintained under different conditions remains; according to Mead the evidence indicated that it was receptors indicating the stretch of the lungs—lung receptors—rather than those indicating stretch of the intercostal muscles—spindles—that provided the information.

Importance of Vagal Reflexes

In animals (but not in man), section of the vagus slows respiratory rate but the tidal volume increases, so that the alveolar ventilation remains the same and the end-tidal PCO_2 and PO_2 remain normal. Thus for eupnoeic breathing the Hering-Breuer reflex is relatively unimportant so far as lung ventilation is concerned.* However, when the responses to raised PCO_2 are considered, the relation between total ventilation and PCO_2 is altered by vagal section, due primarily to a failure of the frequency of respiration to increase (Guz *et al.*, 1966).

Vagotomy and Frequency

This is shown by the three parts of Fig. 3.21; in (a) the total ventilation, V_E, is plotted against alveolar PCO_2; in the normal animal (open

---

* Oberholzer and Schlegel (1957) noted that bilateral section of the vagi in the guinea-pig caused death in expiration within some 30–180 min if the animals were waking or anaesthetized with barbiturates. Under urethane they retained their rhythmical breathing for many hours.

symbols) there is a linear increase in ventilation up to about 55 mm Hg, when the curve flattens off; in the vagotomized animal the relation is altogether flatter indicating that, for any alveolar PCO_2, the ventilation is very much smaller. In (b) the volume of tidal air, V_T, is plotted; this increases with PCO_2, but in the normal animal there is a sharp break at about 45 mm Hg indicating that, beyond this, increases in ventilation are achieved largely by increases in frequency of breathing;

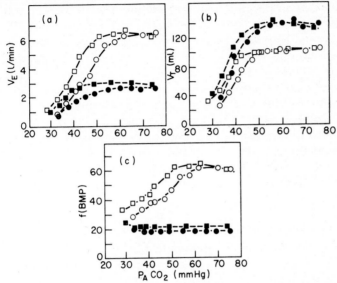

Fig. 3.21. The effect of vagotomy on the respiratory patterns of the decerebrate cat. Open symbols control, filled symbols after vagotomy. In (a) vagotomy reduces the normal increase in total ventilation (V_E) in response to raised PCO_2. In (b) the normal break in the control curve of tidal volume V_T against PCO_2 is lost with vagotomy indicating that, in the intact animal, above a PCO_2 of 50 mm Hg, increases in ventilation are achieved by increasing rate and not depth. In (c) the vagotomized animal has lost its frequency-response (f) to changes in PCO_2. Circles at 37°C, squares at 39·5°C. (Euler *et al.*, *Resp. Physiol.*)

this occurs at about half the vital capacity, and emphasizes that, when breathing under a strong hypercapnic drive, the animal is not expanding its lungs to anything like maximal capacity, and we may presume that the Hering-Breuer reflexes govern this restraint on tidal volume since, as Fig. 3.21(b) shows, in the vagotomized animal this sharp break does not occur. In Fig. 3.21(c) it is clear that, in the vagotomized animal, the response of frequency, f, to PCO_2 has been lost; in the normal, as indicated, increasing P_ACO_2 above about 50 mm Hg fails to produce any further increase in frequency.

Importance of Inhibition

In general, then, we must consider that the normal rhythmicity of the central respiratory neurones is subjected to a certain drive, governed by the afferent impulses from the chemoreceptors and the general level of H^+ in the blood and cerebrospinal fluid; an increased drive on these neurones results in increased discharge to the motor neurones of the intercostal muscles and diaphragm. This would result in more *rapid* inspiration and, unless the Hering-Breuer inhibitory impulses intervened, in a more *prolonged* inspiration. In fact, the Hering-Breuer impulses become effective, but at a later stage in inspiration, so that tidal volume is increased and the facilitation of the expiratory neurones helps to accelerate the expiratory phase and bring on the new inspiratory phase. Thus frequency and tidal volume increase. In the absence of the vagus the Hering-Breuer inhibition cannot take place, and so the increased chemoreceptor drive results in prolongation of inspiration and now the end of this is governed by the inherent rhythmicity of the central neurones. As the Figures show, for any given level of chemoreceptor drive, the ventilation is now less adequate because the increased tidal volume does not compensate for the lost increase in frequency.

The V_E–V_T Relationship

It is customary in many studies to plot the total ventilation, $\dot{V}_E$, against the tidal volume, V_T, as in Fig. 3.22; this emphasizes the

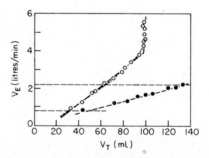

Fig. 3.22. The relationship between total ventilation ($\dot{V}_E$) and tidal volume (V_T), in a rebreathing decerebrate cat. Open circles control; filled circles after vagotomy. (Euler *et al.*, *Resp. Physiol.*)

failure of the tidal volume, V_T, to increase after a limiting ventilation rate is achieved, and the linear portion is described by the simple equation:

$$\dot{V}_E = k(V_T - V_0)$$

where k indicates the slope of the straight portion and V_0 is the extra-polated value of V_T when $\dot{V}_E$ is zero. In the vagotomized animal the slope of the line alters, and the break fails to occur.

Rate of Inspiration and Expiration

Duration of Phases

The frequency of breathing, f, is governed by the sum of the times taken for inspiration, T_I, and expiration, T_E, i.e. $f = 1/(T_I + T_E)$. Thus to characterize a breath we require its volume, V_E, and T_I and T_E. It is remarkable that, because of the increased drive on the

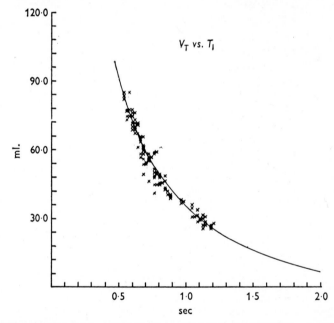

Fig. 3.23. The relation between tidal volume (V_T) and duration of inspiration (T_I) in an anaesthetized cat during rebreathing. (Clark and Euler, *J. Physiol.*)

respiratory centre provoked by high PCO_2, for example, the duration of inspiration decreases in spite of the increased tidal volume. Thus in experiments by Clark and Euler (1972) on cats rebreathing their own expired air, the increased tidal volume was associated with decreased inspiration-time, T_I, as in Fig. 3.23 where the hyperbolic relation between the two variables is shown. As we have seen, vagotomy destroys this relationship, so that it depends on feed-back from the lung-volume. The duration of the expiratory phase was also investigated by Clark and Euler who found it to be a simple linear function of the inspiratory time, i.e.

$$T_E = nT_I + p.$$

On simple mechanical grounds a relationship between inspiratory and expiratory times is understandable, the greater the expansion of the lung the longer will it take to collapse, although such a simple linear relation would not be predictable, and has been questioned (p. 241).

Control Model. In man, a similar hyperbolic relation between T_I and V_I was observed, but now there was a striking difference

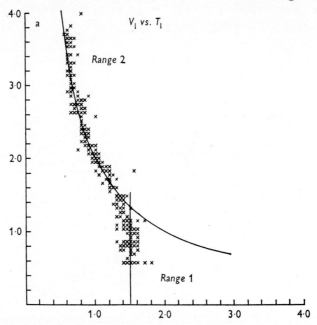

Fig. 3.24. The relationship between the duration of inspiration (T_I) and the inspiratory volume (V_I) in man. Note that at low tidal volumes (Range 1) the time for inspiration was independent of the tidal volume. Ordinate, V_I (litres); Abscissa, T_I (secs). (Clark and Euler, *J. Physiol.*)

at low tidal volumes when the time for inspiration was independent of tidal volume, as indicated in Fig. 3.24, the values of T_I being constant at about 1·5 sec for tidal volumes up to about 1·3 litres. This suggests that, in man, the vagal feedback does not operate at small lung expansions, and agrees with the finding that, in man, the Hering-Breuer reflex is absent during eupnoeic breathing. Clark and Euler thus divide the inspiratory phase into two periods, *Range 1*, where feedback seems not to be operative, and *Range 2*, where it is.

On this basis they have developed a hypothetical control model that describes the relations between the three variables, rate of inspiration, volume of inspiration, and total ventilation. Thus the fundamental relations are the hyperbolic relation between V_I and T_I, and the

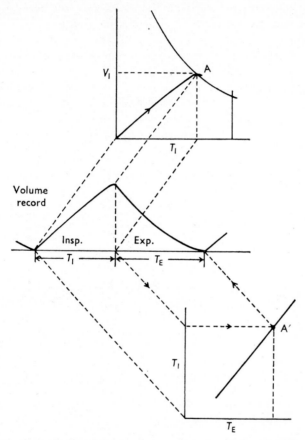

Fig. 3.25. Schematic diagram of a respiratory control system model. The phases of a hypothetical spirometer volume trace, middle record, have been related to the hyperbolic relation between the tidal volume (V_T) and respiratory period (T_I), upper graph, and to the linear relation between the inspiratory period (T_I) and expiratory period (T_E), lower graph. (Clark and Euler, *J. Physiol.*)

linear relation between T_I and T_E. These relations have been put into the composite diagram of Fig. 3.25, which also shows a hypothetical volume-record for the lung during a single breath. For the particular value of the inspiratory volume, V_I, given by the point A on the uppermost graph, the volume of inspired air, indicated on the middle graph, will rise approximately linearly and will be completed in the tmie, T_I, given on the uppermost graph. The time for expiration will be governed by the simple linear relation between T_I and T_E, and will correspond to the point A′ on the lowest graph; and the phase of expiration, recorded on the middle graph, will be given by the second part of the curve. Variations in breathing, due to altered CO_2-tension in the inspired air, as in rebreathing, would be governed by setting a new point on the $V_I - T_I$ curve, which would give, not only new values for tidal volume and time of inspiration, but also a new value for expiration time; since the sum of the inspiration and expiration times, $T_I + T_E$, determines rate of breathing, f, the breathing characteristics are completely defined.

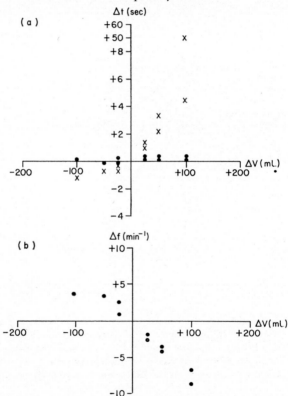

Fig. 3.26. Effects of changed lung-volume (ΔV) on (a) duration (Δt) of inspiration (filled circles) and expiration (crosses), and (b) on respiratory frequency (Δf) during respiratory paralysis with vagi intact. Note that the effect of ΔV on respiratory frequency is almost entirely due to changes in the duration of expiration. Note marked influence of lung-volume on respiratory frequency in the absence of lung movements. (Bartoli *et al.*, *J. Physiol.*)

Expiration Time

Clark and Euler's analysis attributes a dominant role to the vagal inspiratory discharge in controlling frequency of breathing, in the sense that it is the relation between T_I and V_T that determines the breathing characteristics. However, a recent study by Bartoli *et al.* (1973), employing the cardiopulmonary bypass described later, which permits the maintenance of adequate oxygenation of the blood in the absence of respiratory movements, indicates that the duration of expiration is reflexly controlled by a similar feedback mechanism.

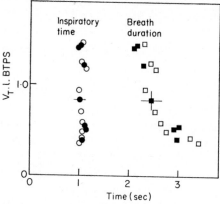

Fig. 3.27. The relationship between tidal volume V_T and duration of a single breath in man. On the right-hand side (squares) it can be seen that, as the size of the breath increases, the time of each breathing cycle decreases. On the left-hand side (circles) the inspiratory time is seen to be virtually constant, so that the shortening of the breath cycle must have been achieved by shortening of the expiratory period. (Cunningham and Gardner, *J. Physiol.*)

Thus, when the lung-volume was altered and held at this new value, there was a marked change in the duration of the expiration, measured by the discharge in the phrenic nerve; an increase in volume caused an increase in expiratory duration, and *vice versa*. As Fig. 3.26 shows, there was remarkably little effect on the duration of the inspiratory discharge, so that under these conditions the effects of the tidal volume on frequency of breathing would appear to be exerted on the duration of the expiratory discharge in the phrenic nerve.

Experiments on Man. It might be argued that the conditions of Bartoli *et al.*'s experiments were highly artificial, but studies on man, breathing different concentrations of CO_2, carried out by Cunningham and Gardner (1972), have given a similar result. This is illustrated by Fig. 3.27, in which the tidal volume, V_T, has been plotted against duration of a single breathing cycle; if we look at the right-hand set of points (squares), it is clear that the larger the breath the shorter the time of the whole cycle; if we look at the left-hand group of points (circles), we see that the inspiratory time remains virtually constant, so that the shortening of the breath-cycle must be achieved by shortening of the *expiratory* period.

It appears, then, that Clark and Euler's control scheme is too simple, and that we must take into account feedback mechanisms operating during both inspiration and expiration; and it may be that the effects described represent the two extremes between which variations in both expiratory and inspiratory periods take place.

Effect of P_ACO_2 on Vagal Reflexes

Vagotomy and Raised P_ACO_2

In view of the powerful effects of CO_2 on the respiratory centre and the carotid body reflexes, we might expect influences on respiratory rate to be governed entirely by these; nevertheless, there is some evidence that vagal reflexes arising from the direct stimulus of CO_2 in the lungs play a role in governing the duration of the inspiratory phase, and thus influence ventilatory rate. Thus the tachypnoea of inhalation of CO_2 is abolished by vagotomy in rabbit, cat, and man; the fact that it is also abolished in man is of some interest since in this species vagotomy does not affect normal respiratory frequency. It could be argued, of course, that the increase in respiratory frequency with inhaled CO_2 was due to more active vagal discharge resulting from the more intense inspiratory movement evoked by the direct CO_2 stimulus on the respiratory centres, bringing this movement to a close sooner and thus increasing frequency. In this case we do not have to invoke any direct effect of CO_2 on vagally innervated CO_2-sensitive lung receptors.

Single Fibre Discharge

There is good evidence, however, that some stretch-receptors in the lungs, and presumably those responsible for the Hering-Breuer inhibition of inspiration, are sensitive to CO_2. Thus Mustafa and Purves (1972) isolated single fibres of the vagus whose discharge was modulated by inspiratory movements, and which adapted slowly, this latter feature being a characteristic that is associated with fibres concerned in the Hering-Breuer type of reflex. The discharge-rate of the fibres increased linearly with expansion of the lung. Exposure of the lungs to high concentrations of CO_2 considerably modified the pattern of discharge as shown in Fig. 3.28; it will be seen that the expiratory discharge was considerably reduced at high levels of P_ACO_2, and the peak-frequency in inspiration also fell. It seems, then, that vagal discharge in both inspiration and expiration is decreased at high levels of inspired CO_2; if the discharges are, like the Hering-Breuer reflex discharges, inhibitory to the respiratory centre, we can understand that blocking

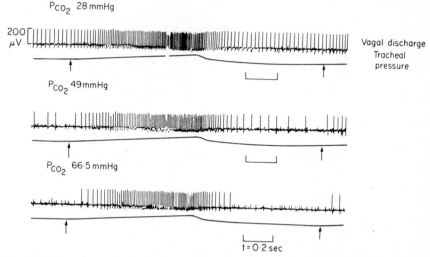

Fig. 3.28. The effect of increased levels of PCO_2 on the rate of discharge from vagally innervated stretch-receptors in the lung. As carbon dioxide tension increases, the rate of discharge falls from 265 impulses/sec at 28 mm Hg to 192 impulses/sec at 66·5 mm Hg. Upper trace of each record, vagal discharge; lower trace, tracheal pressure. (Mustafa and Purves, *Resp. Physiol.*)

the vagus would modify the response to CO_2, releasing the respiratory centre from inhibitory impulses and thus increasing the total ventilation.

Cardiopulmonary Bypass

This study, and a comparable one by Schoener & Frankel (1972), which demonstrated a marked increase in sensitivity to stretch with lowered P_aCO_2, indicated definitely that vagal, and presumably inhibitory, discharge is affected by CO_2 independently of the blood-level; but of course it is not possible to deduce the consequences on frequency and depth of breathing solely from the altered pattern of discharge. Direct evidence that inspired CO_2 can affect ventilation independently of blood arterial PCO_2 has been provided by Bartoli *et al.* (1974), who employed dogs with a cardiopulmonary bypass, illustrated by Fig. 3.29. A cannula was introduced into the external ileac vein and pushed back to the right atrium; blood from here was bypassed through an external oxygenator and returned to the left side of the heart by way of the external ileac artery by means of a pump. Thus the gas tensions of the blood could be held constant by means of the oxygenator whilst the tension of inspired air could be varied independently.

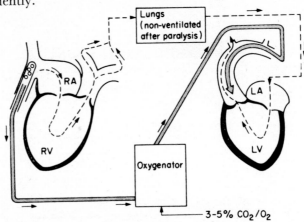

Fig. 3.29. Schematic diagram of closed-chest cardiopulmonary bypass. RA, right atrium; RV, right ventricle; LA, left atrium; LV, left ventricle. Interrupted line shows right-to-left shunt that may develop with an inadequate bypass. (Bartoli *et al.*, *J. Physiol.*)

Reduced Expiratory Time. When the PCO_2 of the inspired air was increased abruptly to 30 mm Hg (Fig. 3.30, bottom record) there was an equally abrupt increase in ventilation (V_E); since the inspiratory time was unaltered (T_I top graph), and the tidal volume was also unaltered, the increased ventilation was achieved by a shortened expiratory time (T_E) which led to an increased frequency (f). It will be recalled that Mustafa and Purves (1972) found a reduced vagal inhibitory discharge with high PCO_2, and this might well be reflected in a shortened expiratory phase, the absence of inhibition permitting a more powerful expiratory effort; but it is unwise to make any dogmatic statement in this connexion since it could be argued that a more prolonged expiratory (i.e. less inhibited) discharge would be reflected in a more lengthy expiratory phase.

CO_2-Sensitive Receptors in Birds

The actual receptors in the lung sensitive to CO_2 have not been identified; they presumably lie close to the airway surface. In this

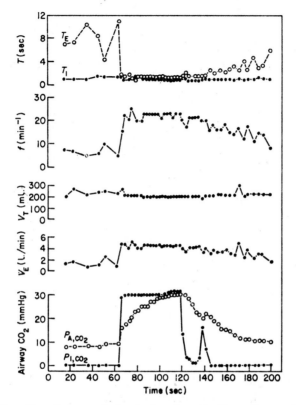

Fig. 3.30. The effect of changes in inspired carbon dioxide tension on the respiratory pattern of the dog on cardiopulmonary bypass. The bypass enabled gas tensions of the blood to be held constant while those in the inspired air could be varied. Records from the top show the duration of expiration (T_E) and inspiration (T_I), respiratory rate (f), tidal volume (V_T) ventilation ($\dot{V}_E$) and the inspired (P_ICO_2) and end-tidal (P_ACO_2) CO_2-tensions. The effect of inhaling CO_2 is solely on the duration of expiration, T_E. (Bartoli et al., *J. Physiol.*)

connexion we may note that the respiratory passages of birds contain receptors that are remarkably sensitive to CO_2, receptors that are important in controlling respiration. Thus passing air, containing less than 4 per cent CO_2 through the lungs by way of the trachea, and out into the atmosphere through opened abdominal air-sacs caused rapid onset of apnoea, and this was prevented by increasing the concentration to 6 per cent CO_2 (Ray and Fedde, 1969). The sensory fibres are carried in the pulmonary branches of the vagus in the chicken, and when a stream of gas was passed through the trachea and out through the opened air-sacs, the discharge varied inversely with the concentration of CO_2 in the gas (Fedde and Peterson, 1970). Hypoxia or hyperoxia had no effect. In Molony's study, out of forty-five units firing in phase with breathing, some twenty-five showed decreased firing when CO_2 was added to the inspired air. According to Molony, the receptors may, in fact, be primarily sensitive to mechanical stretch, like those concerned in the Hering-Breuer reflex in mammals; superimposed on this mechanical sensitivity is one to CO_2. Thus Leitner (1972) found that half of the vagal fibres carrying impulses in response to lung-inflation were sensitive to CO_2, which decreased their discharge. As with mammals, however, the location of the receptors has not been achieved.

Physiological Significance

It would seem, then, that in mammals, and particularly in birds, the PCO_2 within the air-ways can exert a control over respiration by modifying the inhibitory activity of pulmonary receptors; a high concentration of CO_2 betokens inadequate ventilation, and the reduced vagal discharge, by increasing the duration and force of respiratory movements, tends to compensate for this.

Vagotomy and Response to Exercise and Hyperthermia

Exercise

According to Phillipson *et al.* (1970), although conscious dogs, with their vagi blocked, failed to increase the frequency of breathing with high P_ACO_2, as shown by Euler *et al.* (1970), the response to exercise was not so seriously impaired; the minute-volume per unit of O_2-consumption was unaltered, and the frequency of breathing increased, although not to the same extent as in normals.

Hyperthermic Polypnoea

The increased respiratory frequency, or panting, typically seen in the dog, is controlled through a hypothalamic centre (p. 23), and so we might expect it to be differently affected by vagal block from the polypnoea of high PCO_2. In fact Anrep and Hammouda (1932) found that panting in cats and dogs was unaffected by vagotomy; moreover, it is interesting that during hyperthermic panting it is not possible to evoke a Hering-Breuer inhibition of breathing, as in the eupnoeic dog. When different species are compared, there are some striking variations in respect to hyperthermic panting; thus the rabbit, cat and lamb are similar to the dog, but Richards (1968) has shown that, in the guinea-pig and rat, vagotomy during hyperthermic panting causes a drop in breathing-rate and, in the guinea-pig, severe respiratory distress.

THE BRAIN-STEM RESPIRATORY NEURONES

Diverse Discharge Patterns

We have already seen that, in the medulla, groups of neurones have been discovered, giving rhythmic bursts of discharges related to one or other phase of the respiratory cycle, which may be described as inspiratory or expiratory neurones. A very exhaustive study of such

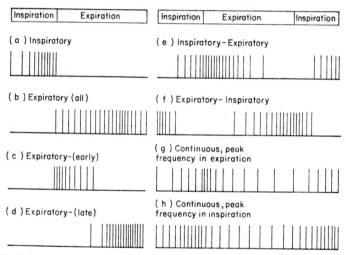

Fig. 3.31. Schematic classification of major discharge patterns of medullary respiratory neurones. Each pattern is derived from spike counts of a representative neurone. (Cohen, *Breathing*, Ciba Symp.)

neurones is that of Cohen (1968, 1969, 1970) in the cat, and it has revealed a much greater diversity than had been suspected. Fig. 3.31 shows the major discharge patterns during breathing; *a* is the typical inspiratory neurone, discharging only during inspiration; *b* to *d* are expiratory neurones but their discharges occur throughout expiration (*all*) or in the early or late phases. These discharges bear strong analogies with discharges in the muscles of respiration, so far as their time-relations to the cycle are concerned, and it may be that the neurones giving these discharges are closely related to the muscles of respiration, e.g. the inspiratory neurones to the phrenic nerve and the nerves supplying the external intercostals; the early expiratory to the laryngeal expiratory fibres, and so on. The other group is classed as phase-spanning, with discharges that are not confined to one or other phase of the cycle (*e-h*). These occur predominantly in the pons, by contrast with the neurones locked to a phase, which are found predominantly in the medulla; and it may be that they are concerned with coordinating the medullary neurones to produce a smooth transition from inspiration to expiration, and *vice versa*.

Responses to Inflation

The responses to lung-inflation are of special interest owing to the importance of the Hering-Breuer reflex; in general, lung-inflation inhibits inspiratory muscle discharges and facilitates those of the expiratory muscles (Sears, 1964), so that we may expect corresponding

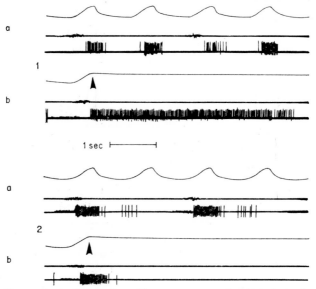

Fig. 3.32. Comparison of occlusion effects on two predominantly early-expiratory neurones having opposite responses to inflation (1, excited; 2, depressed). a, control state (2:1 synchronization); each neurone fires in two bursts. b, occlusion at peak inflation in early expiratory phase. The discharge of 1 is increased; that of 2 is decreased. (Cohen, *Breathing*.)

responses in the brain-stem neurones. This was usually true, the inspiratory neurones being depressed by inflation and the expiratory neurones being excited; however, as Fig. 3.32 shows, two predominantly expiratory neurones, quite close to each other, had opposite effects, the one (1) having its discharge prolonged during inflation and the other having it inhibited (2). In a similar way, inspiratory neurones could be found that were facilitated by inflation. We may conclude that such "anomalous" neurones were in fact interneurones; thus the inspiratory neurones excited by inflation would be inhibitory to the inspiratory neurones that promote inspiratory motor discharge, whilst the expiratory neurones that are depressed by inflation are inhibitory to the expiratory neurones which promote expiratory motor discharge. On this basis, inspiratory neurones that are excited by inflation are anti-inspiratory and expiratory neurones that are depressed by inflation are anti-expiratory in function.

Brain-Stem Stimulation

In a similar way, a duality in response of medullary neurones may be observed when higher regions of the brain-stem are stimulated electrically; thus stimuli localized to the dorsolateral rostral pons—the so-called "pneumotaxic centre" considered to dominate rhythmicity (p. 209)—would cause either facilitation of inspiration or of expiration according to the region stimulated. When the discharges in medullary neurones were examined during electrical excitation of these regions, some inspiratory neurones would respond with increased discharge but other inspiratory neurones would be inhibited.

Origin of Rhythmicity

According to Cohen, who has also studied the effects of lowered PCO_2 on the respiratory neurones, the contrasting responses indicate the presence of antagonistic neuronal circuits; and it is essentially the interplay of these that leads to the rhythmicity of the final discharges to the motor neurones of respiration. This view contrasts with that which attributes rhythmicity to an innate tendency to discharge in a cyclical fashion, similar to the rhythmicity of smooth muscle and cardiac cells.

Vagal Motor Units

In this connexion it must be remembered that the brain-stem contains neurones that may well be discharging in relation to the respiratory cycle, yet not be governing this periodicity. This would almost certainly be true of the vagal motor units in the medulla that innervate the intrinsic muscles of the larynx; according to Eyzaguirre and Taylor (1963), many vagal motor neurones may be found with an inspiratory rhythm corresponding in time with discharges in the phrenic nerve; not all of these stopped at expiration so that some continued and could thus be described as "phase-spanning". In eupnoeic breathing only inspiratory vagal neurones fired, and these would be concerned in widening the glottis.

Cough-Reflex

The expiratory neurones, which tend to close the glottis, become active when the intrathoracic pressure rises and are presumably concerned in the cough-reflex, which consists of powerful expiratory movements, with a narrowed glottis, evoked by mechanical or chemical stimuli to the tracheobronchial tree.

THE INTEGRATED BREATHING PATTERN

Decerebrate Animal

Having discussed the factors influencing the various parameters involved in breathing, we may return to consider briefly the possible relations of the "breathing centres" to each other and to the respiratory motor neurones. Tang (1967) has proposed the scheme illustrated in

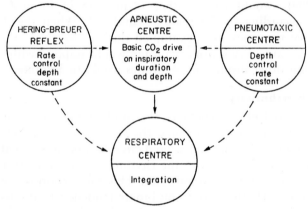

Fig. 3.33. Diagram illustrating the control of respiratory depth and rate by the Hering-Breuer reflex, the pneumotaxic centre, the apneustic centre and the medullary respiratory centre in response to CO_2 drive. (Tang, *Resp. Physiol.*)

Fig. 3.33, based on his experiments on the effects of breathing high concentrations of CO_2 in decerebrate cats subjected to additional brain-lesions.

Removal of Pneumotaxic Centre

Respiration is eupnoeic in the decerebrate animal; on removing the "pneumotaxic centre", by sucking away a portion of the isthmus region of the pons, the breathing pattern changed, with each inspiration appearing to approach a depth-limit; the change was especially manifest when the effects of breathing 5 per cent CO_2 were considered. In decerebrate animals the effects are manifest in large increases in depth of respiration and only smaller increases in rate, but in these additionally lesioned animals it appeared that a limit was imposed on depth of breathing, so that increased ventilation had to be achieved by increased rate.

Vagotomy. When the vagi were cut, typical *apneustic breathing* occurred, i.e. prolonged inspiratory spasms interspersed with gasps; the gasps were apparently due to anoxia, since they were prevented by breathing 100 per cent O_2, when breathing consisted in a succession of prolonged inspiratory cramps. Thus the vagus, presumably acting through the Hering-Breuer inflation reflex, modifies the activity of the remaining parts of the brain-stem concerned in maintaining rhythm, i.e. those parts left after removing the pneumotaxic centre. This is illustrated by Fig. 3.33 where the Hering-Breuer reflex is indicated as influencing the *apneustic centre*, the centre which, together with the medullary centre, remains after removal of the pneumotaxic centre. According to this scheme, the pneumotaxic centre controls depth of breathing, since breathing 5 per cent CO_2 failed to increase depth appreciably when this centre had been removed. In the absence of a Hering-Breuer reflex and of the pneumotaxic centre, breathing is apneustic, or a succession of inspiratory cramps.

Medullary Centre. When the brain is sectioned below the apneustic centre, leaving only the medullary centre, breathing becomes a succession of gasps; in this situation the respiratory centre proper, containing neurones with a tendency to discharge rhythmically, controls breathing, to give the uncoordinated series of gasps. Under these conditions, according to Tang, the gasping rate was virtually uninfluenced by breathing 7 per cent CO_2, so that the basic CO_2-drive is attributed to the apneustic centre, which controls mainly rate since, as we have seen, when the pneumotaxic centre has been removed, the response to high CO_2 is largely restricted to changes in rate, rather than depth.

According to Fig. 3.33, then, the medullary respiratory centre integrates the nervous impulses it receives primarily from the apneustic centre, which provides the basic CO_2-drive on inspiratory duration and depth; this apneustic centre is influenced by the Hering-Breuer reflex and by the pneumotaxic centre, whilst both of these may influence the medullary respiratory centre directly.

THE RESPIRATORY RESPONSE TO EXERCISE

Accuracy of Adjustment

The ventilation of the lungs is very finely adjusted to the work performed by the body, so that if we plot the one against the other, as in

Fig. 3.34, we obtain a linear relation up to a very high level of energy consumption; the difference between the trained athlete and the untrained subject is essentially the point at which ventilation suddenly becomes much greater than necessary, and it is soon after this point has been reached that the "break point" occurs, and exercise has become intolerable. This beautiful adjustment of ventilation to energy

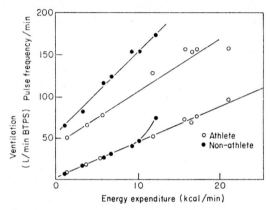

Fig. 3.34. Pulse frequency and ventilation during graded exercise in a middle-distance runner of world fame and in a non-athlete. (Upper two lines: pulse rate Lower lines: ventilation.) (Cotes, *Brit med. Bull.*)

expenditure obviously betokens an accurate feedback mechanism whereby the altered state of the blood, due to exercise, influences the respiratory centres, both directly and through peripheral reflex mechanisms.

Changes in P_aO_2 and P_aCO_2

Nevertheless, it is extremely difficult to demonstrate how the altered blood-composition exerts its effects since, although the PO_2 and PCO_2 of the venous blood, returning to the heart, are vastly different at the height of exercise from their resting values, so efficient is the ventilation process in the lungs that the corresponding parameters for the arterial blood are virtually unchanged, especially when a steady state of ventilation has been reached. Thus the mean level of PO_2 for arterial blood is 90–95 mm Hg up to the breaking point, and so it would appear that there would not be a very strong chemoreceptor drive in action. Similarly the PCO_2 of the arterial blood shows no striking changes; at the onset there may be a transient fall; later it tends to rise as the steady state of ventilation is approached, and subsequently it returns to its original level or, if exercise is severe, it falls below this.

Because of the small and sometimes opposite effects on PCO_2, it has been argued that there are receptors on the venous side or in the pulmonary circulation that mediate reflex changes in ventilation, and some experimental support has been provided for this claim, for example by Armstrong. However, it may well be that the changes in acid-base characteristics of the arterial blood, although small, can account for the altered respiratory rate both qualitatively and quantitatively.

Time-Course of Ventilation

Let us examine the changes in ventilation (Fig. 3.35); at the beginning it increases rapidly, too rapidly for any change in blood composition to have had time to take effect; and for this reason the rise is attributed to nervous mechanisms, possibly through receptors in the exercising muscles, but the exact manner in which the initiation of exercise brings about this increase in ventilation is still unsettled.

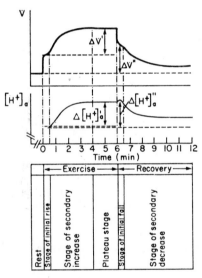

Fig. 3.35. Basic form of the time-course of ventilation ($\dot{V}$) during exercise and recovery (heavy line). Also shown schematically is the time-course of arterial [H$^+$] (from arterial pH recordings). The nomenclature used for the various stages in exercise and recovery refer solely to the observed changes in $\dot{V}$. $\Delta\dot{V}'$ represents the increment of $\dot{V}$ from its mean value during the stage of initial rise to that in the plateau stage, $\Delta\dot{V}''$ represents the difference between the mean value of $\dot{V}$ during the stage of initial fall in recovery and its resting level. Note that the $\Delta\dot{V}/\Delta[H^+]_a$ ratios in the plateau stage were the same as in the stage of initial fall in recovery. (Matell, *Acta physiol. scand.*)

It seems certain that it is reflex rather than cortical in origin since, as Fig. 3.36 shows, the ventilation of men voluntarily exercising their legs is the same as that when their legs are made to go through similar motions with the aid of a machine.

Plateau Level. After this rapid rise, which may amount to 50 per cent of the increase during exercise, and which lasts a few seconds, there is a slower rise to reach a plateau, the height of which is governed by the rate of energy consumption; on cessation of the exercise there

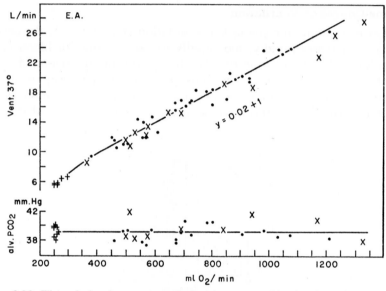

Fig. 3.36. The relation between ventilation (upper graph), alveolar PCO_2 (lower graph) and the rate of working as represented by the oxygen consumption. Note that the ventilatory response to work is the same for man exercising voluntarily ($\times$) as those whose legs were made to move by aid of a machine ($\bullet$). (Asmussen *et al.*, *Acta. physiol. scand.*)

is a rapid fall in ventilation, presumably corresponding to the cessation of the neural component, and this is followed by a slow fall.

Blood Changes. Simultaneous analyses of the arterial blood PO_2, PCO_2 and pH, carried out by Matell, showed that, during the initial stages of the increase in ventilation there were, indeed, small changes in these, but usually by the time the plateau of ventilation had been reached the PO_2 and PCO_2 had returned to their initial values, and had even altered in the reverse direction from that expected, i.e. the PO_2 had *increased* and the PCO_2 *decreased*. However, as Fig. 3.35 shows, the H^+-ion concentration of the arterial blood rose in parallel with the increase in ventilation, i.e. the blood was acid. The main problem that confronts the investigator in the control of respiration is to determine how the increased respiration is brought about, and sustained at the plateau-level appropriate to the rate of exercise. It may well be that the neurogenic factor, together with the transient changes in blood-chemistry, are sufficient to bring the respiration to the plateau level, but the return of PCO_2 and PO_2 to their resting values raises the question as to the nature of the drive at the height of sustained exercise. Cunningham has argued that the changed pH of the arterial blood, combined with the existing chemoreceptor drive determined by the arterial PO_2, in accordance with his equation (p. 226), could account for at least 60 per cent of the extra ventilation, if we exclude that component due to neural factors.

Chemoreceptor Drive

The importance of the chemoreceptor drive, operating through the arterial blood PO_2, is easily demonstrated by switching the inspired air from normal to one rich in O_2; there is an immediate reduction in ventilation, as occurs also at rest, but the amount of this reduction during severe exercise seems to be proportional to the existing ventilation, namely about 16 per cent; hence the chemoreceptor drive is responsible for a greater absolute ventilation rate during exercise than at rest, and the contradiction remains.

Temporal Fluctuations in Blood Gas Tensions

Injections of CO_2

An experiment of Yamamoto and Edwards (1960) is instructive in this context; they simply injected CO_2 into a rat by equilibrating blood in an extracorporeal circuit with 100 per cent CO_2, as in Fig. 3.37; they found that the extra CO_2 was removed by increased ventilation in proportion as the CO_2 was injected, i.e. there seemed to be perfect homoeostasis respecting the CO_2-content, and thus PCO_2, of its arterial blood. The amount injected was equivalent to what would have been produced in severe exercise, but under these conditions the only stimulus to remove the CO_2—i.e. to hyperventilation—was the CO_2 itself. Clearly, if an animal can dispose of this unwanted and artificially introduced CO_2 without permitting a significant change in the P_aCO_2, the same mechanism could be employed during exercise. What, then, is the stimulus? Why is the rat breathing five times as fast at one time as at another when its $PaCO_2$ is the same at both times? Yamamoto and Edwards suggested that it was temporal

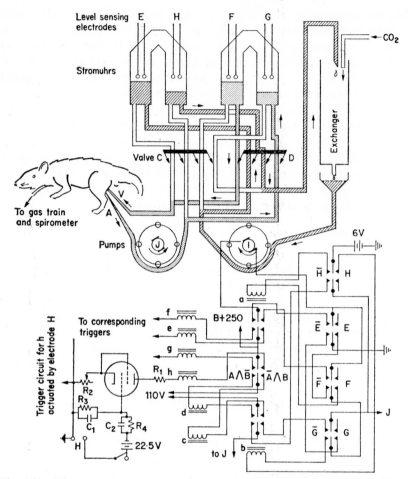

Fig. 3.37. Diagram of extracorporeal perfusion apparatus. Blood flow indicated would occur with valve D open and valve C closed. Animal is filling G and being infused from F. Exchanger is filling E and being loaded from H. (Yamamoto and Edwards, *J. appl. Physiol.*)

fluctuations in the PCO_2 of the arterial blood that provided the essential signal; thus, under his conditions, as soon as he raised the CO_2-content of the animal the blood returning from the lung would contain a higher PCO_2 for at least one respiratory cycle; the increased ventilation caused by excitation of the chemoreceptors would bring the P_aCO_2 down, but if CO_2-infusion continued, the next lot of blood flowing through the lungs would be hypercapnic and excite the chemoreceptors, and so on. Thus the production of extra CO_2 (or its injection) provides an oscillating signal, and clearly the greater the rate of production of CO_2, i.e. the more severe the exercise, the greater will these breath-to-breath oscillations be. Hence the brain must interpret an *oscillation* in P_aCO_2 (or pH or PO_2) rather than the mean or steady level.

Breath-to-Breath Fluctuations

The values of PCO_2 and PO_2 of arterial blood, employed in relating these to ventilation, are mean values and take no account of the fluctuations that must take place from one breath to another. Modern electrode techniques permit the rapid and continuous monitoring of the blood pH, PCO_2 and PO_2, so that it is possible to measure fluctuations taking place within a second or less (Purves, 1966).

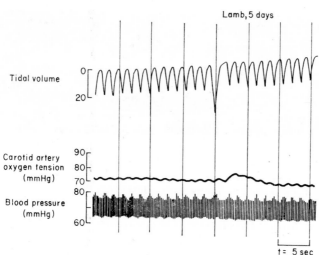

Fig. 3.38. Fluctuations in carotid artery oxygen tension in a 5-day-old lamb. From above down: tidal volume (inspiration downwards), carotid artery oxygen tension, carotid artery blood pressure. The lamb took a deep breath and this was followed 2·3 sec later by a rise in mean P_aO_2. (Purves, *Resp. Physiol.*)

P_aO_2 **Fluctuations.** Fig. 3.38 shows a typical curve obtained in a young lamb, the PO_2 of its arterial blood fluctuating by 1·5 mm Hg around a mean of 72 mm Hg; the peak of each fluctuation coincided with the trough of the respiratory fluctuation in blood-pressure; when the animal took a deep breath this was followed 2·3 sec later by a rise in mean P_aO_2, whilst the amplitude of variation increased to ±3 mm Hg. We may conclude that these fluctuations correspond with similar fluctuations in the alveolar tension with each respiratory cycle. Thus the very short time spent by blood in the pulmonary capillaries, and the rapid equilibration during this time, ensure that the blood flowing out of the lungs at any moment reflects the PO_2 of the alveolar air, which tends to fall during expiration and rise during inspiration. To some extent these fluctuations will be damped by intraventricular mixing, but such effects only produce small step-like interruptions in the wave-pattern. The interval of 2·5–3·2 sec between peak inspiration and peak of arterial PO_2 corresponds to the lung-to-carotid circulation time.

pH Fluctuations. Fluctuations in pH of the blood related to the ventilatory rate have also been frequently described, e.g. by Band, Cameron and Semple (1969), obviously related to corresponding changes in P_aCO_2. The fluctuation was of the order of 0·02 pH units.

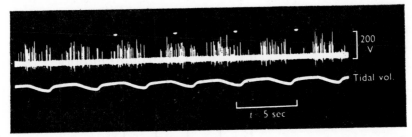

Fig. 3.39. Chemoreceptor activity (upper trace), measured in a baroreceptor-free strand of the sinus nerve, and respiration (lower trace), inspiration downwards. Each chemoreceptor discharge group is probably related to changes in alveolar gas tensions in the previous respiratory cycle. (Biscoe and Purves, *J. Physiol.*)

Carotid Sinus Discharge. Corresponding with these changes in blood-chemistry we find a fluctuation in activity in the carotid sinus nerve, as Fig. 3.39, from Biscoe and Purves shows, where each burst of chemoreceptor discharges is presumably related to the previous respiratory cycle. The cyclic effects were not related to changes in blood-flow, whilst a possible baroreceptor activity in the fibres was excluded by showing that they were unresponsive to clamping the common carotid whilst their discharge was inhibited by inspiration of O_2.

P_aCO_2 **versus** P_aO_2. When Fitzgerald *et al.* (1969) carried out intermittent injections of hypercapnic blood into the common carotid artery close to the bifurcation, they found that the discharges in the carotid sinus nerve could follow the frequency of injection up to some 60/min (Fig. 3.40); with hypoxic blood injections, however, there was very little evidence that the chemoreceptors could follow frequencies ranging from 27 to 54 per min, so that, although the chemoreceptors have generally been considered to be operated primarily through hypoxia, where the response to oscillations is concerned it appears that it will be the oscillations in PCO_2 or pH that will be the signal governing increased ventilation during exercise. This does not mean that the fluctuating hypoxia of exercise will not be important, since we have seen that a high sensitivity of the chemoreceptors to altered

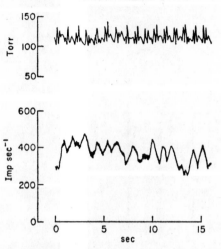

Fig. 3.40. The response of the carotid sinus nerve to intermittent infusions of hypercapnic blood administered up the common carotid artery at a rate of 60 min^{-1}. Upper trace: carotid blood pressure. Lower trace: carotid nerve afferent activity. The animal is breathing room air. (Fitzgerald *et al.*, *Resp. Physiol.*)

PCO_2 depends on a background of hypoxia, the combined effect of hypoxia and hypercapnia being greater than the sum of their individual effects.

Timing of the Chemoreceptor Stimuli

The respiratory neurones are considered to pass through cyclic changes in excitability, reflected in cyclical depolarization and repolarization; reflex modifications in respiratory rate and depth are brought about by changing the time-relations of this cyclical event; thus an increase in rate will require a more rapid depolarization and shorter periods between firing and repolarization; increased depth will require more prolonged discharge for any inspiration, and so on. Such changes could be achieved by the arrival of excitatory or inhibitory impulses from the chemoreceptors, but clearly the effect on an

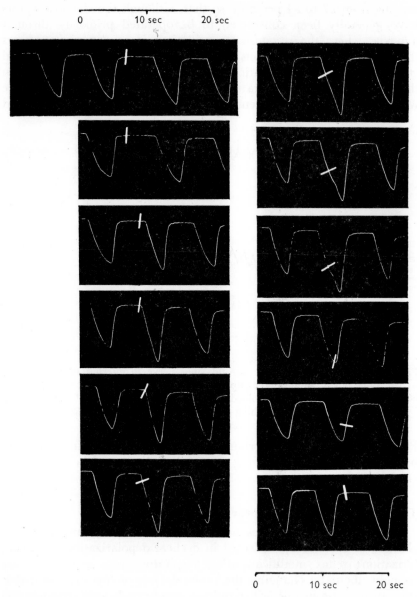

Fig. 3.41. The effect of 0·5 ml Ringer solution, equilibrated with 100 per cent CO_2 and injected retrogradely into the external carotid artery, on the pattern of breathing in the cat. At the bar on each trace the injection was made and its effects depend on the phase in respiration. (Black and Torrance, *J. Physiol.*)

inspiratory neurone, for example, will depend on the timing of the impulses.

Retrograde Injections. The importance of this was first demonstrated by Black and Torrance who injected saline with a high PCO_2 retrogradely down the external carotid artery and observed a prolongation of inspiration which increased the tidal volume of the breath taking place at the time of arrival at the carotid body; if the injection reached it during expiration this was prolonged, thereby militating against ventilation (Fig. 3.41). Clearly, then, an oscillatory chemical stimulus, arriving at the respiratory neurones during inspiration,

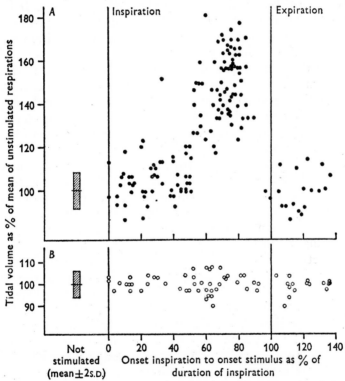

Fig. 3.42. A) The change in tidal volume resulting from carotid body chemoreceptor stimulation (0·3 ml. CO_2-bicarbonate solution) at various times in the respiratory cycle in a cat. One carotid sinus nerve is intact. Tidal volume changes occurring with stimulation are shown as a percentage of the mean of unstimulated breaths. Vertical bars represent the mean ± 2 S.D. for unstimulated control breaths. Stimulation has little effect on tidal volume until over half of inspiration has been completed. Expiratory stimulation (greater than 100 per cent on time scale) has no effect. (B) Same cat, with both carotid nerves cut. Injection of CO_2-bicarbonate solution now has no effect on tidal volume. (Eldridge, *J. Physiol.*)

would be a more useful stimulus to increased ventilation than a continuous one, which would prolong both inspiratory and expiratory phases.

Stimulation of Sinus-Nerve. A more accurate study of the importance of timing is provided by electrical stimulation of the carotid sinus nerve; using this technique, as well as chemical stimulation of the chemoreceptors, Eldridge (1972) showed that the maximal effect, measured as a change in tidal volume, was obtained if the stimulus reached the carotid sinus at the end of inspiration (Fig. 3.42). If the carotid sinus nerve was not intact there was no change in ventilation. As Fig. 3.42 shows, if the stimulus arrived during expiration the tidal volume was not significantly changed. Moreover, it has been established that the effects of a stimulus falling during expiration are not carried over to the next inspiration, so that the inspiratory neurone has a "memory" shorter than a single respiratory cycle. Eldridge postulated that the carotid sinus-nerve impulses tended to depolarize inspiratory neurones whenever they arrived, and would thus add their effects to the depolarization already taking place and so prolong inspiration. If they arrived when the neurones had repolarized they would have little effect since, of themselves, they would not be able to depolarize the neurones to the firing threshold.

Relation to Oscillatory Stimulus. These studies have an obvious bearing on the effectiveness of an oscillatory stimulus discussed above; thus it may be that the peak of the oscillating chemoreceptor signal tends to entrain the respiratory neurone rhythm, thereby assuring an appropriate relation between the peak-signal and inspiration; and it is interesting, in this connection, that there is often a whole-number relation between heart-rate and respiratory rate, a relation that, in the dog, is intensified by manoeuvres that increase the carotid body chemoreceptor output, e.g. in exercise, or exercise plus hypoxia, and eliminated by section of the carotid sinus nerve (Weiss and Salzano, 1970). Thus the time of arrival of the oscillatory signal at the respiratory neurones will clearly depend on the heart-rate, so that if respiration is entrained by the changing carotid body stimulus, there will be a clear-cut relation of heart-rate to respiration-rate.

Build-Up of Ventilation. If, then, during exercise, there is not only an increase in reflex afferent activity but also a sharpening of the grouping of impulses arriving centrally at a favourable phase in the respiratory cycle, we may account for the build-up of very large ventilation rates during exercise with only small mean changes in arterial gas tensions. When P_aCO_2 is high, the reflex hypoxic drive is small, as Bhattacharyya et al. (1970) have shown; this rather surprising result could well be accounted for by a change to less favourable phasing of the afferent discharge so that even though its mean value, in terms of impulses per sec, were increased, it would be far less effective.

Injections of Hypercapnic Blood. An ingenious experiment that emphasizes the importance of oscillatory changes in P_aCO_2, as opposed to continuous ones, was carried out by Cameron, Linton and Miller (1974); they measured the response as the ratio between the increase in ventilation over the increase in P_aCO_2. When hypercapnia is induced in the rabbit by an intravenous infusion, we may expect the stimulus arriving at the chemoreceptors to be pulsatile, each heart-beat causing a surge of hypercapnic blood into the carotid sinus. Under these conditions the ratio was $78 \pm 33 \cdot 6$ ml. min^{-1} mm Hg^{-1} PCO_2. When hypercapnia was induced by inhalation, the oscillations were presumably not so great and frequent, and the ratio became $31 \cdot 6 \pm 15 \cdot 4$ ml min.

Tube-Breathing. Experimentally, in man, the time-profile of alveolar CO_2 and O_2 can be altered by breathing through a tube, which increases the dead-space of the respiratory system; of the various profiles established by this method Cunningham *et al.* (1973) found the most effective to be that when the peak P_aCO_2 occurred late in the inspiratory phase.

Sympathetic Stimulation

Just as with the cardiovascular responses, stimulation of the sympathetic supply changes the respiratory reflex sensitivity of the carotid

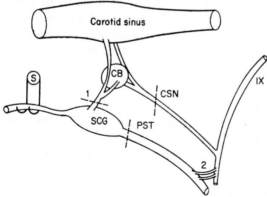

Fig. 3.43. Diagrammatic representation of the sympathetic innervation of the carotid body and sinus in the cat. Medial view of structures on the right side. CB, carotid body; CSN, carotid sinus nerve; IX, glossopharyngeal nerve; SCG, superior cervical ganglion, PST, post-ganglionic sympathetic trunk; 1, post-ganglionic branch to carotid body and sinus; 2, connections through which sympathetic, post-ganglionic fibres enter sinus nerve. (Mills and Sampson, *J. Physiol.*)

body. Thus stimulation of the cervical sympathetic causes an increase in ventilation, presumably by increasing the sensitivity of the chemoreceptors to the existing levels of P_aO_2 and P_aCO_2. The effect was blocked by section of the carotid sinus-nerves, and also fairly completely by cutting the branch from the superior cervical ganglion to the carotid bifurcation; complete block was obtained by cutting the postganglionic sympathetic trunk as well, since some fibres run from there in the carotid sinus nerve (Fig. 3.43). We may assume that, in severe exercise, the liberation of adrenal hormones will contribute to increase the drive on the respiratory neurones through the carotid and aortic bodies.

The Limiting Factor in Severe Exercise

Cardiac Output

Let us conclude this discussion of the control of respiration in exercise by considering what it is that puts a limit to the rate of doing work. At the breakpoint, the subject is "breathless", so that it might be inferred that the limit was given by his power of ventilation of the blood; in the normal subject, whether untrained or an athlete, this is not true, however. In fact, at the breakpoint, the subject is ventilating his lungs far in excess of the requirements of gas-exchange, so that the tension of O_2 in the arterial blood is higher than at rest, and that of CO_2 lower. It is the failure of the cardiac output to keep pace with the demands of the exercising muscles; as a result of inadequate blood-flow through these, the work performed becomes more and more anaerobic so that more and more lactic acid accumulates in the blood, and it is the *metabolic acidosis*, so created, that produces the respiratory distress.

Raised Body-Temperature

Contributing to the failure is the raised body-temperature that reflexly increases the drive on respiration, thereby increasing this still further, beyond the requirements of oxygen intake.

Work of Breathing

If it is appreciated that breathing requires expenditure of energy, the unnecessary increase in breathing-rate creates further demands on the organism; in fact, it has been calculated that, with a ventilation of 140 litres/minute, any increase in rate is useless since the increase will be required for the extra muscular effort of breathing.

Effects of Raised P_aCO_2

Perhaps the best demonstration that respiratory rate is not limiting is that, when a subject breathes an oxygen-enriched air during exercise, although his ventilation is reduced for any given rate of work, he is able to sustain this work for longer periods. The higher oxygen tension of the blood resulting from the increased tension in the inspired air permits a more efficient oxygenation of the tissues and so reduces accumulation of lactic acid. The maximum effect is with 66 per cent O_2; at higher concentrations there is an effect on the cerebral circulation that opposes the benefits to the exercising limbs.

Training

Economy of Effort

A well trained subject is able to carry out a given work-load with less demands on his cardiovascular and respiratory systems than an untrained subject; in other words the muscular effort is achieved more economically, and this is revealed, for example, in the relation of cardiac output, or pulse-rate, to rate of working (Fig. 3.34, p. 252); with both non-trained and trained subjects the relations are linear, but the trained subject has a smaller pulse-rate or cardiac output for a given rate of work.

Stroke-Volume. The same point is made by comparing the increases in stroke-volume of athletes and normal subjects; when Bevegård et al. (1963) did this they found that, with both their groups, the maximum increase was of the order of 10 per cent. It must not be thought, however, that the well trained athlete has the same maximum cardiac output as that of the untrained subject; in fact it is indeed, greater, and since the maximum pulse-rate is the same this means that the stroke-volume during maximum work is larger in the trained person. If, as is claimed, the athlete does not increase his stroke-volume by a greater amount than the non-athlete, this means that the athlete's *resting* stroke-volume is larger, and this is true. As an example, untrained subjects during severe exercise involving O_2-consumption of 3·2 litres/min, reached a cardiac index of 10·5 litres/min/m² at a heart-rate of 187 beats/min, so that the stroke-index was 57 ml/m². By contrast, at an average oxygen consumption of 4·7 litres/min, the athletes attained a cardiac index of 13·7 litres/min/m² at a heart-rate of 189 beats/min, so that their stroke-index was 73 ml/m². At rest, in the supine position, the average heart rates were 67 beats/min for the untrained subjects and 58 beats/min for the athletes; the cardiac indices were 3·5 and 3·8 litres/min/m² for untrained and athletes respectively, so that the corresponding stroke-indices were 52 and 65 ml/min.

Physical Working Capacity. Associated with this greater cardiac output, of course, the athlete has a greater "physical working capacity", indicated by PWC_{170}, and representing the working intensity, in kg.m/min, that the subject can perform at a pulse-rate of 170/min, i.e. at very nearly the maximum pulse-rate during severe exercise.

Shift of Breakpoint. Corresponding to the greater efficiency of muscular effort and increased cardiac output, the degree of oxygenation of the muscles for a given work-load will be better in the athletes, and this is reflected in a greater capacity to carry out aerobic muscular contraction; hence the point, during exercise, when lactic acid accumulates in the blood to cause a metabolic acidosis is delayed in the athlete. This is reflected in the shifting of the breakpoint of exercise to higher work-outputs, since an important element in reaching the breakpoint is the concentration of lactic acid in the blood.

A–V O_2-Difference. Finally, the athlete can make use of the oxygen carried by the blood more efficiently, in the sense that the arterio-venous difference in oxygen content, both at rest and during maximum exercise, is larger; thus in maximum exercise the athletes studied by Bevegård extracted an extra 3 ml of O_2 out of every 100 ml of blood, by comparison with the untrained subjects.

ADAPTATION TO HIGH ALTITUDES

Changes in Alveolar Air Composition

The atmospheric pressure, and therefore the partial pressure of O_2 in the atmosphere, falls almost linearly with altitude, so that at a height of 5500 metres (18,000 feet) the atmospheric PO_2 is just 80 mm Hg, or about half that at sea-level. At this height the PO_2 of the alveolar air will be reduced disproportionately because of the contribution of CO_2 and H_2O which will not be halved. When the alveolar air of subjects living at high altitudes, i.e. of well adapted subjects, is compared with that of those living at sea-level, a remarkable reduction in the PCO_2 of the alveolar air is manifest.

This is shown by Table I; at sea-level the PCO_2 of alveolar air was 38 mm Hg and the PO_2 106 mm Hg; at, say, 12,500 feet (3792 m) the barometric pressure is 489 mm Hg, the alveolar PCO_2 is 30 mm Hg and the alveolar PO_2 is 58·5 mm Hg. At 22,700 feet (6885 m) the alveolar PCO_2 is only 17·7 mm Hg, the PO_2 being 40·7 mm Hg.

TABLE I

Alveolar air composition of sojourners and permanent residents at various altitudes.

Altitude 1000 ft	Bar. Press. mm Hg	Alveolar PCO_2	PO_2
0	760	38·0	106·0
·55	748	38·1	100·7
1·00	733	37·7	100·3
4–14			
6·2	610	33·3	79·5
9·2	543	34·0	64·0
10·0	525	31·5	61·9
		31·5	63·9
12·5	489	30·0	58·0
14·0	446	25·9	51·6
14·2	458	26·8	53·7
14·2	458	27·9	52·6
15·4	429	28·0	46·9
17·5	401	25·6	42·3
20·1	356	21·4	37·7
21·2	331	17·7	42·5
22·8	310	15·6	37·0
22·7	337	17·7	40·7

Hyperventilation

The lowered PCO_2 in the alveolar air is indicative of an increased ventilation of the lungs, presumably induced by the hypoxia of the inspired air. Thus at high altitudes the PCO_2 of the inspired air remains the same, whereas that of O_2 is reduced, so that the hypoxic stimulus causes a hyperventilation that tends to wash CO_2 out of the lungs more effectively than at sea-level. The increased ventilation will tend to improve the oxygenation of the blood, which at low levels of PO_2 is very highly sensitive to small alterations in PO_2 in the alveoli, i.e. the haemoglobin lies on the steep portion of the O_2-dissociation curves (Vol. 1). In the normal subject at sea-level, the blood leaving the lungs is fully saturated, and this is because the PO_2 in the alveoli, although less than atmospheric, is high enough. As PO_2 in the inspired air is lowered, a point is reached when the degree of saturation of the haemoglobin must be less than 100 per cent, but the degree of unsaturation will depend on the efficiency with which the alveolar air is replaced by inspired air, i.e. by the alveolar ventilation, so that some improvement in oxygenation will be achieved by increased ventilation, which helps to maintain the PO_2 in the alveolar air close to that of the inspired air. Thus the hyperventilation may be regarded as a purposive response to the lowered PO_2 mediated through the chemoreceptors of the carotid and aortic bodies, but the lowered PCO_2, and its consequent alkalosis, are the price that is paid.

The Adaptive Process

The figures shown in Table I are derived from subjects that either lived at the high altitudes or had sojourned long enough to adapt. The nature of the adaptation is revealed by Fig. 3.44 which shows (black dots) the alveolar PCO_2 of non-acclimatized men in response to acute exposure to simulated high altitudes, as indicated by

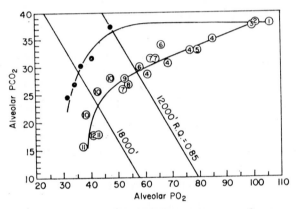

Fig. 3.44. Differences in alveolar PCO_2 between man acutely exposed to various altitudes (solid circles) and man acclimatized at various altitudes (open circles). Two iso-altitude lines for an R.Q. = 85 are represented as diagonals. (Rahn and Otis, *Amer. J. Physiol.*)

the PO_2 on the abscissa; this is compared with the figures of Table I represented as open circles. It is clear from Fig. 3.44 that the unacclimatized men, acutely exposed to simulated high-altitudes, failed to hyperventilate as much as acclimatized men living at these altitudes; in fact it will be seen that it was not till the PO_2 fell to 50–60 mm Hg that unacclimatized men, acutely exposed to lowered PO_2, developed any hyperventilation. By contrast, the men living at high altitudes develop an increased ventilation at relatively low altitudes.

Effect of Alkalosis. The failure of unadapted subjects to develop a hyperventilation when acutely exposed to low PO_2 is at first sight surprising, since we know by "single-breath tests" (p. 227) that the respiration is being driven by the PO_2 to some extent even at an alveolar PO_2 of 100 mm Hg. This, however, is due to the opposing effect of the alkalosis that develops immediately on increasing respiration; thus initially the subjects did hyperventilate but the alkalosis due to lowered PCO_2, developing within the first few minutes, counteracted the hypoxic stimulus, and the net effect was unchanged ventilation. The acclimatized subjects are apparently able to prevent this inhibition of the reflex hyperpnoea of low PO_2.

C.S.F.-Bicarbonate. Within a short time, however, the unacclimatized subject, exposed to low PO_2, develops a hyperventilation with lowered P_aCO_2, and this is due to the correction of the alkalosis by a reduction in the bicarbonate of the cerebrospinal fluid, so that a more acid pH may be maintained by a given PCO_2 in accordance with the Henderson-Hasselbalch relationship. Later the bicarbonate of the blood is also reduced through renal action, thereby further stabilizing the chemical drive. The basis for the decrease in bicarbonate in the cerebrospinal fluid seems to be the production of lactic and pyruvic acids by the brain, stimulated by the hypoxia (Sørensen, 1971), which pass from the brain into the cerebrospinal fluid and decompose the bicarbonate. In this adapted state, then, the animal, or man, has a lower PO_2 in the blood and alveolar air, together with a lower-than-normal PCO_2. The alveolar PO_2 is higher than in the unadapted state, and this is equivalent to being at a lower altitude, and thus permits the performance of more work than would have been possible in the unadapted state.

Chemoreceptor Origin. It was considered, e.g. by Rahn and Otis (1949), that in the adapted state the hypoxic drive mediated by the carotid and aortic bodies was no longer operating, the hyperventilation being due to failure of the central respiratory neurones to buffer against CO_2 of metabolic origin. However, there is no doubt from studies on animals with denervated carotid and aortic bodies, and from applying the single-breath O_2-test to men at high altitude, that the hyperventilation of high altitude is of chemoreceptor origin (Dejours *et al.*, 1957; Gilfillan *et al.*, 1958; Bouverot *et al.*, 1973).

Lowered Sensitivity to Hypoxia. It was pointed out by Chiodi (1957) that men born and bred at high altitudes apparently had a lower sensitivity to reduced PO_2 than lowlanders recently adapted to the same high altitude. This was manifest in the higher P_aCO_2 of the highlanders compared with that of the lowlanders at the same altitude; moreover, whereas the P_aCO_2 of the lowlanders decreased linearly with altitude, falling to about 28 mm Hg at 4500 metres, that of the highlanders was some 32 mm Hg at 2000 m and remained the same up to 4500 m. This finding, repeated frequently, suggests a lowered sensitivity of the chemoreceptors to changed PO_2, and Chiodi found that, when highlanders were tested with breathing pure O_2, the depression of ventilation was always less than in the lowlanders. Again, using the response to hypoxia, Severinghaus *et al.* (1966) found, in Peruvian tests, that the highlanders at Cerro de Pasco (4330 m) gave an increased ventilation in response to a PO_2 of 40 mm Hg of only 5·6 litres/min/sq metre of body surface, compared with 21 litres for lowlanders acclimatized for 1–40 weeks. The sensitivities of the highlanders to altered PCO_2 were apparently no different from those

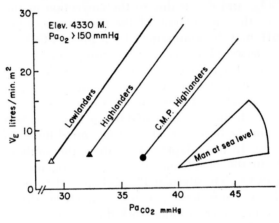

Fig. 3.45. Changes in ventilation with altered P_aCO_2 in human subjects at an elevation of 4330 metres and with high P_aO_2. C.M.P. highlanders are those suffering with chronic mountain polycythaemia. Note slopes of lines are the same within experimental error. Figures for man at sea level were taken from Lambertsen. (Severinghaus *et al.*, *Resp. Physiol.*)

of lowlanders; this is indicated by the similar slopes of $\dot{V}_E$ against P_aCO_2, but for a given P_aCO_2 the ventilation of the lowlanders was considerably lower, indicating a different "setting" of the central respiratory chemosensitive neurones (Fig. 3.45).

Irreversibility. The lowering of sensitivity to hypoxia found in highlanders seems to be an irreversible phenomenon since Sørensen and Severinghaus (1968) found that the hypoxic sensitivity of Andean highlanders, dwelling at low altitudes, remained the same; it appeared that it only required a child to live at high altitudes for a few years before this hypoxic insensitivity was acquired. That it was not a genetic characteristic belonging to those of Mongol type, e.g. the Sherpa or Andean native, was shown by studying Caucasian children born with cyanotic heart disease, after their condition had been corrected. These children had thus been subjected to blood anoxia since birth; they, like the highlanders, showed depressed hypoxic sensitivity.

REFERENCES

Adrian, E. D. (1933). Afferent impulses in the vagus and their effect on respiration. *J. Physiol.*, **79**, 332–358.
Adrian, E. D. and Buytendijk, F. J. J. (1931). Potential change; in the isolated brain stem of the goldfish. *J. Physiol.*, **71**, 121–135.
Andersen, P. and Sears, T. A. (1970). Medullary activation of intercostal fusimotor and alpha motoneurones. *J. Physiol.*, **209**, 739–755.
Anrep, G. V. and Hammouda, M. (1932). Observations on panting. *J. Physiol.*, **77**, 16–34.
Armstrong, B. W., Hurt, H. H., Blide, R. W. and Workman, J. M. (1961). The humoral regulation of breathing. *Science*, **133**, 1897–1906.
Asmussen, E., Nielsen, M. and Weith-Pedersen, G. (1943). Cortical or reflex control of respiration during muscular work? *Acta physiol. scand.*, **6**, 168–175.
Band, D. M., Cameron, I. R. and Semple, S. J. G. (1969). Oscillations in arterial pH with breathing in the cat. *J. appl. Physiol.*, **26**, 261–267.
Band, D. M., Cameron, I. R. and Semple, S. J. G. (1970). The effect on respiration of abrupt changes in carotid artery pH and PCO_2 in the cat. *J. Physiol.*, **211**, 479–494.
Bartoli, A., Bystrzycka, E., Guz, A., Jain, S. K., Noble, M. I. M. and Trenchard, D. (1973). Studies of the pulmonary vagal control of central respiratory rhythm in the absence of breathing movements. *J. Physiol.*, **230**, 449–465.
Bartoli, A., Cross, B. A., Guz, A., Jain, S. K., Noble, M. I. M. and Trenchard, D. W. (1974). The effect of carbon dioxide in the airways and alveoli on ventilation: a vagal reflex studied in the dog. *J. Physiol.*, **240**, 91–109.
Batsel, H. L. (1964). Localization of bulbar respiratory center by microelectrode recording. *Exp. Neurol.*, **9**, 410–426.
Bertrand, F. and Hugelin, A. (1971). Respiratory synchronizing function of nucleus parabrachialis medialis: pneumotaxic mechanisms. *J. Neurophysiol.*, **34**, 189–207.
Bevegård, S., Holmgren, A. and Jonsson, B. (1963). Circulatory studies in well trained athletes at rest and during heavy exercise, with special reference to stroke volume and the influence of body posture. *Acta physiol. scand.*, **57**, 26–50.
Bhattacharyya, N. K. *et al.* (1970). Hypoxia, ventilation, PCO_2 and exercise. *Resp. Physiol.*, **9**, 329–347.
Biscoe, T. J. (1971). Carotid body—structure and function. *Physiol. Rev.*, **51**, 437–495.
Biscoe, T. J. and Purves, M. J. (1967). Observations on the rhythmic variation in the cat carotid body chemoreceptor activity which has the same period as respiration. *J. Physiol.*, **190**, 389–412.
Black, A. M. S. and Torrance, R. W. (1967). Chemoreceptor effects in the respiratory cycle. *J. Physiol.*, **189**, 59–61P.
Bouverot, P., Candas, V. and Libert, J. P. (1973). Role of the arterial chemoreceptors in ventilatory adaptation to hypoxia of awake dogs and rabbits. *Resp. Physiol.*, **17**, 209–219.
Cameron, I. R., Linton, R. A. F. and Miller, R. (1974). The respiratory response to intravenous infusion of hypercapnic blood in the anresthetized rabbit. *J. Physiol.*, **239**, 20–21P.

Chiodi, H. (1957). Respiratory adaptations to chronic high altitude hypoxia. *J. app. Physiol.*, **10**, 81–87.

Clark, F. J. and Euler, C. von. (1972). On the regulation of depth and rate of breathing. *J. Physiol.*, **222**, 267–295.

Cohen, M. I. (1968). Discharge patterns of brain-stem respiratory neurones in relation to carbon dioxide tension. *J. Neurophysiol.*, **31**, 142–165.

Cohen, M. I. (1969). Discharge patterns of brain-stem respiratory neurons during Hering-Breuer reflex evoked by lung inflation. *J. Neurophysiol.*, **32**, 356–374.

Cohen, M. I. (1970). How respiratory rhythm originates: evidence from discharge patterns of brainstem respiratory neurones. In *Breathing*. Hering-Breuer Symposium, Ciba, pp. 125–150. Churchill, London.

Cotes, J. E. (1963). Exercise limitation in health and disease. *Brit. med. Bull.*, **19**, 31–35.

Cunningham, D. J. C. (1963). Some quantitative aspects of the regulation of human respiration in exercise. *Brit. med. Bull.*, **19**, 25–30.

Cunningham, D. J. C. and Gardner, W. N. (1972). The relation between tidal volume and inspiratory and expiratory times during steady-state CO_2 inhalation in man. *J. Physiol.*, **227**, 50–51P.

Cunningham, D. J. C., Howson, M. G. and Pearson, S. B. (1973). The respiratory effects in man of altering the time profile of alveolar carbon dioxide and oxygen within each respiratory cycle. *J. Physiol.*, **234**, 1–28.

Cunningham, D. J. C., Lloyd, B. B., Miller, J. P. and Young, J. M. (1965). The time course of human ventilation after transient changes in P_ACO_2 at two values of P_AO_2. *J. Physiol.*, **179**, 68–70P.

Davis, J. N. and Sears, T. A. (1970). The proprioceptor reflex control of the intercostal muscles during their voluntary activation. *J. Physiol.*, **209**, 711–738.

Dejours, P. (1959). La régulation de la ventilation au cours de l'exercice musculaire chez l'homme. *J. Physiol. (Paris)*, **51**, 163–261.

Dejours, P. (1962). Chemoreflexes in breathing. *Physiol. Rev.*, **42**, 335–358.

Dejours, P. *et al.* (1957). Existence d'un stimulus oxygène de la ventilation après acclimatation à l'altitude de 3,613 m. chez l'homme. *C.r. Acad. Sci. Paris*, **245**, 2534–2536.

Deshpande, S. S. and Devanandan, M. S. (1970). Reflex inhibition of monosynaptic reflexes by stimulation of type J pulmonary endings. *J. Physiol.*, **206**, 345–357.

D'Silva, J. L., Gill, D. and Mendel, D. (1966). The effects of acute haemorrhage on respiration in the cat. *J. Physiol.*, **187**, 369–377.

Eldridge, F. L. (1972). The importance of timing on the respiratory effects of intermittent carotid body chemoreceptor stimulation. *J. Physiol.*, **222**, 319–333.

Eldridge, F. L. (1972). The importance of timing on the respiratory effects of intermittent carotid sinus nerve stimulation. *J. Physiol.*, **222**, 297–318.

Elftman, A. C. (1943). The afferent and parasympathetic innervation of the lungs and trachea of the dog. *Amer. J. Anat.*, **72**, 1–28.

Euler, C. von, Herrero, F. and Wexler, I. (1970). Control mechanism determining rate and depth of respiratory movements. *Resp. Physiol.*, **10**, 93–108.

Eyzaguirre, C. and Taylor, J. R. (1963). Respiratory discharge of some vagal motoneurons. *J. Neurophysiol.*, **26**, 61–78.

Fedde, M. R. and Peterson, D. F. (1970). Intrapulmonary receptor response to changes in airway-gas composition in *Gallus domesticus*. *J. Physiol.*, **209**, 609–625.

Fillenz, M. and Widdicombe, J. G. (1972). Receptors of the lungs and airways. In *Enteroreceptors* (Ed. F. Neil), pp. 81–112. Springer, Berlin.

Fitzgerald, R. S., Leitner, L.-M. and Liaubet, M.-J. (1969). Carotid chemoreceptor response to intermittent or sustained stimulation in the cat. *Resp. Physiol.*, **6**, 395–402.

Gautier, H., Remmers, J. E. and Bartlett, D. (1973). Control of the duration of expiration. *Resp. Physiol.*, **18**, 205–221.

Gilfillan, R. S., Hansen, J. F., Kellogg, R. H., Pace, N. and Cuthbertson, E. M. (1958). Physiologic study of the chemoreceptor mechanism in the dog at sea level and at high altitude (12,600 ft). *Circulation*, **18**, 724.

Green, J. H. and Neil, E. (1955). The respiratory function of the laryngeal muscles. *J. Physiol.*, **129**, 134–141.

Guz, A. *et al.* (1966). Peripheral chemoreceptor block in man. *Resp. Physiol.*, **1**, 38–40.

Guz, A. and Trenchard, D. W. (1971). Pulmonary stretch receptor activity in man: a comparison with dog and cat. *J. Physiol.*, **213**, 329–343.

Head, H. (1889). On the regulation of respiration. *J. Physiol.*, **10**, 1–71.

Hornbein, T. F., Griffo, Z. J. and Roos, A. (1961). Quantitation of chemoreceptor activity; interrelation of hypoxia and hypercapnia. *J. Neurophysiol.*, **24**, 561–568.

Howe, A. and Neil, E. (1972). Arterial chemoreceptors. In *Enteroreceptors* (Ed. E. Neil), pp. 47–80. Springer, Berlin.

Joels, N. and Neil, E. (1961). The influence of anoxia and hypercapnia, separately and in combination, on chemoreceptor discharge. *J. Physiol.*, **155**, 45–46P.

Koller, E. A. and Ferrer, P. (1970). Studies on the role of the lung deflation reflex. *Resp. Physiol.*, **10**, 172–347.

Langrehr, D. (1964). Receptor-afferenzen in Halsvagus des Menschen. *Klin. Wschr.*, **42**, 239–244.

Leitner, L. M. (1972). Pulmonary mechanoreceptor fibres in the vagus of the domestic fowl. *Resp. Physiol.*, **16**, 232–244.

Leusen, I. (1972). Regulation of cerebrospinal fluid composition with reference to breathing. *Physiol. Rev.*, **52**, 1–56.

Loeschke, H. H., De Lattre, J., Schläfke, M. E. and Trouth, C. O. (1970). Effects on respiration and circulation of electrically stimulating the ventral surface of the medulla oblongata. *Resp. Physiol.*, **10**, 184–197.

Luck, J. C. (1970). Afferent vagal fibres with an expiratory discharge in the rabbit. *J. Physiol.*, **211**, 63–71.

Matell, G. (1963). Time-course of changes in ventilation and arterial gas tensions in man induced by moderate exercise. *Acta physiol. scand.*, **58**, Suppl. 206.

Mead, J. (1960). Control of respiratory frequency. *J. appl. Physiol.*, **15**, 325–336.

Mills, E. and Sampson, S. R. (1969). Respiratory responses to electrical stimulation of the sympathetic nerves in decerebrate, unanaesthetized cats. *J. Physiol.*, **202**, 271–282.

Mills, J. E., Sellick, H. and Widdicombe, J. G. (1969). Activity of lung irritant receptors in pulmonary embolism, anaphylaxis and drug-induced broncho-constrictions. *J. Physiol.*, **202**, 337–357.

Miserocchi, G., Mortola, J. and Sant'Ambroggio, G. (1973). Localization of pulmonary stretch receptors in the airways of the dog. *J. Physiol.*, **235**, 775–782.

Mitchell, R. A., Loeschke, H. H., Massion, W. H. and Severinghaus, J. W. (1963). Respiratory responses mediated through superficial chemosensitive areas on the medulla. *J. appl. Physiol.*, **18**, 523–533.

Molony, V. (1971). Some characteristics of the CO_2-sensitive receptors present in the lower respiratory tract of the chicken. *J. Physiol.*, **219**, 35–36P.

Mustafa, M. E. K. Y. and Purves, M. J. (1972). The effect of CO_2 upon discharge from slowly adapting stretch receptors in the lungs of rabbits. *Resp. Physiol.*, **16**, 197–212.

Nesland, R. S., Plum, F., Nelson, J. R. and Seidler, H. S. (1966). The graded response to stimulation of medullary respiratory neurons. *Exp. Neurol.*, **14,** 57–76.

Oberholzer, R. J. H. and Schlegel, H. (1957). Die Bedeutung des afferenten Lungvagus für die Spontanatmung des Meerschweinchens. *Helv. Physiol. Acta*, **15,** 63–82.

Otis, A. B., Fenn, W. O. and Rahn, H. (1950). Mechanism of breathing in man. *J. appl. Physiol.*, **2,** 592–607.

Paintal, A. S. (1972). Cardiovascular receptors. In *Enteroreceptors* (Ed. E. Neil). Springer, Berlin.

Paintal, A. S. (1966). Re-evaluation of respiratory reflexes. *Quart. J. exp. Physiol.*, **51,** 151–163.

Paintal, A. S. (1969). Mechanism of stimulation of type J pulmonary receptors. *J. Physiol.*, **203,** 511–532.

Paintal, A. S. (1970). The mechanism of excitation of type J receptors and the J reflex. In *Breathing.* Hering-Breuer Centenary Symposium, Ciba, Churchill. (Ed. R. Porter), pp. 59–70.

Pappenheimer. J. R. (1965/66). The ionic composition of cerebral extracellular fluid and its relation to the control of breathing. *Harvey Lectures*, **61,** 71–94.

Pappenheimer, J. R., Fencl, V., Heisey, S. R. and Held, D. (1965). Role of cerebral fluids in control of respiration as studied in unanaesthetized goats. *Amer. J. Physiol.*, **208,** 436–450.

Phillipson, E. A. *et al.* (1970). Effect of vagal blockade on regulation of breathing in conscious dogs. *J. appl. Physiol.*, **29,** 475–479.

Purves, M. J. (1966). Fluctuations of arterial oxygen tension which have the same period of respiration. *Resp. Physiol.*, **1,** 281–296.

Rahn, H. and Otis, A. B. (1949). Man's respiratory response during and after acclimatization to high altitude. *Amer. J. Physiol.*, **157,** 445–462.

Ray, P. J. and Fedde, M. R. (1969). Response to alterations in respiratory PO_2 and PCO_2 in the chicken. *Resp. Physiol.*, **6,** 135–143.

Richards, S. A. (1968). Vagal control of thermal panting in mammals and birds. *J. Physiol.* **199,** 89–101.

Salmoiraghi, G. C. and von Baumgarten, R. (1961). Intracellular potentials from respiratory neurones in brain-stem of cat and mechanism of rhythmic respiration. *J. Neurophysiol.*, **24,** 203–218.

Schläfke, M. E., See, W. R. and Loeschke, H. H. (1970). Ventilatory response to alterations in H^+ ion concentration in small areas of the ventral medullary surface. *Resp. Physiol.*, **10,** 198–212.

Schoener, E. P. and Frankel, H. M. (1972). Effect of hyperthermia and P_aCO_2 on the slowly adapting pulmonary stretch receptor. *Amer. J. Physiol.*, **222,** 68–72.

Sears, T. A. (1964). Efferent discharges in alpha and fusimotor fibres of intercostal nerves of the cat. *J. Physiol.*, **174,** 295–315.

Sears, T. A. (1970). The respiratory motoneurone: integration at spinal segmental level. In *Breathlessness* (Ed. Howell, J. B. L. and Campbell, E. J. M.). Blackwell Scientific, Oxford.

Sellick, H. and Widdicombe, J. G. (1970). Vagal deflation and inflation reflexes mediated by lung irritant receptors. *Quart. J. exp. Physiol.*, **55,** 153–163.

Severinghaus, J. W., Bainton, C. R. and Carcelen, A. (1966). Respiratory insensitivity to hypoxia in chronically hypoxic man. *Resp. Physiol.*, **1,** 308–334.

Sørensen, S. C. (1970). Ventilatory acclimatization to hypoxia in rabbits after denervation of peripheral chemoreceptors. *J. appl. Physiol.*, **28,** 836–839.

Sørensen, S. C. (1971). The chemical control of ventilation. *Acta. physiol. scand.*, Suppl. 361.

Sørensen, S. C. and Severinghaus, J. W. (1968). Irreversible respiratory insensitivity to acute hypoxia in man born at high altitude. *J. appl. Physiol.*, **25**, 217–220.

Tang, P. C. (1967). Brain stem control of respiratory depth and rate in the cat. *Resp. Physiol.*, **3**, 349–366.

Trouth, C. O. and Loeschke, H. H. (1969). Histologisches Substrat chemosensibler Strukturen unter der ventralen oberflache der Medulla oblongata der Katze. *Pflüg. Arch. ges. Physiol.*, **312**, R54.

Wang, S. C. and Ngai, S. H. (1964). General organization of central respiratory mechanisms. *Handbk. Physiol.*, Section 3, Vol. 1, pp. 487–505.

Wang, S. C., Ngai, S. H. and Frumin, M. J. (1957). Organization of central respiratory mechanisms in the brain stem. *Amer. J. Physiol.*, **190**, 333–342.

Weil, J. V. *et al.* (1970). Hypoxic ventilatory drive in normal man. *J. clin. Invest.*, **49**, 1061–1072.

Weiss, H. R. and Salzano, J. (1970). Formation of whole number ratios of heart rate and breathing frequency. *J. appl. Physiol.*, **29**, 350–354.

Widdicombe, J. G. (1954). The site of pulmonary stretch receptors in the cat. *J. Physiol.*, **125**, 336–351.

Widdicombe, J. G. (1961). Respiratory reflexes in man and other mammalian species. *Clin. Sci.*, **21**, 163–170.

Widdicombe J. G. (1964). Respiratory reflexes. *Handbk. Physiol.*, Section 3, Vol. 1, pp. 585–630.

Widdicombe, J. G., Kent, D. C. and Nodel, J. A. (1962). Mechanism of bronchoconstriction during inhalation of dust. *J. appl. Physiol.*, **17**, 613–616.

Wyss, O. A. M. (1964). Die nervose Steuerung der Atmung. *Erg. der Physiol.*, **54**, 1–413.

Yamamoto, W. S. and Edwards, Mc. I. W. (1960). Homeostasis of carbon dioxide during intravenous infusion of carbon dioxide. *J. appl. Physiol.*, **15**, 807–818.

CHAPTER 4

Control Mechanisms in the Alimentary Process

The Digestive Process

The basic processes concerned in alimentation have been described in Vol. 1. These consist in the chewing of the food, accompanied by secretion of saliva; the act of swallowing or deglutition; the transport of the bolus along the oesophagus; the accumulation of the food in the stomach and its partial digestion, brought about by the secretion of acid and enzymes, accompanied by movements that tend to mix the contents. By a type of peristaltic movement, the chyme is passed out of the stomach into the small intestine where digestion is completed through secretion of juices from the pancreas, the intestinal glands, and from the liver by way of the gall-bladder and bile-duct. The intestinal processes are aided by segmental mixing movements, whilst propulsion is continued by peristalsis. In the colon, absorption of water and salts occurs, and the final residues—the faeces—are propelled, once again by peristalsis, to the rectum and eliminated. In practically all these processes the muscular activity is carried out by smooth, or involuntary, muscle controlled by the autonomic nervous system, whilst the secretion of the juices is brought about by secretory cells, which are likewise activated. In the present chapter we shall concentrate on the humoral and nervous mechanisms concerned with the control of these digestive and absorptive processes. Before these processes can begin, of course, the animal must eat, so that we may logically begin this Chapter with a consideration of some of the factors governing the intake of food, i.e. the factors that determine hunger, or appetite.

THE INTAKE OF FOOD

If an animal is allowed plenty of food and water, it will eat and drink periodically and, over a long period of time, its food-intake will be adjusted fairly accurately to its caloric requirements, so that it will tend to remain at a constant weight. The two main problems are: What determines the onset and cessation of eating at any given meal? i.e. What is the basis for the hungry sensation that impels eating, and the satiety that brings this to a close? Secondly: What is the mechanism of the long-term adjustments that permit the maintenance of a constant weight in the face of variable caloric requirements? Rather similar problems are presented with respect to the control of water-intake, but in view of the connection of this with the general problems of renal function and the control of water- and salt-balance, we may defer till later the study of the physiological mechanisms at the basis of thirst and its alleviation.

Hunger and Satiety

Denervated Stomach

Objectively we may measure hunger, at any rate in rough terms, by the size of a meal that an animal takes, and by the trouble it will

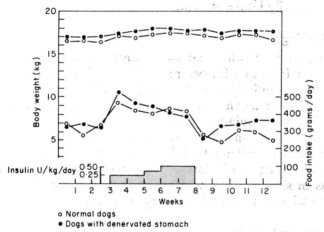

o Normal dogs
• Dogs with denervated stomach

Fig. 4.1. The lack of effect of vagotomy on the insulin-induced hunger response in dogs. Both control and vagotomized dogs increased their food intake in response to intravenous insulin, so that vagally increased gastric motility cannot be considered the prime hunger drive in dogs. Upper pair of curves, body weight. (Grossman *et al.*, *Amer. J. Physiol.*)

take to find and obtain it; thus, after a period of 24 hours of deprivation, rats will eat more over the next 24 hours than in a control period, and this will be achieved by eating for longer periods and reducing the inter-meal period. In his classical discussion of the subject of hunger, Cannon suggested that the increased gastric motility that occurred during hunger*—hunger pangs—governed the intake of food, whilst satiety was indicative of a cessation of these hunger contractions. However, whilst this may be a factor it is by no means the whole since, when the stomach is extrinsically denervated, thereby removing the afferent impulses to the brain, hunger is still felt and the animal, or man, continues to eat without loss of appetite. Thus Grossman, Cummins and Ivy (1947) showed that the increased feeding in dogs caused by treatment with insulin was, indeed, accompanied by high gastric motility; the increased motility was abolished by vagotomy but this had no influence on their food intake (Fig. 4.1).

Pre-Feeding

Moderate pre-feeding of dogs some 20 minutes before their meal had little effect on the regular intake, but pre-feeding a large volume did inhibit subsequent feeding; this was not related to the caloric value of the pre-fed material, so that gastric distension was the predominant factor. In confirmation, a water-filled balloon in the stomach reduced the normal daily intake of food.

Sham-Feeding

The effects of chewing and swallowing, *oropharygeal stimulation*, are best studied in dogs with oesophagostomies, i.e. sham-feeding. Dogs allowed to feed entirely by this method, i.e. without food entering their stomachs, ate for much longer periods than normal but did, finally, show satiety by stopping. The duration of sham-feeding was inversely related to the amount of intragastric feeding. Thus both oral and gastric factors contribute to bringing about the satiety that brings feeding to an end; oral factors can apparently bring feeding to a stop alone, as in sham-feeding, whilst gastric feeding, or distension, must cooperate with oral factors to be very effective.

Gastric Emptying Time

If distension of the stomach contributes to satiety, then clearly the emptying time, governed by its motility, will be a factor. The prolonged satiety consequent on a heavy fat meal may be attributed to the entero-

* The contractions during fasting have been described in detail by Quigley (1955). After 24 hours of fasting the periods of contraction, consisting of peristaltic waves involving in sequence the fundus, corpus, antrum and proximal duodenum, occur at intervals of 1–1·5 hours; with longer fasting the periods become more prolonged until activity becomes continuous. It is probably best to avoid definitions in this sphere; however, hunger may be said to involve unpleasant sensations accompanying gastric motility, whilst appetite the pleasant sensations accompanying eating.

gastrone activity of the fat in the duodenum, inhibiting release of gastrin and thus motility.

Matching Caloric Need with Intake

Intragastric Feeding

Although physical factors, such as gastric distension and oropharyngeal stimuli, obviously affect intake of food and influence satiety, it is clear that the composition of the blood must exert an influence, especially when the long-term matching of caloric intake and energy expenditure is considered, when the blood-borne factor will be dominant. Intragastric feeding can be used to study the effects of caloric

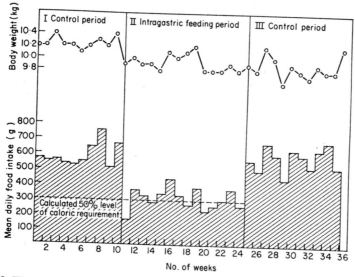

Fig. 4.2. The effect of intragastric feeding of 50 per cent of the calculated required calories on the oral intake of food. In period II intragastric feeding was commenced and an almost matched decrease in oral intake is seen. (Janowitz and Hollander, *Ann. N.Y. Acad. Sci.*)

intake, as opposed to mere expansion of the stomach, if this is carried out over prolonged periods and if the intragastric feeding is carried out so long before the normal meal-time of the animal that stomach distension does not enter as a factor. In this case it is found that the animal compensates for the ingested food fairly precisely, as indicated in Fig. 4.2, where 50 per cent of the animal's calories were absorbed intragastrically. That adjustment is not perfect is shown by giving

100 per cent of the caloric requirements through the gastric fistula, in which case eating is not completely suppressed. "The dogs would sniff at the food offered them daily, often take one or two mouthfuls, and then sit down in the corner of the cage and pay no more attention to it during the remainder of the time the food was in the cage" (Janowitz and Hollander, 1955).

The Blood-Borne Stimuli

What, may we ask, is the means whereby the caloric intake, and its subsequent digestion, influence the urge to eat? In view of the importance of carbohydrate metabolism and its close relations with fat metabolism, the level of glucose in the blood has been considered as governing food intake, contributing its chemical stimulus to the other stimuli already considered (Mayer, 1955).

Glucostatic Hypothesis. This *glucostatic hypothesis* has some plausibility since it is well known that a low blood-sugar induces gastric motility (p. 341), a physiological change brought about by low sugar in the brain, since 2-deoxyglucose, which suppresses glucose uptake into the brain in spite of a normal blood-level, has the same effect. The relation between satiety and blood-sugar, if it exists, is by no means straightforward, however; thus experimentally induced hyperglycaemia, by large intravenous infusions of glucose, had no effect on voluntary food-intake by dogs (Janowitz and Grossman, 1949), and the glucostat hypothesis was modified by Mayer to allow for glucose utilization, as measured by the arterio-venous difference of concentration; thus a low utilization, or low a-v-difference, corresponds to a state of hunger whilst a high utilization, with large a-v-difference, is considered to correspond to a state of satiety (Stunkard and Wolff, 1954), but the evidence favouring this modification of the glucostat hypothesis is rather tenuous.

Glucose-Sensitive Brain Cells. Nevertheless, the concept of cells within the brain sensitive to the level, or availability, of glucose in the blood is experimentally sound, since the release of gastrin, for example, is triggered off at a very reproducible level of hypoglycaemia (p. 341), and the same is said to be true of the induction of hypoglycaemic convulsions.

Other Factors. Of other blood-borne factors we may mention amino acids, the temperature-rise following the absorption of food— the specific dynamic action—and the relation between the fatty acids of the blood and the fat depots, as revealed by the level of fatty acids in the blood. This last, *lipostatic hypothesis*, of Kennedy (1953) seems the most promising where the long-term control over food-intake is concerned, and will be discussed later; we must now pass to the location of any hypothetical centres governing food-intake.

Hypothalamic Centres

Satiety Centre

A case of obesity associated with a tumour of the pituitary was described by Mohr in 1840, but the cause was the damage done by the tumour to the overlying hypothalamus, since Hetherington and Ranson were able to induce obesity and hyperphagia in rats by stereotaxically directed lesions in this region of the diencephalon. The area responsible was the medial hypothalamic region containing the ventromedial nuclei—the *ventromedial hypothalamus*, or *VMH*. This region has come to be called the *satiety centre* that presumably maintains a tonic inhibition of the hunger mechanism; stimulation of the region electrically, in animals with implanted electrodes, caused aphagia in food-deprived animals.

Feeding Centre

Another region of the brain, in the lateral hypothalamus (LH), was identified by Anand and Brobeck in 1951; destruction of this

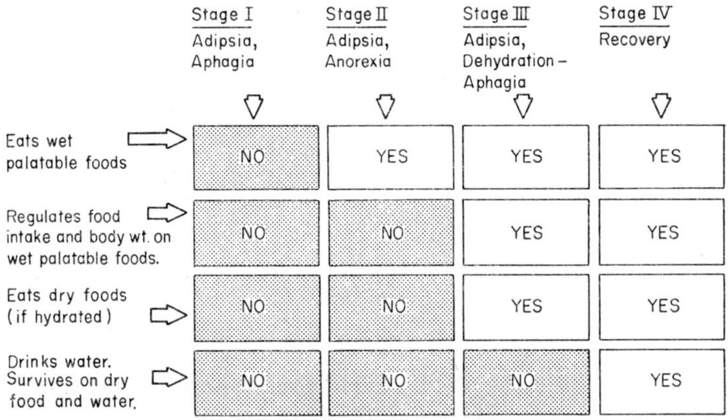

	Stage I Adipsia, Aphagia	Stage II Adipsia, Anorexia	Stage III Adipsia, Dehydration – Aphagia	Stage IV Recovery
Eats wet palatable foods	NO	YES	YES	YES
Regulates food intake and body wt. on wet palatable foods.	NO	NO	YES	YES
Eats dry foods (if hydrated)	NO	NO	YES	YES
Drinks water. Survives on dry food and water.	NO	NO	NO	YES

Fig. 4.3. Stages in the recovery of rats with a region in the lateral hypothalamus destroyed. Rats with this area destroyed suffer from aphagia and adipsia and will only survive if they are fed by the intragastric route until the normal pattern of feeding and drinking has been re-established. (Teitelbaum and Epstein, *Psychol. Rev.*)

caused aphagia so that rats with this type of lesion, unless fed intragastrically, died of inanition. If the feeding was maintained for several weeks there was a gradual recovery so that ultimately they ate and drank normally (Teitelbaum and Epstein, 1962). The stages of this recovery are interesting and are illustrated by Fig. 4.3; it will be seen that the animals also failed to drink—adipsia—but at stage III the animals would survive on wet food but not when given dry food and water—they were adipsic, and so, when given dry food and water, they would die of *adipsic dehydration aphagia*.

Interaction between VMH and LH

On the basis of these two centres, VMH and LH, a fairly consistent mechanism for the control of food intake was elaborated, as indicated in Fig. 4.4 from Anand. According to this, peripheral nervous and

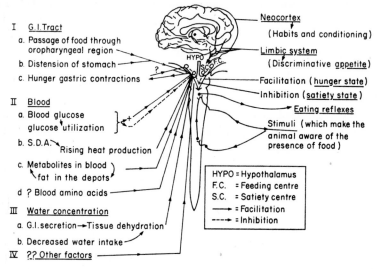

Fig. 4.4. An outline of neural mechanisms regulating food intake. (Anand *Physiol. Rev.*)

blood-borne factors exert their effects predominantly on the ventro-medial satiety centre; excitation of this, e.g. by gastric distension, brings about an inhibition of the lateral hunger centre. Thus longitudinal cuts in the hypothalamus, such as would separate connections between the two centres, resulted in hyperphagic obesity comparable with that obtained by destruction of the ventromedial centre (Sclafani, 1971) although the hyperphagia was not so great and, interestingly, if the diet was replaced by a more palatable one, the difference between the two hyperphagic states disappeared.

Effect of Gold Thioglucose

Some apparent support for the glucostatic hypothesis was provided by the observation of Waxler and Brecher (1950) that the compound, gold thioglucose, specifically attacked the ventromedial hypothalamus, causing lesions that led to obesity; and it was considered that the glucose compound reacted with the glucose receptors of the hypothalamus. Certainly the lesion is associated with deposition of gold in the oligodrendroglia (Debons *et al.*, 1970), and another gold compound, gold thiomalate, does not cause deposits in this region although it apparently penetrates the brain. However, this seems to be due to a failure to cause necrosis of the tissue, so if bipiperidyl mustard, which does cause necrosis of the centre, is given at the same time as gold thiomalate, then gold deposits accumulate. Thus the action of gold thioglucose is probably not due to a special affinity for a glucose-receptor.

Effect of Blood-Glucose

Again, Anand, Dua and Singh (1961) measured EEG-activity in the hypothalamic food-sensitive centres and found that hyperglycaemia caused increased electrical activity in the ventromedial "satiety" centre and reduced activity in the lateral "feeding" centre. Gastric distension increased activity in the ventromedial centre (Sharma *et al.*, 1961). When single units were examined in cats and monkeys, the spike-frequency varied in a predictable manner with the level of blood-glucose (Fig. 4.5). Thus treatment with insulin, causing hypoglycaemia, reduced the frequency in the ventromedial satiety centre and increased that in the lateral feeding centre.

Local Injection of Glucose

Finally, local application of glucose solution through a micropipette modified the spontaneous activity of single units in both ventromedial and lateral hypothalamic centres. Many of those in the lateral centre responded also to NaCl injection, and were probably osmoreceptors (p. 409) concerned with water-regulation; none of those in the ventromedial centre responded in this way (Oomura *et al.*, 1969).

Lipostatic Hypothesis

Kennedy (1950, 1953) studied rats made hyperphagic and obese by ventromedial hypothalamic lesions. He observed that, as they became obese, there was a marked change in their feeding behaviour, so that they ate less and finally reached a static condition in which

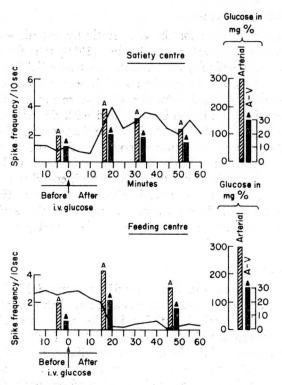

Fig. 4.5. Spike frequency of a unit from the satiety centre and a unit from the feeding centre, from two different cats, correlated with changes in arterial blood glucose and arteriovenous glucose difference, produced by intravenous infusion of glucose. The frequency of the units at any time was determined by counting the spikes for 1 min and taking their mean values. The inverse relationship of changes in activity of satiety and feeding centres is well demonstrated. (Anand *et al.*, *Amer. J. Physiol.*)

their intake was little different from normal, although they remained obese. They now became very "choosy" in what they ate, so that by giving them unpalatable food they could be reduced in weight, but then they became voracious on restoring their diet to the original palatable one. It was postulated that the hypothalamus controlled urges to eat that were initiated in other parts of the central nervous system, and that it operated by controlling the intake of calories. In opposition to Brobeck (1948), who considered that the heat-production *per se* was the stimulus to increased eating—"animals eat to keep warm, and stop eating to prevent hyperthermia"—Kennedy suggested that the hypothalamic centre was sensitive to a whole complex of metabolites, and so could respond to excessive fat-storage by limiting food intake, and *vice versa*.

Pharmacology of Centres

It is possible to apply small amounts of transmitters to localized region of the brain of waking animals by passing minute crystals, e.g. of noradrenaline, along implanted tubes. When noradrenaline and adrenaline were introduced into the ventromedial areas, there was an increased food-intake in satiated rats; acetylcholine inhibited the food intake of hungry rats. It is of some interest that both satiety and hunger manifestations were induced from the same locus in the hypothalamus. The effects on water-intake were opposite, so that the adrenergic mechanism inhibited drinking by thirsty rats whilst acetylcholine stimulated it. When α- and β-adrenergic mechanisms were examined, Leibowitz (1971), with a tube implanted in the lateral region of the hypothalamus, found that α-adrenergic agonists elicited eating whilst β-adrenergic agonists, such as isoproterenol, caused suppression, or anorexia. This difference between α- and β-agonists is of interest since, first, it suggests that the cholinergic inhibitory mechanism cooperates with the β-adrenergic one, and secondly it might account for the effects of amphetamine, a drug that releases catecholamines from tissues, and causes anorexia or loss of appetite. If the release resulted in predominantly β-action the effects could be understood.*

Eating and Drinking Reflexes

The opposite effects on eating and drinking revealed by these transmitters are of physiological interest; animals eat and drink alternately, so that it is reasonable that the various feeding reflexes that come into operation when food is placed in the mouth should inhibit the drinking reflexes, and *vice versa*.

Modern Trends

A number of more recent observations militate against the rather simple view of a ventromedial satiety centre that, responding to intake of food and its metabolic consequences, brings eating to a halt by inhibiting the lateral hypothalamic feeding centre. Thus hyperphagic

---

* A more convincing demonstration of the existence of an adrenergic mechanism, stimulating eating, is provided by injections into the hypothalamus of a substance that causes endogenous catecholamine to be liberated through depletion of catecholamine-containing neurones. Evetts, Fitzsimons and Settler (1972) injected 6-hydroxydopamine into satiated rats, thereby causing them to eat; the effect was inhibited by phentolamine, an α-blocking agent, and by MJ-1999, a β-blocking agent.

rats, with ventrolateral lesions, exhibit regular periods of eating and cessation of eating, as in normals, i.e. they do show satiety; moreover, they respond like normals to alterations in sugar-availability induced by insulin and 2-deoxyglucose. This would not be expected in these lesioned rats if the satiety centre were the central region governing eating behaviour in response to peripheral stimuli. Instead, modern workers, such as Le Magnen (1973), emphasize the inter-relationships between fat and sugar metabolism.

Changed Metabolic Pattern. Thus an animal that has failed to eat enough for its energy requirements is adapting its carbohydrate metabolism to the breakdown of fat—gluconeogenesis—whilst the animal that has eaten too much is converting its glucose to fat. If the hypothalamic centres influence the switch from one type of metabolism to another, then lesions in the centres will have effects on feeding behaviour, but the precise manner in which a given lesion will manifest itself will depend on just how the neurones destroyed by the lesion were involved, either through release of metabolically important hormones—such as insulin, glucagon, adrenaline, thyroxine—or through responsiveness to blood-borne metabolites and peripheral nervous messages. Thus the hyperphagic rat, with its ventromedial "satiety centre" lesion, behaves as though it were secreting more than the normal amount of insulin, i.e. as though destruction of the centre had released the pancreas from a tonic inhibition. This is revealed experimentally by the rat's more efficient disposal of a load of glucose given intravenously, and by its high degree of lipogenesis, with its correspondingly high respiratory quotient.

Fat Synthesis. When the adipose tissue of the hyperphagic rat was examined *in vitro*, it was found that treatment with adrenaline released only one quarter of the fatty acids released from the fat of control animals. Thus the hyperphagic rat is directing its metabolism towards the synthesis of fat, and it may be that this is more nearly the cause of the hyperphagia than the effect, i.e. the lesion may be causing the animal to increase its fat depots, the hyperphagia being secondary to this.

Parabiotic Pair. That there is a defective response to some factor in the blood of the hyperphagic rat is suggested by Hervey's study on a pair of parabiotic rats*; when one was made hyperphagic by a hypo-thalamic lesion the other became thin, as though the laying down of fat were being inhibited by the circumstance that its twin was doing so. Thus the metabolic conditions, as reflected in the blood, indicated to the normal twin that fat should be mobilized and not laid down,

* A parabiotic pair, or "Siamese twins", are produced experimentally by opening their peritoneal cavities and uniting the four cut edges of muscle and peritoneum.

whereas the hyperphagic animal, because of its hypothalamic deficit, was unable to respond to this message.

Diurnal Rhythm of Eating. LeMagnen was impressed by the cyclical character of a rat's eating behaviour. Thus, although in any 24-hour period a rat will adjust its food-intake to its metabolic requirements fairly accurately, during the night it eats more, and is thus hyperphagic, whilst during the day it eats less and is hypophagic (Fig. 4.6). If the food eaten during the night is labelled with ^{14}C it is found that this is utilized during the day, so that the excess eaten in

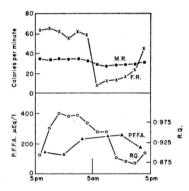

Fig. 4.6. The diurnal rhythm of eating in rats. In the upper graph is shown the relative variation in feeding (FR) and metabolic rate (MR) over 24 hours. In the lower graph the plasma free fatty acids (PFFA) and the respiratory quotient (RQ) are shown for the same period. Note at night the rat is hyperphagic by some 77 per cent while during the day it is hypophagic. (Le Magnen, *et al., J. comp. physiol. Psychol.*)

the night does influence the amount eaten during the day. During the night it is found that synthesis of fat dominates the metabolic picture, and during the day fat mobilization with synthesis of glucose prevails (Fig. 4.7). In the ventromedially lesioned rats this cycle no longer prevails, in that the daily hypophagia is absent along with the failure of mobilization of fat, as revealed by the failure of the plasma free fatty acids (FFA) to rise (Fig. 4.7).

Function of VMH. Thus we may consider the ventromedial centre as one that is intimately related to carbohydrate and lipid metabolism, being influenced by the concentrations of metabolites in the blood and itself influencing the hormonal metabolic control mechanisms. The influence exerted on the food-intake may well be through the lateral centre, stimulation of which provokes eating, but the simple picture postulated by Anand and Brobeck, of a satiety centre, acting as a brake on food intake, the destruction of which allows for runaway eating, is

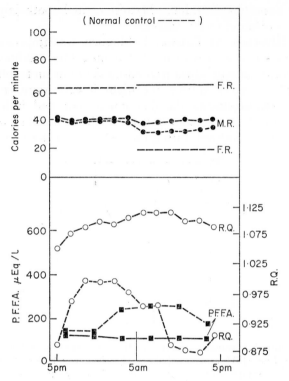

Fig. 4.7. Rats with ventromedial lesions showing loss of the normal diurnal rhythm in feeding. From the top are shown the calorific intake (FR), the metabolic rate (MR), the respiratory quotient (RQ), the plasma free fatty acid level (PFFA) during a 24 hour period. The feeding rate is very high and constant throughout the period and widely in excess of the O_2 consumption (MR) which is itself almost constant. The RQ is at a high level and cyclic variation in PFFA is not seen. (Le Magnen *et al.*, *J. comp. physiol. Psychol.*)

not sustained. Perhaps the most significant finding in this respect is that hyperphagic rats with ventromedial lesions seem to respond to short-term feeding demands normally; thus intragastric feeding reduces their food intake to the same extent as in normals (Fig. 4.8) indicating that there is a "satiety centre" capable of responding to gastric distension. On the other hand, these lesioned rats exhibit obvious defects in responding to food-deprivation; whereas a normal rat increases its food intake by some 28 per cent after a 24 hour fast, the "hyperphagic" rats only increased theirs by 4 per cent; thus the defect is nor in achieving postprandial satiety, but rather in adjusting the food-intake to changes in the animal's stores, whether these are

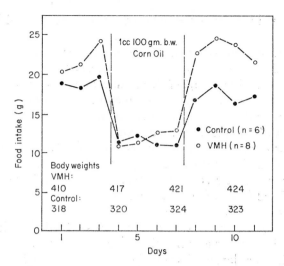

Fig. 4.8. A comparison of the daily food intakes of control rats with those which have been lesioned in the ventromedial hypothalamus (VMH). As can be seen the lesioned rats responded to short-term feeding demands in the same way as the control animals. During days 4-7 all rats were fed directly into the stomach with corn oil. Mean body weights at 3-day intervals shown in the lower part of the figure. (Panksepp, *Physiol. Behav.*)

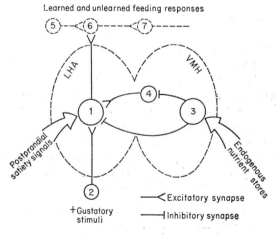

Fig. 4.9. A simple neural model of the organization of the feeding centres. LHA, lateral hypothalamic area; VMH, ventromedial hypothalamus. (Panksepp, *Physiol. Behav.*)

depletions, as in deprivation, or excesses, as in its normal hyperphagic state.

Function of LH. What then becomes of the function of the lateral hypothalamic centre, removal of which causes aphagia and stimulation of which causes hyperphagia? According to a suggestion by Panksepp (1971), this centre is the one responsive to post-prandial satiety stimuli, such as gastric distension, blood-sugar and amino acids, and also to gustatory and olfactory stimuli; and he cites electrophysiological evidence for the sensitivity of this region to local injections of glucose, and olfactory and gustatory stimuli (e.g. Emmers, 1969).

Organization of Feeding Centres. On this basis the organization is that depicted in Fig. 4.9 with the lateral centre as the final common pathway operating on the various feeding reflexes. According to this scheme, the long-term influences of endogenous nutrient stores operate on centre 3 in the ventromedial region, and this acts directly on centre 1 in the lateral hypothalamus, together with postprandial signals and gustatory stimuli. The ventromedial centre also acts indirectly through centre 4, which facilitates feeding and thus re-inforces gustatory stimuli. In the ventromedially lesioned rat this reinforcement is lost so that, although the animal is hyperphagic due to the loss of the inhibitory control from centre 3, it is actually less motivated to obtain food and becomes more finicky with regard to its quality, these being, in fact, features of the hyperphagic animal.*

Single Units

Obviously a great deal of work must be done, employing recording of individual neurones and fibres in the hypothalamic feeding centres. So far, unequivocal evidence for units in the lateral centre that increase their firing during eating has not been obtained; all those studied by Hamburg (1971) actually decreased their spontaneous activity during eating; on withdrawal of food the activity would increase, even though the animal was still chewing. Thus electrical stimulation of the lateral hypothalamic region might well stimulate eating through activation of nervous tracts running through it, rather than through activation of neurones with their cell-bodies in this region; it is from the cell-bodies of neurones that records would be the most likely to be taken in this sort of study, rather than from the fibres of the tracts.

* An interesting feature of the animals recovered from lateral hypothalamic lesions is that they show *higher motivation* to eat than hyperphagic or normal animals, in so far as they take more trouble to discover food (Devenport and Balagura, 1971). This fact, and the reduced motivation of the hyperphagic animal, emphasize the need for delicate tests of function in studies on the effects of lesions; it is not sufficient to measure the amount of food eaten.

Hypothalamus as a Controlling Region

There is little doubt from the studies of lesions, and the effects of localized stimulation, that the hypothalamus contains neuronal organizations, or centres, that, by receiving afferent input from the viscera and initiating efferent output to the appropriate effectors, permit control over such functions as eating, drinking, defence, and so on. It has to be emphasized, however, that the methods of delineating these centres anatomically and functionally are crude. Electrical stimulation by an electrode implanted in a given region is a very unphysiological stimulus and may well activate groups of neurones simultaneously that have opposing effects. Localized lesions do not distinguish between destruction of the cell bodies of neurones constituting a putative centre and tracts of fibres either passing through or making synaptic contacts, or both.

Limbic System. Thus the *median forebrain bundle* is an important tract carrying impulses to the hypothalamus from higher centres such as the amygdala and septum, and, in general, relating it to the other parts of what has been called the *limbic system* or, *visceral brain*. Lesions in the hypothalamus that interrupt the tracts which connect it with the visceral brain will produce effects equivalent to destruction of centres elsewhere. Thus the lesions in the lateral hypothalamus that cause aphagia and adipsia, presumably by destroying eating and drinking centres, can be imitated by bilateral cuts either anterior or posterior to the hypothalamus, but not affecting the lateral hypothalamus itself. It is probable that the median forebrain bundle, which passes through the whole lateral hypothalamic area, is the region severed by these cuts; as just indicated, this bundle relates the hypothalamus to the septal area which receives connexions with the hippocampus and amygdala, whilst there is a more direct communication with the same regions.

THE DIGESTIVE PROCESSES

Innervation of the Alimentary Tract

Contraction and Relaxation

The smooth muscle of the alimentary tract is supplied by both parasympathetic and sympathetic nerves; on the classical view, their actions on any given portion are antagonistic, the parasympathetic, e.g. the vagus, being excitatory and the sympathetic being inhibitory, causing relaxation of existing tone. Thus stimulation of the vagus nerve in the neck causes strong contractions of the stomach that are blocked by atropine, an effect that is opposed by stimulation of the sympathetic outflow. At the sphincters, controlling passage of material from one portion of the tract to the other, the roles are reversed, so that as the body of the viscus contracts the sphincter relaxes to allow passage of the contents.

Non-Cholinergic-Non-Adrenergic Inhibition. As we shall see, however, this view of the actions of parasympathetic and sympathetic innervation is too simple; thus an important mechanism of inducing relaxation, i.e. inhibition, is through the parasympathetic innervation, so that, when the vagus is stimulated in the presence of atropine and of adrenergic blockers, a definite relaxation of the stomach can be observed. We may therefore speak of a *non-cholinergic-non-adrenergic inhibition*; and, on the modern view, the marked inhibition associated with certain reflexes—descending inhibition of peristalsis and the intestino-intestinal inhibition—are mediated by this non-adrenergic mechanism.

Sympathetic

The essential features of the autonomic outflow to the viscera have been indicated earlier (Vol. 2), and are summarized in Fig. 4.10 for convenience.

As indicated, the sympathetic outflow to the abdominal viscera passes through the sympathetic chain without relaying, forming the splanchnic nerves, and passing to various collateral ganglia, e.g. the coeliac, where the synapses are made. Postganglionic fibres travel along blood vessels and, together with some preganglionic fibres and numerous scattered small ganglia, form elaborate plexuses along the main arteries of the abdomen; these plexuses are named after the arteries, e.g. the *renal plexus, coeliac plexus, mesenteric plexus*, and so on. From these plexuses the postganglionic sympathetic fibres pass to the complex intramural plexuses of the gastrointestinal tract, namely the submucous and myenteric plexuses (*Meissner's* and *Auerbach's plexuses*). These plexuses represent a local (*intrinsic*) autonomic nervous system through which the activities of the smooth muscle of the alimentary tract and the blood vessels are coordinated. The postganglionic sympathetic neurones relay with neurones within the plexuses, or innervate the smooth muscle directly.

Parasympathetic

The parasympathetic supply is from the vagus and the sacral autonomic outflow from the cord. The efferent root of the vagus in the medulla sends fibres to most of the abdominal viscera, passing to the various autonomic plexuses in which, as well as in the walls of the

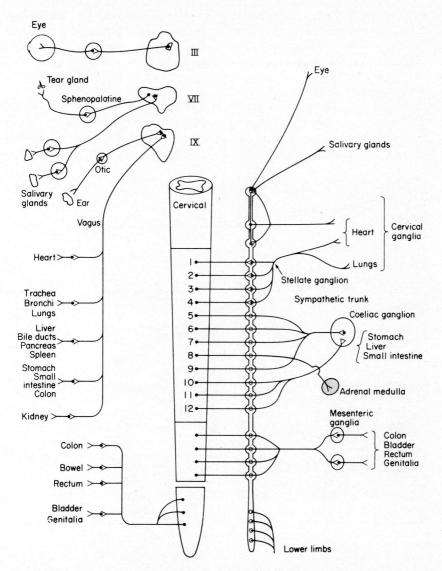

Fig. 4.10. A diagrammatic representation of the distribution of the sympathetic and parasympathetic parts of the autonomic system. On the left is the parasympathetic distribution with long preganglionic fibres and short postganglionic fibres, the parasympathetic ganglion being very close to the innervated organ. On the right is the sympathetic distribution with the chain of sympathetic ganglia alongside the cord. Note that there is a bilateral distribution of both systems and one from each side has been shown in the diagram.

organs themselves, are placed the ganglia containing the post-ganglionic neurones. The large intestine, rectum and bladder are supplied by the sacral outflow, the *pelvic visceral nerves*, or *nervi erigentes*; these relay in ganglia placed mostly on their walls.

Intramural Plexuses

In general, the ganglia of the sympathetic are outside the wall of the alimentary tract and may be called *extramural*; those of the parasympathetic may be both extra- and intra-mural, the latter occurring in the nodes of Meissner's and Auerbach's plexus. The arrangement

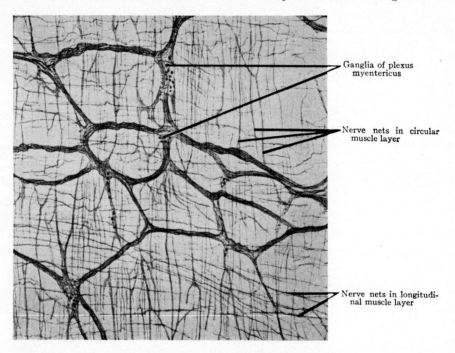

Ganglia of plexus myentericus

Nerve nets in circular muscle layer

Nerve nets in longitudinal muscle layer

Fig. 4.11. A schematic diagram of the intramural plexuses of the wall of the alimentary tract. (Greep, *Histology.*)

of the nerve fibres and ganglia in the myenteric plexus is illustrated in Fig. 4.11.

In general, the myenteric plexus (Auerbach's) may be divided into *primary*, *secondary* and *tertiary* plexuses according to the size and position of the nerves making them up; thus the primary plexus consists of large nerve bundles in a wide meshwork containing ganglion cells; as Fig. 4.11 shows, the interstices of this are traversed by thinner

secondary nerve bundles, and a tertiary system of finer fibres of some
3–$10\,\mu$ in diameter. The extrinsic nerves pass through the muscle coat
to end in the primary plexus. Fine bundles from these plexuses pass
inwards to Meissner's submucosal plexus and the mucosa, whilst nerve
bundles from the tertiary plexus run to supply the muscle coats,
running parallel with the main axis of the muscle fibres, branching
into smaller and smaller bundles and finally terminating in restricted
areas, free of Schwann cell covering. At nodes in the plexus are scattered
the ganglion cells; some idea of the number is given by the statement
that there are over 5 million ganglion cells in Auerbach's plexus and
10–15 million in Meissner's. Some of the terminations on the ganglion
cells are definitely adrenergic, as indicated by the granular type of
synaptic vesicles.

Intrinsic and Extrinsic Innervation. The intramural plexuses
are described as the *intrinsic innervation*, and there is little doubt that a
great deal of the coordinated activity of the muscular walls of the
alimentary tract can be executed through these intrinsic plexuses, so
that the *extrinsic system*, operating through the sympathetic and parasympathetic outflows from the central nervous system, may be considered to exert a modifying influence on activities that can be largely
executed independently of them.

The Transmitters

Parasympathetic

The extrinsic nervous supply to the gastrointestinal tract can
operate directly on the glands and smooth muscle; in this event the
transmitter of parasympathetic postganglionic neurones is acetylcholine,
acting on muscarinic receptors on the effector cells, with its effects
abolished by atropine. A great deal of this activity is, however, not
exerted directly but indirectly through interneurones of the intramural
plexuses, so that the cholinergic activity is exerted at a synapse and
may be classed as nicotinic, being blocked by curarine.* The neurones
of the intramural plexuses seem to be largely cholinergic since, when
they are activated directly by transmural stimulation, catecholamines
are not released whereas acetylcholine is (Paton and Zar, 1968).

Sympathetic

The sympathetic postganglionic neurones are adrenergic, exhibiting
both a- and β-actions, and at one time it was considered that they

* Some transmission in the plexuses may be muscarinic, and blocked by atropine, in a
similar way to that in the superior cervical ganglion (Eccles and Libet, 1961).

exerted their influence on the smooth muscle directly, but modern techniques of identifying adrenergic neurones through their fluorescence, developed by Falck and Hillarp, have shown that most, if not all, of the adrenergic neurones pass to the intramural plexuses and not to the muscular layers; within the plexuses they terminate in relation to ganglion cells of these plexuses; and only in the colon are there appreciable numbers of fibres running to the muscle (Norberg, 1964). It seems, therefore, that although adrenaline and noradrenaline can hyperpolarize smooth muscle cells, thereby inhibiting contraction, exerting both α- and β-actions, the extrinsic influence on muscle activity is mainly through interneurones of the intramural plexuses.*

α- and β-Receptors. This indirect action is brought about through

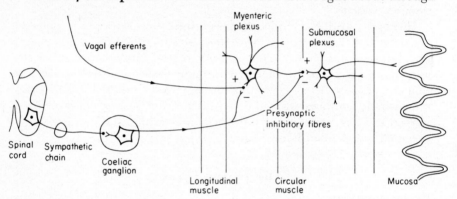

Fig. 4.12. Sympathetic presynaptic inhibition of parasympathetic preganglionic fibres.

α-receptors, since it is not blocked by β-blockers, such as phentolamine; where both α- and β-activity is demonstrated, the β-activity is brought about by a direct action on the muscle. Thus relaxation of smooth muscle may be brought about by sympathetic activity when α-action is blocked specifically, e.g. by dibenamine.

Adrenergic Presynaptic Inhibition. When the interneurones of the plexus are activated directly in an isolated piece of gut by transmural stimulation, and records of activity in the neurones are made with an intracellular electrode, synaptic potentials and spikes occur. These are due to excitation of nerve fibres within the plexus that make synaptic contacts, since they are blocked by tetrodotoxin, which, it

* There is not complete agreement on this point; Silva, Ross and Osborne (1971) found that, whereas the longitudinal muscle of the ileum had little or no adrenergic innervation, the circular muscle was densely innervated, as well as the neurones of the myenteric plexus. Thus in circular muscle inhibition can be brought about directly on the smooth muscle and indirectly through the intramural plexus.

will be recalled, blocks transmission along axons but not at synapses. Paton and Vizi (1969) found that these potentials were blocked by tubocurarine but not by adrenergic blockers; and this indicated that, in this preparation of guinea pig longitudinal muscle, the adrenergic nerves do not make synaptic contacts with the neurones belonging to the plexus. How then can the sympathetic act as an inhibitor of muscular contractions? The answer is by inhibiting the release of acetylcholine by the cholinergic fibres, which would cause contraction. This is an example of *presynaptic inhibition*, the adrenergic nerve fibre terminating in relation to the endings of the cholinergic preganglionic fibre, as in Fig. 4.12, and inhibiting the release of transmitter by depolarizing the terminal. Thus, when isolated strips of intestine were treated with adrenaline and noradrenaline, the release of acetylcholine that normally takes place was reduced, and the larger release that follows transmural electrical stimulation was also reduced. The effect was inhibited by α-blockers such as phentolamine, phenoxybenzamine and ergotamine, whilst exhaustion of catecholamine supplies, by treatment with reserpine or guanethidine, allowed a greater-than-normal release of acetylcholine.

Parasympathetic Background Motility. We may conclude, therefore, that Nature works economically in the extrinsic control over the gastrointestinal tract; acetylcholine is released by the tonic action of the parasympathetic innervation, and this provides a background of motility; inhibition is brought about by release of noradrenaline which opposes the release of acetylcholine by the tonically active cholinergic neurones. In this way we may account for the very pronounced motility that occurs when the sympathetic is blocked, e.g. by reserpine; now the gut is under the sole control of tonically active cholinergic neurones.

When contraction of the stomach or gut is brought about experimentally by application of acetylcholine, this may be inhibited by sympathetic stimulation, but the evidence indicates that this is not a direct action of the adrenergic inhibitor on the muscle, i.e. a hyperpolarization due to noradrenaline, but is brought about indirectly through a ganglion of the intramural plexus (Jansson and Martinson, 1966).

Purinergic Transmission

As indicated above, an inhibition of gastro-intestinal smooth muscle may be evoked by stimulation of the parasympathetic supply in the presence of cholinergic and adrenergic blocking agents; the same inhibition may be observed by direct stimulation of the intramural nervous supply—Auerbach's and Meissner's plexuses—when cholinergic activity is blocked with atropine and adrenergic activity with bretyllium; and Burnstock has provided a large amount of evidence supporting the role of ATP as a transmitter.

Effects of ATP. Thus when inhibition is induced in the perfused stomach by vagal stimulation, adenosine may be collected in the perfusate (Satchell and Burnstock, 1971); ATP certainly causes relaxation of the stomach muscle and causes hyperpolarization of smooth muscle cells of the guinea pig taenia coli, i.e. longitudinal muscle from the colon.

Further support is given by a study of Tomita and Watanabe (1973) who compared the effects of ATP with those of electrical stimulation (transmural) and of noradrenaline and its α-antagonist phentolamine. ATP in a concentration of $10^{-3}M$ caused a marked hyperpolarization of the intestinal membrane, and this was accompanied by an increase in conductance, presumably due to increased K^+-permeability. These changes were accompanied by the abolition of spontaneous spikes and relaxation of the muscle. Noradrenaline had roughly similar effects, and these were due to its α-action since the effects were abolished by phentolamine. Transmural stimulation produced an inhibitory potential which was reduced by ATP; this latter effect is to be expected, however, if transmural stimulation and ATP act in the same way, namely to increase the K^+-conductance and hyperpolarization of the muscle cell. Clearly, if ATP has already hyperpolarized the membrane by increasing its conductance, the possibility of further hyperpolarization, by transmural stimulation, is reduced. Thus the inhibitory potential must now take off from a background of hyperpolarization, and is consequently smaller when measured as a change.

Dual Inhibitory Mechanism. There are thus two ways of inhibiting smooth muscle of the guinea pig taenia coli, namely through release of the catecholamines, noradrenaline and adrenaline, and through the release of ATP. The smooth muscle cells contain separate receptors responsive to these substances; most commonly the adrenergic substances noradrenaline and adrenaline would be released from the adrenal gland whilst the direct nervous action would be through the purinergic sympathetic neurone.

Adrenergic Activation of Intramural Neurones. Although some workers have found little postsynaptic excitatory action of noradrenaline on the intramural neurones, there is little doubt from Ohkawa and Prosser's (1972) study of cat intestine that many neurones of both plexuses were activated by adrenaline, the effect being blocked by phentolamine, an α-blocker. It could well be that these neurones

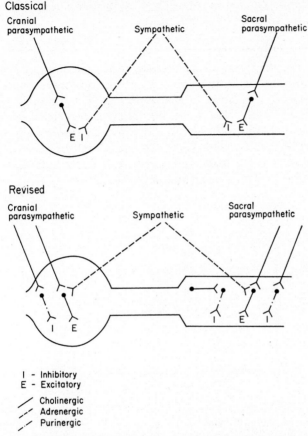

Fig. 4.13. In the upper part of the diagram is shown the classical view of the autonomic innervation of the gut. In the lower part is shown the latest ideas incorporating the purinergic pathways which can inhibit the gut via the parasympathetic nervous supply by the release of ATP. The purinergic neurones are under the influence of the sympathetic nervous system. (Courtesy of Prof. G. Burnstock.)

were the purinergic neurones discussed above, being activated synaptically by adrenergic neurones of the sympathetic (Fig. 4.13).

Control Mechanisms Summarized

Myogenic Activity

To summarize the basic nervous mechanisms operating in the control over the smooth muscle of the gastrointestinal tract, we may state that there is a primary myogenic activity manifest in the rhythmic contractions described in Vol. 2, and accompanied by electrical activity in the individual muscle fibres.

Tonic Neurogenic Activity

By means of the intramural plexuses, either operating independently or as distributors of extrinsically active nerves, there seems to be a tonic neurogenic activation of the smooth muscle, opposed by a tonic neurogenic inhibition. The tonic inhibition is revealed very strikingly by the study of spike discharges in individual neurones and correlating this with the spontaneous spike discharge in circular muscle. As Fig. 4.14 shows, as the mean spike-frequency in the submucous plexus decreased that of the circular muscle increased.

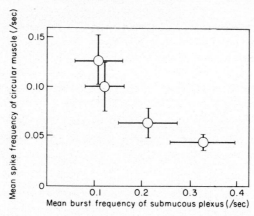

Fig. 4.14. The relation between mean spike activity in the submucous plexus and that in the circular muscle of the gut. As the activity in the submucous plexus increases the spike activity in the muscle decreases. Each point is the mean and standard deviation for the two variables. (Ohkawa and Prosser, *Amer. J. Physiol.*)

Stimulation of the sympathetic division causes inhibition of the musculature of the stomach—adrenergic inhibition—mediated largely, if not exclusively, by interneurones in the intramural plexuses. Tonic activation of the muscle fibres occurs through cholinergic neurones, and is manifest as a continuous release of acetylcholine in the resting muscle; treatment with eserine, which prevents hydrolysis of the liberated transmitter, increases the amplitude of rhythmic contractions.

Reflex Release of Adrenal Hormones

Finally, to complicate the situation further, we find that, when inhibition of intestinal motility is brought about reflexly, for example by haemorrhage, or occlusion of the common carotid arteries, this inhibition is unaffected by cutting the extrinsic sympathetic nerve supply to the intestine, and is actually due to the activation of the suprarenal glands with liberation of adrenaline into the blood stream; thus the reflex fails in the adrenalectomized animal, whilst in the normal animal the time taken for it to take effect is governed by the circulation-time for the blood leaving the adrenals to reach the intestine (Kock, 1959).

Effects of Drugs on Motility

Acetylcholine

The complexities in the neurology of the smooth muscle of the alimentary tract are necessarily reflected in an even greater complexity in unravelling the effects of drugs, so that only a few general statements can be made. The cholinergic transmitter, acetylcholine, causes contraction by virtue of its muscarinic action, an effect abolished by atropine and mimicked by acetyl β-methyl choline (methacol); this is a direct action on the muscle through activation of the muscarinic receptor. Acetylcholine may influence the tissue through its nicotinic action, an effect mimicked by carbamylcholine; here the action is on the postsynaptic membranes of neurones, e.g. the neurones of the peripheral ganglia of the vagus; the effect is abolished by high concentrations of nicotine or by hexamethonium and tubocurarine.

Adrenergic Drugs

Adrenergic drugs may influence both α- and β-receptors on the smooth muscle; both influences cause relaxation. The α-action seems to be exerted rapidly because the drug acts on the membrane of the responsive tissue, be it neurone or muscle; the β-action is delayed because the action on the smooth muscle apparently involves intracellular events mediated by cyclic AMP (Vol. 2). When α-receptors are concerned, adrenaline is as effective as, or more effective than, noradrenaline, and both are much more effective than isopropylnoradrenaline (isoprenaline, isoproterenol), and the action is blocked by the specific α-blockers, such as dibenamine, dibozane, tolazoline, phentolamine, etc. Phenylephrine selectively stimulates through α-receptors, having no action on β-receptors, which are characteristically activated by isopropylnoradrenaline (isoprenaline). Typical β-blockers are dichlorisoprenaline (DCI), pronethanol and propanolol.

Cholinergic Blockers. As we have seen, adrenergic nerves influence smooth muscle largely indirectly, either by causing the liberation of catecholamines from the adrenal gland, or by activating adrenergic receptors on neurones of the intramural plexuses. It is not surprising, therefore, that cholinergic blockers, such as curare, can inhibit adrenergic activity, since many of the neurones activated by the α-action liberate acetylcholine.

Sphincteric Muscle

Contraction of smooth muscle, as in peristalsis, may be associated with relaxation of sphincteric muscles; and it is generally stated that the parasympathetic supply causes the contraction of the smooth muscle of the alimentary tract except for the sphincteric muscles, which it causes to relax. Thus we might expect acetylcholine to cause inhibition of sphincteric muscle, but this seems not to be true (Daniel, 1965).

Electrotonic Spread

Again, it has been shown by Harry (1963) that the circular muscle of the ileum does not contract under the influence of acetylcholine when it is separated from Auerbach's plexus and the longitudinal muscle, so it has been argued that the contraction of the intact tissue relies on activation of the longitudinal muscle and spread of activity electrotonically to the circular muscle.

Adrenergic Contraction

As with cholinergic activity, so with adrenergic, there are exceptions from the main generalization that adrenergic drugs cause relaxation; thus these drugs cause constriction of the smooth muscle of the bile duct at its junction with the duodenum (sphincter of Oddi—Vol. 1) but relaxation of the smooth muscle of the duodenum with which it is related; the final effect is relaxation of the sphincter with increased flow of bile (Benzi *et al.*, 1964). Again, the longitudinal smooth muscle of the cat's oesophagus contracts in response to α-adrenergic drugs in a manner similar to the effects of acetylcholine; β-adrenergic drugs, on the other hand, cause relaxation.

Serotonin

5-Hydroxytryptamine, or serotonin, is a transmitter in the central nervous system; it is localized in granules of the enterochromaffin cells at the base of the mucosal epithelium of the intestine, and has been considered, e.g. by Bülbring, to be a transmitter in the gut, operating in the peristaltic reflex (p. 307). Whilst 5-HT undoubtedly acts on smooth muscle, causing either contraction or relaxation according to the particular tissue, it is considered that physiologically it does not act as a transmitter in the alimentary tract. Thus Bouillin maintained rats on a tryptophan-deficient diet until the 5-HT content of the gut had fallen to 10 per cent of normal, but the peristaltic response to the presence of food in the gut was quite unaffected. Pharmacologically, 5-HT acts in several ways; its direct action enhances motility, an effect antagonized by lysergic acid; indirectly it can cause contraction through its action on cholinergic neurones of the intramural plexus, an effect that is blocked by atropine.

Histamine

This is another natural drug that has strong actions which are, however, without physiological significance; it usually acts indirectly causing release of acetylcholine and thus increasing motility, although the gastric fundus is an exception.

Prostaglandins

Recent discoveries on the functions of prostaglandins are contributing to our understanding of visceral muscle behaviour; but the position will remain complex for a long time. The substance extracted by Vogt from intestine, and called *Darmstoff*, turns out to be a mixture of PGF_1 and PGF_1a; the material is released from frog intestine on stimulating its nervous supply. In general, the A and B prostaglandins

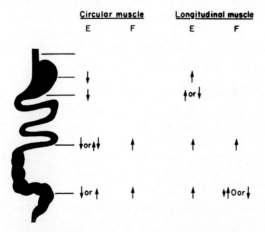

Fig. 4.15. A diagrammatic representation of the effects of PGE_1, E_2, $F_{1\alpha}$ and $F_{2\alpha}$ on the circular and longitudinal muscle layers of the human isolated gut. ↑, contraction; ↓, inhibition; ↕, small contraction followed by a relaxation; ↕, small relaxation followed by a contraction; O, no response. The size of response is indicated roughly by the size of arrow. Blank areas, information is not available. (Bennett and Fleshler, *Gastroenterology*.)

have little effect on gastrointestinal muscle, whereas the E's and F's are active, E_1, E_2, F_1a and F_2a having been extracted. Longitudinal muscle contracts in response to E and F in most tissues, but the behaviour of circular muscle is more diverse, F causing contraction, and E causes relaxation or opposes the stimulating action of drugs. Thus PGE_1 and PGE_2 are both inhibitory transmitters to circular muscle of the stomach; they also inhibit the secretion of acid provoked by pentagastrin, and it is probably for these reasons that aspirin, which inhibits synthesis of prostaglandins (Vol. 2), may cause gastric ulcers, releasing the stomach from a tonic inhibition. In Fig. 4.15 the effects of PG's on different parts of the gastrointestinal tract are indicated schematically.*

Sensory Mechanisms

From the moment that the act of swallowing has been initiated, the processes of digestion and absorption take place reflexly, and we must therefore seek for receptors that will respond to the appropriate stimuli that bring about the reflexes. To a small extent the human subject is aware of events taking place in his gastrointestinal tract—e.g. satiety is indicated as a sense of fullness related to the distension of either the stomach or some other portion of the tract, whilst pain is the result of a more powerful distension. In general, the stimuli to which the tract is responsive are *mechanical*, involving a change in tension of the muscles or deformation of the mucosa, and *chemical*, involving sensitivity to the presence of acid, secretogogues, and perhaps changes of osmolality, as in the effects of hypertonic solutions in slowing gastric emptying (p. 325).

Visceral Sensory Fibres

The anatomical and physiological study of sensory mechanisms is handicapped by the extreme complexity of the innervation of the tract, containing as it does both an intrinsic and extrinsic system, and also by the circumstance that the sensory fibres are mainly unmyelinated and not easy to study as single units. Although the percentage of sensory fibres in the extrinsic nerves of the abdomen—vagus and splanchnic—is extremely high, being some 80 per cent in the abdominal vagus, for example, the amount of sensory influx from the gastro-intestinal tract is small, and this is understandable in view of the high degree of autonomy exerted through its intrinsic plexuses that are capable of providing the neurone-arcs for such well integrated activities

---

* The effects of the prostaglandins on the gastrointestinal tract have been reviewed by Bennett and Fleshler (1970).

as peristalsis and segmenting movements. In general, the sensory nerve fibres terminate as fine nonmyelinated fibres reaching the longitudinal and circular muscles, the submucosal muscle, and thence the mucous membrane, terminating in relation to epithelial cells. The terminations vary in character with species and with position in the tissue, but well organized receptor organs, comparable with Pacinian corpuscles or muscle spindles, are either rare or absent, so that both mechanical and chemical sensitivity may well be a feature of the nerve terminals themselves, requiring no "transduction" from specialized receptor cells.

Responses to Stretch

Paintal recorded from single unmyelinated fibres of the vagus and found many that responded to inflation of a balloon in the stomach; Fig. 4.16 shows the response of one unit, and it will be seen that the

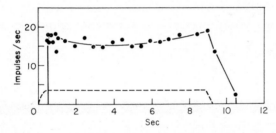

Fig. 4.16. Response of a gastric stretch-receptor to maintained distension of the stomach. The frequency after 9 sec is as high as the initial peak frequency following rapid distension. The interrupted line indicates onset and duration of distension. (Paintal, *J. Physiol.*)

discharge is maintained at a steady level with little sign of adaptation, i.e. of diminution in discharge. With others, however, the discharge fell off rapidly in spite of maintaining the tension in the stomach wall, and we may assume that the two types of nerve fibre subserve different functions; the non-adapting perhaps to indicate the sense of fullness or satiety, and the other to produce a response to distension, as in peristalsis.

Location in Series. In a similar type of study Iggo (1957a) identified, in the unmyelinated C-fibres of the vagus, single units that responded to distension of either the stomach or gut; when the gut contracted, either spontaneously or as a result of faradic stimulation, the fibre was activated, so that unlike a skeletal muscle spindle, which only responds to stretch, and is therefore in parallel with the muscle fibres, it would seem that the receptors in the gastrointestinal tract are in series with the contractile elements, being excited either by stretching or shortening of the muscle fibres.

Movement Receptor

Bessou and Perl (1966) have described responses in single thin myelinated fibres of the mesenteric nerve that are clearly differentiated from the typical stretch receptors described by Iggo and Paintal. The receptors are located on the outermost part of the intestine and so can be activated by traction on the mesentery; the response is phasic, i.e. a burst of discharge on activation that rapidly declines, and the authors consider that the receptor responds specifically to movement of the gut, rather than pressure within it. The receptor is not sensitive to vibration and is thus differentiated from the Pacinian corpuscle (Vol. 5).

Chemical Sensitivity

The secretion of acid in the stomach, and the passage of this into the intestine, bring about reflex changes demanding the presence of sensors

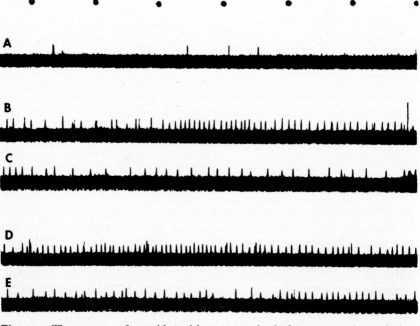

Fig. 4.17. The response of an acid-sensitive receptor in the intact stomach to solutions put into the stomach through the cardiac sphincter. A 0·03 N HCl, pH 1·5; B, 0·1 N HCl; C, the same unit 30 sec later with the acid still in the stomach; D, 0·2 N HCl; and E, 30 sec later as in C. Time marks, 1 sec. (Iggo, *Quart. J. exp. Physiol.*)

to altered pH. Thus acid in the duodenum reflexly depresses gastric motility. Iggo (1957) isolated single fibres of the vagus that gave discharges when acid was put into the intact stomach of the cat (Fig. 4.17). The receptors, or nerve endings, must have been in the mucosa, rather than the muscle, since scraping away the innermost third of the mucosa abolished the response in many of the units.* Harding and Leek (1972) obtained high-frequency spike discharges in single vagal fibres by stroking the mucosa; the same fibre gave responses to acid and alkaline solutions, and sometimes to changes in osmolality.

Pain

Pain can arise from distension of the viscera, so that it is likely that some of the fibres responding to distension mediate this. They would presumably be high-threshold fibres since the tensions developed during normal peristalsis do not provoke awareness. Thus the powerful contractions of the oesophagus developed by inserting an incompressible balloon are intensely painful, whereas the normal tensions developed by swallowing are not noticed.

Local Reflex Activity: Peristalsis

Bayliss-Starling Law

The fundamental feature of this process is the ring of contraction of circular muscle passing down the alimentary tract in an aboral direction; the contraction is preceded by a greater or less degree of relaxation of the muscle immediately in front. It is provoked by the stretch of the gut by the bolus, and as formulated by Bayliss and Starling's *Law of the Intestine*, this stimulation produces excitation above the stimulated point—*ascending contraction*—and inhibition below the stimulated point—*descending inhibition*. The process is independent of the extrinsic innervation of the gut; nevertheless it is a highly coordinated reflex mediated by the neurones of the intrinsic innervation, a reflex that is initiated by sensory endings in the mucosa that are responsive to stretch; thus the *myenteric reflex*, as we must call it, is abolished by treatment of the mucosa with cocaine, a drug that blocks sensory transmission. We may assume that sensory neurones within the intrinsic plexus transmit impulses to interneurones and motor neurones that lead to contraction and relaxation of the smooth musculature.

* Iggo (1957) also described alkali-sensitive receptors in the stomach; their presence is a puzzle as they are unlikely to be activated normally.

Longitudinal and Circular Muscles

The involvement of both longitudinal and circular muscles in the reflex has been invoked; for example, when Trendelenburg (1917) examined the tensions developed in both, he found that the initial step was contraction of the longitudinal muscle, which caused a shortening of the intestinal segment under study; this was followed by contraction of the circular muscle in a wave travelling in an aboral direction and expelling the contents, while the longitudinal muscle relaxed. Trendelenburg distinguished in this way a *preparatory*, or *filling phase*, and an *emptying phase*. It could be postulated that the stretch-receptors in the gut wall governing the longitudinal muscle had the lower threshold and would cause reflex contraction of this; this would cause a rise in intraluminal pressure that would activate the stretch-receptors governing the circular muscle, causing this to contract reflexly, whilst at the same time causing a relaxation of the previously contracted longitudinal muscle.

Independent Contractions

However, the careful experimental study of Kosterlitz *et al.* (1956) has definitely ruled out any theory that attributes an excitatory role to the contraction of the longitudinal muscle, i.e. their work has shown that the peristaltic wave of contraction of the circular muscle can take place in the absence of contractions of the longitudinal muscle. They measured the development of tension in the longitudinal muscle by connecting this to a strain-gauge, whilst the contraction of the circular muscle was measured by the development of pressure within the piece of isolated gut; this was accompanied by expulsion of fluid aborally, which was also measured. When the gut was distended by a low internal pressure, only a contraction of the longitudinal muscle occurred, and the tension developed was sustained for as long as the stimulating distension continued. There was no contraction of the circular muscle, and the pressure developed in the lumen of the gut was negligible. On increasing the stimulating distension beyond a threshold value of about 1·5 cm H_2O intra-intestinal pressure, the contraction of the longitudinal muscle was followed by a contraction of the circular muscle, as revealed by the rapid development of internal pressure, and the emptying of fluid aborally. Now the longitudinal muscle no longer sustained its tension, which passed through a peak, and relaxation began very soon after the beginning of the circular contraction, or "emptying phase". Thus, although contractions of the longitudinal and circular muscles follow a definite temporal pattern, the contraction of the circular muscle seems not to be the consequence of the contraction of the longitudinal muscle, but requires its own stimulus of gut-distension. When it contracts it causes an inhibition of the longitudinal muscle.

Effects of Drugs. This independence is emphasized by the effects of drugs; thus treatment of the gut with a high concentration of acetylcholine inhibits the contraction of the longitudinal muscle, but leaves that of the circular muscle unaffected. In a reverse manner, the independence of the longitudinal contraction from that of the circular muscle was demonstrated by Feldberg and Lin (1949), who

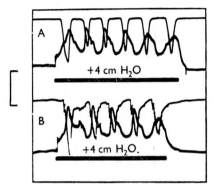

Fig. 4.18. Absence of dependence of peristalsis on the state of tone of longitudinal muscle. In A the longitudinal muscle is under isometric conditions and not able to shorten, while in B it is under isotonic conditions. In each record the upper trace is the tension, or shortening, of longitudinal muscle and the lower trace is intra-intestinal pressure. During the signal bar the intra-intestinal pressure was raised by 4 cm H_2O. Calibration: A, 3·2 g tension, 5 cm H_2O; B, 1·5 cm shortening, 4·4 cm H_2O. (Kosterlitz *et al.*, *J. Physiol.*)

showed that ganglion-blocking agents, such as tubocurarine and nicotine, inhibited the reflex contraction of the circular muscle but left that of the longitudinal muscle unaffected.

Isotonic versus Isometric Contraction. The unimportance of the longitudinal muscle in peristalsis is further emphasized by Fig. 4.18, which shows that the cycles of contraction of the circular muscle, revealed by the development of intra-intestinal pressure, are the same whether the longitudinal muscle is allowed to shorten—isotonic—or whether this is prevented by an isometric arrangement.

Significance of Longitudinal Muscle. The fact that the wave of peristalsis can occur independently of longitudinal muscular contraction does not mean that the latter, or "filling phase", is without physiological significance. Raiford and Mulinos (1936), in their classical description of the contractions of longitudinal and circular muscle in a piece of transplanted intestine, considered that the contraction of the longitudinal muscle tended to open the lumen in preparation for the propulsive phase caused by the circular contraction, and this is confirmed by the absence of any propulsion until circular muscle contraction begins. According to Kosterlitz *et al.* (1956), the contraction might well favour mixing in preparation for propulsion.

The Adequate Stimulus

In the presence of a ganglion-blocking agent, such as hexamethonium, the stimulus for contraction of the longitudinal muscle can be studied in isolation. The adequate stimulus is deformation of the receptors by radial distension rather than pressure itself; so that, if distension is prevented by slipping a tube over the gut, the effects of increased pressure are nullified (Kosterlitz and Robinson, 1959); and the same is true for the initiation of the emptying phase, i.e. contraction of the circular muscle (Ginzel, 1959). When the stretch is applied along the long axis of the gut, no contraction is evoked, and this contra-indicates a myogenic origin to the contraction.*

Electrical Stimulation of the Gut

By using coaxial electrodes, it is possible to activate the nerve fibres within the gut wall, and by using low-frequency stimulation it is possible to activate the motor fibres to the longitudinal muscle alone; on increasing the frequency, the circular muscle can be brought into action. When only the longitudinal muscle was activated, Kottegoda found that this was sufficient to initiate the whole peristaltic reflex; the longitudinal muscle contracted first, and this was followed by contraction of the circular muscle and relaxation of the longitudinal muscle in spite of the fact that the stimulation was being maintained (Fig. 4.19).

Reflex Inhibition. This strongly suggests that a *reflex inhibitory discharge* to the longitudinal muscle is being generated, of sufficient strength to overcome the excitatory effects of the electrical stimulation.

Intra-Intestinal Pressure. That the reflex was being evoked by the development of pressure within the lumen was shown by removing

---

* Raiford and Mulinos (1936) pointed out that the longitudinal muscle is connected to sensory nerves from the mucosa at and below its own level, whilst the circular muscle is connected to sensory nerves above the same level. Thus the distension created by the bolus tends to activate longitudinal muscle below it and circular muscle above it by virtue of this topographical arrangement.

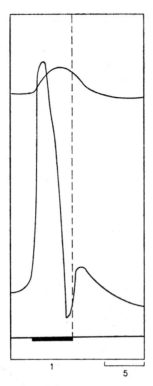

Fig. 4.19. The response of the guinea pig ileum to stimulation of the longitudinal muscle. The lower trace shows the contraction of the longitudinal muscle followed in the upper trace by a contraction of the circular muscle. Note the contraction of the longitudinal muscle is inhibited by a reflex, since the muscle relaxes although the electrical stimulation is continuous throughout this period. Co-axial electrical stimulation 0·1 msec pulses 1 per sec for 5 sec. (Kottegoda, in *Smooth Muscle*, Bülbring *et al.*, Arnold.)

fluid from it, in which case the contraction of the longitudinal muscle failed to generate sufficient pressure, and hence stretch of the receptors, to activate the contraction of the circular muscle. According to Kottegoda, therefore, the pressure developed within the gut by contraction of the longitudinal muscle was acting as a stimulus for the "emptying phase" of the peristaltic reflex, i.e. for the contraction of the circular muscle. However, in view of the results of Trendelenburg and of Kosterlitz, on the contractions evoked reflexly, one hesitates to argue from the effects of transmural electrical stimulation to the natural condition. Quite clearly if, under Kottegoda's conditions, the electrical stimulus caused the longitudinal muscle to develop a high intra-intestinal pressure, this would act as a stimulus to the contraction of the circular muscle, but the consensus of opinion is that, normally, contraction of the longitudinal muscle does not raise intra-intestinal pressure significantly, in fact it favours the filling of the gut.*

Ascending Contraction and Descending Inhibition

These studies on the interaction of the longitudinal and circular muscles tend to obscure the basis of peristalsis and the Bayliss-Starling Law of the Intestine, which is that the stimulus—distension—is associated with excitation of muscle on the oral side—*ascending excitation*—and inhibition on the anal side—*descending inhibition*. In view of

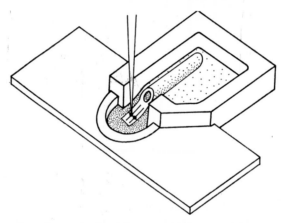

Fig. 4.20. Drawing of organ bath used to mount the preparation of intestinal segment with attached flap of longitudinal muscle and myenteric plexus. The base of the circular chamber consists of a microscope coverslip coated with silicone rubber; an individual neurone was impaled with a micro-electrode, using an inverted compound microscope. (Hirst and McKirdy, *J. Physiol.*)

the powerful nature of the circular muscle and its obvious function in closing the lumen, we must expect to find these opposing responses in this muscle alone; and the best way to study this would be to make recordings of electrical changes in individual muscle fibres on the anal and oral sides of a piece of intestine when it was stimulated.

Intestinal Flap. Hirst and McKirdy (1974) prepared a flap of intestine attached to a length of intact intestine as in Fig. 4.20; the

* The actual time-relations of contraction of longitudinal and circular muscles in the *colon* have been studied by MacKenna and McKirdy (1972); rather surprisingly they find that the two muscles contract and relax in phase rather than reciprocally; this similarity in behaviour was maintained when nervous activity had been abolished by tetrodotoxin, and this suggests electrical linking of the two muscles, perhaps through the nexus-type of junction.

flap could be on the oral or anal side of the intact region. With micro-electrodes, the activities of individual muscle fibres could be recorded as well as of individual neurones of the myenteric plexus. When the flap was anal to the segment, continuous activity was recorded in the S-type of neurones,* consisting of excitatory junctional potentials indicative of tonic synaptic input from other neurones, either inter-neurones, or sensory neurones of the myenteric plexus (Fig. 4.21). Associated with this neural activity there were inhibitory junctional potentials in the circular muscle fibres, suggesting that the neurones

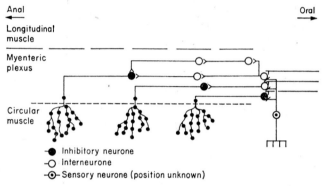

Fig. 4.21. Schematic representation of the descending inhibitory pathway. Afferent processes of the sensory neurone (cell-body ⊙) are stimulated by distension; efferent processes impinge on the cell-body of an interneurone (○) or may impinge directly on the cell-body of an inhibitory neurone (●). Inhibitory fibres run in an anal direction; inhibitory transmitter is assumed to be released from varicosities (small filled circles).
(Hirst and McKirdy, *J. Physiol.*)

activated were inhibitory to the circular muscle. Stretching the segment by inflation with saline caused increased activity. All these effects were abolished by tetrodotoxin, and were thus neurally mediated. When the flap was on the oral side of the segment the picture was entirely different; there was no spontaneous activity in the neurones nor yet did they show excitatory junctional potentials on distension of the segment, whilst the circular muscle fibres failed to give any hyper-polarizing inhibitory junctional potentials. The longitudinal muscle cells showed no response to distension of the segment, and this was true of both oral and anal flaps.

Thus, so far as descending inhibition is concerned, the Bayliss-

* Electrophysiologically two types of myenteric plexus neurone have been characterized; the S-neurones receive a large synaptic input and can be caused to discharge at high frequency with intracellular stimulation; the other, AH-neurone, has no synaptic input and after an action potential in its soma exhibits a prolonged after-potential.

Starling Law applies to the circular muscle of the guinea pig small intestine. This descending inhibition could be detected because the nervous pathways were long, so that an impulse initiated in the intact segment could be recorded in the flap. The ascending excitation may well be very close to the site of stimulation, and thus escape recording under these conditions.

Purinergic Inhibition. The transmission of the afferent impulses to the effector neurone in the inhibitory responses is blocked by curare, indicating a cholinergic step; however, inhibitory junctional potentials in the circular muscle fibres could be detected at some distance from the point of stimulation of the gut in the presence of atropine and guanethidine, so that the effector neurone seems to be neither cholinergic nor adrenergic, and may well belong to the purinergic class.

Local Reflex Activity: The Intestino-Intestinal Reflex

Pearcy and Van Liere (1926) observed that distension of any portion of the gastrointestinal tract caused relaxation of other parts, excluding the ileocolic sphincter. Experimentally this intestino-intestine reflex may be studied by preparing two Thiery-Vella loops (Vol. 1) and exciting one by distension, or in some other way, and observing the spontaneous contractions in the other; there is a rapid inhibition of the spontaneous activity (Youmans *et al.*, 1938).

Reflex Pathway

The reflex pathway is through the splanchnic nerve which acts as the afferent limb; the visceral afferent neurones, excited by stretch, relay in the cord and the efferent motor pathway is once again along the spinal sympathetic outflow. Thus the reflex is retained when the vagus is sectioned, showing that this is not essential; removal of the thoracolumbar sympathetic chain on both sides abolishes the reflex.

Coeliac Ganglion. It has been argued, e.g. by Kuntz, that the reflex could be mediated independently of the spinal cord, the afferent neurones from the intestine relaying with motor neurones in a peripheral ganglion, such as the coeliac (Fig. 4.22), but the bulk of the evidence is against this. Thus Freund and Sheehan (1943) could find no evidence for reflex activity through the coeliac and other ganglia; so long as one sympathetic chain and one splanchnic nerve were intact the reflex could be obtained. A further fact pointing to a spinal reflex is the influence of supraspinal activity on it.

Medullary Inhibition. It is well established that the activities of spinal motor neurones can be modified by visceral afferent impulses;

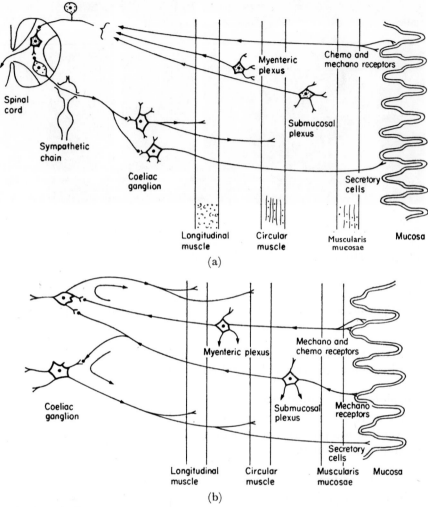

Fig. 4.22. Reflex pathways in the intestine. In (a) the spinal reflex pathways are
shown. In (b) the postulated intestino-intestinal reflex pathway, independent of the
spinal cord. (Modified from Davenport, *Physiology of the Digestive Tract*, Year Book
Med. Publishers.)

e.g. stimulation of the splanchnic nerve affects the activities of intercostal motor neurones, and this influence can be abolished by stimulation of a higher brain-stem centre. In a similar way Johansson *et al.*
(1965) were able to abolish the reflex response to distension of the gut
by stimulating the medulla (Fig. 4.23). It would seem that the medulla

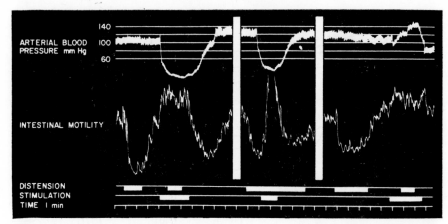

Fig. 4.23. Left panel: Effects of graded gut distension on intestinal motility before and during stimulation of medullary depressor area. Note that no intestinal inhibition is obtained by distension during stimulation of the medulla. Middle panel: Effect of identical bulbar stimulation during prolonged period of distension. Intestinal tone is considerably increased under these circumstances (cf. effect of bulbar stimulation in the left panel). Right panel: Same series of procedures as in the left panel but with stimulation of a different point in the medulla. Note that stimulation here gives blood pressure rise together with elimination of the intestino-inhibitory response to distension. (Johansson *et al.*, *Acta physiol scand.*)

exerts a tonic restraint on the intestino-intestinal reflex since dorsal hemisection of the cervical spinal cord enhanced the response.

Physiological Significance

We may regard the intestino-intestinal reflex as a mechanism for preventing too powerful contractions of the gut such as to completely obliterate the lumen.

Gastro-Intestinal Interaction

The intestino-intestinal reflex may well be a manifestation of a more general interaction between the different parts of the gastro-intestinal tract; for example, stimulation of the gut causes inhibition of motility in the stomach; thus Herrin and Meek obtained complete lack of appetite, with vomiting, in dogs by distension of a Thiery-Vella loop, but by splanchnectomy and excision of the lumbar sympathetic chain they were able to abolish the vomiting although the loss of appetite remained. When to these operations they added vagotomy, the appetite returned. It may be, as Lalich *et al.* (1936) argued, that both vagal and splanchnic pathways are available for this intestino-gastric reflex since the spinal sympathetic column did not have to be intact in order to evoke it, by contrast with the intestino-intestinal reflex.*

Gall-Bladder and Peritoneum

Stimulation of other regions of the alimentary tract than the intestine will also evoke inhibitory responses; thus distension of the gall-bladder or mechanical stimulation of the peritoneum cause inhibition of the intestine. According to Youmans, the manifestations of nausea and vomiting in response to these manoeuvres require activation of vagal fibres in the sensory limb, but as indicated above, the intestino-intestinal reflex operates independently of this.

SALIVARY SECRETION

Stimulus

We may now proceed to a description of the control processes involved in successive stages of digestion. In many species, such as the horse, the mere act of chewing seems to be the adequate stimulus to provoke secretion of saliva; and in a ruminant, like the sheep, there is steady flow apparently independent of any stimulus. We may presume that, in the horse, receptors in the mouth are stimulated by the food since, if the mouth of a horse is anaesthetized with a local anaesthetic, secretion is inhibited. In other animals, such as man and especially the dog, the mere sight of food is adequate to provoke salivation.

Motor Pathway

The motor pathway, as with other visceral systems, is through the autonomic, namely the glossopharyngeal (N IX), chorda tympani branch of the facial (N VII) and the hypoglossal (N XII); these relay in ganglia closely related to the glands. The actions of the nerves may be mimicked by acetylcholine or pilocarpine, whilst atropine abolishes the secretion, causing a dry mouth. Sympathetic stimulation also causes secretion of saliva, e.g. in the submaxillary, and it is interesting that the chemical composition of saliva secreted in response to sympathetic stimulation may be different from that induced by the parasympathetic; e.g. there is a much greater concentration of protein in the sympathetically evoked fluid. To the extent that adrenaline can mimic sympathetic stimulation, there is a hormonal control of the

---

* According to Jansson and Martinson (1966), however, the intestino-gastric reflex depends on an intact spinal pathway. We may note that the vagus, besides being excitatory to gastric muscle, will also cause relaxation; this form of inhibition is not brought into play by the intestino-gastric reflex, however.

salivary glands; also, when a sheep becomes depleted of Na^+, we have seen that K^+ becomes the dominant cation in the saliva; this ability to substitute K^+ depends on the presence of the adrenal glands, which exert control over the salt and ionic balance of the whole animal.*

Myoepithelial Cells

Ejection of saliva is favoured by contraction of the myoepithelial cells, so that if these are differently innervated from the secretory cells we may expect to be able to provoke ejection without increased secretion; in fact, parasympathetic stimulation of the submaxillary and parotid glands of the dog could raise the pressure in the duct even when no secretion was provoked. Sympathetic stimulation will also provoke salivation in the dog, and here it is possible to show that the myoepithelial cells contain α-receptors, and the secretory cells β-receptors; isoprenaline, which activates β-receptors, only raises the pressure when it provokes secretion, whereas noradrenaline, by activating the myoepithelial cells, could raise the pressure without necessarily provoking secretion (Emmelin et al., 1969).

SWALLOWING

The process of swallowing, or deglutition, involves the coordinated contractions and inhibitions of many voluntary muscles that force the bolus into the back of the mouth and into the pharynx; at the same time inspiration is inhibited, and entry into the trachea is blocked by contractions of the true and false vocal cords, elevation of the trachea, and closure of the glottis by the epiglottis. The initiation of this, the *buccopharyngeal phase*, gives rise to a reflex relaxation of the upper and lower sphincters controlling the entry of the bolus into the oesophagus and stomach respectively, together with a wave of peristalsis that propels the bolus into the cardia of the stomach.

Swallowing Centre

The highly elaborate process, whereby, in sequential order, the activities of more than twenty voluntary muscles of the mouth, pharynx and larynx, and the voluntary and smooth muscle of the oesophagus,

---

* The protein kallikrein (Vol. 2), liberated into the salivary gland interstitial space during secretion, has attracted some interest; it acts as an enzyme splitting off a polypeptide (kallidin) from plasma protein, the polypeptide in this case being a powerful vasodilator, causing increased flow of blood through the gland. The weight of evidence is against its being significant in controlling secretion (Beilenson et al., 1968).

are controlled, requires the presence of a central group of neurones, which have been called the *swallowing centre*.

Afferent Impulses to Centre

We may expect such a centre to receive messages from higher regions including the motor region of the frontal cortex since the act of swallowing may be initiated voluntarily. Furthermore, we may expect it to be played upon by afferent impulses from the mouth and oesophagus, since there is no doubt that most of the features of deglutition can be brought about by natural or artificial stimuli applied to these regions, i.e. to the tongue, epiglottis, larynx and so on. For example, sudden distension of the oesophagus, by inflation of a balloon in its lumen, will induce a wave of peristalsis down the whole length of the oesophagus, together with relaxation of both upper and lower sphincters, and it may even induce a swallowing movement. This so-called *secondary peristalsis* is not a locally induced response through intramural plexuses, but is a true reflex centrally controlled, since it will occur if the oesophagus is cut across above the balloon, and resected, thereby destroying the possibility of upward transmission along the intramural system of nerves. Furthermore, it is well known that it is much easier to swallow if there is something in the mouth, so that sensory influx from the mouth contributes to the firing off of the coordinated response organized by the hypothetical centre; in fact it has been argued that swallowing is essentially a reflex response *facilitated* by voluntary centres.

Oesophageal Muscles

The effectors in swallowing are the many voluntary muscles of the mouth, pharynx, and larynx, and the muscles of the oesophagus. The muscular wall of this region of alimentary tract is composed of inner circular and outer longitudinal layers, as with the other regions; unlike the remainder of the tract, however, the muscles are both striated and non-striated, the relative proportions varying with different species; in man, the upper third consists of striated muscle, that in the lower two-thirds being smooth, with an intermediate zone containing both types of fibre. In the dog, the muscles are entirely striated, but, irrespective of the types of muscle present, the propulsive movement of peristalsis is remarkably uniform, consisting in a caudad movement of a band of contracting circular muscle. Since the resting state of the oesophagus is one of relaxation, a "preceding wave of relaxation", characteristic of gastric and intestinal peristalsis, is unnecessary except in so far as it "pre-empts" the muscular system for contraction at the appropriate time.

Motor Pathway

The motor neurones concerned are located in the motor nuclei of the trigeminal (N V), the facial (N VII), glossopharyngeal (N IX), and hypoglossal (N XII), whilst the dorsal nucleus of the vagus (N X) probably controls the smooth muscle of the oesophagus. These motor nuclei are all fairly close together in the medullary and mesencephalic regions of the brain-stem.

Sensory Pathway

The sensory influx concerned with swallowing is derived from the trigeminal (N V) the glossopharyngeal (N IX) and the vagus; as

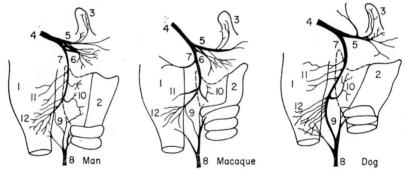

Fig. 4.24. Distribution of internal branch of superior laryngeal nerve (SLN): 1, pharynx; 2, larynx; 3, epiglottis; 4, SLN; 5, ascending fascicle; 6, middle fascicle; 7, descending fascicle; 8, recurrent laryngeal nerve; 9, anastomosis between recurrent and SLN; 10, fascicles to cricoarytenoid area; 11, pharyngeal fascicles; 12, fascicles to pharyngoesophageal area. (Doty, *Handbook of Physiol.*, Amer. Physiol. Soc.)

Fig. 4.24 illustrates, the internal branch of the superior laryngeal nerve (SLN) supplies both larynx and pharynx with sensory fibres. Electrical stimulation of this nerve, as well as of the maxillary branch of N V and of the glossopharyngeal nerve, will induce swallowing movements. The central pathway of the afferent neurones probably involves the tractus and nucleus solitarius in the medulla.

Localization of Centre

Thus it is reasonable to seek here, namely the medulla, a region which, when destroyed, abolishes the capacity to swallow or, when stimulated electrically, induces the complete act. By transection of the brain-stem at various levels the region within which the centre lies can be approximately delineated; thus transection at the level of the rostral medulla has no influence; if the centre were above this level clearly the motor nuclei and sensory stations would be inaccessible to impulses from the centre and section should abolish swallowing. Again, a section at the caudal end of the medulla, at the level of the obex, likewise has no effect, so that the centre must lie between these levels.

Split 1
Split 2

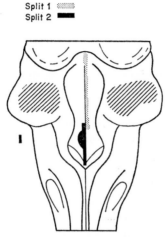

Fig. 4.25. The area within the medulla in which division of the midline modifies the swallowing reflex in response to stimulation of the superior laryngeal nerve. Split 1 has no effect on swallowing, but extension of the incision more caudally (split 2) causes the reflex to become unilateral. (Doty, *Handbook of Physiol.*, Amer. Physiol. Soc.)

Its exact location is easy to determine because it is organized in a strictly bilateral manner, in the sense that, if a midline incision is made through it, stimulation of the SLN on one side will produce a unilateral swallow confined to the muscles of this side.*

Midline Medullary Incisions. Thus we may make incisions of this sort in the medulla and determine the extent of the medulla that has to be divided to make the reaction completely unilateral. Using this technique, Doty located the centre exactly between the posterior pole of the nucleus of N VII and the rostral pole of the inferior olive, 1–3 mm dorsal to this and 1·5 mm off the midline. In Fig. 4.25 the dotted line indicates a large longitudinal split that had no effect on swallowing;

* The term "unilateral swallowing" is not completely correct; the efferent pathway to some of the constrictor muscles of the pharynx is crossed, so that whilst most of the swallowing activity is indeed unilateral, after hemisection, some of the constrictors of the opposite side contract whilst those of the same side are inhibited.

by carrying this a little further caudally, the response to SLN stimulation became unilateral. It is interesting that, if both SLN were stimulated together, a well coordinated bilateral swallow resulted; and this is made possible by some degree of motor interaction between the two centres.

Oesophageal Phase

Peristaltic Wave

The peristaltic wave of the oesophagus is not the result of a myenteric reflex, as with other regions of the alimentary tract; it depends on the extrinsic innervation and represents a sequential activation of the circular muscle fibres, passing as a wave down the oesophagus and involving both striated and smooth muscle fibres. Once the process has begun it continues to completion but, unlike the buccopharyngeal phase of deglutition, it *can* be affected by sensory feedback from the oesophagus; for example, distension can bring about inhibition of the wave distal to the point of distension.

Sequential Nervous Activation

That the wave progresses as a result of sequential nervous activation is shown by removal of a section of the oesophagus, when the wave passes over the non-conducting gap. When the blood supplying the brain was cooled, moreover, the wave of peristalsis was slowed, presumably because the activities of the neurones of the swallowing centre were slowed. As to whether the contraction-wave is preceded by a phase of inhibition, as in peristalsis of the small intestine, is not certain; thus there is no tonic activity in the striated muscle of the oesophagus, so that inhibitory influences would not normally be detected.

Sphincter Controls

Upper Sphincter Relaxation

The entrance to the oesophagus is normally closed, as may be demonstrated by the force required to push a tube into it, or by direct observation; opening of the pharyngeo-oesophageal orifice occurs when the act of swallowing is initiated, and such an action has been attributed to relaxation of the cricopharyngeus muscle as a result of inhibitory impulses from the swallowing centre. However, it is now considered unlikely that this muscle is tonically active, and the "upper sphincter" is considered to be held closed essentially by the elasticity of the surrounding tissues; opening is thought to be due to a passive result of laryngeal movements, but this is, of course, facilitated by inhibitory discharges to the cricopharyngeus muscle which have the negative effect of pre-empting any contraction that would otherwise occur.

Lower Sphincter Relaxation

In a similar way the tonic activity of the smooth muscle of the oesophageo-gastric junction, or *lower oesophageal sphincter* (LES), may be more apparent than real, apart from the inherent tone of the smooth muscle; stimulation of the vagus, which causes contraction of the oesophagus, causes relaxation of the smooth muscle at the oeso-phageal gastric junction.

Independence of Peristalsis. The opening of the lower sphincter occurs as a part of the complete swallowing process and is not dependent on the wave of propulsion—the *oesophageal phase of deglutition*—reaching it; thus a pressure-recording device held in the sphincter region shows relaxation well before the arrival of the peristaltic wave. Furthermore, the opening of the sphincter—the *gastro-oesophageal phase*—is clearly independent of peristalsis as shown by the fact that, with repeated swallows, the lower sphincter remains relaxed, although peristalsis is inhibited by the successive swallows; only when the final swallow has taken place does the wave of peristalsis pass along the oesophagus.

Again, as we have already indicated, the relaxation, which includes the relaxation of the cardia of the stomach that allows the bolus to enter without raising the intraluminal pressure appreciably—*receptive relaxation*—occurs well before the peristaltic wave reaches the junction, and may occur in isolation by a distension of the oesophagus too weak to excite a propagated wave of peristalsis. As to the nervous mechanism bringing about relaxation, adrenergic drugs apparently cause both contraction and relaxation of the circular muscle at the junction with the stomach; the relaxation is due to β-receptors, since it is mimicked by isoproterenol and blocked by propranolol. As Christensen (1970) has demonstrated, the smooth muscle of the last few centimetres of the oesophagus is differentiated from the adjacent muscle both pharma-cologically and by its response to electrical stimulation.

Preliminary Inhibition

The first detectable electrophysiological sign of swallowing seems to be the inhibition of all motor activity in the appropriate muscles; it is as though the swallowing centre signals to the large variety of muscles, many of which are concerned in other activities than swallowing, such as respiration and speech, that they are required for the special act of swallowing. An instance of this inhibitory influence is the forestalling of oesophageal contraction, due to local distension, by the act of swallowing; the inhibition occurs before any muscular signs of buccopharyngeal activity.

Inhibition of Respiration. This inhibitory activity extends to inhibition of the nearby respiratory centre, necessary if inhalation of food is not to take place. In this respect we may note that in man, some 89 per cent of swallows take place during expiration; in infants who are suckling, clearly the suck, swallow, and inhibition of respiration, must be well coordinated; and in fact the usual situation is a one-to-one coupling of these processes, the swallow occurring during expiration and setting the rhythm. An apnoeic pause, lasting some 1·5 sec, follows the swallow.

GASTRIC DIGESTION

The gastric processes consist, first, of the reception of the food from the oesophagus; and this involves the capacity to enlarge without the development of high tensions in the wall—*receptive relaxation*. Having taken up the food, the stomach must secrete acid and enzymes, whilst the peristaltic and other movements leading to mixing of the contents and emptying of the stomach through the pylorus must be initiated and maintained.

Distension Reflexes

Afferent Traffic

The signal caused by the entry of food is one of distension of the stomach, developing tension within its wall; and this excites the stretch—or distension—receptors innervated by the predominantly unmyelinated fibres of the vagus and sympathetic afferent system. The features of these receptors have been indicated earlier; most are slowly adapting units, so that a sustained message to the intramural ganglia and brain will be received. The signal will initiate reflex contractions of the muscle wall and ultimately, when the stomach has been emptied, these signals will cease and most of the afferent fibres will become silent. Contraction of the muscle may well also stimulate the receptors in the tissue, since it is likely that they are in series with the muscle and thus are more like Golgi tendon-organs than muscle spindles. Hence, throughout the ingestion of food and its subsequent digestion, there will be a busy traffic of sensory discharge from the endings in the stomach; these will pass through a maximum and eventually subside.

Satiety. Most of the fibres become silent when the stomach has emptied, although about one third continue to discharge at about 1–10 impulses per second (Paintal, 1963). These afferent discharges will be responsible for the sense of satiety resulting from filling the stomach but also, of course, they will represent the afferent limb in reflexes controlling the emptying through the pylorus.

Motor Limb

The motor limb of the reflexes causing gastric contractions is mainly through the vagus, but it will be appreciated that the highly co-ordinated peristaltic contractions are brought about through the intramural plexuses rather than through reflexes involving the central nervous system. As indicated earlier, the effects of stimulation of either division of the autonomic are not clear-cut; thus stimulation of the vagus causes both excitation—low threshold fibres—and inhibition —high threshold fibres—of the stomach.

Receptive Relaxation. It is this high-threshold system, mediated by purinergic nerves, that probably permits the large increase in volume of the stomach, without appreciable increase in pressure, that has given rise to the term "receptive relaxation". It is accompanied by enhanced secretion of acid and pepsin.

Gastric Emptying Time

The stretch caused by the presence of food in the stomach is an adequate stimulus to initiate the peristaltic and other movements that finally result in emptying the contents into the duodenum. However, there is a feedback mechanism from the duodenum such that the presence of the chyme in this region of the tract tends to inhibit empty-ing, and this may be the basis of the intestino-gastric inhibition described earlier. In this way the amount of chyme presented to the small intestine for digestion and absorption in a given time is con-trolled, thereby permitting adequate time for the intestinal phase of digestion.

Nature of the Meal. The *gastric emptying time* is thus compounded of two opposing tendencies. Hunt found that the emptying time for test-meals, introduced directly into the stomach, depended critically on the nature of the meal, and he concluded that there were receptors in the duodenum responsive either to chemical stimulants, such as H^+-ions, or to the osmolality of the solution bathing them. There is certainly a wide variety of substances whose presence in the duodenum inhibits gastric emptying, and the mechanism by which this occurs is probably complex; thus with many substances cutting off the sensory nerves from the stomach (vagus) abolishes the influence, so that the phenomenon is described as an *enterogastric reflex*.

Enterogastrones. With other substances, particularly fat, which has a powerful inhibitory action, section of the nerve supply is without effect, and it seems that a chemical mediator, liberated into the blood by the duodenum, is responsible. This factor was called *enterogastrone*, and the name was reserved for the principle contained by the duodenal mucosa that was apparently liberated in response to the presence of fat in the duodenum, and which inhibited the secretion of acid. Since the presence of acid in the duodenum also inhibits gastric secretion independently of the nervous system, it is best to include in the term enterogastrone the substance or substances that are liberated by the duodenal mucosa in response to acid or fat and secretogogues. As we shall see, it is likely that the two intestinal hormones, secretin and cholecystokinin, inhibit gastric acid secretion and may be described as enterogastrones.

Phases of Digestion

The secretion of juices (and changes in gastric motility) have been divided into three phases. Thus, well before the food has entered the stomach, the secretion has begun; this is called the *cephalic phase*, and is a reflex response to the sight of food and its presence in the mouth, and it is most easily demonstrated by *sham-feeding*, namely allowing the food to be eaten but causing it to be diverted from the stomach by an oesophagostomy. The second, or *gastric phase*, results from the presence of food in the stomach; and finally the transfer of the acid contents into the adjacent duodenum exerts a reflex action to give the *duodenal phase*.

Cephalic Phase

The cephalic phase of secretion is brought about through the vagus, whose postganglionic neurones in the myenteric plexus act directly on the secretory cells, stimulating release of acid from the oxyntic cells, and pepsin from the chief cells. This vagal action can be mimicked by acetylcholine or pilocarpine; another potent substance in provoking secretion is histamine (p. 339). It has long been known that extracts of stomach, particularly of the antral region, when given subcutaneously will cause gastric acid secretion, and this is due to the presence of a hormone, *gastrin*, elaborated predominantly by the cells of the antral region.

Gastrin

The hormone is a polypeptide containing seventeen amino acids, and was isolated in pure form by Gregory and Tracy (1964); the amino acid sequence of pig gastrin is illustrated in Fig. 4.26; the remarkable feature is the large number of dicarboxylic acid residues, imparting a strong acidity to the molecule. Several different gastrins have been isolated according to the species, and the differences have

Pig	Glu . Gly . Pro . Trp. Met. Glu. Glu. Glu. Glu. Glu . Ala . Tyr . Gly . Trp . Met . Asp . Phe . NH₂
Human	_____ Leu _____
Cow/Sheep	_____ Val _____ Ala _____
Dog	_____ Met——————— Ala _____
Cat	_____ Leu _____ Ala _____

Fig. 4.26. The amino acid sequences in a variety of mammalian gastrins. (Kenner and Sheppard, *Frontiers in Gastrointestinal Hormone Res.*)

involved substituting one or more amino acids for those in the pig molecule; for example, human gastrin contains leucine in plac of the methionine residue at position 5 (Fig. 4.26). In all species, two gastrins have been isolated, called Gastrin I and Gastrin II, Gastrin II having the tyrosine residue in position 12 sulphated. The remarkable feature of all gastrins is that the physiological activity is governed by the C-terminal four amino acids, so that a synthetic "pentagastrin" has been prepared, containing the C-terminal tetrapeptide of pig gastrin, elongated at the amino-end by a *t*-butylcarbonyl-β-alanyl residue; this has all the activity of natural gastrin.

Cellular Localization. By preparing a fluorescent antibody to gastrin and treating histological sections of stomach with it, the hormone could be demonstrated in special cells of the epithelial lining of the pyloric gastric gland; assay of regions showing high gastrin activity correlated well with regions of high fluorescence (McGuignan, 1968). The hormone is contained in 150–200 μ granules, identified in the electron microscope by labelling with an antibody tagged with horseradish peroxidase (Greider *et al.*, 1972). When portions of gastric mucosa from different areas of stomach were analysed for gastrin activity, this was found to be highly localized to the antral region, characterized histologically by the absence of acid- and pepsinogen-secreting cells (Fig. 4.27).

Gastrin is not confined to the antral region of the stomach; according to Lai (1964) the amounts in unit weight of tissue of antral, duodenal, jejunal, ileal and colonic mucosae were 46, 33·5, 12, 4, and 0·5 units respectively. In the pancreas—

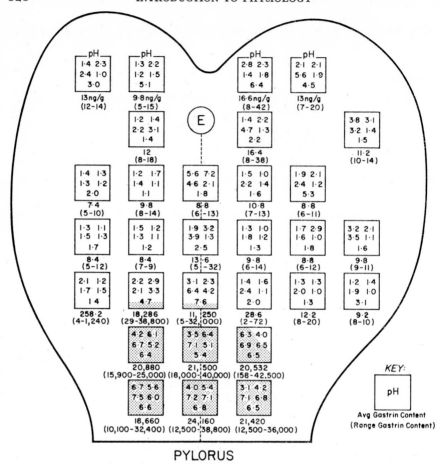

PYLORUS

Fig. 4.27. Diagram of the mucosal surface of the canine stomach showing average mucosal gastrin concentration, pH levels and histological demarcation between antrum and fundus in five dogs. E denotes oesophagus. The dotted lines between the oesophagus and the pylorus represent the lesser curvature of the stomach. The mean gastrin concentration (and the range of gastrin content) is given beneath each square as nanogrammes of gastrin per gramme of mucosa (ng/g). Individual pH determinations for all five dogs are given within the squares. The shading represents the area that was histologically typical antrum. (Jackson *et al.*, *Amer. J. Surg.*)

islets of Langerhans—the enzyme has been demonstrated in D-cells by the immuno-fluorescence technique.

Gastrin Precursors. Yalow and Berson (1970) showed that the circulating gastrin, when examined electrophoretically and by gel-filtration, was associated with a considerably larger molecule—molecular weight some 6000–9000—than the synthetic heptadecapeptide—molecular weight about 2100. Crude extracts of the antrum contained both the high and low molecular-weight material. Later (1972) they described a "big big" gastrin, with a molecular weight close to that of serum albumin. Both these large gastrins could be converted to the heptadecapeptide by treatment with trypsin. It would seem that, as with ACTH and insulin, the enzyme is stored primarily in a conjugated form.

Half-Life. When liberated into the blood from gastricmucosa gastrin passes into the portal vein and thus traverses the liver before reaching its target organ (Jaffe *et al.*, 1970); according to Thompson *et al.* (1973) there is some loss of activity on passage through the liver, and this may account for the short half-life of gastrin in the circulation, namely 3 minutes.

Vagus-Gastrin Interaction

It was suggested by Straaten (1933) that secretion of acid could be provoked by a dual mechanism, namely a direct effect of the vagal postganglionic fibres on the secreting cells, and less directly by a vagally induced liberation of gastrin from the antrum. This hypothesis

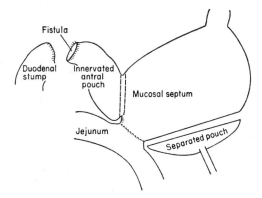

Fig. 4.28. Diagram to show the completed preparation of isolated innervated antrum and separated pouch. (Pe Thein and Schofield, *J. Physiol.*)

appeared to be disproved by the observation of Babkin and Schachter (1944) that complete extirpation of the pyloric region of stomach, responsible for gastrin release, did not affect the secretion in response to vagal stimulation. As Pe Thein and Schofield (1959) showed, however, a complicating factor is the inhibition of gastrin release caused by acidity of the mucosa, so that with an empty stomach the acid released by direct vagal action would bring the pH to sufficiently low values to prevent gastrin secretion. By preparing a separated pouch of the Heidenhain type, i.e. with innervation removed (Fig. 4.28) and by separation of the antrum, i.e. the region for secretion of gastrin, as another, innervated pouch, whose pH could be maintained high by infusion of buffer, they showed that, when the dog was sham-fed, there was a large and sustained secretion of acid by the separated pouch

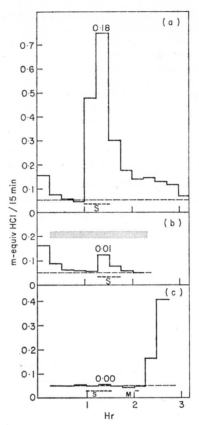

Fig. 4.29. Acid secretion by a separated pouch of dog stomach (Heidenhain pouch) in response to various stimuli. (a) Typical response to sham-feeding with isolated vagus-innervated antrum. (b) Similar experiment during irrigation of the antrum with 0·04 N HCl. (c) Sham-feeding following denervation of antral pouch. At the end of this experiment (M) the animal was given 300 g meat with the oesophagostomy held closed so that the food passed into the stomach. In all diagrams total acid output (m-equiv/15 min) is shown by the continuous black line; the fine interrupted line indicates the control level or titration value of the 10 ml 0·005 N HCl placed in the pouch every 15 min; the figures adjacent to each acid response indicate the total output in m-equiv during the first hour following sham-feeding. Sham-feeding is indicated by S and short lines indicating the duration of the sham-feeding periods. Acidification of the antrum is indicated by a band of horizontal cross-hatching.
(Pe Thein and Schofield, *J. Physiol.*)

(Fig. 4.29a). This must have been due to a blood-borne hormone— released presumably from the innervated antral region. If the antrum was irrigated with acid the response was considerably reduced (Fig. 4.29b), and the same was true of sham-feeding when the antrum was denervated. That the stomach was capable of secreting acid under these conditions was shown by feeding the animal with meat, allowing it to pass into the stomach. Local reflex secretion of gastrin was possible due to the buffering action of the meat, and this was reflected in acid secretion in the separated pouch.

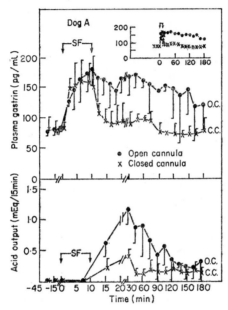

Fig. 4.30. Gastric acid secretions from Pavlov pouches (plotted at end of collection period) and gastrin concentrations before and after sham-feeding with or without the gastric fistula open. Each symbol represents the mean of three experiments. Vertical bars represent 1 SD. Note uneven time scale in large drawing. Gastrin concentrations are repeated with linear time scale in small drawing. (Nilsson *et al.*, *Gastroenterology*).

Sham-Feeding. The more recent development of the radio-immunoassay technique for estimating the concentration of circulating hormone in the blood has permitted a more direct demonstration that gastrin is released into the blood as a result of sham-feeding. Fig. 4.30 shows the large rise in both plasma gastrin and acid output from Pavlov pouches of dogs* after sham-feeding. If the acid formed in the main part of the stomach was allowed to remain in it, gastrin secretion and acid secretion fell back, indicating the inhibitory action of the acid; removal through a fistula permitted a maintained high blood-

---

* The Pavlov pouch retains its extrinsic innervation, by contrast with the Heidenhain pouch.

level of gastrin. Atropinization of the animal markedly inhibited release of gastrin into the blood, thereby demonstrating the cholinergic mechanism of gastrin release.

Cooperation. Thus vagal activity and hormonal activity apparently cooperate in producing the flow of gastric juice; according to Andersson and Olbe (1964), there is probably a tonic vagal discharge that potentiates the effects of gastrin on acid secretion, so that the response to gastrin in a Heidenhain pouch (denervated) was less than the same dose in a Pavlov pouch (innervated). In a similar way the liberation of acetylcholine from the stomach, caused by gastrin, may be expected to cooperate in promoting secretion. Thus Vizi *et al.* (1972) showed that acetylcholine was released from Auerbach's plexus by gastrin; whilst it has been known for some time that the secretory and motility effects of gastrin on the stomach could be inhibited by atropine.

Inhibition

Secretion of acid and motility of the stomach may be inhibited by central nervous activity. This is manifest typically in the effects of rage, pain or strong physical exercise, when gastric secretion may be completely inhibited, so that we may speak of a *cephalic inhibition* as well as a cephalic phase of secretion and motility. The sympathetic division inhibits secretion and motility, effects that are abolished by α-blocking agents and may act through the pre-synaptic mechanism suggested by Paton and Vizi (p. 297), i.e. through preventing release of acetylcholine from cholinergic neurones. At any rate Vizi *et al.* showed that the acetylcholine release, induced by gastrin from Auerbach's plexus of the guinea pig ileum, was inhibited by noradrenaline. As indicated earlier (p. 295, footnote), the results of stimulation of the vagus are complex, low-threshold fibres causing contraction whilst high-threshold fibres cause relaxation of the stomach muscle, and enhance acid and enzyme secretion. Thus sympathetic stimulation leads to inhibition of both motility and digestion, whereas parasympathetic inhibition allows the stomach to distend whilst enhancing digestion. It has been suggested that some vagal fibres liberate 5-HT as their transmitter substance; this would activate post-ganglionic neurones that cause inhibition of the stomach muscle. Certainly 5-HT, applied to the stomach, causes inhibition.

Effects of Gastrin on Motility. The basic reflex mechanisms governing 'stomach motility have been described earlier; it must be emphasized that the cooperation between vagal and hormonal activity is not confined to the secretory processes; gastrin has a powerful effect on gastric motility, an effect abolished by atropine, and so probably mediated by cholinergic neurones of the myenteric plexus. Of special significance in this respect is the abolition by tetrodotoxin; this abolishes neuronal conduction without affecting transmission at the endings, and so it must be concluded that the hormonal action involves at least one neurone. Simultaneously with these contractions of the body of the stomach, there is an increase in tension of the lower oesophageal sphincter (LES), thereby preventing regurgitation of the stomach contents. Thus the circular muscle of the oesophagus in this sphincteric region is characteristically different in its pharmacological behaviour from adjacent muscle (Christensen, 1970); this is especially true of its response to gastrin, it being a thousand times more sensitive than adjacent muscle, and 108 times more sensitive to gastrin than to acetylcholine (Lipschutz, Tuch and Cohen, 1971).

Effects of Gastrin on Non-Gastric Muscle. Gastrin causes contraction of the guinea pig ileum, *in vitro*, and many of the pharmacological aspects of gastrin action have, in fact, been demonstrated on this muscle rather than on stomach muscle because the effects on this were not easy to demonstrate (see, for example, Bennett, 1965). With human material, on the other hand, Bennett *et al.* (1967) found that isolated strips of stomach muscle responded to gastrin, whereas small intestinal muscle did not. In this tissue, local anaesthesia or treatment with neostigmine or hyoscine had no influence, and this suggests that gastrin was acting directly on the muscle rather than through the cholinergic mechanism demonstrated in isolated gut preparations, or in gastric pouch experiments on animals such as the dog. As mentioned above, gastrin causes contraction of the sphincteric muscle in the terminal few centimetres of the oesophagus, an effect that is inhibited by secretin (Cohen and Lipschutz, 1971).

Gastric Phase of Digestion

Distension and Secretogogues

The gastric phase of secretion is stimulated by the mechanical distension of the stomach together with the presence of the products of digestion—the so-called *secretogogues*; this process may be abolished by cocainization of the mucosa, and thus depends on a nervous mechanism that causes the release of gastrin. The demonstration that this is due to local influences is given by the preparation illustrated in Fig. 4.31, which shows a gastric pouch consisting of a piece of oxyntic (acid-secreting) area which is completely separated from the nervous system by denervation; the presence of secretogogues, such as meat extract, in the pyloric region causes secretion of acid in this denervated pouch by the liberation of gastrin into the blood by the cells in the pyloric region. Moreover, if the antral pouch illustrated in Fig. 4.31 is separated from the rest of the stomach and implanted under the skin, distension of this pouch causes secretion of acid by the rest of the stomach, due to

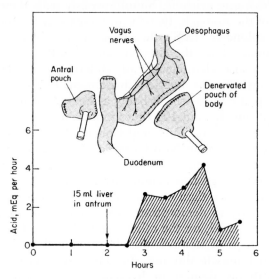

Fig. 4.31. Effect of inserting 15 ml of homogenized beef liver into denervated antral pouch of a dog. The graph shows the acid secreted by the denervated test pouch of the body of the stomach. (Davenport, *Physiology of the Digestive Tract*, Year Book Med. Publications.)

liberation of gastrin into the circulation, since this was vagally denervated (Grossman, Robertson and Ivy, 1948).

Acid Inhibition of Gastrin Release

It has been abundantly proven that liberation of acid inhibits release of gastrin; Andersson and Olbe (1964) measured the acid secretion in response to sham-feeding in dogs, with Pavlov pouches made from the antral region; when the pH in the pouch was maintained greater than 2·5 acid liberation was maximal, but between pH 1 and 1·5 there was a substantial reduction of acid liberation, an effect that could be eliminated by low doses of gastrin. They concluded that the physiological mechanism by which acidification acts is through suppression of release of gastrin. This could be a reflex mechanism mediated by the acid-sensitive receptors described by Iggo (p. 307), but there is strong evidence for a direct action of acidity on the gastrin-secreting cells. Thus acidity blocks the release of gastrin mediated by irrigating the stomach with acetylcholine (Thompson *et al.*, 1973), i.e. acidity can directly antagonize the effects of the cholinergic transmitter, and this suggests that both transmitter and H^+-ions act at the same locus, namely the gastrin-releasing cell.

Relation to Hormone Structure. The gastrin molecule is a strongly acidic one due to the 5 glutamic acid residues, and it may be that suppression of its ionic dissociation, by high concentrations of H^+-ions, in some way prevents its release, perhaps by preventing it from separating from a complex. It is interesting that the secretion of secretin is *activated* by the presence of acid in the duodenum (p. 347), and this molecule is strongly basic, so that if it is bound as a salt within the secretory cells of the duodenum, it is possible that acidification breaks this binding, permitting its release. Thus in the one instance acidity promotes binding, and in the other, promotes separation.

Physiological Significance. The function of this inhibition is obvious, being an autoregulatory device terminating the gastric phase of gastric secretion, i.e. when no further acid secretion is desirable, its production is temporarily shut off until the successive portions of HCl have passed into the duodenum. In general, then, the pH of the stomach contents seems to play a very large part in the control of secretion; thus in the resting stomach the pH of the antrum is low and gastrin release is inhibited; as soon as food enters the stomach the small amount of acid in it is neutralized and the pH of the fluid in the pyloric gland area rises, and this facilitates the release of gastrin provoked by the cephalic and secretogogue phases of digestion. Acid is thus secreted and its formation continues at a high rate until the buffering power of the food is exhausted, when the pH of the antrum and pyloric region falls to such acid values (ca pH 1·5) that release of gastrin is brought to a halt.

Secretogogues

The secretion of acid by the stomach is strongly influenced by the chemical nature of the food; thus protein, or its hydrolytic products—e.g. commercial peptone—is a strong secretogogue. Part of the effect of protein and amino acids may well be the buffering of the acid, preventing acid-inhibition, but there is little doubt that certain molecules have a specific excitatory action. For example ethyl alcohol has a strong action, and when different alcohols are compared the action is confined to ethanol and propyl alcohol; moreover, even the change from *n*- to *iso*-propyl alcohol was sufficient to abolish activity (Elwin, 1969). When commercial protein hydrolysate—peptone—was fractionated, Elwin (1973) found that the fraction containing the smallest molecules—amino acids and small peptides—was active in lowest concentration. It is generally assumed that the actions are reflexly brought about since they are inhibited by local anaesthetics in the stomach.

General Control Mechanism

The various influences on gastrin release described in the previous pages may be illustrated in Fig. 4.32, whilst Fig. 4.33 summarizes the control mechanisms in gastric digestion as a whole.

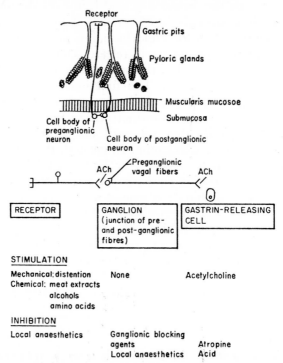

Fig. 4.32. Hypothetical mechanisms controlling release of gastrin from the antrum. (Elwin, *Frontiers in Gastrointestinal Hormone Research*, Ed. S. Andersson.)

Secretion and Motility. The control mechanisms operate in two ways, first to promote the secretion of acid, pepsin, and mucus, and to induce waves of peristalsis; these initiate digestion and gradually drive the food into the small intestine. They are brought about by direct nervous influences on the muscle and glands and by local reflexes involving distension of the stomach wall; these actions are powerfully reinforced by the liberation of gastrin, which is provoked either through direct nervous action, as in the cephalic phase; through local reflexes, as in the response to stretch of the antrum; and in response to the presence of secretogogues in the pyloric gland area. Secondly, the control mechanisms operate to restrain the passage of the partially digested material into the small intestine, thereby protecting its mucosa from being exposed to a highly acid medium, and from over-

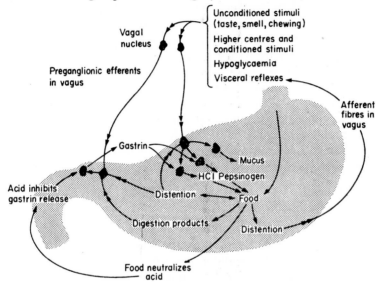

Fig. 4.33. The control of gastric secretion. (Davenport, *Physiology of the Digestive Tract*, Year Book Med. Publications.)

loading its digestive abilities. This restraint operates through feedback mechanisms; thus acid in the pyloric region inhibits the liberation of gastrin, whilst the presence of acid in the duodenum, and of fat and amino acids, provokes the liberation of secretin and of cholecystokinin-pancreozymin (CCK-PZ), both of which inhibit the action of gastrin, not only in respect to its acid secreting activity but also in respect to its action on motility. As we shall see, these enzymes also provoke the secretion of enzymes and bicarbonate by the pancreas, and the contraction of the gall-bladder.

Duodenal Phase

Enterogastrone

The final stage in gastric digestion is governed by the passage of the acid chyme into the duodenum; the acidification of the duodenum and the presence of fat and amino acids provoke the liberation of two intestinal hormones, namely secretin and cholecystokinin-pancreozymin (CCK-PZ) both of which have an enterogastrone activity in so far as they inhibit the release of gastrin, thereby reducing acid secretion and gastric motility. It was considered by Johnson and Grossman (1968, 1970) that the "physiological enterogastrone" was, in fact, the combination of secretin and CCK-PZ. However, Brown and Pederson (1970) compared a relatively crude preparation of CCK-PZ with a more highly purified one and found that the purer product only *stimulated* acid secretion, i.e. it had no enterogastrone activity; and this suggested that the activity described earlier was due to a contaminant. Later they isolated a polypeptide with strong inhibitory action, and finally its complete amino-acid sequence was determined; it contained 45 amino acids, 15 of the first 26 occupying the same positions as those in porcine glucagon (Ch. 5) and 9 the same positions as in secretin (Brown and Dryburgh, 1971). By developing a technique of radioimmunoassay they showed that the concentration of the gastric inhibitory polypeptide (GIP) in the blood increased after a meal.

Duodenal Acidity

So far as the acidification of the duodenum is concerned in the inhibition of gastrin release, there is no doubt that bringing the duodenal pH as low as 2, or less, inhibits the release of gastrin by a humoral mechanism independent of innervation of the gastrin-releasing part of the stomach. However, it has been questioned whether the duodenum would ever become so acid as this, but by isolating the duodenal bulb

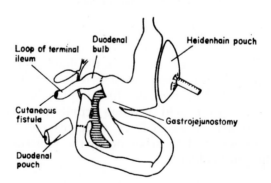

Fig. 4.34. The preparation used to study the effect of acid in a duodenal pouch on the rate of acid secretion by a denervated gastric [Heidenhain] pouch in the dog. The pyloric region of the stomach is connected via a fistula to the jejunum isolating the duodenal region. (Andersson *et al.*, *Frontiers in Gastrointestinal Hormone Research*, Ed. Andersson)

from the stomach surgically, as in Fig. 4.34, it could be shown that this was the sensitive region of the small intestine, acidification of which would inhibit secretion of acid by the denervated gastric pouch. Acidification of the distal regions failed to inhibit secretion, so it is just the region of the duodenum where the acid first enters that is responsible for the inhibitory action. Studies of the pH of this region under normal conditions showed that it was, indeed, low, so that when it was between 1 and 2 in the antrum of the stomach it was between 1 and 3 in the duodenal bulb, and 6·5 to 7·5 in the postbulbar duodenum (Andersson *et al.*, 1973).

Negative Feedback

Thus the intestinal phase is essentially a manifestation of negative feedback that graduates the passage of chyme into the intestine so that it is not overloaded and does not become too acid.

Further Humoral Mechanisms

Histamine

Experimentally the secretion of acid by the stomach is usually provoked either by pilocarpine or by histamine; the response to pilocarpine, which mimicks acetylcholine and hence mimicks the action of the vagus, is understandable, but the effect of histamine is not, and it is by no means certain that histamine plays any role in the normal activation of the secretory mechanism. It is certainly true that the gastric mucosa contains histamine, and large amounts of the enzyme—*histidine decarboxylase*—that is responsible for the synthesis of histamine; in fact Kahlson states that, in the rat, half of all the histamine formed in the animal is produced in the stomach wall, but this is not true of other animals.

Lowering the histamine content of the gastric mucosa, by treating pyridoxine-deficient rats with semicarbazide, to a small fraction of normal did not influence the response to gastrin, so it is unlikely that the histamine present in the mucosa is involved in the response to gastrin; however, the level of histidine decarboxylase in the mucosa does correlate with secretory activity, whilst histological studies suggest that the enzyme is associated with the parietal cells, so that Kahlson *et al.* (1964) have suggested that gastric acid secretion is, indeed, mediated through histamine, operating even when the amounts stored in the tissue have been reduced by some 95 per cent. Stimuli to secretion would release histamine from its stores which are continually being replenished by synthesis, a synthesis that is accelerated by

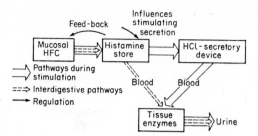

Fig. 4.35. Proposed pathway of histamine mobilized and synthesized in the gastric mucosa. The histamine store is assumed to be within, or close to, the parietal cell, as is the histidine decarboxylase. Because of the short life-time of histamine in the store, even in the interdigestive state, histamine is continuously entering the blood stream and excreted as free histamine or derivatives. (Kahlson *et al.*, *J. Physiol.*)

synthesis of new enzyme (Fig. 4.35). Certainly infusion of graded doses of pentagastrin in rats, producing increasing rates of acid secretion, were accompanied by excretions of graded amounts of histamine, amounts that must have come from the stomach since excretion was abolished by gastrectomy (Lundell, 1974).

Adrenal Cortex

The increased incidence of gastric ulcers during glucocorticoid therapy suggests an influence of adrenal cortical hormones on gastric acid secretion; adrenalectomy reduces acid secretion, which is restored to normal by administration of glucocorticoids, e.g. dexamethasone. As with other effects, the action of the hormone is permissive in so far as, in the normal animal, administration of the hormone does not increase acid secretion; thus the hormones are necessary to maintain, but not to stimulate, gastric acid secretion. According to Domschke *et al.* (1972), the reduction in acid secretion was accompanied by a drastic decrease in cyclic AMP content of the mucosa, which was prevented by dexamethasone (Fig. 4.36).

Cyclic AMP

This demonstration of the importance of cAMP in the mediation of gastric secretion conforms with the studies of Harris *et al.* (1969) on secretion by the isolated frog's stomach. However, attempts to prove a role for this "second messenger" in gastric secretion of the dog have not been successful; for example, Mao *et al.* (1972) found that the stimulation of secretion by histamine did not result in an increase in adenylcyclase activity in the mucosa, nor did dibutyryl cAMP initiate secretion when infused into a gastric artery. Moreover, when a positive

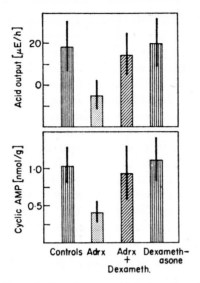

Fig. 4.36. Effects of bilateral adrenalectomy (Adrx) and replacement therapy with dexamethasone (Adrx + Dexameth), respectively, on gastric acid output and on cyclic AMP content of gastric mucosa in rats. Values obtained from sham-operated rats without (Controls) and with preceding dexamethasone treatment are depicted for comparison. (Domschke *et al.*, *Gastoenterology*.)

effect was found, e.g. by Levine and Wilson (1971), this was an inhibition, probably due to an effect on blood circulation.*

Insulin

The hypoglycaemia induced by insulin causes increased gastric acid escretion, and this is associated with an increase in the concentration of gastrin in the blood (Jaffe *et al.*, 1970) an effect that depends on an intact vagal supply to the antrum (Nyhus *et al.*, 1960). The effect manifests itself when the plasma level of glucose falls below 72 mg/ 100 ml.

Cerebral Hypoglycaemia. The hypoglycaemia directly influences the brain and its effects may be mimicked by reducing access of glucose to the brain by injecting a competitor that inhibits passage of glucose out of the blood into the brain (Colin-Jones and Himsworth, 1969). Thus the blood-brain barrier to glucose shows facilitated transfer kinetics (Chapter 6); a non-utilizable hexose, such as 3-O-methyl-

---

* Caffeine increases gastric secretion in dog, cat and man (Roth and Ivy, 1944) and this suggests an action of cAMP since, as we have seen, caffeine inhibits the enzyme that breaks down cAMP, namely phosphodiesterase (Vol. 2). According to Bieck *et al.* (1973), this class of compounds increase the cAMP output of the stomach in man and dogs.

glucose, when infused into the blood, caused gastric secretion in spite of the normal blood-glucose. Because hypoglycaemia also provokes secretion of the adrenal glands—the liberated adrenaline causing a rise in blood-sugar—the experiments must be carried out on adrenalecto-mized animals. Local application of another competitor, 2-deoxy-glucose, to the lateral hypothalamus in rats also produced secretion, and by making selective lesions in the brain Kadekaro *et al.* (1972) have shown that neurones in the median forebrain bundle* in the medial and posterior levels of the hypothalamus may be those that, as a result of hypoglycaemia, trigger off the response through the vagus. It is interesting that the food-ingestion centre is close, and animals that failed to respond to 2-deoxyglucose were also unable to feed themselves. It seems likely that the centre that triggers off the secretion of acid also triggers the secretion of the adrenal gland.

The Secretion of Pepsin

Chief Cells

In the great majority of studies on gastric secretion it is the production of acid that has been studied; since pepsin (or rather pepsinogen) is secreted by different—the *chief* as opposed to the *parietal*—cells, it would not be surprising to find differences in the effects of hormonal and nervous factors in the relative degrees to which one or other secretory product was produced. In general, the differences are mainly quantita-tive but there are some qualitative ones too.

Effects of Gastrin and Secretin

Thus, when they studied secretion by the denervated Heidenhain pouch, Dutt and Magee (1972) found that gastrin and pentagastrin did not stimulate pepsin release, although the cholinergic drug metha-choline did, and it seems that, in dogs at any rate, a background of cholinergic activity is necessary for gastrin to exert its effects, so that cutting the vagal supply to the stomach tends to inhibit the secretion of pepsin in response to, say, histamine or gastrin (Emas and Grossman, 1967).† Again, secretin, which, as we have seen, antagonizes the action of gastrin, tends to favour secretion of pepsin—it is a *pepsagogue* (Nakajima *et al.*, 1969).

* The median forebrain bundle runs between the fornix and internal capsule; it is not just a fibre-bundle but a complex system of fibres and cell-bodies and may contain both the afferent and efferent elements in the response to 2-deoxyglucose.

† The importance of vagal action was demonstrated very neatly by Sewing (1967) who cross-circulated two cats, one of which had its vagi cut. Stimulation of the vagus in the other cat provoked both acid and pepsin secretion in this animal, but only acid secretion in the other, this being evoked by the gastrin liberated into the blood of the vagus-stimulated cat.

Acidity

A further factor governing secretion of pepsin is the acidity of the gastric mucosa; if a pouch is made of an oxyntic cell region of stomach, and HCl of various strengths is infused into it, the secretion of pepsin is increased three-fold when 100 mN acid is present, compared with that at pH 7·5. Secretin, we have just seen, is a pepsagogue, and when combined with acid in the pouch there was a twelve-fold increase in secretory rate. Teleologically this relation between acidity and pepsinogen release is important, since it means that a high rate of pepsinogen secretion will not occur unless there is sufficient acid to hydrolyse it to pepsin.

Control Scheme

Figure 4.37 is a hypothetical scheme showing the factors governing release of pepsinogen into the stomach; according to this, the H^+-ions are the stimulus to an intrinsic neurone that excites the peptic cell, which can also be activated directly by the vagus. Secretin acts as a blood-borne hormone.

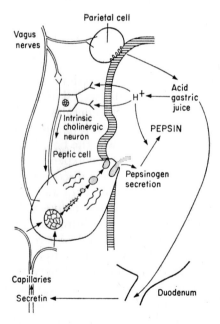

Fig. 4.37. Schematic diagram of mechanisms and agents involved in pepsinogen secretion and activation. (Johnson, *Amer. J. Physiol.*)

Secretion of Mucus

Stimulation of the vagus provokes secretion of mucus, so that during the cephalic phase, at any rate, all three parameters of gastric secretion are brought into play. According to Vagne and Fargier (1973) the output of mucus, as indicated by uronic acids, fucose and galactose, is increased by secretin but inhibited by pentagastrin. It seems, then, that the intestinal hormone, secretin, acts as secretogogue to both pepsin and mucus, but as an inhibitor of acid secretion.

INTESTINAL DIGESTION

Pancreatic Secretion

The main features of the control of intestinal movements have been discussed earlier (p. 291); so we need concern ourselves here only with the control mechanisms in the secretion of the digestive juices. The liberation of gastrin into the blood provokes, not only gastric movements and secretion of gastric juice, but also secretion of pancreatic juice, hence the intestine will be, at least to some extent, prepared for the reception of the chyme while the food is still in the stomach; before this, however, sham-feeding experiments show that there is a "cephalic phase" of pancreatic secretion within a minute or two of eating.

Secretin

Stimulation of the vagus causes secretion of enzymes, and this may be the motor route for this cephalic secretion. As Bayliss and Starling showed in 1902, the intestinal wall contains a hormone, which they called *secretin*, which, when injected into the blood, causes copious secretion of pancreatic juice. This was the first description of hormonal action, and Martin's description of the experiment is worth recording:

"I happened to be present at their discovery. In an anaesthetized dog a loop of jejunum was tied at both ends and the nerves supplying it dissected out and divided so that it was connected with the rest of the body only by its blood-vessels. On the introduction of some weak HCl into the duodenum, secretion from the pancreas occurred and continued for some minutes. After this had subsided, a few cubic centimetres of acid were introduced into the denervated loop of jejunum. To our surprise a similarly marked secretion was produced. I remember Starling saying: 'Then it must be a chemical reflex'. Rapidly cutting off a further piece of jejunum he rubbed its mucous membrane with sand in weak HCl, filtered, and injected it into the jugular vein of the animal. After a few moments the pancreas responded by a much

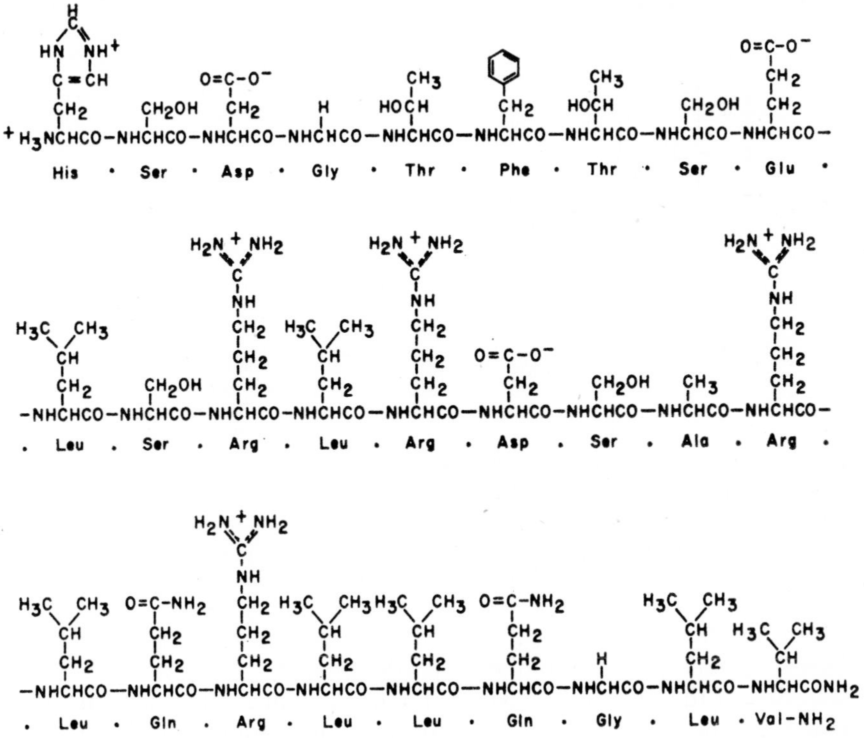

SECRETIN

Fig. 4.38. Structural formula of porcine secretin. (Jorpes, *Frontiers in Gastrointestinal Hormone Research*, Ed. S. Andersson.)

greater secretion than had occurred before. It was a great afternoon."

Amino-Acid Sequence. The hormone may be isolated from the wall of the small intestine, the largest amounts being obtained from the duodenum. It has been prepared in pure form and is a polypeptide containing 27 amino acids (Fig. 4.38); a synthetic product has identical activity (Mutt and Jorpes, 1968). Unlike that of the other gastrointestinal hormones, its activity depends on maintenance of the whole structure, so that cleavage products have little or no activity. The hormone not only provokes secretion in the denervated pancreas but also stimulates the secretion of bile.

Pancreozymin

It has been subsequently found that the main action of secretin is to provoke the secretion of salts, mainly bicarbonate, and of water,

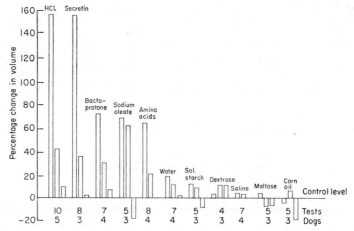

Fig. 4.39. Relative effectiveness of different foodstuffs introduced into the intact duodenum of conscious dogs in stimulating volume-flow (secretin liberation) of juice from the transplanted pancreas. The bars are arranged in groups of three, representing consecutive 20-minute collection periods. (Wang and Grossman, in Gregory *Secretory Mechanisms of the Gastrointestinal, Tract.*)

whilst another hormone, called by its discoverers Harper and Raper (1943) *pancreozymin*, stimulates predominantly the synthesis and secretion of the digestive enzymes. Pancreozymin is liberated into the blood by the same factors that cause the liberation of secretin, but these factors, such as presence of acid, peptones, amino acids, etc. in

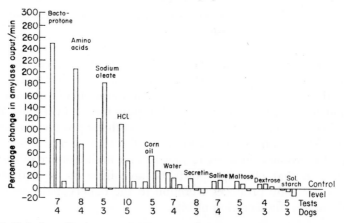

Fig. 4.40. Relative effectiveness of different foodstuffs in stimulating enzyme output (pancreozymin liberation) by the transplanted pancreas. (Wang and Grossman, in Gregory, *Secretory Mechanisms in the Gastrointestinal Tract.*)

the duodenum, have quantitatively different effects; thus acid is more effective in promoting secretin liberation, whilst peptones and amino acids are more effective in promoting liberation of pancreozymin (Figs. 4.39 and 4.40).

Acid Chyme in Duodenum

In so far as the natural secretion of the pancreatic juice during a meal is concerned, it seems that the most significant factor is the appearance of the acid chyme in the duodenum; this brings the pH into the acid region, with the result that secretin is liberated, and the flow of the alkaline juice occurs; this tends to neutralize the acid, and under certain conditions it may be shown that, by this process of "titration", a steady pH of about 4 is maintained. When acid chyme ceases to flow in, the pH rises and further liberation of secretin ceases. As to what the precise stimulus is, it is not easy to say; over the range of pH 0–3 acidity is unimportant; at more alkaline reactions than pH 3 there is a very close relation between acidity and rate of bicarbonate secretion, so that at pH 4·5 to 5·0 there is an absolute threshold at which there is no secretion at all. According to Grossman, it is the length of small intestine that has been acidified below a critical pH that governs the release of secretin, and the consequent secretion of bicarbonate.

Fat

When fat constitutes an appreciable portion of the meal, then the stimulus seems rather to be the products of fat digestion, fatty acids, etc., and the pH is maintained because of the enterogastric reflex (p. 337) that slows the emptying of the stomach when fat is in the duodenum.

Cyclic AMP

According to Scratcherd and Case (1973), secretin acts on the perfused pancreas through cAMP to stimulate water and bicarbonate secretion; they found only a marginal effect on enzyme secretion. By contrast, Knodell *et al.* (1970) found a strong effect of cAMP on enzyme secretion and little effect on salt- and water-secretion in the isolated rabbit pancreas.

Bile Secretion

The bile acids, synthesized in the liver and stored in the gall-bladder, are important for the digestion of fat. During digestion, both synthesis of further quantities of bile and expulsion of the stored material are excited, the latter being the result of contractions of the muscular wall. Secretion by the liver is under nervous control, so that stimulation of the peripheral end of the vagus causes a 2-4-fold increase. As indicated earlier, secretin provokes, in many species, an increased flow of bile and is thus to be classed with the *choleretics*, but there is some doubt as to whether the concentrations of secretin normally reached in the blood during digestion are adequate to be of significant influence on bile flow.

Bile Salts as Choleretics

Chemical agents in the blood that stimulate bile secretion are called choleretics, and of these, as we have seen, the bile salts are themselves very powerful; thus, after a meal when bile has been ejected into the duodenum, after functioning in fat absorption, the salts are themselves absorbed into the blood and the increased concentration in the portal blood causes the secretion of more bile to make up for that expended in digestion.

Gall-Bladder Contraction

Contraction of the gall-bladder may be evoked by stimulation of the vagus, and is part of the cephalic phase of digestion. A completely denervated gall-bladder contracts in response to the presence of chyme in the duodenum; the same process can be evoked by extracts of intestinal mucosa, and the active principle was described by Ivy and Oldberg (1928) as *cholecystokinin*. Thus three enzymes are extractable from the duodenum, namely secretin, stimulating bicarbonate secretion of the pancreas, pancreozymin, provoking enzyme secretion by the same gland, and cholecystokinin, causing contraction of the gall-bladder.

CCK–PZ. When Mutt and Jorpes (1973) attempted to prepare a pure specimen of cholecystokinin, they found that, with each step in purification, the activities of both pancreozymin and cholecystokinin increased in parallel, and they concluded that the two activities belonged to the same molecule which must, if this is true, be called cholecystokinin-pancreozymin—CCK–PZ. Like gastrin and secretin, CCK–PZ is a polypeptide; it will be recalled that the active site for gastrin is the C-terminal tetrapeptide-amide—Trp-Met-Asp-Phe-NH$_2$ —and it is interesting that CCK–PZ contains the same terminal sequence (Fig. 4.41), and its activity is governed by the C-terminal octa- and dodecapeptides, which have all the activity of the pure hormone. Corresponding with its similarity to gastrin, it has a weak stimulating action on gastric secretion. Secretion of CCK–PZ by the duodenum is provoked by the presence of the products of digestion, such as peptone, amino acids, or fatty acid soaps, so that perfusion of a solution of, say, phenylalanine through the duodenum, in the intact human through a catheter, provokes a prolonged secretion of pancreatic enzymes mediated by CCK–PZ. Not all amino acids are effective, in fact only the essential, so that a solution of eight of these

Pig CCK-PZ	Asp.Tyr.(SO_3).Met.Gly.Trp.Met.Asp.Phe-NH_2
Pig Gastrin	Glu.Ala.Tyr(SO_3).Gly-Trp.Met.Asp.Phe-NH_2
Caerulein	Asp.Tyr(SO_3).Thr.Gly.Trp.Met.Asp.Phe-NH_2

Fig. 4.41. A comparison of the C-terminal sequences of pig CCK-PZ, pig gastrin, and of caerulein. (Mutt and Jorpes, *Frontiers in Gastrointestinal Hormone Research*. Ed. S. Andersson.)

provoked as vigorous a secretion as that obtainable by intravenous administration of secretin (Go, Hofmann and Summerskill, 1970). It is interesting that these amino acids are absorbed by the same transport mechanism and are also present in the CCK–PZ molecule. When different regions of the intestine are studied, release of hormone is greatest at the duodenal end.

SOME HORMONE INTERACTIONS

Enterogastrones

Reference has already been made to the postulated hormone, enterogastrone, a term originally invented to account for the humoral mechanism that inhibited gastric acid secretion when fat was in the duodenum; as Grossman has emphasized, it is best to extend the term to the humoral factor, or factors, that inhibit gastric acid secretion and motility when acid, or hypertonic solutions, are present in the duodenum as well.

Inhibitory Action of Secretin

The preparation of pure secretin, and its synthesis, have permitted the accurate comparison of the effects of acid in the duodenum with those of secretin. Thus with the preparation illustrated in Fig. 4.42, secretion of acid by the Heidenhain pouch was measured in response to infusion of acid into the duodenum through a Gregory tube, whilst any natural secretion of acid was diverted through a fistula. Injection of secretin into the animal caused 100 per cent inhibition of gastrin-

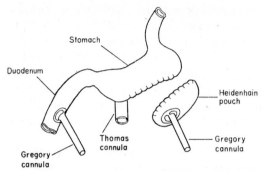

Fig. 4.42. The preparation used to study the effects of intravenous secretin on gastric acid production. Natural acid secretion is diverted through a Thomas cannula, and the effect of acid on the duodenum is studied by infusion of acid into the Gregory cannula, and compared with the effect of an intravenous infusion of secretin. (Johnson and Grossman, *Amer. J. Physiol.*)

provoked secretion, comparable with the inhibition produced by infusing HCl through the duodenum.

Inhibition by CCK–PZ

Similar experiments showed that pure cholecystokinin inhibited the acid secretion provoked by gastrin. The doses required for this gastric inhibition were well below those required for maximal pancreatic secretion and gall-bladder contraction, so that physiologically CCK–PZ could, indeed, act as an enterogastrone. The inhibition seems to be of the competitive type, as indicated by its Michaelis-Menten kinetics[*] so we may imagine a receptor on the mucosal cell that takes up both gastrin and CCK–PZ by virtue of their similar terminal amino-acid sequences (Johnson and Grossman, 1970). Both of these substances inhibit motility in a vagally isolated antral pouch.

Pyloric Closure. The pylorus, which controls entry of chyme into the duodenum and prevents regurgitation of intestinal contents into the stomach, is influenced by the presence in the duodenum of secretogogues such as amino acids and HCl; according to Fisher *et al.* (1973), these substances, which cause closure of the sphincter, effect this through the liberation of CCK–PZ into the blood. Thus an intravenous injection of the hormone caused a rise in pressure in the sphincter in human subjects, an effect that was opposed by gastrin,

---

[*] Inhibition of gastrin activity by secretin, on the other hand, seems to be non-competitive, so that the two hormones do not act at the same site (Johnson and Grossman, 1969).

whilst similar effects were obtained on isolated sphincter-muscle of the opossum.

Intestinal Feedback

Thus, as indicated earlier, the intestine cooperates in an efficient feedback mechanism that ensures that the emptying of the stomach matches the requirements of the small intestine, preventing the chyme from becoming too acid and the digestive system from being overloaded. Whether the hormones secretin and CCK–PZ are the important enterogastrones, or whether it is the polypeptide isolated by Brown and Dryburgh (p. 333) that is the most important, remains to be seen.

Secretin-Pancreozymin

It is customary to refer to the action of secretin on the pancreas as the stimulation of fluid and HCO_3^- secretion, whilst that of pancreozymin is to stimulate enzyme secretion. In fact there is little doubt that both hormones influence all three parameters; this is indicated by Table I from Henriksen and Worning's study on the dog. It will be seen, too, that the effects are additive. Again, Meyer *et al.* (1971) provoked the secretion of CCK–PZ by perfusing essential amino acids through the duodenum, and the result of this release of endogenous

TABLE I

Interaction of secretin and pancreozymin on external pancreatic secretion in dogs
(Henriksen and Worning, 1967)

	Secretin	Pancreozymin	Combined
Fluid (ml/min)	1·25	0·30	1·65
Bicarbonate (meq/litre)	120	81	135
Bicarbonate rate (meq/min)	150	24	223
Protein	7·6	17·5	23

hormone was to increase the HCO_3^- secretion provoked by a given dose of secretin; similarly the pancreatic enzyme secretion, brought about by the endogenously released CCK–PZ, was increased by intravenous secretin.

INTESTINAL SECRETION

So far as the intestinal secretions are concerned, Brünner's glands respond to the presence of food in the stomach and/or intestine; this is demonstrated by making a pouch of duodenum at the junction of the pylorus where the submucosa is rich in Brünner's glands. The secretion occurs in the completely isolated pouch, free from nervous influences and access to food, and this demonstrates a hormonal response which other experiments indicate is almost certainly not due to secretin; and it may well be that the secretion follows secondarily from an increased motility of the duodenum caused by the liberated hormone. Even more doubtful is the existence of a hormonal mechanism for secretion of the intestinal glands (crypts of Lieberkühn) in response to food; the mechanical stimulus resulting from its presence is certainly adequate of itself to promote secretion, and this is seen by exciting motility in an intestinal loop by insertion of a balloon; as the balloon is expelled from the lower end it is preceded by a few millilitres of secretion.

ELECTRICAL ACTIVITY

Stomach

A great deal of the motility of the stomach is "spontaneous", i.e. it is essentially independent of extrinsic nervous activity, and probably also of its intrinsic nervous plexuses; there is a strong element of *myogenic activity* in it. It is therefore of great interest to examine the electrical activity of the tissue in the intact organ. If electrodes are placed in the muscle of the stomach, records of spontaneous activity are obtained; these consist of rhythmic changes of potential, at 4–7 cycles/sec, on which may be superimposed spike activity.

Basic Electrical Rhythm

The slow potential changes have been described as the *basic electrical rhythm* (BER); when spike activity is superimposed on this, it is associated with muscular contraction; by contrast, the basic electrical rhythm can occur independently of contraction and is regarded as a pace-setter potential, governing the time-relations of the locally acting spike potentials (Fig. 4.43). Thus the frequency of the peristaltic type of contraction corresponds exactly with that of the basic electrical rhythm, the maximum frequency being, in man, some 3/min; when peristalsis occurs at its maximum rate, then the bursts of action potentials occur with each wave of the basic electrical rhythm. The BER is propagated over the stomach in a cephalad (head) to caudal (tail) direction, and the velocity can be measured by recording from electrodes spaced at intervals over the stomach wall; the speed increases as the antrum is approached and reaches one of 2–4 cm/sec or more

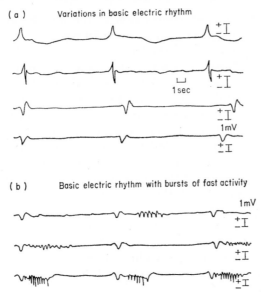

Fig. 4.43. Basic electrical rhythm (BER) of canine gastric antrum with and without action potentials. (Bass *et al.*, in Code and Carlson, *Handbook of Physiology*, Amer. Physiol. Soc.)

in the terminal regions; since the spread of the BER is accompanied by spikes and contraction of the stomach, it is easy to see how the contraction in the terminal antrum is nearly simultaneous over the whole. When food is present in the stomach the BER rhythm remains unaltered but the frequency with which a cycle of BER is accompanied

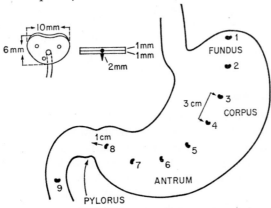

Fig. 4.44. Design of silver-silver chloride electrodes (inset) and sites of implantation used to study the basic electrical rhythm on canine stomach and duodenum. (Kelly *et al.*, *Amer. J. Physiol.*)

by spikes, and therefore contraction of the muscle, increases from a basic frequency of 13 per cent to some 70 per cent. When the animal is treated with pentagastrin the frequency is increased.

Pacemaker Zone. By sewing electrodes into different regions of the dog's stomach, as in Fig. 4.44, Code showed that the BER began just below the fundus, and travelled over the body of the stomach towards the antrum; no BER activity was recorded from the extreme oral part of the fundus. It was concluded, because the frequency of the BER was highest here, and because its activity dominated that of other regions, that this region acted as a pacemaker zone, in the same way that the SA-node of the heart is able to impose its rhythmicity on that of other parts of the heart, in spite of their own inherent rhythmicities.

Conducting Tissue. By making incisions in either the circular muscle or longitudinal muscle it was shown that the pathway for conduction was along the longitudinal muscle so that circumferential excision of a band from this muscle abolished propagation (Bedi *et al.*, 1972).

The Small Intestine

Spread from Stomach

When the wave of slow-potential in the stomach (the BER) reaches the junction between stomach and duodenum it is extinguished, presumably because the protoplasmic continuity is broken by a ring of connective tissue; thus spread along the stomach wall occurs by virtue of the syncytial nature of the smooth muscle, the depolarization of one cell being transmitted to an adjacent one by virtue of the presence of gap-junctions. If the stomach tissue cells are not joined to intestinal cells by similar contacts, then we must expect the electrical activity, if it is myogenic, to fade out at the connective-tissue gap.

Duodenal Rhythm

In the duodenal cap a new rhythm of slow potential is found, much more rapid, namely 17–19/sec, and propagated caudally at 20 cm/sec; and by arranging electrodes both radially and longitudinally in the duodenum, as illustrated in Fig. 4.45, it could be shown that the BER occurs simultaneously all round the perimeter of the duodenum and travels longitudinally as a "sleeve" of electrical activity; propagation is along the longitudinal muscle. As with the stomach, the occurrence of spikes on the slow wave was accompanied by contraction of muscle, as measured by a rise in pressure of a balloon in the lumen;

the greater the frequency of the spikes in a given burst, the more powerful the contraction, which was of the segmenting type, by contrast with the peristaltic type of rhythmic contraction that accompanies the gastric BER.

Effect of Morphine. By treating the intestine with morphine, the bursts of spikes became more frequent, and this was accompanied by more forceful contractions. The spread of BER occurs along the longitudinal muscle, whilst spike activity seems to be mainly confined

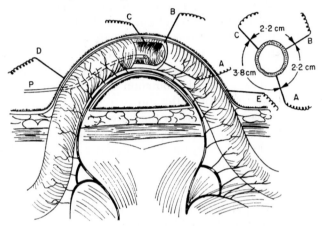

Fig. 4.45. Radial and longitudinal arrangements of electrodes in loop of duodenum. ABC are radial electrodes, BDE form a longitudinal array, P is the pressure-detecting catheter. (Bass *et al., Amer. J. Physiol.*)

to the circular muscle, so that it may be that the segmental contractions, involving the circular muscle, are initiated by the pull of the longitudinal muscle. This difference in character of the longitudinal and circular muscles is brought out further by the effects of morphine; this increases the frequency of spike bursts and also the tension, in circular muscle, but leaves the tension in the longitudinal muscle unchanged.

Effects of Food. As with the stomach, so the effect of feeding is to increase the frequency with which a cycle of BER in the duodenal cap is accompanied by a burst of spike potentials, so that once again the control mechanism is effected through a potentiation of the smooth muscle fibres that makes them respond more actively to the locally and centrally determined inflow of nervous activity, whilst the BER governs the time-relations of these responses and thereby ensures the basic rhythm that gives rise to a smooth wave of contraction and relaxation.

Gastro-Duodenal Independence

As we might expect from the different BERs of stomach and small intestine, there is no relation between gastric and duodenal motor activity; thus the antrum and pyloric ring behave as one unit, and the duodenal cap behaves as another.

Pacemaker Zone

The frequency of the BER decreases as we pass down the intestine and, as with the stomach, there seems to be a pacemaker zone; this has been identified in the region of entry of the bile duct in the duodenum; if the duodenum is resected, i.e. cut and the ends sewn together, propagation of the wave does not occur across the join, and now the more distal—jejunal—region acquires its own slower rhythm of 3–5 per min. The same phenomenon may be demonstrated in a reversible fashion by clamping the gut at regions progressively closer to the entry of the bile duct; when the latter region is reached there is an immediate decrease in frequency of BER. Thus the duodenal pacemaker zone imposes a rhythm on the remainder of the small intestine, but this is not the same for the whole, diminishing aborally.

Segmenting Movement

The most prominent spontaneous activity of the small intestine is the segmenting movement, which often occurs at a characteristic frequency, and this frequency corresponds with the BER.

Rhythm and Intensity of Contraction

In general, then, we may look on the BER as a means whereby a rhythmic form of contraction can be maintained; of itself it does not cause contraction, but by synchronizing the spike activities of the cells, it controls the rhythm of the spontaneous activity. Intensity of the contractions is governed by the frequency of spike activity, and this is presumably governed by the extrinsic nerve supply, by hormonal, and other chemical influences.

THE LARGE INTESTINE

The control mechanisms of main interest in the large intestine are those concerned with its movements, especially the final phase of expulsion into the rectum and defaecation.

Nervous Pathways

Neurones of the superior mesenteric plexus supply the caecum, and ascending and transverse colons, including both sympathetic and vagal components; the descending colon and sigmoid are supplied by the inferior mesenteric plexus. The rectum receives its sympathetic supply from the upper and lower divisions of the hypogastric nerves, and its parasympathetic supply from the sacral autonomic outflow—the pelvic visceral nerves.

Reflexes

Passage from ileum to caecum through the ileocaecal valve results from a propulsive wave in the terminal ileum. The valve is held closed by intrinsic mechanisms, in the sense that complete cutting off of the extrinsic nervous supply does not affect the closure, so we may regard the opening as one more example of the *receptive relaxation* that precedes the propulsive contractions. During a meal, the activity of the terminal ileum increases—the so-called *gastro-ileal reflex*—but the neuronal mechanism for this is obscure. A reverse type of reflex, whereby distension of the ileum inhibits gastric motility, is called the *ileo-gastric reflex*.

Gastro-Colic Reflex. By the *gastro-colic reflex* is meant the greatly increased motility of the colon that follows taking a meal, or, experimentally, by distension of the stomach; it usually occurs at the same time as the gastro-ileal reflex, but it is independent of this since it will occur in an isolated colon after ileostomy has diverted the contents of the ileum from it. It is very likely that a predominant factor in the elicitation of this response is the liberation of gastrin into the blood; certainly, when administered to man or the dog, it induces colonic motility similar to that observed after eating.

Extrinsic Nervous Effects. So far as the direct effects of nervous stimulation are concerned, the results are often contradictory, simply because, in the colon perhaps more than elsewhere, activity is dominated by local myenteric reflexes as well as by humoral activity, so that the extrinsic innervation merely modifies this; moreover, more and more evidence is accumulating to show that a given branch of the autonomic, e.g. the parasympathetic, may contain both excitatory and inhibitory fibres. Perhaps all that may be said, regarding the overall effect of the extrinsic innervation, is that the predominant influence is inhibitory, so that destruction of the lumbosacral cord results in excessive motility.

Peristaltic Wave

In the small intestine, the preparation phase for peristalsis is a contraction confined to the longitudinal muscle, and the essential feature of the peristalsis is the subsequent contraction of the circular muscle, which is sufficiently powerful to cause expulsion of the contents even if the longitudinal muscle fails to relax. In the large intestine, the relaxation phase ahead of the circular contraction is more important, presumably because the large intestine must expel solid contents, in which case the relaxation is more necessary.

Descending Inhibition. When a cat's colon was stimulated by inflating a balloon in its lumen, there was an initial contraction of the longitudinal muscle, followed by contraction of the circular muscle above the bolus and a relaxation of this below; this is seen in Fig. 4.46,

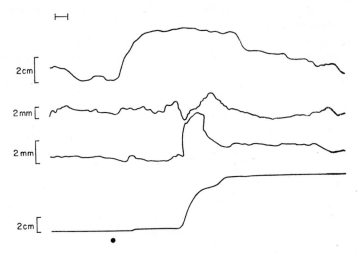

Fig. 4.46. The peristaltic reflex in the isolated cat colon. At the black circle a balloon was distended in the lumen of the colon. The top trace shows how the longitudinal muscle has contracted and remains contracted while the balloon moves aborally (bottom trace). The second record, down, shows the relaxation of the circular muscle below the bolus preceding the contraction of the circular muscle above the bolus (third record, down). Ordinates muscular movement. Time mark 10 secs. (Crema *et al.*, in Bulbring *et al.*, *Smooth Muscle*.)

which shows how the longitudinal muscle contracts and remains contracted while the balloon moves aborally (bottom record); the second record down shows the relaxation of the circular muscle below the bolus preceding the contraction of the circular muscle above the bolus. It is this *descending inhibition* that is the prominent feature of peristalsis in the colon. This inhibition is not mediated by the intrinsic adrenergic nerves, but may well be cholinergic since atropine abolishes the descending inhibition without affecting the contraction. Under these conditions, distension of the balloon causes contraction of the circular muscle both above and below the bolus; hence the inhibitory mechanism is normally polarized so as to inhibit circular muscle below the region of distension; thus the polarity of this portion of the gut, which ensures that peristalsis always runs aborally, depends on this polarized method of inhibition rather than on a polarization in the contraction process. If the inhibition fails, propulsion also fails.

Basic Electrical Rhythm

In the colon there is a basic rhythm of electrical and muscular activity (BER), with the caecum probably acting as pacemaker zone; the rhythm is slow, about 2/min, and is presumably associated with rhythmic fluctuations in tone of this part of the gut. It is remarkable that the BER of the internal sphincter is rapid by comparison with that of the rectum, varying from 6 to 26 c/min. The development of tension coincides with the BER although no spikes can be seen on the record.

THE RECTUM AND ANUS

The Sphincters

The final stage of the gastrointestinal tract is the rectum, which normally remains empty; it is terminated by the anal canal, the latter being surrounded by the two muscular sphincters, the *external* being composed of voluntary striated muscle and the *internal* of smooth

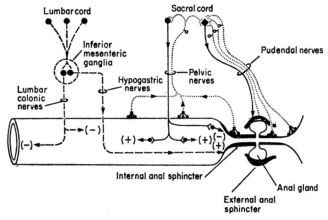

Fig. 4.47. Innervation of the distal colon and anal canal of the cat. The lumbar sympathetic inhibits the colon and is motor to the internal anal sphincter. The sacral parasympathetic outflow in the pelvic nerves is motor to the colon and inhibits the internal sphincter. The pudendal nerves innervate the external sphincter; sensory fibres from the circumanal skin, etc. run in the pudendal nerves. (Schuster and Mendeloff, *Handbook of Physiology*, from Bishop *et al.*)

muscle. The external sphincter receives motor innervation through the pudendal nerves, derived from S2–S4, which are excitatory, as with other somatic motor nerves; the internal sphincter receives an excitatory sympathetic outflow through the hypogastric nerves and an inhibitory parasympathetic supply through the pelvic visceral nerves (Fig. 4.47).

Tone

Both sphincters exert tone, that exerted by the internal being much the stronger and therefore the more important in maintaining continence. The tone is measured by insertion of balloons, and register-

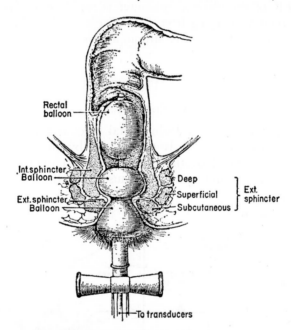

Fig. 4.48. A diagram of the balloons used to investigate the tone of the rectum and anal sphincters. (Schuster *et al.*, *Bull. Johns Hopkins Hosp.*)

ing the pressures within them, as in Fig. 4.48; to some extent the results may be artefactual since distension of the rectum and sphincters by the balloon may evoke reflex contractions. The tone in the external sphincter, as with tone in other voluntary muscles, relies on a reflex mediated through muscle spindles, with afferent fibres in the dorsal fibres of S2 and efferent fibres in the pudendal nerve. Thus section oj the dorsal roots of S2 abolishes tone in the external sphincter (Fig. 4.47).

Anal Reflexes

Reflexes that augment this basic tone in the external sphincter are
called *phasic reflexes*, and result from stimuli in the anal region, e.g.
perianal scratching (*anal reflex*) or penetration of the anus (*guarding
reflex*). Another powerful anal reflex operates through the bladder,
micturition producing sudden and complete relaxation of the external
anal sphincter; the afferent pathway for these bladder-sphincter
responses passes through both pelvic and hypogastric nerves to the
spinal cord with the efferent pathway by the pudendal nerves.

Flutter Valve

Whether a tonic sustained contraction of the anal musculature is
adequate to maintain normal continence in the face of sudden variations

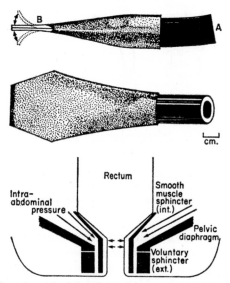

Fig. 4.49. Illustrating the principle of the flutter valve. Walls of the valve remain
approximated as long as pressure at B exceeds pressure at A. When enough air is
blown into A to exceed pressure at B, the walls of the valve separate and flutter.
Bottom: Diagrammatic application of flutter-valve principle to anal canal; increase of
intraabdominal (as opposed to intrarectal) pressure serves to close valve more tightly.
(Schuster, *Handbook of Physiology*, Amer. Physiol. Soc. From Phillips and Edwards.)

in intra-abdominal pressure, or whether additional factors are
necessary, is difficult to say. Phillips and Edwards (1965) have suggested that a raised intra-abdominal pressure can exert a force on a
section of the anal canal that makes its walls collapse, as in Fig. 4.49.
Such a mechanism would help to counteract increased intra-abdominal

pressure but of course would be useless against an increased pressure in the rectum. Cinematographic studies indicated that, when intra-abdominal pressure was raised, a portion of the anal canal was emptied of its contents.

Continence

Rectosphincteric Reflex

When the rectum is distended a reflex relaxation of the internal sphincter and contraction of the external sphincter take place (Fig. 4.50); this contraction of the external sphincter represents an important

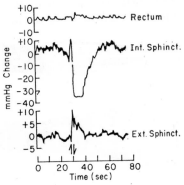

Fig. 4.50. Distension of the rectum (at arrow) causes a reflex relaxation of the internal sphincter (middle record) and a contraction of the external sphincter (bottom record). (Schuster, *Handbook of Physiology*, Amer. Physiol. Soc.)

factor in the continence of man and many other animals. Of primary importance, though, is the *reservoir function* of the rectum which, by virtue of its compliance, or receptive relaxation, allows material to pass into it without creating high rectal pressures. Thus continence is not impaired after colonic resection if the distal 7–8 cm of rectum are retained.

Rise in Colonic Pressure. When sufficient material enters the rectum to cause a significant rise in pressure, then the *rectosphincteric reflex*, operating on the external sphincter, acts as a retaining force. Because this reflex is not sustained for long, it probably acts as an emergency mechanism dealing with sudden rises in pressure, as when the intra-abdominal pressure rises in coughing. Thus, when a saline enema is given to the limit of tolerance, repeated rectal contractions take place, and these are accompanied by contractions of the external sphincter that outlast the rectal contraction, and with strengths that become greater the greater the force of rectal contraction (Brody *et al.,* 1960).

Relaxation of Internal Sphincter. The relaxation of the internal sphincter in response to rectal pressure operates against continence, in so far as the first barrier has been broken down; however, it permits a momentary contact of the rectal contents with the sensitive anal lining which permits discrimination of its nature so that voluntary control, or differential passage of flatus or faeces, is possible. If retention is decided on, voluntary contraction of the external sphincter contributes to the retentive force, whilst the receptive relaxation of the rectum allows the pressure to return to the normal resting state.

Defaecation

In general, then, the presence of faeces in the rectum sufficient to distend it induces reflex responses that tend towards continence; the conscious awareness, however, of this distension, brought about by activation of sensory pathways that reach the cortex, leads to the recognition of the necessity for defaecation. The subsequent, voluntarily controlled, activities, lead to an increase in intra-abdominal pressure and relaxation of the pelvic floor and external anal sphincter which, it will be recalled, is composed of striated muscle.

Defaecatory Reflex

The initiation of these steps brings into play the complex activities that make up the defaecatory reflex, which are coordinated by neurones of the sacral autonomic system. The sensory information that supports this reflex activity is derived largely from the rectum, and perhaps more importantly from the skin of the anus. This reflex activity includes an increased motility of the colon that sweeps faeces into the rectum. Centres in the brain concerned in defaecation are present in the midbrain and medulla, exerting influences on the descending colon and rectum.

Cortical Activity

The cerebral cortex is also important in so far as it receives sensory input from the descending colon and rectum, informing it that the left colon is ready to empty itself. It also initiates the variety of muscular actions that first increase intra-abdominal pressure and later relax the pelvic floor and external sphincter.

THE STORAGE AND VOIDING OF URINE

It is customary to discuss the physiology of micturition at the end of the description of the mechanism of formation of the urine. However, the physiological problems connected with the *formation* of the urine have nothing to do with the problems concerning the storage and voiding of this fluid, so that it is more appropriate to consider these in relation to the closely related problems of the storage and voiding of the products of digestion. Without further apology, therefore, we may break with tradition, and take up the subject of micturition and its obverse, continence, now. Urine is normally formed continuously and passes along the ureters to the bladder where it is stored and ultimately voided by the process of *micturition*, i.e. the flow of urine through the urethra.

Ureters

The ureters are tubes made essentially of smooth muscle, and transport of urine is brought about by peristaltic waves; this active driving of fluid is necessary since the pressure within the bladder

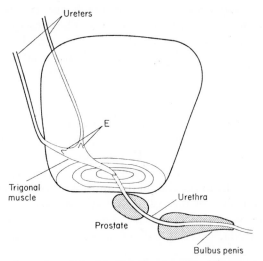

Fig. 4.51. Schematic section of the bladder showing the oblique entry of the ureters into the trigonal muscle at the base and the paired exits (E) on the inside. Note the flat floor of the bladder and the position of the prostate gland which surrounds the urethra.

exceeds that of the renal pelvis for the majority of the storage period. As Fig. 4.51 shows, the ureters enter the bladder at its base, traversing the smooth muscle of the wall at an oblique angle, so that the tone of the bladder compresses the ureters here and prevents reflux towards the kidneys. Moreover, according to Hutch (1972), the longitudinally arranged muscle fibres of the ureter within the wall of the bladder are surrounded by a sheath of circularly arranged muscle—*Waldeyer's sheath*—whose constant tonus maintains a closing pressure similar to that of the urethral sphincter.

The ureters are innervated by both sympathetic and parasympathetic divisions of the autonomic system by fibres from the splanchnic and hypogastric nerves, and we may assume that nervous activity modifies the otherwise spontaneous peristaltic activity that occurs with a frequency of some three waves per minute, travelling at a velocity of some 2–3 cm/sec. Thus section of the nerves does not abolish this spontaneous peristalsis. According to Rosen *et al.* (1971), a rise in pressure in the bladder is associated with an increased frequency of action potentials recorded from the smooth muscle of the ureter.

The Bladder

The bladder is composed of three layers of smooth muscle and lined internally with transitional epithelium (Fig. 4.52). The outer layer runs longitudinally from the neck to the fundus and is sometimes described as the detrusor urinae; the middle layer is the thickest and is arranged circularly to form a continuous layer. The inner muscular

Fig. 4.52. A diagram of the arrangement of the smooth muscles of the bladder wall showing the longitudinal external and internal layers and medial circular layer. 1, bulbus penis; 2, prostate gland; 3, apex vesicae; 4, external sphincter. (Nyberg-Hansen, *Acta neurol. scand.* From Andreasen.)

layer is thin and incomplete. Emptying of the bladder is a consequence of contractions taking place in all three layers, so that the name "detrusor" should be applied to all three equally and not just to the outermost layer.

Trigonum

The triangular part of the bladder-wall between the orifices of the ureters and the internal urethral orifice is called the *trigonum vesicae*; and its musculature is continuous with the longitudinal extension of the detrusor behind the urethra. According to Bro-Rasmussen *et al.* (1965), muscle fibres from the internal longitudinal layer make up a special *musculus trigonalis*, which develops embryologically from mesoderm, by contrast with the endodermal origin of the rest of the bladder. Hutch (1972) emphasizes the close relation structurally and embryologically of the deep portion of the trigone with the urethra.

The Sphincters

Leakage of urine from the bladder is prevented by the sphincters; the *internal sphincter*, or *sphincter vesicae*, consists in a modification of the muscular layer at the base of the bladder over the trigonum. Thus the internal orifice of the urethra is surrounded by crossing bundles of smooth muscle fibres continuous above with the detrusor muscle. There is probably no true ring of muscle fibres forming a sphincter proper; rather the fibres seem to be continuations of the longitudinal muscles of the detrusor, passing around the urethra in a postero-inferior direction, and forming a band of obliquely running smooth muscle fibres behind the urethral outlet (Clegg, 1957). Emptying of the bladder may be induced experimentally by insertion of a cannula up the urethra until its tip has passed through the internal sphincter. Two other muscles, composed this time of striated fibres, contribute to preventing flow of urine along the urethra; together they form the *external sphincter*, or *sphincter urethrae*. They can be closed voluntarily, e.g. during micturition, but are only opened reflexly and as part of the total act of micturition. The chief one, the *compressor urethrae*, forms a flat ring around the second part of the urethra extending, in the male, from the prostate to the bulb; the other is the *bulbo-cavernosus* in the bulb.

The muscular arrangements vary with the species, but in general we may always speak of an *internal sphincter*, composed of smooth muscle, and an *external sphincter* composed of voluntary muscle, although in the latter case smooth muscle fibres may be intermixed with the striated ones (Clegg, 1957).

In the normal animal, including man, flow of urine is held up at the internal meatus by the internal sphincter; so that the urethra distal to the internal sphincter is free of urine even when the bladder is fully distended. Under certain pathological or experimental conditions the internal sphincter is forced and urine is now retained by the stronger compressor.*

Innervation of the Bladder

Pelvic Nerves

The innervation of the bladder and sphincters is illustrated by Fig. 4.53. The important motor and sensory nerves are the parasympathetic *pelvic nerves* (*nervi erigentes*), with their motor neurones in the cord at the levels of S2 and S3 and their sensory neurones in the corresponding dorsal root ganglia. The preganglionic parasympathetic fibres mix with fibres from the hypogastric nerve to form the *hypogastric plexus* with its ganglia. Fibres to the bladder in this plexus pass from here to the *vesical plexus* and enter the vesical musculature. Some of the fibres terminate in the hypogastric plexus, so that their postganglionic fibres are relatively long compared with those from the vesical plexus on the bladder itself. Ganglia are especially numerous in the bladder-wall near the entrance of the ureters.

Hypogastrics

In most animals the preganglionic sympathetic fibres innervating the bladder are derived from the anterior roots of L2–L5; most of these "white rami", or preganglionic fibres, terminate in the inferior mesenteric ganglion, and postganglionic fibres attain the bladder wall via the hypogastric and vesical plexuses. Some preganglionic fibres do not relay in the inferior mesenteric ganglion but pass on in the hypogastric nerves to the peripheral plexus, and thus have very short postganglionic fibres.

* Hutch (1972) has described in some detail the anatomy of the human bladder in relation to the trigone, the sphincters and the urethro-vesical junction (UVJ), and has formulated interesting theories concerning the mechanics of continence and micturition. He describes *three* urinary sphincters. According to his description, the internal sphincter is composed of smooth muscle of the bladder and is presumably the equivalent of the physiologist's internal sphincter. The *urethral sphincter* consists of rings of muscle, predominantly smooth in the proximal urethra, and mixed with striated muscles (paraurethral striated muscles), coming up from the urogenital diaphragm, in the distal urethra. The *external sphincter* is composed of striated muscle, its basic portion being the circular striated muscle that lies between the two layers of the urogenital diaphragm through which the urethra passes; from here muscle is reflected up the urethra, forming rings around the lower urethra. Hutch emphasizes that incontinence does *not* follow paralysis of the external sphincter, and he attributes an important role to it in ejaculation as well as the voluntary cessation of micturition.

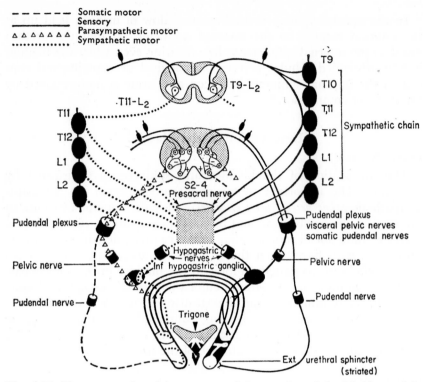

Fig. 4.53. The segmental and intrasegmental innervation of the bladder and its sphincters. (Bors. *J. nerv. ment. Dis.*)

Pudic Nerve

This is an ordinary somatic nerve originating, in man, from S3 and S4; it carries motor fibres to the voluntary muscles associated with the bladder, notably the external sphincter or compressor, and auxiliary muscles, such as the perineal. Thus electrical stimulation of the peripheral stump of the cut nerve in man causes contraction of the compressor but, according to Bors (1952), it also causes contraction of the neck of the bladder.

Sensory

All three nerves contain sensory fibres originating in the bladder or urethra; the afferent sympathetic fibres in the hypogastric nerves enter the cord through the lower thoracic and first and second lumbar roots; those in the pelvic nerve through S2 and S3 and those in the pudic mainly through S3 and S4. There seems little doubt that some of the afferent impulses relating to bladder distension are carried in the hypogastric nerves, and this means that some sensation may be felt when the cord is transected considerably higher than T10, in fact the sensation of bladder-distension is only abolished by sections higher than T6–T4 (Bors, 1952). However, the sensation of bladder-filling, leading eventually to the desire to void and to micturition, is mediated through the pelvic nerves in normal human subjects; and it would seem that the sympathetic afferents mediate mainly pain, although this may also be carried by the pelvic nerves (Nyberg-Hansen, 1960).

Distribution within the Bladder

El-Badawi and Schenk (1966) have reviewed the conflicting descriptions of the detailed innervation of the bladder tissue; in their own work they employed histochemical identification of neurones through their content of cholinesterase and catecholamine. On this basis they were able to show that all parts of the bladder contained both sympathetic and parasympathetic innervation, so that the claim that the trigone was only sympathetically innervated seems unsound. Throughout the tissue there were ganglion cells, so that a high degree of intrinsic coordination of muscular activity is possible. These authors (1968, 1971) emphasize the interrelationships between the two types of innervation; thus preganglionic sympathetic and parasympathetic neurones were seen synapsing with a single ganglion cell. The terminal ramifications of parasympathetic neurones probably come into relation with every muscle cell, whereas the terminal arrangements of sympathetic fibres are more restricted, and vary considerably with the part of the bladder considered, so that in the bladder-dome there are relatively few fibres in relation to the muscle cells. Moreover, the degree of sympathetic innervation shows marked species variations.

Tonus and Reflex Micturition

Man and several other species, such as the cat and dog, are able to void their bladders at will,* whilst with others this occurs automatically when a certain degree of bladder-filling has been reached. With voluntary micturition it would seem that the basic course of events is the same as with reflex micturition once the normal inhibition that sustains continence has been released.

Pressure-Volume Relation

Experimentally the relation between the pressure developed within the bladder, and the volume contained within it, is determined most

---

* See, however, p. 392.

simply by inserting a cannula through the urethra into the bladder; connected with the cannula through a side-arm is a manometer or pressure-transducer (Fig. 4.54). Alternatively, two concentric cannulae may be introduced, filling being carried out through the internal one and pressure being measured through the outer one; with this arrangement, by having the tip of the internal catheter in the bladder and the tip of the external one within the urethra, effects of bladder distension on sphincteric action may be measured. Fluid may be introduced in regular amounts into the bladder and the pressure recorded.

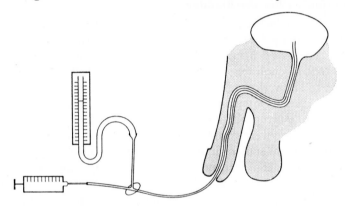

Fig. 4.54. A method used to record the pressure within the urinary bladder.

Each new introduction causes a phasic rise in pressure which then falls—a process that has been called *accommodation* and is probably equivalent to the receptive relaxation of the stomach. This accommodation may amount to about 80 per cent when the bladder is not greatly distended.

Laplace Law. An important element in this receptive relaxation, however, is the relation between tension in the wall of a hollow elastic body and the pressure within it. This has been discussed in relation to the vascular and respiratory systems (Vol. 1); it will be recalled that the tension, T, is related to the internal pressure, P, by the relation:

$$P = \frac{2T}{R}$$

R being the radius of the hollow spherical elastic body. Initially, when fluid is being introduced, the pressure rises; this causes dilatation with a consequent stretching and increase in T. Thus both R and T increase together, so that the change in P may be very small.

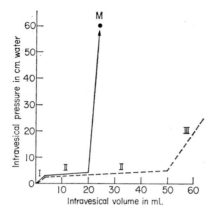

Fig. 4.55. Schematic cystometrograms. M indicates peak-pressure during micturition contraction. Segment I, or the initial rise, is segment from zero to first point of inflection. Segment II, or the initial limb, begins at first inflection point and either ends at micturition contraction (solid line) or, in the absence of micturition reflex, continues into segment III (dotted line). Segment III, or the ascending limb, is a sharply rising terminal limb. (Tang and Ruch, *Amer. J. Physiol.*)

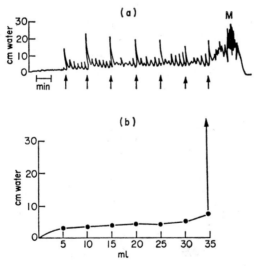

Fig. 4.56. (a) Cystometrogram from cat bladder with intact nerve supply. Volume increments of 5 ml at arrows were produced by rapid injections through a three-way valve connecting the bladder cavity to the pressure-transducer. Tube connection to the transducer was shut during injection, then opened for intravesical recording. M, micturition. (b) Graphic reproduction of the cystometrogram in (a) by plotting prefilling pressure-levels (in cm water) against volume (in ml). (Gjone, *Acta physiol. scand.*)

Cystometrogram

The steady-state pressure, achieved after this accommodation, is plotted against the volume, and the resulting *cystometrogram* may be illustrated schematically in Fig. 4.55. The course of events in a typical measurement is illustrated by Fig. 4.56; in (a) the acute rises in pressure and subsequent oscillations in response to individual injections of 5 ml into the cat's bladder are shown, whilst in (b) the steady pressures finally achieved have been plotted against volume.

Micturition Reflex

As Guyon first showed in 1900, at a certain level of filling there is a steep increase in pressure that is reflected in expulsion of the contents around the side of the cannula; and this corresponds to the initiation of the full *micturition reflex*, which for the moment we may describe as the powerful and sustained contraction of the detrusor accompanied by opening of the internal sphincter and relaxation of the voluntary muscle of the external sphincter.

Tonus

The slope of Phase II in the schematic cystometrogram has been called the *tonus* of the bladder, so that a *hypertonic* bladder would be one with a steep slope, a small increment of volume producing an unusually high pressure; a *hypotonic* bladder would be one giving a flat tonus-slope. When pressure increases to a certain *threshold*, micturition begins. Thus the cystometrogram contains two parameters of interest, namely the tonic phase and the threshold pressure, or volume, required to induce micturition.

Micturition

The process of micturition, once started, proceeds to completion, i.e. to the complete emptying of the bladder as a result of sustained contraction of the detrusor. Failure to empty the bladder completely indicates a partial failure of the mechanism. The emptying is achieved primarily by contraction of the detrusor; the relaxation of the internal sphincter is almost certainly the mechanical consequence of this; it is certainly not due to a reflex inhibition of a tonic contraction that normally keeps it closed. By contrast, the inhibition of the external sphincter, mediated through the pudendal nerves, is a part of the micturition reflex, so that cutting the motor roots of the pudendal nerves increases the pressure required to void urine. The reflex nature of micturition is demonstrated by cutting the pelvic nerves, in which case fluid may be introduced into the bladder indefinitely without provoking the coordinated contraction of the detrusor and relaxation of the sphincters; instead, when pressure is raised, fluid tends to escape in spurts, and the bladder may be said to be automatic.

Peripheral Nerves and Tonus

The bladder has two motor supplies, namely through the pelvic (parasympathetic) and hypogastric (sympathetic) nerves; and the two main problems are the extents to which the motor nerves are involved in detrusor contraction during the micturition reflex, and in the normal tonus, as exhibited by the slope of Phase II of the cystometrogram (Fig. 4.55). The involvement of the pelvic nerves in detrusor contraction during micturition is unequivocal, the reflex being abolished on section of these nerves, whilst their electrical stimulation produces a sustained and powerful contraction of the bladder wall. Section of the hypogastrics leaves micturition apparently unaffected; stimulation, however, does not produce a simple relaxation as might be anticipated by analogy with other viscera, in fact, Kuntz and Saccomanno (1944) found an initial sharp rise in pressure followed by a fall in the pressure-volume curve below the pre-stimulatory level; this was associated with abolition of rhythmical activity. Whatever the cause of the rise in pressure, this seems never to be adequate to cause micturition (Gjone, 1965).

Nerve Section and Micturition

The effects of cutting the nerves also emphasize the dominant importance of the pelvic nerves; thus cutting the hypogastric nerves does not interfere with micturition, whereas cutting the pelvic nerves leads to retention of urine with final overflow when pressure develops sufficiently to overcome sphincter tone. According to Barrington (1914), overflow ceases after some days and the animal passes small quantities of urine reflexly, retaining large amounts. When the pudic nerves were also cut, thereby releasing tonic control over the external sphincter, voluntary micturition ceased and there was continuous dribbling. Cutting the pudic nerves alone leads to incontinence in cats, through lack of control over the external sphincter, but the process of micturition takes place as a coordinated act.*

* According to Hutch (1972) failure of the external sphincter in humans does not lead to incontinence. This is reasonable, since in the female this muscle is not well developed.

Tonus

The tonus of the bladder muscle is revealed in two ways, namely as the slope of the cystometrogram, or as the rhythmic contractions of the bladder, which become more and more evident as the bladder fills. Since the classical studies of Elliott (1907), for example, had shown that these rhythmical contractions persisted in the extrinsically denervated bladder, but disappeared when the intrinsic plexuses and ganglia were removed, it was concluded that this tonus was a feature of the intrinsic plexuses rather than being analogous with the postural tone of skeletal muscle, which Sherrington's studies had shown to be

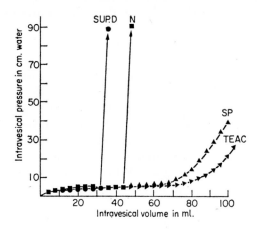

Fig. 4.57. The effect of nerve section on micturition. The traces show normal (N), supracollicular decerebrate (SUP.D) and spinal (SP) cystometrograms, and cystometrogram following intramuscular injection of tetra-ethyl ammonium chloride (TEAC). (Tang and Ruch, *Amer. J. Physiol.*)

due to reflex contractions initiated by stretch in the muscle, a tone that was abolished by cutting the sensory or motor roots of the nerves supplying the muscle. So far as the slope of the cystometrogram is concerned, there is little doubt, from the studies of Langley and Whiteside (1951) on dogs and Tang and Ruch (1955) on cats, that this tonus is *not* a reflex phenomenon. Thus the reflex-sensitivity of the bladder, measured by the threshold for micturition, can be altered by several means; for example, the sensitivity can be increased by a supracollicular decerebration (p. 386) and reduced to the point of complete abolition of the reflex by spinal transection yet, as Fig. 4.57 shows, the slope of the cystometrogram remains the same. When autonomic blockade is established with TEAC the slope remains the same.*

Nerve Section and Tone. That the peripheral extrinsic nerve-supply is not without influence on the rhythmic activity of the bladder was shown by Gjone (1965), who avoided the danger of overdistension of the bladder by inserting his cannula into the bladder directly, after a laparotomy; thus the urethral opening was unobstructed by a catheter and, when the micturition reflex was initiated, it could proceed without hindrance. Figure 4.58 shows the effects of successively

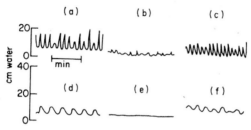

Fig. 4.58. Intravesical pressure variations at constant bladder volumes. Upper records: bladder filled with 20 ml saline solution. (a) Intact nerves; (b) efferent parasympathetic nerve supply cut and (c) in addition sympathetic supply bilaterally interrupted. Lower records: bladder filled with 10 ml fluid. (d) Intact nerves; (e) afferent parasympathetic nerves bilaterally sectioned, and (f) efferent parasympathetic nerves and sympathetic supply also cut. (Gjone, *Acta physiol. scand.*)

cutting the parasympathetic and sympathetic supplies; there is a marked reduction in the rhythmical contractions (b) on cutting the parasympathetic supply, but these return to nearly their former amplitude when the sympathetic is cut as well, suggesting that, so far as these tonic contractions are concerned, the two divisions of the autonomic system oppose each other. The results show, as well, that the denervated bladder is nearly as reactive, so far as these contractions are concerned, as the innervated one. Thus, there is an inherent tone, probably mediated through the intrinsic nervous plexuses, but this is modified by both sympathetic and parasympathetic supplies, acting in opposition.

When Gjone (1965) applied the same nerve-sectioning techniques to the measurement of the slope of the cystometrogram, he found an essential antagonism between the two divisions of the autonomic supply.

* Langley and Whiteside (1951) drew attention to the marked loss of tone in a bladder if it has been maintained in a distended state for some time. After spinal transection, unless the animal is catheterized, the bladder is greatly distended, and it is to this, rather than to any loss of nervous influences, that the "atonic" bladder of spinal transection may be attributed.

This is revealed by Fig. 4.59; I indicates the normal animal; in II the afferent supply from the bladder was removed by sectioning the dorsal roots from L7 to S3. This abolishes the micturition reflex, as we should expect, but it also reduces the tone, as measured by the slope of the pressure-volume curve. In III the sympathetic supply was

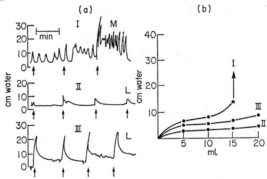

Fig. 4.59. (a) Cystometrograms at various stages of bladder denervation. M, micturition reflex initiated by gradual bladder filling; L, regular micturition act replaced by dribbling leakage of fluid from the vesical cavity. I, All nerves intact. II, Bilateral section of nerve roots L 7-S 3. Micturition reflex abolished. Reduction of rhythmic bladder contractions and decrease in vesical tone. III, Both sympathetic chains cut in addition. Rhythmic activity and tone of the bladder again increased, although complete normalization is not seen. The micturition reflex still absent. (b) Graphic reproduction of the three cystometrograms. Arrows indicate 5 ml volume increments. (Gjone, *Acta physiol. scand.*)

cut, and it is seen that there is a marked increase in tone, indicating an inhibitory action of this division.

Micturition Threshold

In a third study, involving the act of micturition, Gjone (1965) found that section of the sympathetic supply caused a marked reduction

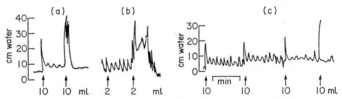

Fig. 4.60. Effects of progressive nerve section. (a) Intact vesical nerve supply. A regular micturition act was induced by injection of 20 ml saline solution into the vesical cavity. (b) Both sympathetic chains cut. Hyperactive bladder; vigorous rhythmic contractions at an intravesical volume of 2 ml. Micturition induced by further distension of the bladder with 2 ml fluid. (c) All extrinsic autonomic nerves interrupted. Micturition reflex abolished. (Gjone, *Acta physiol. scand.*)

in the threshold for micturition; this is shown in Fig. 4.60; in (a) it required two injections of 10 ml to bring about the act of micturition; in (b), with the sympathetic nerves cut, the introduction of 2 ml caused marked rhythmic contractions, and a second injection of 2 ml caused the act of micturition with complete emptying of the bladder; (c) shows the effects of subsequent cutting of the pelvic nerves, when reflex micturition was abolished.

Spontaneous Activity

When a bladder is filled with warm saline, spontaneous fluctuations in pressure take place, due to well coordinated contractions of the whole musculature; according to Plum and Colfelt (1960) the rhythmic waves became more prominent as bladder-filling increased, so that micturition resulted from a tetanic fusion of these smaller fluctuations. Elliott (1907) found that complete extrinsic and intrinsic denervation abolished spontaneous activity, but Plum and Colfelt found that this was retained under these conditions and also with complete autonomic blockade with TEAC or atropine, so that the spontaneous rhythmicity is myogenic, the effects described by Elliott being probably due to the loss of tone that occurs when the bladder has been allowed to distend abnormally, a condition that would pertain in the operated cat unless steps were taken to catheterize it regularly.

Species Variations

Elliott (1907) pointed out that the relative degrees of parasympathetic innervation to the bladder varied considerably with species, and Barrington (1914) emphasized that the inhibitory action of the hypogastric nerves on bladder motility observed by him in the cat might well be peculiar to this species; this animal is able to contain its urine for long periods and so may require a more powerful inhibitory apparatus than other species.

Inhibition of Micturition

Stimulation of the sympathetic nerves during micturition caused a cessation of this process for as long as the stimulation lasted; on cessation of stimulation the act proceeded to completion. As indicated earlier, stimulation of the hypogastric nerves in the resting bladder causes an initial increase in pressure, but this is never accompanied by expulsion of urine, and it may well be concerned with coitus.*

* Thus during ejaculation the musculature of the trigone and bladder-neck, as well as of the prostatic urethra, contract, thereby preventing flow of seminal fluid into the bladder.

Internal Sphincter

Stimulation of the sympathetic caused inhibition of rhythmic contractions in both the bladder and in the urethra; thus the relaxing effect of sympathetic stimulation applies to both regions, and is accompanied by closure of the sphincter as examined cystoscopically. It will be recalled that contraction of the bladder is accompanied by opening of the internal sphincter, a process that is considered to be the mechanical consequence of the contraction; it is reasonable to expect, then, that relaxation of the bladder, induced by sympathetic stimulation, should also lead to closure of the internal sphincter, the sphincter being, essentially, a continuation of the detrusor muscle, and its contraction causing a widening of the urethral orifice (Plum, 1960); thus its relaxation should passively close the orifice.

External Sphincter

Stimulation of the pudendal nerve causes contraction of the external sphincter; during micturition, the action is coordinated with contraction of the detrusor, so that it is not possible to cause the external sphincter to relax unless the detrusor is contracting; however, it can be caused to contract when the detrusor is active, so that in man it is possible to bring micturition to a close before the bladder has emptied. Whether the contraction of the external sphincter is the primary event in bringing micturition to an end voluntarily is still a matter of opinion; it may be that this, like the relaxation at the beginning of voluntary micturition, is just part of a series of reactions begun by contraction of other voluntary muscles of the pelvis (p. 309). Relaxation of the external sphincter is probably accomplished by reflex inhibition of tonic pudendal impulses from afferent impulses arising from contraction of the bladder-wall and/or urethra during contraction of the detrusor (Nyberg-Hansen, 1966).

Afferent Messages

Electrophysiological evidence for the presence of receptors responsive to stretch in the bladder is obtained by examining discharges in single fibres of the pelvic plexus (Iggo, 1955), but identification of the structures, or transducers, responsible for converting stretch into a nervous discharge relies on histological study, preferably combined with studies on single fibres discharges. Figure 4.61 shows the steady increase in frequency of discharge of a single fibre as the volume of the bladder of a cat was steadily increased by injection of fluid; when a powerful isometric contraction was sustained, i.e. when the bladder contracted but was not allowed to change in volume, then the frequency of discharge, which reached a peak of 30–40/sec when the pressure exceeded 50 mm Hg, steadily declined, i.e. it adapted, but was sustained at a lower rate of some 20/sec for as long as the tension was maintained. Thus, this type of receptor is capable of conveying messages regarding sudden changes in tension in the muscle and also regarding the steady level, i.e. the state of filling at a given moment.

Fig. 4.61. The steady increase in frequency of discharge of a single fibre from the pelvic plexus as 50 ml of saline was steadily infused into a cat bladder. Upper trace: intravesical pressure. Lower trace: nerve discharge. Time 1 sec on the intravesical pressure tracing. (Iggo, *J. Physiol.*)

It was clear from Iggo's studies on the bladder-, and also on gastric receptors that not only stretch, as in filling, but also development of tension, as in contraction, caused discharge. The receptors thus differ from the voluntary muscle spindle (Vol. 4) which is in parallel with the muscle fibres and shows diminished firing with muscular contraction; the receptors of the bladder are said to be "in series" with the muscle, and become deformed either by stretch or shortening.

The Receptors. As to the nature of the receptors, histological examination has revealed a great variety of structures coming into relation with the sensory nerve terminals, many of these being analogous with receptors in the skin and subcutaneous tissue, such as Pacinian corpuscles, Ruffini-like endings, and so on (Baba, 1959, quoted by Kuru, 1965).

Pain. According to Talaat (1937), who carried out a similar study on dogs, distension of the urethra gave discharges in hypogastric, pelvic and pudendal nerves, whereas the flow of urine through the urethra, an important stimulus in the maintenance of bladder emptying (p. 380), caused discharges only in the pelvic nerves. Talaat concluded that discharges in the hypogastric nerves were mainly due to pelvic nerve fibres running in their trunks; moreover, discharges in the hypogastrics might well subserve pain since much higher degrees of stretch were usually required to evoke them.

Barrington's Micturition Reflexes

Barrington (1921) found that it was possible to divide the bladder at its neck, i.e. just approximal to where the urethra begins to expand, and tie a cannula into both cut ends, so that the pressures of urethral resistance, and of bladder-distension, could be observed at the same time. By this method he identified five separate reflexes, all concerned in the total act of micturition, three leading to contraction of the bladder and two to relaxation of the urethra.

First Reflex. The *first reflex* is essentially what we have already described as the "micturition reflex", namely the contraction of the detrusor in response to stretch of the bladder; he found that it depended on the intactness of the pelvic nerves for its afferent and efferent limbs, and, as already indicated, he found that it was abolished by spinal transection; and by sectioning the brainstem at various levels he localized a "hind-brain centre" to the pons. He considered that the reflex arc consisted in the passage of afferent impulses up the cord to a relay neurone in the pons, leading to an efferent message down the cord to the parasympathetic motor neurone of the sacral cord.

Second Reflex. The *second reflex*, leading to powerful bladder contraction, was evoked by running water through the urethra; thus the bladder was only partially filled so that no reflex contraction was evoked; the pressure in the urethral catheter was raised until fluid began to flow through the external meatus. After a short latency of some 2 sec, the pressure in the bladder rose and remained high until the flow of fluid ceased. The reflex was abolished by spinal section or by cutting both pelvic nerves. Section of the pudic nerves almost invariably abolished the reflex, suggesting an afferent pathway through these.

Third and Fourth Reflexes. A *third reflex*, different from the second, was observed during injections through the urethra, and it appeared that the stimulus was expansion of the posterior part of this rather than flow through it; the reflex pathway was through the hypogastric nerves and was unaffected by division of the cord. The *fourth reflex* results in relaxation of the urethra, and is evoked by the passage of fluid through it; thus to quote his experimental protocol: "The pressure (of fluid in the urethra) was gradually raised till escape of water from the meatus started when it was 34 cm, in the next half minute it fell to $10\frac{1}{2}$ cm, when the escape stopped and in consequence the pressure remained constant; the pressure was then increased again by 5 cm each minute, escape of water from the meatus started again when the pressure was between 30 and 35 cm, and in the next half-minute fell to 11 cm, when the escape stopped and the pressure remained constant." Thus the fact that flow was prevented even when the pressure was above 11 cm and below 30 cm, whereas if flow was occurring it persisted down to pressures of 11 cm, indicates that the flow itself was evoking a relaxation of the sphincter(s). The reflex was abolished by cutting the pudic nerves; division of the pelvic nerves or spinal section did not abolish the reflex.

Fifth Reflex. The *fifth reflex* represents a relaxation of the external sphincter in response to a rise in intravesical pressure; thus the tube inserted into the urethra from the proximal (bladder) end is connected to a manometer tube which is filled with water to a height insufficient to cause flow through the closed sphincter. Fluid is injected into the bladder through its tube, and it is found that the reactionary rise in vesical pressure is accompanied by a flow of fluid through the urethra. Division of both pelvic nerves abolished the effect and it was also abolished by cocainization of the bladder; it was unaffected by spinal transection.*

Sequential Action. These five reflexes are of such a nature that, when one starts, the others are brought into action automatically, with

TABLE II

Barrington's seven reflexes (Garry, Roberts and Todd, 1959)

Reflex	The stimulus	Ingoing path	"Centre"	Outgoing path	Response of the effector
1	Distension of the bladder	Pelvic nerves	Hind-brain	Pelvic nerves	Contraction of the bladder
2	Running water through the urethra	Pudendal nerves	Hind-brain	Pelvic nerves	Contraction of the bladder
3	Distension of the proximal urethra	Hypogastric nerves	Lumbar cord	Hypogastric nerves	Slight transitory contraction of the bladder
4	Running water through the urethra	Pudendal nerves	Sacral cord	Pudendal nerves	Relaxation of the urethra
5	Distension of the bladder	Pelvic nerves	Sacral cord	Pudendal nerves	Relaxation of the urethra
6	Distension of the bladder	Pelvic nerves	Sacral cord	Pelvic nerves	Relaxation of the plain muscle of the urethra in its proximal third
7	Running water through the urethra	Pelvic nerves	Sacral cord	Pelvic nerves	Contraction of the bladder

* Evans (1936) measured the action potentials in the pudendal nerve during distension of the bladder; a tonic motor discharge was observed and, at the moment before flow started to emerge round the cannula, i.e. when the first reflex came into effect, there was an abrupt cessation of discharge in the pudic nerve, which remained quiescent until the micturition had finished.

the result that the bladder is emptied completely. The importance of the second reflex should be stressed; if it did not exist, the lowering of the pressure within the bladder due to the escape of urine would abolish the stimulus provoking the first reflex and so bring urination to a halt.

Sixth and Seventh Reflexes. Subsequent work (Barrington, 1931, 1941) revealed two other reflexes, the *sixth* being a relaxation of the proximal urethra in response to distension of the bladder, mediated through the pelvic nerves and maintained on spinal section; and the *seventh*, a contraction of the bladder due to running water through the urethra (i.e. similar to No. 2) but maintained after spinal section and with its afferent pathway in the pelvic nerves. For convenience the whole set is shown in Table II.

Electrophysiology of Reflexes

By recording action potentials from the striped muscle of the external sphincter of the cat, Garry *et al.* (1959) were able to examine Barrington's

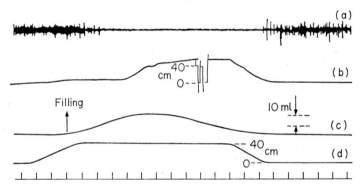

Fig. 4.62. Demonstration of Barrington's fifth and first reflexes by recording from the striped muscle of the external sphincter in the cat. (a) Action potentials from external urethral sphincter; (b) intravesical pressure with calibration in cm H_2O; (c) change in bladder volume; (d) height of reservoir connected with bladder. Two marked responses to bladder filling occur, namely cessation of sphincter activity (fifth reflex) and rise in pressure in bladder leading to return of fluid to the reservoir (first reflex). Contraction of bladder is isotonic and reduction in sphincter activity precedes rise in bladder pressure by about 25 sec. (Garry *et al., J. Physiol.*)

reflexes more precisely; Fig. 4.62 shows the operation of the fifth reflex very lucidly; as the bladder is filled, there is a sudden cessation of spontaneous activity in the sphincter, and this actually precedes the rise in intravesical pressure (Curve b) denoting the onset of the first reflex, i.e. bladder contraction. We may note that the bladder fills with only a small increase in intravesical pressure, so that the stimulus is largely the increased tension in the wall that must occur on physical grounds (p. 370) if a hollow elastic body expands without increase in pressure.

Guard Reflex. When the bladder is empty or contains only a small volume of fluid, an attempt to force fluid along the urethra through a cannula passing from the bladder into the proximal urethra results in an increase in activity in the sphincter; i.e. the sphincter guards against escape of fluid (Fig. 4.63). The main feature of the stimulus is

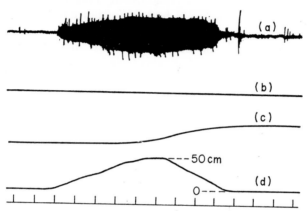

Fig. 4.63. The guard reflex. When the bladder is empty, an attempt to pass fluid through the urethra results in increased sphincteral activity. (a) Action potentials in external sphincter; (b) intravesical pressure; (c) volume of fluid that has passed through urethra—the change in level indicates flow; (d) height of reservoir connected to urethra. As height of reservoir is raised, increasing pressure applied to distal urethra. Activity in the sphincter is aroused; flow along the urethra starts when the pressure reaches 50 cm H_2O and continues even while the pressure is reduced, although the external sphincter is still active. (Garry *et al.*, *J. Physiol.*)

the expansion of the urethra rather than the flow of fluid. This reflex, which clearly operates in the retention of urine, is of obvious importance when continence is considered. When the fifth micturition reflex is in operation, i.e. when the sphincter is relaxed as a result of bladder-distension, then the guard reflex fails to manifest itself. If the bladder is removed to avoid all reflex activity from it, then the only effect of forcing fluid along the urethra is to cause contraction of the external sphincter.

The Fourth Reflex. Garry *et al.* (1959), in discussing their results, indicated that the existence of the fourth reflex—relaxation of the urethra in response to running water through it—was probably an artefact; it would certainly be inconvenient, since an accidental flow, once started, would be at once facilitated and make for incontinence, whereas we have seen that the response to this is the guard reflex, with increased sphincteric activity. The basic observation it will be recalled was that flow could be maintained at lower pressures, after it had been started, than at the pressure required to start it; however, Garry *et al.* point out that this need not be due to a reflex relaxation but could be the consequence of flow along a tube ensheathed with circular muscle. These authors were able to confirm the second and seventh reflexes— contraction of the bladder in response to flow of fluid through the urethra—although others could find no evidence for them in man.

Sixth Reflex. So far as the sixth reflex is concerned, a relaxation of the smooth muscle of the urethra—the internal sphincter—in response to bladder distension, this seems unlikely in view of the continuity of the detrusor with the internal sphincter, contraction of the one being of itself sufficient to cause an opening of the sphincter.

Stages in Micturition

In the light of this work Garry *et al.* divide micturition into two stages. *Stage 1.* Stimulation of the stretch-receptors in the bladder-wall causes reflex relaxation of the external sphincter (Reflex No. 5); and contraction of the detrusor (Reflex No. 1). *Stage 2.* Because Reflex No. 5 is in action, the guard reflex is in abeyance and flow continues, maintaining, and perhaps reinforcing, the contraction of the bladder, Reflexes No. 7 and No. 2 being responsible.

The reflexes continue while the bladder is emptying; as the volume diminishes the area of wall also diminishes, and a point will come when the contractile elements will have shortened as much as they can. Further reduction in area relieves the tension on the receptors in series with the contractile elements and thus reduces the reflex-drive from the bladder, so that both contraction of the detrusor and inhibition of the external urethra subside. If the receptors in the urethra are still active at this stage they are now able to operate the guard reflex, since the inhibition of the external sphincter has been removed. This stops the flow of urine and the bladder gradually refills.

Higher Centres

Pontine Centre

Barrington (1925) showed that destruction of a small part of the pons, just ventral to the internal edge of the superior cerebellar peduncle, was followed by permanent inability to empty the bladder if the lesion

was bilateral. The effects of spinal transection could thus be attribut-
able to cutting off the sacral cord from this region; as indicated above,
Barrington considered that the afferent pathway in the reflex ran up
to the pontine centre. Barrington had shown that the spinally transected cat at first was unable to pass urine, so that a condition of
retention existed, the rise in pressure due to filling being insufficient
to force urine through the tonically active sphincter. With the passage
of time, the bladder became automatic, in the sense that urine was
expelled at intervals as a result of filling, but according to Barrington
these acts of expulsion could not be described as the result of the
micturition reflex, which depended for its afferent limb on ascending
neurones to the pontine centre.

Automatic Bladder. Denny-Brown and Robertson (1933b), in
their studies of human cases of spinal transection, concluded that it
was probably only in the early stages after transection that the true
reflex was lost, in the sense that a coordinated response, involving
reflex pathways through the cord by way of the pelvic afferent and
efferent fibres, was absent. They considered that the later development
of the fully automatic bladder represented a taking over of control by
the sacral segments of the cord. When the lesion involved destruction
of the sacral segments, then control was less complete and was exerted
through the intrinsic plexuses of the bladder.

The Sacral Cord. It must be appreciated that the nervous pathway
for a micturition reflex does, of course, exist in the animal with its
spinal cord severed above the sacral level; moreover, the sacral and
coccygeal segments below S2 are very different from the rest and are
obviously related to the functions of defaecation, micturition, coitus
and parturition, so that it is reasonable to postulate the existence of a
sacral micturitional centre, subject of course to the influence of higher
centres, but capable of some autonomous activity when separated from
these. This view is held by Tang and Ruch (1950), who suggest that
Barrington's pontine "centre" is essentially a region sending down
tonic facilitatory impulses to the spinal pelvic motor neurones; spinal
transection removes this facilitation and produces a condition of
"spinal shock" similar to the areflexia observed in respect of the
somatic motor neurones following spinal transection. The somatic
reflexes return after a time, and it may be that the difference between
the visceral reflex and the somatic one is only quantitative, so that the
voiding by the automatic bladder is, indeed, a reflex phenomenon,
mediated by the sacral cord, but less effective through the loss of
facilitatory influences. In this respect we must emphasize again the
fact that most studies have been carried out on the cat which may not

be typical of mammals; thus Goltz and Sherrington (see Kuru, 1965) both stated that, in the spinal dog, large quantities of urine were periodically voided in a steady stream that nearly emptied the bladder.

Other Regions of Brain

Barrington, in his study of brain lesions designed to delineate his "pontine centre", found that bilateral destruction of the midbrain from the ventral half of the side of the posterior end of the aqueduct outwards to just beyond the mesencephalic root of N V, did not impair the micturition reflexes, but left the cat with a permanent loss of consciousness of the need to micturate or defaecate. Thus he states of one cat with this type of lesion: "In most cases where micturition was seen, it was evident she had no knowledge of its coming on. She spent a large amount of time playing with balls or paper and the commonest

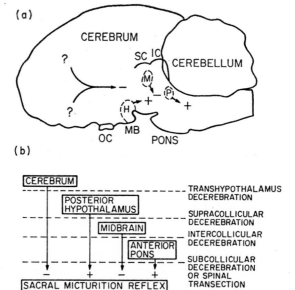

Fig. 4.64. (a) Schematic sagittal section of a cat's brain showing the locus of areas (H, M, P) as determined by transections and Horsley-Clarke lesions which facilitate (+) and inhibit (−) micturition. SC and IC, superior and inferior colliculi; MB, mammillary bodies; OC, optic chiasma. (b) A summarizing diagram indicating the net facilitatory or inhibitory action of various levels of the nervous system deduced from surgical procedures shown at the right. For simplicity, the diagram does not take into account the possibility that the descending pathways from the higher structures terminate on lower ones, including the bulbar reticular inhibitory and facilitatory areas of Kuru and co-workers. (Tang, *J. Neurophysiol.*, and Tang and Ruch, *J. comp. Neurol.*)

circumstance in which micturition started was when she was actively engaged in this. She would then stand quite still without squatting until the stream had stopped."

Tegmental "Centres". Tang and Ruch (1956) used the micturition threshold, i.e. the volume introduced into the bladder just sufficient to start the reflex, as a measure of the reflex activity after lesions throughout the brain; the importance of a centre higher than the pons was shown by the pronounced fall in threshold from 40 ml to only 4–12 ml on decerebration, suggesting that above this level there was a strong inhibitory centre, so that the section released the spinal

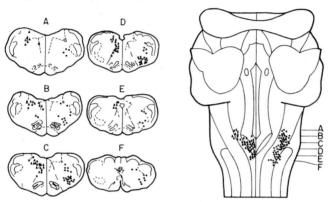

Fig. 4.65. On the left-hand side is shown the distribution of points, stimulation of which resulted in a contraction (right, dot) or in a relaxation (left, triangle) of the bladder. Results obtained in 128 cats on both sides of the medulla were transferred on either half superimposing points in neighbouring sections upon respective representative section. On the right the dorsal view of the lower brain stem of the cat with the cerebellum removed. The location of points, stimulation of which elicited contraction (right, dot) or relaxation (left, triangle) of the bladder is diagrammatically shown projected upon the dorsal surface of the medulla. The lettering from A to F on the right side of the figure indicates the level of the sections on the left. (Tokunaga and Kuru, *Jap. J. Physiol.*)

centre of this inhibition. They concluded from the effects of transections at the levels indicated in Fig. 4.65, that there were regions of facilitation and inhibition; they felt that there were no specific nuclei that could be described as micturition centres, but rather that the brain tegmentum was fractionated into areas of specific function. No medullary region was found.

Medullary "Centres". However, the elaborate microelectrode studies of Tokunaga and Kuru (1959) have revealed sites from which localized stimulation will evoke either contraction or relaxation of the bladder (Fig. 4.65). The vesico-constrictor "centre" is close to the termination of the sacrobulbar tract in the lateral funiculus of the cord, whilst the vesico-relaxor "centre" is close to the para-alar nucleus where the "pelvic sensory vagus", in the dorsal funiculus, and a part of the sacrobulbar tracts terminate. These tracts carry impulses from the parasympathetic and somatic afferent neurones passing into the cord; thus the tract ending in the para-alar region is analogous with the sensory root of the vagus nerve, and action potentials may be recorded in it on stretching the bladder (Yamamoto *et al.*, 1956). The two regions seem to be regions where the centripetal impulses from the bladder are converted into centrifugal impulses, directed either towards the bladder or towards other brain regions. Thus we may cut the pelvic nerve and stimulate its central end, i.e. its afferent neurones. This causes reflex contraction of the bladder; if the brain is transected between the pons and the medulla this response survives, showing that the pontine centre is apparently not necessary. Transection below the medulla abolishes the response to afferent stimulation. When both centres were stimulated, an antagonism between the two could be demonstrated (Kuru *et al.*, 1961). These authors discuss the relation of the pontine centre of Barrington to these two medullary centres; they consider that the pontine centre has two descending outlets, one to the medullary centres and one to the sacral motor neurones, whilst there are ascending pathways to the thalamus and midbrain. It is because of its double connexions that the pontine centre occupies such an important post in the neural control; efferent activity from the pontine centre would be exerted reciprocally through the two medullary centres, excitation of the vesico-contractor centre being accompanied by a reciprocal inhibition of the vesico-relaxor centre, and in this way continuous voiding of urine, despite the fall in intravesical pressure, is achieved. A rather similar mode of activation of the medullary and spinal centres is brought about by the midbrain centre (Kuru *et al.*, 1961).

Reflex Activity in Single Units

Spontaneous Discharges

A modern electrophysiological study of De Groat and Ryall (1969) promises to reconcile the opposing views of Barrington and of Denny Brown and Robertson on the existence of a sacral reflex centre for micturition. They recorded from neurones of the pelvic visceral nerve in the sacral cord and measured the changes in discharge when the bladder was distended, or when the afferent nerve was stimulated. Figure 4.66 shows the bursts of efferent discharge associated with the

Inhibitory Discharges

De Groat and Ryall also noted strong inhibitory discharges on the pelvic neurones, and here it must be emphasized that inhibition, besides excitation, must be a very important feature of bladder behaviour. Inhibition of the internal sphincter seems not to be a necessary feature of the micturition reflex, since this opens probably as a mechanical consequence of the contraction of the detrusor; however there must be inhibition of pudendal motor neurones, during micturition, and a continuous inhibition of the detrusor mechanism during continence.

The Course of Bladder Emptying

As De Groat and Ryall summarize reflex micturition, there are initially small contractions of the vesical musculature of purely peripheral origin, i.e. coordinated through the intramural plexus; these may depend on the intravesicular pressure, as described by Plum (1960). As the bladder fills, these rhythmic contractions increase to the point that the afferent discharges are sufficient to evoke responses in spinal pelvic neurones through a supraspinal mechanism, i.e. through the medullary and pontine centres. This represents an overcoming of the normal inhibition of these neurones, and the whole reflex is Barrington's first reflex. This leads to a mechanical opening of the proximal urethra—internal sphincter—and simultaneously there is a relaxation of the external urethra, by a viscero-somatic spinal reflex (Barrington's fifth reflex). Passage of fluid through the urethra induces a discharge in afferent fibres in the pudendal nerve which, by a supraspinal mechanism, reinforces excitation of pelvic neurones (Barrington's second reflex), and in this way contraction is sustained whilst discharge in the tension-receptors increases, which itself reacts on the parasympathetic neurones. Inhibition is generally reduced largely through the afferent excitation, and possibly as a result of the removal of voluntary restraint. Thus, if we consider only these three reflexes and the associated reduction in inhibition, there is a progressive self-reinforcing cycle which increases and maintains contraction of the vesical musculature during micturition. As the bladder empties the cycle reverses. As we have indicated above, in the chronic spinal animal, essentially the same series of changes take place, but now confined to the spinal level, and it is possible that this taking over of function by the lower centre reveals plastic changes in synaptic connexions in the sacral cord following transection.

Responses in Conscious Man to Bladder Filling

Rhythmic Waves

Plum (1960) inserted a catheter into human bladders and measured changes in pressure with increasing volume; the results were by no means uniform, so that some subjects developed rhythmic waves leading to micturition during filling up to 600 ml, whilst at the other extreme, there was a very flat cystometrogram interrupted by neither waves nor micturition. Invariably rhythmic activity preceded reflex micturition; if this occurred, it developed as a series of waves, building one upon the next to produce a sustained high pressure exceeding 70 cm H_2O and causing fluid to leak round the catheter. The subjects who failed to micturate when the vesicular volume had reached 600 ml nevertheless showed rhythmic waves which, however, never fused to give the coordinated powerful contraction of micturition.

Sensation

So far as sensation was concerned, three distinct sensations accompanied filling; vague lower-abdominal fullness appeared first at volumes between 135 and 190 ml, and this was unaccompanied by any cystometric change. The onset and rising phase of each rhythmical contraction were associated with a sensation of "urgency" confined to the suprapubic and perineal regions and lasting a few seconds. When contractions fused, urgency became prolonged and vigorous efforts were required to "hold" the urine. As earlier workers had found, over-distension of the bladder led to a considerable flattening of the cysto-metrogram, i.e. the bladder became atonic.

Voluntary Initiation and Interruption of Micturition

We have so far concerned ourselves almost exclusively with the reflex voiding of urine; of equal importance for civilized man and for many animals, of course, is the problem of continence and the voluntary relaxation of this continence.* The detrusor is an involuntary muscle, and, as we have indicated, it is impossible to cause relaxation of the striated external sphincter by voluntary effort (Denny-Brown and Robertson, 1933a); thus the question arises as to what is the initial

* Muellner (1958) emphasizes that true voluntary micturition, in the sense of voiding urine independently of the degree of fullness of the bladder, is peculiar to man, and may well have been made possible by the loss of the tail and the associated redeployment of the muscles concerned in its movement. The frequent micturition in small quantities by the dog is not an expression of voluntary micturition; it is a sexual ritual of the male and can be abolished by castration or induced, in the female, by androgens.

event in the voluntary initiation of micturition. Is there a simple removal of cortical inhibition of the micturition reflexes arising through distension of the bladder, or, as suggested by Denny-Brown and Robertson (1933a), does man make significant muscular efforts, and if so are these really necessary, and what do they do?

Downward Pull on Bladder-Neck

According to Muellner (1951, 1958) a group of voluntary muscles, including the diaphragm, muscles of the abdominal wall and the levator ani muscle, are all involved in both voluntary initiation and cessation of micturition. Thus voluntary micturition is initiated by contraction of the diaphragm and muscles of the abdominal wall, on

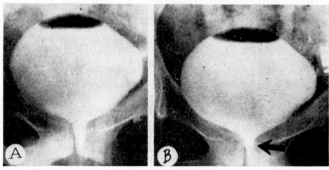

Fig. 4.68. Cystograms of the bladder before (A) and during (B) initiation of micturition. Note the displacement downward of the neck as shown by the arrow in B. (Muellner, *J. Urol.*)

the one hand, and relaxation of the muscles of the pelvic floor including the levator ani. These two processes cause a downward tug on the bladder-neck sufficient to activate contraction of the detrusor. This downward movement* of the neck of the bladder is illustrated by the cystograms of Fig. 4.68, and it is considered that the stretch on the detrusor muscle in the neck is an adequate stimulus to induce a co-ordinated contraction of the whole bladder-wall, mediated through the intrinsic plexus and extrinsic innervation.

Raised Intra-Abdominal Pressure

According to Muellner, the essential feature of the muscular contraction and relaxation is a small rise in intra-abdominal pressure

---

* Hutch's (1972) elaborate description of the functional anatomy of the pelvic musculature in relation to micturition has been mentioned earlier; if he is correct, there is no downward movement of the neck of the bladder, but rather a change in shape of the base from an initially flat plate to a funnel.

directed towards the neck of the bladder; it is comparable with the rise in pressure concerned in coughing or clearing the respiratory passages, but directed towards a different end. The rise in intra-abdominal pressure is small and not comparable to that involved in "straining", so that voluntary micturition can be prevented by just a slight contraction of the levator ani.

Interruption at Will

Interruption of micturition at will is started, in Muellner's view, by contraction of the muscles of the pelvic floor, e.g. the levator ani, which in turn elevates the entire bladder base so that the vesicle neck snaps shut. Certainly Denny-Brown and Robertson (1933a) in their study of catheterized human subjects, found that voluntary efforts directed towards micturition or retention were accompanied by changes in activity of the perineal musculature.

Muscle Paralysants

Lapides *et al.* (1957) have argued against this view on the basis of studies involving paralysis of the voluntary musculature by muscle relaxants; when "all muscles were paralysed" the human subjects could void at will although cessation at will was much slower. Muellner (1958) has pointed out, however, that complete paralysis of the voluntary musculature may not have been achieved; thus the external sphincter was operative so this certainly had not been put out of action.

Detrusor Micturition

The gradual development of continence in the infant emphasizes the importance of cortical inhibition in the suppression of the micturition reflexes; at low intravesical pressures this suppression is entirely unconscious. As the pressure rises and the desire to micturate becomes strong, conscious holding efforts are made. When the desire becomes very urgent the micturition taking place requires no voluntary effort but simply a release from cortical inhibition, but Muellner argues that this form of voiding should be called "detrusor micturition". True voluntary micturition must be studied against a background of only a partially full bladder, and under these conditions mere release of cortical inhibition is inadequate and detrusor activity must be initiated by something more positive.

REFERENCES

Anand, B. K. (1961). Nervous regulation of food intake. *Annu. Rev. Physiol.*, **41**, 677–708.

Anand, B. K. (1967). Central chemosensitive mechanisms related to feeding. *Hdb. Physiol.*, Sect. 6, Vol. I, pp. 249–263.

Anand, B. K. and Brobeck, J. R. (1951). Localization of a "feeding center" in the hypothalamus of the rat. *Proc. Soc. exp. Biol. Med., N.Y.*, **77**, 323–324.

Anand, B. K., Dua, S. and Singh, B. (1961). Electrical activity of the hypothalamic "feeding centres" under the effect of changes in blood chemistry. *Electroenceph. clin. Neurophysiol.*, **13**, 54–59.

Andersson, S., Nilsson, G., Sjodin, L. and Uvnas, B. (1973). Mechanism of duodenal inhibition of gastric acid secretion. In *Frontiers in Gastrointestinal Hormone Research* (Ed. Andersson, S.), pp. 223–238. Almqvist and Wiksell, Stockholm.

Andersson, S. and Olbe, L. (1964). Inhibition of gastric acid response to sham feeding in Pavlov pouch dogs by acidification of antrum. *Acta physiol. scand.*, **61**, 55–64.

Babkin, B. P. and Schachter, M. (1944). The chemical phase of gastric secretion and the surgery of the stomach. *McGill Med. J.*, **13**, 127–136.

Barrington, F. J. F. (1914). The nervous mechanism of micturition. *Quart. J. exp. Physiol.*, **8**, 33–71.

Barrington, F. J. F. (1921). The relation of the hind-brain to micturition. *Brain*, **44**, 23–53.

Barrington, F. J. F. (1925). The effect of lesions of the hind- and mid-brain on micturition in the cat. *Quart. J. exp. Physiol.*, **15**, 81–102.

Barrington, F. J. F. (1931). The component reflexes of micturition in the cat. Pts. I and II. *Brain*, **54**, 177–188.

Barrington, F. J. F. (1941). The component reflexes of micturition in the cat. Pt. III. *Brain*, **64**, 239–243.

Bass, P., Code, C. F. and Lambert, E. H. (1962). Motor and electric activity of the duodenum. *Amer. J. Physiol.*, **201**, 287–291.

Bayliss, W. M. and Starling, E. H. (1899). The movements and innervation of the small intestine. *J. Physiol.*, **24**, 99-143.

Bayliss, W. M. and Starling, E. H. (1902). The mechanism of pancreatic secretion. *J. Physiol.*, **28**, 325–353.

Bedi, B. S., Kelly, K. A. and Holley, K. E. (1972). Pathways of propagation of the canine gastric pacesetter potential. *Gastroenterology*, **63**, 288–296.

Beilenson, S., Schachter, M. and Smaje, L. H. (1968). Secretion of kallikrein and its role in vasodilatation in the submaxillary gland. *J. Physiol.*, **199**, 303–317.

Bennett, A. (1965). Effect of gastrin on isolated smooth muscle preparations. *Nature*, **208**, 170–173.

Bennett, A, and Fleshler, B. (1970). Prostaglandins and the gastrointestinal tract. *Gastroenterology*, **59**, 790–800.

Bennett, A., Misiewicz, J.J. and Waller, S. L. (1967). Analysis of the motor effects of gastrin and pentagastrin on the human alimentary tract *in vitro*. *Gut*, **8**, 470–474.

Benzi, G., Bertò, F., Crema, A. and Friggo, G. M. (1964). Action of sympathomimetic drugs on the smooth muscle at the junction of the bile duct and duodenum studied in situ. *Brit. J. Pharmacol.*, **23**, 101–114.

Bessou, P. and Perl, E. R. (1966). A movement receptor of the small intestine. *J. Physiol.*, **182**, 404–426.

Bieck, P. R., Oates, J. A., Robison, G. A. and Adkins, R. B. (1973). Cyclic AMP in the regulation of gastric secretion in dogs and humans. *Amer. J. Physiol.*, **224**, 158–164.

Born, G. V. R. (1970). 5-hydroxytryptamine receptors. In *Smooth Muscle* (Ed. Bülbring *et al.*), pp. 418–450. Arnold, London.

Bors, E. (1952). Segmental and peripheral innervation of the urinary bladder. *J. nerv. ment. Dis.*, **116**, 572–578.

Bouillin, D. J. (1964). Observations on the significance of 5-hydroxytryptamine in relation to the peristaltic reflex of the rat. *Brit. J. Pharmacol.*, **23**, 14–33.

Brobeck, J. R. (1948). Food intake as a mechanism of temperature regulation. *Yale J. Biol. Med.*, **20**, 545–552.

Brody, G. S., McCorriston, J. R. and Skoryna, S. A. (1960). Observations on fecal continence mechanisms. *J. Amer. Med. Assoc.*, **173**, 226–229.

Bro-Rasmussen, F. *et al.* (1965). The structure and function of the urinary bladder. *Urol. int. (Basel)*, **19**, 280–295.

Brown, J. C. and Dryburgh, J. R. (1971). A gastric inhibitory polypeptide. II. The complete amino acid sequence. *Canad. J. Biochem. Physiol.*, **49**, 867–872.

Brown, J. C. and Pederson, R. A. (1970). A multiparameter study in the action of preparations containing cholecystokinin-pancreozymin. *Scand. J. Gastroent.* **5**, 537–541.

Brown. J, C. and Pederson, R. A. (1970). Cleavage of a gastric-inhibitory polypeptide with cyanogen bromide and the physiological action of the C-terminal fragment. *J. Physiol.*, **210**, 52–53P.

Bülbring, E., Brading, A. F., Jones, A. W. and Tomita, T., Eds. (1970). *Smooth Muscle*. Arnold, London.

Bülbring, E. and Gershon, M. D. (1967). 5-hydroxytryptamine participation in the vagal inhibitory innervation of the stomach. *J. Physiol.*, **192**, 823–846.

Burnstock, G. (1972). Purinergic nerves. *Pharmocol. Rev.*, **24**, 509–581.

Burnstock, G., Campbell, G., Satchell, D. and Smythe, A. (1970). Evidence that adenosine triphosphate or a related nucleotide is the transmitter substance released by non-adrenergic inhibitory nerves in the gut. *Brit. J. Pharmacol.*, **40**, 668–688.

Cannon, W. B. and Washburn, A. L. (1912). An explanation of hunger. *Amer. J. Physiol.*, **29**, 441–454.

Christensen, J. (1970). Pharmacologic identification of the lower esophageal sphincter. *J. clin. Invest.*, **49**, 681–691.

Clegg, E. J. (1957). The musculature of the human prostatic urethra. *J. Anat.*, **91**, 345–351.

Code, C. F. and Carlson, H. C. (1968). Motor activity of the stomach. *Hdb. Physiol.*, Sect. 6, Vol. IV, 1903–1916.

Cohen, S. and Lipschutz, W. (1971). Hormonal regulation of human lower esophageal sphincter competence: interaction of gastrin and secretin. *J. clin. Invest.*, **50**, 449–454.

Colin-Jones, D. G. and Himsworth, R. L. (1969). The secretion of gastric acid in response to lack of metabolizable glucose. *J. Physiol.*, **202**, 97–109.

Crema, A. (1970). On the polarity of the peristaltic reflex. In *Smooth Muscle* (Ed. E. Bülbring *et al.*), pp. 542–548. Arnold, London.

Daniel, E. E. (1965). The electrical and contractile activity of the pyloric region in dogs and the effects of drugs. *Gastroenterology*, **49**, 403–418.

Daniel, E. E. (1968). Pharmacology of the gastrointestinal tract. *Hdb. Physiol.*, Sect. 6, Vol. IV, pp. 2267–2324.

Debons, A. F., Krinsky, I., From, A. and Cloutier, R. J. (1970). Site of action of gold thioglucose in the hypothalamic satiety center. *Amer. J. Physiol.*, **219**, 1397–1402.

Debons, A. F., Krinsky, I., From, A. and Cloutier, R. J. (1970). Gold thioglucose induction of obesity: significance of focal gold deposits in hypothalamus. *Amer. J. Physiol.*, **219**, 1403–1408.

De Groat, W. C. and Ryall, R. W. (1969). Reflexes to sacral parasympathetic neurones concerned with micturition in the cat. *J. Physiol.*, **200**, 87–108.

Denny-Brown, D. and Robertson, E. G. (1933a). On the physiology of micturition. *Brain*, **56**, 149–190.

Denny-Brown, D. and Robertson, E. G. (1933b). The state of the bladder and its sphincters in complete transverse lesions of the spinal cord and cauda equina. *Brain*, **56**, 397–463.

Devenport, L. D. and Balagura, S. (1971). Lateral hypothalamus: re-evaluation of function in motivated feeding behavior. *Science*, **172**, 744–746.

Domschke, W., Domschke, S., Classen, M. and Demling, L. (1972). Glucocorticoids and gastric secretion: the role of adenosine-3',5'-monophosphate. *Gastroenterology*, **63**, 252–256.

Doty, R. W. (1968). Neural organization of deglutition. *Hdb. Physiol.*, Sect. 6, Vol. IV, pp. 1861–1902.

Dutt, B. and Magee, D. F. (1972). Pepsin secretion by Heidenhain pouches in dogs. *Amer. J. Physiol.*, **223**, 480–483.

Eccles, R. M. and Libet, B. (1961). Origin and blockade of the synaptic responses of curarized sympathetic ganglia. *J. Physiol.*, **157**, 484–503.

Edvardsen, P. (1966). Changes in urinary-bladder motility following lesions in the nervous system in cats. *Acta Neurol. scand.*, **42**, Suppl. 20, 25–31.

Edwards, D. A. W. and Rowlands, E. N. (1968). Physiology of the gastroduodenal junction. *Hdb. Physiol.*, Sect 6, Vol. IV, pp. 1985–2000.

El-Badawi, A. and Schenk, E. A. (1966). Dual innervation of the mammalian urinary bladder. *Amer. J. Anat.*, **119**, 405–427.

El-Badawi, A. and Schenk, E. A. (1968). A new theory of the innervation of the bladder musculature. Pt. I. *J. Urol.*, **99**, 585–587.

El-Badawi, A. and Schenk, E. A. (1971). A new theory of the innervation of bladder musculature. Pt. II. *J. Urol.*, **105**, 368–371.

Elliott, T. R. (1907). The innervation of the bladder and urethra. *J. Physiol.*, **35**, 367–445.

Elwin, C. E. (1969). Stimulation of gastric acid secretion by irrigation of the antrum with some aliphatic alcohols. *Acta physiol. scand.*, **75**, 1–11.

Elwin, C. E. (1973). Release mechanism of gastrins. In *Frontiers in Gastrointestinal Hormone Research* (Ed. Andersson, S.), pp. 176–183. Almqvist and Wiksell, Stockholm.

Emås, S. and Grossman, M. I. (1967) Effect of truncal vagotomy on acid and pepsin responses to histamine and gastrin in dogs. *Amer. J. Physiol.*, **212**, 1007–1012.

Emmelin, N., Garrett, J. R. and Ohlin, P. (1970). Action of kinins on salivary myoepithelial cells. *J. Physiol.*, **207**, 539–544.

Emmelin, N., Ohlin, P. and Thulin, A. (1969). The pharmacology of salivary myoepithelial cells in dogs. *Brit. J. Pharmacol.*, **37**, 666–679.

Emmers, R. (1969). Modulation of the activity of hypothalamic "feeding neurons" by stimulation of the gustatory nucleus of the cat thalamus. *Physiologist*, **12**, 215.

Epstein, A. N. (1976). Oropharyngeal factors in feeding and drinking. *Hdb. Physiol.*, Sect. 6, Vol. I, pp. 197–218.

Evans, J. P. (1936). Observations on the nerves of supply to the bladder and urethra of the cat, with a study of their action potentials. *J. Physiol.*. **86**, 396–414.

Evetts, K. D., Fitzsimons, J. T. and Settler, P. E. (1972). Eating caused by 6-hydroxydopamine-induced release of noradrenaline in the diencephalon of the rat. *J. Physiol.*, **223**, 35–47.

Falck, B., Hillarp, N.-A., Thieme, G. and Torp, A. (1962). Fluorescence of cate-cholamines and related compounds condensed with formaldehyde. *J. Histochem. Cytochem.*, **10**, 348–354.

Feldberg, W. and Lin, R. C. Y. (1949). The action of local anaesthetics and D-tubocurarine on the isolated intestine of the rabbit and guinea pig. *Brit. J. Pharmacol.*, **4**, 33–44.

Fisher, R. S., Lipshutz, W. and Cohen, S. (1973). The hormonal regulation of pyloric sphincter function. *J. Clin. Invest.*, **52**, 1289–1296.

Freund, S. and Sheehan, D. (1943). Experimental investigation of visceral afferent synapses in coeliac ganglia. *J. Neurophysiol.*, **6**, 263–268.

Garry, R. C., Roberts, T. D. M. and Todd, J. K. (1959). Reflexes involving the external urethral sphincter in the cat. *J. Physiol.*, **149**, 653–665.

Ginzel, K. H. (1959). Investigations concerning the initiation of the peristaltic reflex. *J. Physiol.*, **148**, 75–76P.

Gjone, R. (1965). Peripheral autonomic influence on the motility of the urinary bladder in the cat. I. Rhythmical contractions. *Acta physiol. scand.*, **65**, 370–377.

Gjone, R. (1965). Peripheral autonomic influence on the motility of the urinary bladder in the cat. II. 'Tone'. *Acta physiol. scand.*, **66**, 72–80.

Gjone, R. (1965). Peripheral autonomic influence on the motility of the urinary bladder in the cat. III. Micturition. *Acta physiol. scand.*, **66**, 81–90.

Go, V. L. W., Hofmann, A. F. and Summerskill, W. H. J. (1970). Pancreozymin bioassay in man based on pancreatic enzyme secretion; potency of specific amino acids and other digestive products. *J. clin. Invest.*, **49**, 1558–1564.

Gregory, R. A. (1962). *Secretory Mechanisms of the Gastro-intestinal Tract.* Arnold, London.

Gregory, R. A. and Tracy, H. J. (1964). The constitution and properties of two gastrins extracted from hog antral mucosa. *Gut*, **5**, 103–117.

Greider, M. H., Steinberg, V. and McGuigan, J. E. (1972). Electron microscopic identification of the gastrin cell of the human antral mucosa by means of immunocytochemistry. *Gastroenterology*, **63**, 572–583.

de Groot, J. (1967). Organization of hypothalamic feeding mechanisms. *Hdb. Physiol.*, Sect. 6, Vol. I, 239–247.

Grossman, M. I. (1955). Integration of current views on the regulation of hunger and appetite. *Ann. N.Y. Acad. Sci.*, **63**, 76–89.

Grossman, M. I. (Ed.) (1966). *Gastrin.* Butterworth. London.

Grossman, M. I. (1973). Spectrum of biological actions of gastrointestinal hormones. In *Frontiers in Gastrointestinal Hormone Research* (Ed. Andersson, S.), pp. 17–25. Almqvist and Wiksell, Stockholm.

Grossman M. I., Cummins, G. M. and Ivy, A. C. (1947). The effect of insulin on food intake after vagotomy and sympathectomy. *Amer. J. Physiol.*, **149**, 100–102.

Grossman, M. I., Robertson, C. R. and Ivy, A. C. (1948). Proof of a hormonal mechanism for gastric secretion—the humoral transmission of the distension stimulus. *Amer. J. Physiol.*, **153**, 1–9.

Hamburg, M. D. (1971). Hypothalamic unit activity and eating behavior. *Amer. J. Physiol.*, **220**, 980–985.

Harding, R. and Leek, B. F. (1972). Gastro-duodenal receptor responses to chemical and mechanical stimuli investigated by a "single fibre" technique. *J. Physiol.*, **222**, 139–140P.

Harper, A. A. and Raper, H. S. (1943). Pancreozymin, a stimulant of the secretion of pancreatic enzymes in extracts of the small intestine. *J. Physiol.*, **102**, 115–125.

Harris, J. B., Nigon, K. and Alonso, D. (1969) Adenosine-3'-5'-monophosphate: intracellular mediator for methyl xanthine stimulation of gastric secretion. *Gastroenterology*, **57**, 377–384.

Harry, J. (1963). The action of drugs on the circular muscle strip from the guinea-pig isolated ileum. *Brit. J. Pharmacol.*, **20**, 399–417.

Henriksen, F. W. and Worning, H. (1967). The interaction of secretin and pancreozymin on the external pancreatic secretion in dogs. *Acta physiol. scand.*, **70**, 241–249.

Herrin, R. C. and Meek, W. J. (1945). Afferent nerves excited by intestinal distension. *Amer. J. Physiol.*, **144**, 720–733.

Hervey, G. R. (1959). The effects of lesions in the hypothalamus in parabiotic rats. *J. Physiol.*, **145**, 336–352.

Hetherington, A. W. and Ranson, S. W. (1942). Effect of early hypophysectomy on hypothalamic obesity. *Endocrinol.*, **31**, 30–34.

Hightower, N. C. (1968). Motor action of the small bowel. *Hdb. Physiol.*, Sect. 6, Vol. IV, pp. 2001–2024.

Hirst, G. D. S. and McKirdy, H. C. (1974). A nervous mechanism for descending inhibition in guinea-pig small intestine. *J. Physiol.*, **238**, 129–143.

Hunt, J. N. and Knox, M. T. (1968). Regulation of gastric emptying. *Hdb. Physiol.*, Sect. 6, Vol. IV, 1917–1935.

Hutch, J. A. (1972). *Anatomy and Physiology of the Bladder, Trigone and Urethra.* Butterworths, London.

Iggo, A. (1955). Tension receptors in the stomach and the urinary bladder. *J. Physiol.*, **128**, 593–607.

Iggo, A. (1957a). Gastro-intestinal tension receptors with unmyelinated afferent fibres in the vagus of the cat. *Quart. J. exp. Physiol.*, **42**, 130–143.

Iggo, A. (1957b). Gastric mucosal chemoreceptors with vagal afferent fibres in the cat. *Quart. J. exp. Physiol.*, **42**, 398–409.

Ingelfinger, F. J. (1958). Esophageal motility. *Physiol. Rev.*, **38**, 533–584.

Ivy, A. C. and Oldberg, E. A. (1928). A hormone mechanism for gall bladder contraction and evacuation. *Amer. J. Physiol.*, **86**, 599–613.

Jackson, B. M., Reeder, D. D. and Thompson, J. C. (1972). Dynamic characteristics of gastrin release. *Amer. J. Surg.*, **123**, 137–142.

Jacobson, E. D., Mao, C. C. and Shanbour, L. L. (1973). Mucosal cyclic AMP and secretion in the dog stomach. *Amer. J. Physiol.*, **225**, 893–896.

Jaffe, B. M., McGuigan, J. E. and Newton, W. T. (1970). Immunochemical measurement of the vagal release of gastrin. *Surgery*, **68**, 196–201.

Janowitz, H. D. and Grossman, M. I. (1949). Some factors affecting the food intake of normal dogs and dogs with esophagostomy and gastric fistula. *Amer. J. Physiol.*, **159**, 143–148.

Janowitz, H. D. and Hollander, F. (1955). The time factor in the adjustment of food intake to varied caloric requirement in the dog: A study of the precision of appetite regulation. *Ann. N.Y. Acad. Sci.*, **63**, 56–67.

Jansson, G. and Martinson, J. (1966). Studies on the ganglionic site of action of sympathetic outflow to the stomach. *Acta physiol. scand.*, **68**, 184–192.

Johansson, B., Jonsson, O. and Ljing, B. (1965). Supraspinal control of the intestino-intestinal reflex. *Acta physiol. scand.*, **63**, 442–449.

Johnson, L. R. (1973). Effect of gastric mucosal acidification on the action of pepsigogues. *Amer. J. Physiol.*, **225**, 1411–1415.

Johnson, L. R. and Grossman, M. I. (1968). Secretin: the enterogastrone released by acid in the duodenum. *Amer. J. Physiol.*, **215**, 885–888.

Johnson, L. R. and Grossman, M. I. (1969). Characteristics of inhibition of gastric secretion by secretin. *Amer. J. Physiol.*, **217**, 1401–1404.

Johnson, L. R. and Grossman, M. I. (1970). Analysis of inhibition of acid secretion by cholecystokinin in dogs. *Amer. J. Physiol.*, **218**, 550–554.

Kadekaro, M., Timo-Iaria, C., Valle, L. E. R. and Velha, L. P. E. (1972). Site of action of 2-deoxy-D-glucose mediating gastric secretion in the cat. *J. Physiol.*, **221**, 1–13.

Kahlson, G. and Rosengren, E. (1971). *Biogenesis and Physiology of Histamine.* Arnold, London.

Kahlson, G., Rosengren, E., Svahn, D. and Thunberg, R. (1964). Mobilization and formation of histamine in the gastric mucosa as related to acid secretion. *J. Physiol.*, **174**, 400–416.

Kelly, K. A., Code, C. F. and Elveback, L. R. (1969). Patterns of canine gastric electrical activity. *Amer. J. Physiol.*, **217**, 461–470.

Kennedy, G. C. (1950). The hypothalamic control of food intake in rats. *Proc. Roy. Soc. B.*, **137**, 535–549.

Kennedy, G. C. (1953). The role of depot fat in the hypothalamic control of food intake in the rat. *Proc. Roy. Soc. B.*, **140**, 578–592.

Kenner, G. W. and Sheppard, R. C. (1973). Gastrins of various species. In *Frontiers in Gastrointestinal Hormone Research* (Ed. Andersson, S.), pp. 137–142. Almqvist and Wiksell, Stockholm.

Knodell, R. G., Toskes, P. P., Reber, H. A. and Brooks, F. P. (1970). Significance of cyclic AMP in the regulation of exocrine pancreatic secretion. *Experientia*, **26**, 515–517.

Kock, N. G. (1959). An experimental analysis of mechanisms engaged in reflex inhibition of intestinal motility. *Acta physiol. scand.*, **47**, Suppl. 164.

Kosterlitz, H. W. and Lees, G. M. (1964). Pharmacological analysis of intrinsic intestinal reflexes. *Pharmacol. Rev.*, **16**, 301–339.

Kosterlitz, H. W., Pirie, V. W. and Robinson, J. A. (1956). The mechanism of the peristaltic reflex in the isolated guinea-pig ileum. *J. Physiol.*, **133**, 681–694.

Kosterlitz, H. W. and Robinson, J. A. (1959). Reflex contractions of the longitudinal muscle coat of the isolated guinea-pig ileum. *J. Physiol.*, **146**, 369–379.

Kottegoda, S. R. (1969). An analysis of possible nervous mechanisms involved in the peristaltic reflex. *J. Physiol.*, **200**, 687–712.

Kottegoda, S. R. (1970). Peristalsis of the small intestine. In *Smooth Muscle* (Ed. E. Bülbring *et al.*), pp. 525–541. Arnold, London.

Kuntz, A. and Saccomanno, G. (1944). Sympathetic innervation of the detrusor muscle. *J. Urol.*, **51**, 535–542.

Kuntz, A. and Saccomanno, G. (1944). Reflex inhibition of intestinal motility mediated through decentralized prevertebral ganglia. *J. Neurophysiol.*, **7**, 163–170.

Kuru, M. (1965). Nervous control of micturition. *Physiol. Rev.*, **45**, 425–494.

Kuru, M., Makuya, A. and Koyama, Y. (1961). Fiber connections between the mesencephalic micturition facilitatory area and the bulbar vesico-motor centre. *J. comp. Neurol.*. **177**, 161–178.

Kuru, M., Ozaki, H. and Kurati, T. (1961). Effect of simultaneous stimulations of the bulbar vesico-constrictor and vesico-relaxer centres. *J. comp. Neurol.*, **116**, 195–208.

Lai, K. S. (1964). Studies in gastrin. II. *Gut*, **5**, 334–336.

Lalich, J., Meek, W. J. and Herrin, R. C. (1936). Reflex pathways concerned in inhibition of hunger contractions by intestinal distension. *Amer. J. Physiol.*, **115**, 410–414.

Langley, L. L. and Whiteside, J. A. (1951). Mechanism of accommodation and tone of urinary bladder. *J. Neurophysiol.*, **14**, 147–152.

Lapides, J., Sweet, R. B. and Lewis, L. W. (1957). Role of striated muscle in urination. *J. Urol.*, **77**, 247–250.

Leibowitz, S. F. (1971). Hypothalamic alpha- and beta-adrenergic systems regulate both thirst and hunger in the rat. *Proc. Nat. Acad. Sci. Wash.*, **68**, 332–334.

Le Magnen, J. *et al.* (1973). Role of a lipostatic mechanism in regulation by feeding of energy balance in rats. *J. comp. physiol. Psychol.*, **84**, 1–23.

Levine, R. A. and Wilson, D. E. (1971). The role of cyclic AMP in gastric secretion. *Ann. N.Y. Acad. Sci.*, **185**, 363–375.

Lipschutz, W., Tuch, A. F. and Cohen, S. (1971). A comparison of the site of action of gastrin I on lower esophageal sphincter and antral circular muscle. *Gastroenterology*, **61**, 454–460.

Lundell, L. (1974). Changes in urinary histamine following antrectomy and substitution with pentagagastrin. *J. Physiol.*, **236**, 42–43P.

Mackenna, B. R. and McKirdy, H. C. (1972). Peristalsis in the rabbit distal colon. *J. Physiol.*, **220**, 33–54.

Mao, C. C., Shanbour, L. L., Hodgins, D. S. and Jacobson, E. D. (1972). Adenosine 3′,5′-monophosphate (cyclic AMP) and secretion in the canine stomach. *Gastroenterology*, **63**, 427–438.

Mayer, J. (1955). Regulation of energy intake and the body weight: the glucostatic theory and the lipostatic hypothesis. *Ann. N.Y. Acad. Sci.*, **63**, 15–42.

McGuigan, J. E. (1968). Gastric mucosal intracellular localization of gastrin by immunofluorescence. *Gastroenterology*, **55**, 315–327.

McKirdy, H. C. (1972). Functional relationship of longitudinal and circular layers of the musclaris externa of the rabbit large intestine. *J. Physiol.*, **227**, 839–853.

Meyer, J. H., Spingola, L. J. and Grossman, M. I. (1971). Endogenous cholecystokinin potentiates exogenous secretin on pancreas of dog. *Amer. J. Physiol.*, **221**, 742–747.

Muellner, S. R. (1951). The physiology of micturition. *J. Urol.*, **65**, 805–810.

Muellner, S. R. (1958). The voluntary control of micturition in man. *J. Urol.*, **80**, 473–478.

Mutt, V. and Jorpes, J. E. (1968). *Pharmacology of Hormonal Polypeptides and Proteins* (Eds. Banck, N., Marini, L. and Paoletti, R.), pp. 569–580. Plenum, New York.

Mutt, V. and Jorpes, J. E. (1973). Isolation and primary structure of cholecystokinin —pancreozymin. In *Frontiers in Gastrointestinal Hormone Research* (Ed. Andersson, S.), pp. 169–172. Almqvist and Wiksell, Stockholm.

Nakajima, S., Nakamura, M. and Magee, D. F. (1969). Effect of secretin on gastric acid and pepsin secretion in response to various stimuli. *Amer. J. Physiol.*, **216**, 87–91.

Nilsson, G. *et al.* (1972). Plasma gastrin and gastric acid responses to sham feeding and feeding in dogs. *Gastroenterology*, **63**, 51–59.

Norberg, K. A. (1964). Adrenergic innervation of the intestinal wall studied by fluorescence microscopy. *Int. J. Neuropharmacol.*, **3**, 379–382.

Nyberg-Hansen, R. (1960). Innervation and nervous control of the urinary bladder. *Acta neurol. scand.*, **42**, Suppl. 20, 7–24.

Nyhus, L. M. *et al.* (1960). The control of gastrin release. *Gastroenterology*, **39**, 582–589.

Ohkawa, H. and Prosser, C. L. (1972). Electrical activity in myenteric and submucous plexuses of cat intestine. *Amer. J. Physiol.*, **222**, 1412–1419.

Ohkawa, H. and Prosser, C. L. (1972). Functions of neurones in enteric plexuses of cat intestine. *Amer. J. Physiol.*, **222**, 1420–1426.

Oomura, Y. *et al.* (1964). Reciprocal activities of the ventromedial and lateral hypothalamic areas of cats. *Science*, **143**, 484–485.

Paintal, A. S. (1954). A study of gastric stretch receptors. Their role in the peripheral mechanism of satiation of hunger and thirst. *J. Physiol.*, **126**, 255–270.

Paintal, A. S. (1963). Vagal afferent fibres. *Ergebn. Physiol.*, **52**, 74–156.

Panksepp, J. (1971). Is satiety mediated by the ventromedial hypothalamus? *Physiol. Behaviour*, **7**, 381–384.

Panksepp, J. (1971). A re-examination of the role of the ventromedial hypothalamus in feeding behaviour. *Physiol. Behaviour*, **7**, 385–394.

Paton, W. D. M. and Vizi, E. S. (1969). The inhibitory action of noradrenaline and adrenaline on acetylcholine output by guinea-pig ileum longitudinal strip. *Brit. J. Pharmacol.*, **35**, 10–28.

Paton, W. D. M. and Zar, A. M. (1968). The origin of acetylcholine released from guinea-pig intestine and longitudinal muscle strips. *J. Physiol.*, **194**, 13–33.

Pe. Thein, M. and Schofield, B. (1959). Release of gastrin from the pyloric antrum following vagal stimulation by sham feeding in dogs. *J. Physiol.*, **148**, 291–305.

Pearcy, J. F. and Van Liere, E. J. (1926). Reflexes from the colon. *Amer. J. Physiol.*, **78**, 64–73.

Plum, F. (1960). Autonomous urinary bladder activity in normal man. *Arch. Neurol.*, **2**, 497–503.

Plum, F. and Colfelt, R. H. (1960). The genesis of vesical rhythmicity. *Arch. Neurol.*, **2**, 487–496.

Quigley, J. P. (1955). The role of the digestive tract in regulating the ingestion of food. *Ann. N.Y. Acad. Sci.*, **63**, 6–14.

Raiford, T. S. and Mulinos, M. G. (1936). Studies in gastro-intestinal motility. *Arch. Surg., Chicago*, **33**, 276–296.

Rosen, D. I., Constantinou, C. E., Sands, J. P. and Govan, D. E. (1971). Dynamics of the upper urinary tract: effects of changes in bladder pressure on ureteral peristalsis. *J. Urol.*, **106**, 209–213.

Roth, J. A. and Ivy, A. C. (1944). The effect of caffeine upon gastric secretion in the dog, cat and man. *Amer. J. Physiol.*, **141**, 454–461.

Ruch, T. C. (1960). Central control of the bladder. *Hdb. of Physiology*, Sect. 1, Vol. II, 1207–1223.

Satchell, D. G. and Burnstock, G. (1971). Quantitative studies of the release of purine compounds following stimulation of non-adrenergic inhibiting nerves in the stomach. *Biochem. Pharmacol.*, **20**, 1694–1697.

Schuster, M. M., Hookman, P., Hendrix, T. R. and Mendeloff, A. I. (1965). Simultaneous manometric recording of internal and external anal sphincteric reflexes. *Bull. J. H. Hosp.*, **116**, 79–88.

Schuster, M. M. and Mendeloff, A. I. (1968). Motor action of rectum and anal sphincters in continence and defaecation. *Hdb. Physiol.*, Sect. 6, Vol. IV, pp. 2121–2146.

Sclafani, A. (1971). Neural pathways involved in the ventromedial hypothalamic lesion syndrome. *J. comp. physiol. Psychol.*, **77**, 70–96.

Scratcherd, T. and Case, R. M. (1973). The action of cyclic AMP, methyl xanthines and some prostaglandins on pancreatic exocrine secretion. In *Frontiers in Gastrointestinal Hormone Research* (Ed. Andersson, S.), pp. 191–200. Almqvist and Wiksell, Stockholm.

Sewing, K.-Fr. (1967). On the pepsin response to gastrin analogue. *Gastroenterology*, **53**, 497.

Sharma, K. N., Anand, B. K., Dua, S. and Singh, B. (1961). Role of stomach in regulation of activities of hypothalamic feeding centres. *Amer. J. Physiol.*, **201**, 593–598.

Silva, D. G., Ross, G. and Osborne, L. W. (1971). Adrenergic innervation of the ileum. *Amer. J. Physiol.*, **220**, 347–352.

Straaten, T. (1933). Die Bedeutung der Pylorusdrüsenzone für die Magensekretion. *Arch. klin. Chir.*, **176**, 236–251.

Stunkard, A. J. and Wolff, H. G. (1954). Correlation of arteriovenous glucose differences, gastric hunger contractions and the experience of hunger in man. *Fed. Proc.*, **13**, 157.

Talaat, M. (1937). Afferent impulses in the nerves supplying the urinary bladder. *J. Physiol.*, **89**, 1–13.

Tang, P. C. and Ruch, T. C. (1955). Non-neurogenic basis of bladder tonus. *Amer. J. Physiol.*, **181**, 249–257.

Tang, P. C. and Ruch, T. C. (1956). Localization of brain stem and diencephalic areas controlling the micturition reflex. *J. comp. Neurol.*, **106**, 213–231.

Teitelbaum, P. and Epstein, A. N. (1962). The lateral hypothalamic syndrome. *Psychol. Rev.*, **69**, 74–90.

Thompson, J. C., Reeder, D. D., Davidson, W. D., Jackson, B. M. and Clendinnen, B. G. (1973). Studies on the metabolism of gastrin. In *Frontiers of Gastrointestinal Hormone Research* (Ed. Andersson, S.), pp. 111–133. Lundqvist-Liksell, Stockholm.

Tokunaga, S. and Kuru, M. (1959). Vesico-constrictor centre and vesico-relaxer centre in the medulla. *Jap. J. Physiol.*, **9**, 365–374.

Tomita, T. and Watanabe, H. (1973). A comparison of the effects of adenosine triphosphate with noradrenaline and with the inhibitory potential of the guinea-pig taenia coli. *J. Physiol.*, **231**, 167–177.

Trendelenburg, P. (1917). Physiologische und pharmakologische Versuche uber die Dunndarm Peristaltik. *Arch. exp. Path. Pharmak.*, **81**, 55–129.

Vagne, M. and Fargier, M.-C. (1973). Effect of pentagastrin and secretin on gastric mucus secretion in conscious cats. *Gastroenterology*, **65**, 757–763.

Vizi, E. S., Bertaccini, G., Impicciatore, M. and Knoll, J. (1972). Acetylcholine-releasing effect of gastrin and related polypeptides. *Eur. J. Pharmacol.*, **17**, 175–178.

Vizi, S. E., Bertaccini, G., Impicciatore, M. and Knoll, J. (1973). Evidence that acetylcholine released by gastrin and related polypeptides contributes to their effect on gastrointestinal motility. *Gastroenterology*, **64**, 268–277.

Vogt, M. (1955). Darmstoff: occurrence and properties. In *Polypeptides which Stimulate Plain Muscle* (Ed. Gaddum, J. H.), pp. 39–44. Livingstone, London.

Waxler, S. H. and Brecher, G. (1950). Obesity and food requirements in albino mice following administration of gold thioglucose. *Amer. J. Physiol.*, **162**, 428–433.

Yalow, R. S. and Berson, S. A. (1970). Size and charge distinctions between endogenous human plasma gastrin in peripheral blood and heptadecapeptide gastrins. *Gastroenterology*, **58**, 609–615.

Yalow, R. S. and Berson, S. A. (1972). And now, "big, big" gastrin. *Biochem. Biophys. Res. Comm.*, **48**, 391–395.

Yamamoto, S., Sugihara, S. and Kuru, M. (1956). Microelectrode studies on sensory afferents in the posterior funiculus of cat. *Jap. J. Physiol.*, **6**, 68–85.

Youmans, W. B. (1968). Innervation of the gastrointestinal tract. *Hdb. Physiol.*, Sect. 6, Vol. IV, pp. 1655–1663.

Youmans, W. B., Meek, W. J. and Herrin, R. C. (1938). Extrinsic and intrinsic pathways concerned with intestinal inhibition during intestinal distension. *Amer. J. Physiol.*, **124**, 470–477.

CHAPTER 5

Homeostasis of the Blood Composition

GENERAL CONSIDERATIONS

Glucose

The composition of the blood, in so far as any constituent is concerned, is determined at any given moment by several opposing influences, and its relative constancy must be regarded as a steady state in which a balance is struck between these influences. Thus, to take an example, the concentration of glucose in the blood is governed by absorption from the intestine and further additions or subtractions caused by the liver's activities, namely breakdown of glycogen—*glycogenolysis*—and synthesis—*gluconeogenesis*. Superimposed on these additive and subtractive processes is the large variety of metabolic events in which glucose plays a part, together constituting a continuous drain on the supply circulating in the blood. At any moment, because of the temporary dominance of one factor, the concentration may be on the rise or on the fall, or it may be in a reasonably steady state because of the balance of opposing tendencies. Thus, by the average blood concentration we mean, essentially, the concentration when a steady state has been approximately reached, and the conditions are chosen such that such a steady state is likely. So far as glucose is concerned, the blood would not be withdrawn for analysis immediately after a meal, since now the absorptive factor is dominant and the blood sugar is rising; clearly a more likely state to provide a basal level of blood-sugar would be when the subject is fasting.

Ions

When ions are studied we encounter smaller fluctuations, as we should expect since nutritional and metabolic factors influence their concentrations to a lesser degree, although the Cl^- and HCO_3^- ions might be chosen as exceptions because of their involvement in the acid-base balance of the organism and are influenced by respiratory activity and exercise when, as we have seen, large amounts of lactic acid may be liberated into the blood, decomposing the bicarbonate ion. In this chapter we shall consider the main factors that govern the concentrations of many of the solutes of the blood.

SALT AND WATER BALANCE

Osmotic Regulation

The maintenance of the constancy of the concentrations of the various ions of the blood and interstitial fluid, which we may call a manifestation of *ionic regulation*, is largely carried out by the kidney, the basic mechanisms of whose function have already been described (Vol. 1).

Sodium Excretion

Closely involved in the regulation of the ionic composition is that of the osmolality of the blood, since this is largely governed by the concentration of Na^+; and the level of this ion in the blood will be governed primarily by the extent to which the glomerular filtrate is reabsorbed into the blood. Thus, if the diet contains plenty of Na^+, the body will acquire an excess, and some of the filtrate will be reabsorbed and the excess Na^+ will be excreted. Excretion of Na^+, as well as of other solutes, requires the excretion of water since the urine must be fluid, so that it is easy to envisage a situation in the terrestrial animal in which the requirements for the elimination of Na^+, in the interests of constant osmolality of the blood, will compete with the requirements to retain water when this is not accessible. Thus, during water shortage, the osmolality of the blood tends to rise because of loss from evaporation, but the elimination of salt requires the elimination of water, so that unless the kidney eliminates more salt than it does water, in the sense that it eliminates a hypertonic salt solution, the body will become more dehydrated.

Power to Concentrate Urine. In fact, as we have seen, the elimination of hypertonic urines during hydropenia, or water depletion, is a characteristic feature of the mammal. When different species are compared, with respect to the greatest urinary hyperosmolality that they can achieve during water-deprivation, it is found that animals adapted to a desert life are able to develop much higher hyperosmolalities than, say, man (Table I).

TABLE I

Showing correlation between relative thickness of renal medulla and power of
concentrating urine as indicated by depression of freezing point
(Schmidt-Nielsen and O'Dell, 1961)

Animal	% Long loops	Relative medullary thickness	Max $\triangle$°C Urine
Beaver	0	1·3	0·96
Pig	3	1·6	2·0
Man	14	3·0	2·6
Dog	100	4·3	4·85
Cat	100	4·8	5·8
Rat	28	5·8	4·85
Kangaroo rat	27	8·5	10·4
Jerboa	33	9·3	12·0
Psammomys	100	10·7	9·2

Counter-Current. The basis of this concentrating mechanism is
the counter-current system in the loops of Henle, and in the Table
are included the percentage of long loops and the relative medullary
thickness; the important feature is clearly the medullary thickness,
which is a measure of the lengths of the long loops of Henle.

Blood-Volume

A further complication, however, is the necessity to retain the total
volume of the body-water reasonably constant, and this especially
applies to the volume of the blood, since the heart can only work
sufficiently if this is adequate. Too large a volume may be also deleteri-
ous to pumping efficiency, causing congestion at the venous end. Thus,
under conditions of salt-deficiency, the kidney will retain salt and
eliminate water thereby maintaining the osmolality as high as possible;
however, the elimination of water tends to reduce the total body-
water, and thence the blood-volume, so that there is a conflict between
the requirements of constant osmolality and those of constant body-
water, and the compromise consists in allowing the osmolality to fall
during salt-deprivation.

Haemorrhage. In McCance's classical study of salt-deprivation in
human volunteers, the physical manifestations of fatigue, etc., could be
traced to the diminution in blood-volume consequent on the excretion
of water to reduce the hypo-osmolality that would otherwise have
ensued. Salt-deprivation is not a serious hazard with civilized humans,

although with many animals it is; a more common hazard for humans is haemorrhage, which brings the requirement for reabsorption of extracellular fluid into the blood, together with steps to retain both sodium and water. In seeking control mechanisms influencing salt and water retention or elimination, then, we must seek sensors that are not only responsive to blood osmolality but also to blood- or extra-cellular fluid-volume.

Some Techniques for Study

The investigation of the problems of salt and water balance has stimulated the experimenter to the most remarkable ingenuity in devising methods for measuring reabsorption under different conditions.

Split-Drop

The split-drop technique of Gertz involves placing a drop of isotonic NaCl solution in the tubule between two drops of oil; absorption is measured by simply measuring the length of the droplet as it shrinks, and the "half-time" is a quantitative measure of absorptive rate. In the proximal tubule of the dog, for example, it is about 33 sec.

Transit-Time

Another technique involved the "transit time", i.e. the time required for fluid to pass from glomerulus to a given part of the nephron, e.g. the end of the visible portion of the proximal tubule. The animal is injected with the dye, lissamine green; the appearance in the glomeruli is indicated by a green flush over the surface; later the green appears at specific points in the tubule. Gertz *et al.* (1965) used the time required to reach the point where the tubule dips into the medulla, the beginning of the pars recta. Clearly, the shorter the transit-time, the smaller the amount of reabsorption; and from the measured rate of filtration in a single tubule, and the volume of a given length of tubule, it is possible to calculate the fraction of the filtrate reabsorbed.

Collapse-Time

Another technique measures the time for a tubule to collapse after flow has been brought to a halt by sudden occlusion of the renal artery (Leyssac, 1963).

Microperfusion

Other techniques involve perfusion of a portion of tubule either *in vivo* or *in vitro* (Burg and Orloff, 1968). Not satisfied with perfusing

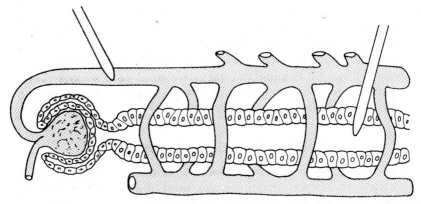

Fig. 5.1. Schematic drawing showing technique of peritubular capillary perfusion and simultaneous micropuncture of a proximal tubule receiving vascular supply from the perfused capillaries. (From Windager *et al.*, in de Wardener, *Brit. med. Bull.*)

and puncturing the various parts of the nephron, others have sampled the blood in the vasa recta, and have even perfused blood through the efferent arteriole, thereby controlling the composition of the blood passing over the tubules (Fig. 5.1).

Vasopressin or ADH

The main mechanisms in the renal control over salt and water balance have been briefly indicated. The antidiuretic hormone— ADH—is secreted by the endings of neurosecretory cells in the posterior pituitary (Vol. 2); the hormone is released into the extracellular space and carried into the general circulation.

Changes in Blood-Concentration

The technique of radioimmunoassay (Vol. 2) has permitted accurate determination of the concentrations of ADH in the circulating blood in response to osmotic and other stimuli. Raising the osmotic pressure of the blood by hypertonic injections caused an increase in the basal level of ADH in the blood, the increase being a linear function of the change in plasma osmolality (Fig. 5.2, open circles). When the blood-volume was decreased by intraperitoneal injections of colloid, keeping the blood-osmolality constant, there was also an increase in ADH secretion (Fig. 5.2, closed circles). During water-lack, both blood-osmolality and blood-volume stimuli come into effect; initially, as the curves show, the blood-osmolality will control the secretion of ADH, but as water-lack progresses and the blood-volume decreases, there will

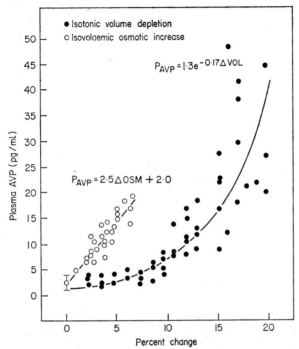

Fig. 5.2. Showing the relation between the concentration of vasopressin (ADH) in the blood plasma (AVP) and the plasma osmolality (open circles) and the plasma volume (filled circles). Ordinates: Concentration of vasopressin in pg/ml; Abscissae: Per cent change in plasma osmolality or volume. (Dunn *et al.*, *J. clin. Invest.*)

be a cooperative action leading to very high levels of ADH in the blood.

Verney's Osmoreceptors

The cell bodies of these secretory neurones are in the hypothalamus; the classical study of Verney demonstrated that the "sensors" governing release of ADH into the blood in response to hyperosmolality of the blood were in the hypothalamus, and subsequent work has identified the supraoptic nucleus as the responsive centre. The *osmoreceptors* of Verney could be the actual secretory neurones, or they could be separate neurones making synaptic contacts with the neurosecretory cells.

Supraoptic Units

To quote a recent study, Hayward and Vincent (1970) implanted electrodes in the supraoptic nucleus of monkeys and recorded the

responses of individual neurones of the unanaesthetized animal when
the osmolality of the blood was altered by intracarotid injections of
hypertonic saline. It is important to appreciate that the antidiuretic
hormone can be released by emotional and sensory stimuli, and it is
therefore desirable to distinguish neurones that are uniquely sensitive
to a change in osmolality of the blood from others that might respond
to different forms of stimulus. Hayward and Vincent were able to
identify many cells that changed their rate of spontaneous firing after
injection of hypertonic saline; these were described as "specific"

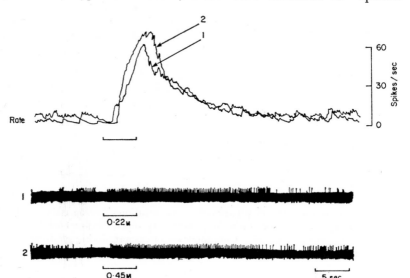

Fig. 5.3. The response of a monophasic specific osmosensitive neurone in the supraoptic nucleus of the conscious monkey to intracarotid injection of hypertonic saline.
Spike discharges in response to 0·22 M NaCl (1) and 0·45 M NaCl (2) are shown in
the lower part of the figure, whilst above are the rates of discharge, in spikes/sec.
(Hayward and Vincent, *J. Physiol.*)

because a variety of sensory or "arousal" stimuli failed to influence
them; moreover, the specific cells fell into two groups according as the
response was mono- or bi-phasic. Thus the *biphasic* type gave an initial
outburst of activity followed by a silent period before resuming the
basic spontaneous discharge. These cells were located in the supraoptic
nucleus exclusively, whilst those giving a *monophasic* response (Fig. 5.3)
occurred in a surrounding zone.

Osmoreceptors. It was considered that the cells responding biphasically were the secretory neurones whose discharge caused liberation of ADH, whilst the monophasically responding cells were the

osmoreceptors of Verney, responding directly to the changed osmolality. On this basis the biphasically responding neurones would be responding post-synaptically to discharges from the osmoreceptors.

Arousal Response. It was noted in the waking animal that the injection of hypertonic solution produced behavioural responses, including irregular sniffing respiration, lip and tongue smacking, chewing, and so on; this "arousal" type of response might well have activated the hypothalamic neurones, and in fact a category of non-specific cells was found distributed diffusely through the anterolateral hypothalamus; these responded to osmotic stimuli but also, unlike the specific cells, they responded to purely "arousal" stimuli, such as noises, flashes, and touching. Thus the same neurosecretory neurone can be activated by purely osmotic stimuli or through a sensory pathway probably related to the ascending reticular arousal system.

Micro-Injection into Hypothalamus

Direct measurements of the change in ADH secretion of anaesthetized cats, following microinjections of hypertonic saline into the supraoptic nucleus, were made by Milton and Paterson (1974) by assaying the level of the hormone in the blood. Only when the micro-injection cannula was in this region of the hypothalamus were increases in blood-ADH observed.

Response to Atrial Distension

Distension of the atria causes a decrease in secretion of ADH, a response that would operate in correcting for an increased blood-volume by diuresis. Menninger and Frazier (1972) found very few single units in the hypothalamus that would respond to expansion of the blood volume, although a number were found that responded to inflation of an atrial balloon. All those responding in this way also responded to hyperosmolality of the hypothalamus and so were, presumably, functional in the release of ADH.

Aldosterone

Addison's Disease

The importance of the adrenal cortex in control over salt balance has been recognized since the discovery that the low blood-Na^+ of Addison's disease was due to adrenal cortical insufficiency and could be remedied by injections of cortical hormones. It was Grundy, Simpson and Tait (1952) who showed that the hormone was aldosterone*, so that injections of this hormone caused retention of salt.

* Deoxycorticosterone (DOC) has "mineralcorticoid" activity in that it causes retention of Na^+ and excretion of K^+, but it is considerably less effective than aldosterone; 18-hydroxy-corticosterone, which is secreted by some patients with hypertension, has about 20 per cent of the activity of DOC (Gotshall and Davis, 1973).

Ascites

The hormone is liberated into the blood in response to haemorrhage, or salt-deprivation, and its effect is to increase the blood-volume by retention of Na^+ and the consequent retention of water; at the same time excretion of K^+ is favoured. In pathological states involving large accretions of extracellular fluid, e.g. the ascites associated with cardiac failure, the causative factor seems to be the secretion of aldosterone into the blood with the consequent salt and water retention.

Receptors

The sensor that responds to the stimulus, e.g. of haemorrhage, may well be located in the low-pressure part of the vascular system, i.e., the atria or great veins. Stretch-receptors here could bring about a reflex secretion of aldosterone and ADH during haemorrhage. The fact that heart failure, involving venous congestion and stretch of the atria and great veins, also causes secretion of aldosterone requires a further hypothesis, i.e. a sensor responsive to a fall in *arterial* pressure. Such a receptor may be in the kidney itself, since there is no doubt that the liberation of aldosterone into the blood can be brought about by the liberation of another chemical mediator, namely renin, synthesized in the kidney. Thus, depletion of sodium will hardly cause any secretion of aldosterone in the hypophysectomized animal if its kidneys have been removed (Binnion *et al.*, 1965).

The Juxtaglomerular Complex

As Fig. 5.4 shows, the afferent arteriole of the glomerulus comes into close apposition with the distal tubule of the same nephron. The epithelial cells here become distinct from those of the rest of the tubule and are called *macula densa* cells. The ordinary smooth muscle cells of the intima of the afferent arteriole are replaced, here, by *epithelioid cells*, which contain granules which, in the electron microscope appear to be secretion granules, being covered by a single membrane similar in appearance to the membranous endoplasmic reticulum. The epithelioid cells, referred to as *granular cells*, contain *renin*, and the degree of granularity of the cells varies, apparently in accordance with the state of salt- or fluid-balance, e.g. they are hypergranulated in generalized oedema.

Angiotensin. Renin is a compound that reacts with a "renin substrate" in plasma or lymph, namely a_2-globulin, from which it splits off a decapeptide, *angiotensin I*; thereafter an octapeptide, *angiotensin II*, is formed from angiotensin I by a *converting enzyme* (Fig. 2.30, p. 141); and it is angiotensin II that is the pharmacologically active agent.

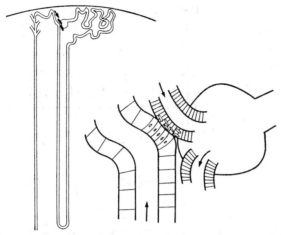

Fig. 5.4. Schematic drawing of the anatomical arrangement of the individual nephron unit and the juxtaglomerular apparatus. At lower right: point of contact between ascending limb of Henle's loop and vascular pole. The tubular cells whose nuclei are shown are the macula densa cells. (Thurau, *Proc. IIIrd Int Congr. Nephrol.*)

Angiotensin II is a powerful vasoconstrictor and by virtue of this action may affect renal function, e.g. by constriction of the afferent arteriole of the glomerulus, thereby reducing filtration. Infusion of ACTH into the adrenal gland, at rates adequate to increase the basic rates of secretion of the glucocorticoids cortisol and corticosterone by 5–20-fold, failed to cause secretion of aldosterone, so that the pituitary is apparently not involved in stimulating release (Blair-West *et al.*, 1962).*

Stimulation of Aldosterone Secretion. Renin appears in the blood under conditions demanding the secretion of aldosterone; thus Fig. 5.5 shows the changes in concentration in the blood of unanaesthetized dogs before and during sodium-deprivation; 24 hours after beginning the experiment the concentration rose by 1·9 ng/ml plasma and remained at this high level for 22 days. Within 48 hours of return to a normal diet the level had fallen to its original value. So far as could be ascertained, it was the concentration of sodium in the blood that determined the release of renin. The secretion of renin into the blood thus seems to be able to provoke the secretion of aldosterone by the adrenal cortex. The manner in which renin provokes the secretion of aldosterone seems to be through an influence of its

* When very high concentrations of ACTH were established, Blair-West *et al.* did find some secretion.

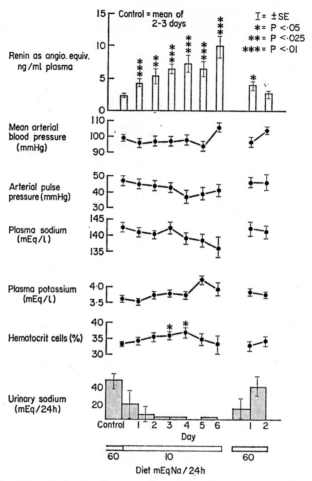

Fig. 5.5. The effect of reducing dietary sodium of dogs from a control value of 60 mEq/24 hr to 10 mEq/24 hr and subsequent return to the control diet. Note rise in renin secretion during salt-depletion. (Brubacher and Vander, *Amer. J. Physiol.*)

derivative, angiotensin II, which stimulates the conversion of cortico-sterone to aldosterone in the adrenal gland; thus in Na^+-depletion the increased aldosterone secretion is accompanied by diminished cortico-sterone secretion (Braverman and Davis, 1973). In discussing the control of salt and water balance, therefore, we have to consider the factors governing the release of renin from the epithelioid cells.

Intrarenal Formation of Angiotensins. It was considered origin-ally that the liberation of the polypeptide angiotensin I was confined to the plasma but it was later found that isolated rat renal glomeruli could release angiotensin I into their incubation medium, a process that was inhibited by inhibitors of protein synthesis (Fischer-Ferraro *et al.*, 1971). The conversion of angiotensin I to angiotensin II likewise occurs within the kidney (Merrill *et al.*, 1973),* and the fact that the concentration of angiotensin II in the kidney lymph is always higher than that in the systemic blood strongly indicates that the intrarenally formed angiotensin is physiologically important. When alterations in renin release are brought about physiologically, e.g. by volume-expansion or treatment with furosemide (p. 509) the changes in renal lymph concentration and systemic blood concentration occur in parallel.

Nervous Mechanisms
Filtration Rate

The completely denervated kidney performs most of its functions quite adequately, so that direct nervous control is considered to be relatively unimportant by comparison with that exerted through the hormones. Nevertheless, the fact that the blood vessels are richly innervated and therefore that the resistance to flow along the afferent, and possibly the efferent, arterioles may be altered, means that the rate of filtration, at least, may be under nervous control, whilst the distribution of blood-flow between cortex and medulla may also be altered. Less directly, but perhaps more powerfully, renal function may be altered by changes in renin secretion brought about by the sympathetic innervation. Thus Vander (1965) infused adrenaline or noradrenaline into dogs, and ensured that the renal arterial pressure was unaltered by controlling a clamp on the aorta; the concentration of renin in the blood was increased, and the same effect could be obtained by stimulation of the renal nerves.

Proximal Reabsorption

A direct action of β-adrenergic stimulation on proximal reabsorption of Na^+ was postulated by Gill and Casper (1971); according to them, infusion of one renal artery with isoproterenol caused increased formation of urine on that side with no influence on glomerular filtration rate or other haemodynamic factors. They suggested that the inhibition of Na^+-reabsorption was mediated by cAMP.

* The activity of the convertase that converts Angiotensin I to II is greatly reduced in low-sodium animals, i.e. in animals in which aldosterone secretion is high. Thus renin activity in the animal can be controlled by alterations in convertase activity (Merrill *et al.*, 1973). We may note here that angiotensin infusion into the blood tends to suppress the release of renin from the kidney—negative feedback (Falchuk *et al.*, 1971).

Let us then keep in mind the three hormonal systems so far un-equivocally concerned in salt and water balance, namely ADH, aldosterone, and renin-angiotensin, and proceed to examine some characteristics of salt and water excretion under different conditions.

The Renal Handling of Sodium

The main features in the handling of Na^+ have been considered in Vol. 1, and are briefly summarized by the diagram of Fig. 5.6. In the proximal tubule some 85–90 per cent of the filtrate is reabsorbed iso-osmotically, in the sense that the solutes are absorbed along with water so that no difference of osmolality is procured; the fate of the remaining 10–15 per cent depends on the state of salt- and water-balance of the animal.

Diuresis

Under conditions of diuresis, when the body is overloaded with water, the problem is to excrete *solute-free water*, i.e. to reabsorb salts in preference to water, to leave a hypotonic urine. This preferential reabsorption of Na^+, to cause gradients of osmolality and Na^+-concentration, is a feature of the distal nephron, i.e. the distal convoluted tubule, the loop of Henle and the collecting duct. If the animal is overloaded with both water and salt, as with salt-infusions, the diuresis is accompanied by *natriuresis*, the reabsorption of salt being restricted.

Antidiuresis or Hydropenia

In antidiuresis, or hydropenia, when the animal is short of water, the 10–15 per cent of the filtrate remaining after passage through the

---

Fig. 5.6. The renal handling of sodium. In the proximal tubule some 85–90 per cent of the filtered sodium is reabsorbed iso-osmotically with water. The remaining 10–15 per cent of sodium is passed to the rest of the nephron and its fate is dependent on the salt- and water-balance of the animal. (a) Hydropenia (antidiuresis). In this state water is reabsorbed by means of an osmotic gradient produced by the active transport of sodium out of the ascending limb of the loop of Henle. Antidiuretic hormone (ADH) makes the collecting duct permeable to water, so that a hypertonic urine is produced. The contribution of sodium to the urine osmolality is dependent on the sodium balance of the animal, and in sodium-deficiency this level can be reduced to a very small amount in the final urine. (b) Diuresis. When there is an excess of water, the animal needs to excrete solute-free water (C_{H_2O}) to reduce salt-loss, and this produces a hypotonic urine. Since ADH is absent in this state, the collecting duct wall is relatively impermeable to water, and sodium is actively reabsorbed by the loop of Henle, the distal convoluted tubule and the collecting duct so that C_{H_2O} is positive.

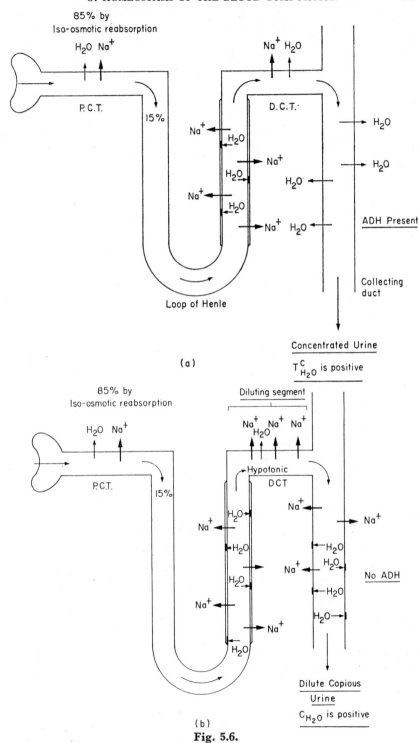

(a)

$T^C_{H_2O}$ is positive

(b)

Fig. 5.6.

proximal tubule is subjected to a concentrating process through selective reabsorption of water by the countercurrent system in the loop of Henle and collecting duct. The extent to which Na$^+$ will contribute to this hyperosmolality of the urine will depend on the state of Na$^+$-balance and the availability of other solutes for excretion. In sodium-deficiency, distal reabsorption of Na$^+$ may be carried to the point that the concentration in the final urine will be very small.

Micropuncture Study

Some of these features are illustrated by the micropuncture study of Malnic *et al.* (1966); Fig. 5.7 shows the changes in tubular fluid/ plasma (TF/P) ratio (upper diagram) for Na$^+$ at different stages in the passage of the filtrate along the nephron. The TF/P ratio is a measure of the change in concentration of Na$^+$; in the proximal tubule

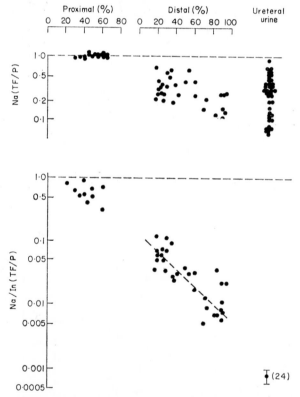

Fig. 5.7. The reabsorption of sodium. Upper graph: TF/P ratio for sodium as function of tubular length. Lower graph: Sodium-to-inulin concentration ratios as function of tubular length. (Malnic *et al.*, *Amer. J. Physiol.*)

there is no change. The ratio of the Na^+ to inulin TF/P ratios measures the fraction of the filtered Na^+ remaining, and it will be seen in the lower graph that, well before the end of the proximal tubule, some 60–70 per cent of the Na^+ has been reabsorbed; and since this has occurred without change in concentration, this means an iso-osmotic reabsorptive process, the reabsorption of Na^+ being accompanied by an amount of water equivalent to that which dissolved this Na^+ in the filtrate. By the distal tubule the concentration of Na^+ has fallen, indicating selective reabsorption *vis-a-vis* water, and the condition in the final urine is variable, from less than 1 per cent of the original concentration to nearly 100 per cent. As the lower curve shows, absolute removal of the Na^+ continues so that the *fractional reabsorption* in the urine is well over 99 per cent.

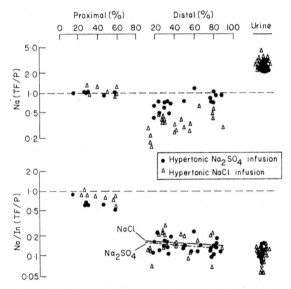

Fig. 5.8. The effects of loading with hypertonic salt solutions on the reabsorption of sodium. Ordinates and abscissae as in Fig. 5.7. (Malnic *et al.*, *Amer. J. Physiol.*)

Hypernatraemia. When the animal is overloaded with sodium the picture changes (Fig. 5.8); at the beginning of the distal tubule the TF/P ratio is still less than unity, indicating selective reabsorption of Na^+ in the loop of Henle, but as we proceed along the distal tubule the ratio returns to unity, indicating a selective removal of water; and by the time the ureter is reached the urine has become strongly hypertonic, the TF/P for Na^+ being greater than 2 indicating that this ion contributes greatly to the hyperosmolality.

Hyponatraemia. Under conditions of sodium-depletion, very low concentrations of Na^+ are achieved in the final urine, the final stages of reabsorption taking place in the collecting ducts; it seems that it is here that the largest gradients of Na^+-concentration across the nephron can be established.

ADH

So far as control is concerned, the antidiuretic hormone acts primarily on the concentrating mechanism, apparently altering the permeability of the collecting ducts to water and making the osmotic absorption of water more effective. In experimental animals, infusion of ADH also causes some extra excretion of salt (saluresis), but this may be due to the artificial conditions of water-loading required to demonstrate antidiuretic action; in human subjects ADH causes increased re-absorption of Na^+ and excretion of K^+ (Barraclough and Jones, 1970).

Aldosterone

Aldosterone, acting on the Na^+-reabsorptive mechanism, favours retention of Na^+ and excretion of K^+. Since the variable portion of Na^+-reabsorption, i.e. the *facultative* portion, takes place in the distal nephron, it is reasonable to assume that aldosterone acts mainly on the distal nephron, and in dogs Lynch *et al.* (1972) found no effects of adrenalectomy on the proximal reabsorptive rate, as calculated from the transit-time or the split-drop technique.*

Angiotensin and Vascular Changes

Renin, causing release of aldosterone, will operate by the same mechanism, but the angiotensin released into the blood, or even acting locally, can alter the vascular dynamics. Such vascular changes can have several influences; thus constriction of the afferent arteriole would decrease filtration rate and on this account might favour salt-retention; vaso-active substances like this might also alter the distri-bution of blood-flow through the kidney, diverting flow from, say, the superficial cortical glomeruli to the deeper ones; if the filtration-reabsorption characteristics of superficial and deep glomeruli were different, we should achieve a change in the handling of salt and water. Again, the ability to concentrate the urine depends on the flow of blood through the medulla; a high blood-flow will militate against the build-up of hyperosmolality in the deep tissue, although the

---

* Wiederholt *et al.* (1966) concluded that aldosterone was necessary for 50 per cent of the proximal reabsorption in the rat.

countercurrent type of flow along the hair-pin vasa recta will tend to compensate this. If blood were diverted to the vasa recta we might expect a diuresis, i.e. a reduced reabsorption of water, due to the levelling up of the osmolality gradient through the medulla.

Blood-Flow in Medulla. Experimentally the blood-flow to the different regions of the kidney may be measured by injecting the animal with radioactive "microspheres", i.e. large particles that block the capillaries as soon as they reach them. The relative degrees of radioactivity in the different regions of the kidney give the relative

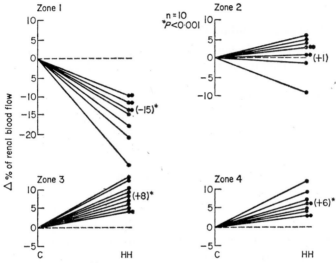

Fig. 5.9. The effect of reduction in blood pressure brought about by haemorrhage on the fractional distribution of renal blood-flow. C, control; HH, after haemorrhage. The kidney tissue has been divided into concentric zones from without inwards. Note that haemorrhage causes a large fall in blood-flow in Zone 1 whilst the innermost layers show a rise in blood-flow. (Rector *et al.*, *Amer. J. Physiol.*)

rates of blood-flow at the time of injection. Using this technique, Stein *et al.* (1971, 1972) found that volume-expansion was accompanied by increased flow to the innermost layers, i.e. that blood-flow had been diverted to the nephrons with long loops of Henle. However, Rector *et al.* (1972) found that haemorrhage, which is accompanied by Na^+-retention, was also associated with diversion of blood-flow to the inner nephrons (Fig. 5.9). Intrarenal epinephrine or angiotensin decreased the total blood-flow but had no specific regional effects, so that the diversion of blood, whatever its significance, was not due to these hormones.

Bradykinin. Bradykinin increases blood-flow through the kidney without affecting the glomerular filtration rate; nevertheless it causes diuresis and natriuresis, which may be prevented by maintaining blood-flow constant with an aortic clamp (Willis *et al.*, 1969). It would seem, then, that increased blood-flow *per se* tends to inhibit reabsorption of Na$^+$ and water, and it could well be that the effects were due to washing out the gradients of Na$^+$ and osmolality established in the medulla; such a wash-out would certainly account for the water diuresis, and it might also account for the natriuresis, reducing the effective active transport of Na$^+$ out of the ascending limb of Henle's loop.

Glomerulo-Tubular Balance

This is the term applied to the tendency for the rate of proximal tubular reabsorption of the filtrate to adjust itself to the rate of glomerular filtration, so that in perfect balance the *fractional* re-absorption of the filtrate is constant, whilst the absolute reabsorption increases with increasing rate of filtration. Such a balance would provide a useful homeostatic mechanism ensuring against large fluctuations in the load of salt and water presented to the distal nephron. On the other hand, if it applied to all conditions, it might limit the kidney's ability to adjust its performance to meet requirements; thus an obvious mechanism for disposing of a large infusion of isotonic saline would be the increased rate of filtration resulting from the lowered osmotic pressure of the plasma; if, however, the reabsorption in the proximal tubule were increased proportionately, the increased filtration would have no homeostatic value. In fact, glomerulo-tubular balance is by no means universal, although under some conditions, as for example, in the experiments of Glabman *et al.* (1965), when they varied the filtration-rate by constricting the abdominal aorta, the fractional reabsorption remained constant in spite of variations of some 6 to 66 per cent in filtration-rate.

Volume Expansion. In general, the casual fluctuations in filtra-tion-rate occurring normally seem to be compensated, but more extreme changes are not necessarily so; hence homeostatic adjustments in the proximal tubule are by no means excluded. Thus Herrera-Acosta *et al.* (1972) examined the functions of single nephrons in the rat in response to blood-volume expansion by infusion of saline. The ratio TF/P for inulin was a measure of reabsorption, and the rate of collection of fluid, and the inulin concentrations in blood and fluid, permitted the calculation of *single nephron glomerular filtration rate* (*sngfr*). From these measurements, the fractional reabsorption was calculated, and this was by no means constant; during moderate blood-volume expansion it fell from 60 per cent in hydropenia, to 36 per cent; the absolute absorptive rate actually decreased too, so that the main factor leading to an increased delivery of filtrate to the distal nephron must have been the increased rate of filtration. Thus, in massive infusions of saline the delivery to the distal nephron increased by 19 nl/min; the rise in glomerular filtration-rate accounted for 16 nl/min, whilst the fall in absolute reabsorption accounted for only 3 nl/min. This work shows, then, that the adjustment to volume-expansion by saline injections consisted in increased filtration-rate *and* decreased proximal reabsorption. The final elimination of the extra salt and water would be accounted for by overloading of the distal reabsorptive processes *per se*, but there is little doubt that a diminished secretion of the hormone aldosterone also influenced reabsorption in the distal nephron.

Significance of Starling Forces

To understand the control of the kidney we must appreciate to the full the operation of simple physical forces governing filtration and reabsorption, to see to what extent there may be built-in homeostatic mechanisms independent of extraneous influences, such as hormonal or nervous action. Thus autoregulation of blood-flow, operating in the kidney so that variations of arterial pressure above about 70 mm Hg have no effect on rate of blood-flow, is itself a homeostatic factor. Since blood-flow through the kidney is closely correlated with filtration-rate, this means that filtration is autoregulated in the face of altered arterial pressure (Deen *et al.*, 1972).

C.O.P. of Efferent Plasma. The colloid osmotic pressure of blood in the efferent arteriole will be greater than that in the glomerulus because of the fact of filtration, and the greater the filtration-fraction the larger will be the colloid osmotic pressure (also called oncotic pressure). In normal hydropenic rats of a strain having its glomeruli on the renal surface, Brenner *et al.* found an average protein concentration of 5·8 g/100 ml in the afferent arteriole and 8·7 g/100 ml in the efferent arteriole. When the plasma had been loaded with saline, to give an afferent arteriolar concentration of 4·6 g/100 ml, the fall in the efferent concentration was not so great, namely to 7·2 g/100 ml, indicating the greater filtration in the saline-loaded animal. If reabsorption from the tubules is influenced by the colloid osmotic pressure of the blood into which this reabsorbed fluid must be collected, we may expect some sort of feedback control leading to *glomerulo-tubular balance*, the greater the filtration-fraction the greater the subsequent reabsorption in the proximal tubule (Fig. 5.10). Such a

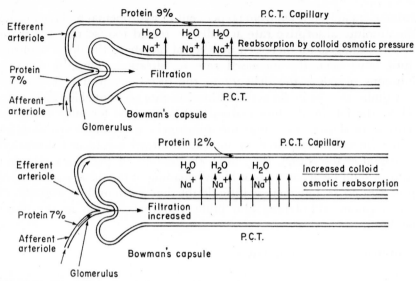

Fig. 5.10. The effect of variation in glomerular filtration rate on the colloid osmotic pressure of the peritubular blood and the subsequent increase in the rate of proximal reabsorption. In the upper figure the increase in colloid osmotic pressure in the efferent arteriolar blood is shown which is the result of hydrostatic ultrafiltration occurring in the renal capsule. In the lower figure is shown the effect of increasing the glomerular filtration rate with the subsequent greater rise in efferent arteriolar colloid osmotic pressure which would lead to increased proximal reabsorption and a balance between filtration and reabsorption.

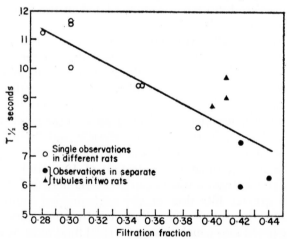

Fig. 5.11. Illustrating the linear relation between filtration fraction and the half-time for fluid reabsorption in the proximal tubule, as measured by the split-drop technique. Thus the greater the filtration-fraction the greater the rate of reabsorption. (Lewy and Windhager, *Amer. J. Physiol.*)

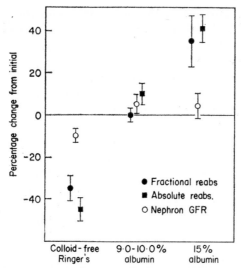

Fig. 5.12. The effect of variation in colloid osmotic pressure of the fluid perfusing the peritubular blood vessels on the fractional reabsorption by the proximal convoluted tubule. Pre-perfusion measurements during normal blood perfusion represent the control situation, from which the changes for each tubule were calculated.
Vertical bars denote ± SE. (Brenner and Troy, *J. clin. Invest.*)

relationship was demonstrated by Lewy and Windhager (1968), and is illustrated in Fig. 5.11 where the half-time for fluid reabsorption, measured by the split-drop technique, is plotted against filtration-fraction.

Tissue-Pressure. Again Brenner and Troy (1971) perfused the

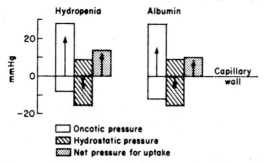

Fig. 5.13. The balance of forces across peritubular vessels of the proximal convoluted tubule favouring uptake of fluid. On the left is the hydropenic state, on the right the effect of raised plasma colloid osmotic pressure which slightly reduces the forces favouring net uptake. The black arrows represent the net forces; positive values absorption into the plasma; negative values, forces opposing this movement. (Knox *et al.*, *Amer. J. Physiol.*)

post-glomerular circulation through a micropipette and showed that, when the colloid osmotic pressure of the perfusion fluid was increased, the fractional reabsorption was increased (Fig. 5.12). However, the extent to which a raised colloid osmotic pressure of the post-glomerular plasma influences reabsorption from the proximal tubule will depend on the interstitial pressure (tissue-pressure) and the concentration of protein in the interstitial fluid. In an attempt to take these factors into account, Knox *et al.* estimated the balance of Starling forces to just favour reabsorption into the tubular blood in the hydropenic animal (Fig. 5.13, *left*). When albumin solutions were infused, the forces favouring uptake were slightly *decreased* due to a rise in colloid osmotic pressure of the interstitial fluid (Fig. 5.13, *right*). As Falchuk *et al.* (1971) concluded, there is little doubt that Starling forces, operating across the proximal tubule, do influence reabsorption of filtrate, but the extent to which they contribute to glomerulo-tubular balance—when this occurs—and to adjustments of proximal re-absorption to physiological changes, such as haemodilution, remains to be proved.

Haematocrit. Changes in the haematocrit of the blood will be determined by the movement of extracellular fluid into the plasma; and so a reduced haematocrit will usually be accompanied by dilution of the plasma proteins; such a dilution should favour salt excretion if Starling forces dominated the situation, and this would be true of volume-expansion by infusion of isotonic saline (Brenner and Galla, 1971). Haemorrhage, however, is accompanied by passage of extra-cellular fluid into the plasma, and the consequent dilution of the plasma proteins might favour salt-excretion; the physiological response, however, is *salt-retention*, brought about by the secretion of renin and aldosterone whose effects outweigh any change in Starling forces favouring salt excretion.

Effects of Haemorrhage

The compensatory response to haemorrhage is retention of salt and antidiuresis; experimentally animals may be bled slowly and the concentrations of hormones in the blood determined. In conscious rabbits, Weber *et al.* found an increase of 300 per cent in the concen-tration of renin, although the loss of blood was insufficient to reduce arterial blood-pressure; if the blood-loss was compensated by a protein-saline injection, there was no increase in renin secretion. Again Clay-baugh and Share (1973), by reducing the blood-volume by only 2·6 per cent, found increased concentrations of both ADH and renin in the blood. The release of ADH in response to haemorrhage is inhibited by blocking afferent impulses through the vagi (Clark and Rocha e Silva, 1967); and the same is true for the release of renin by the kidneys (Hodge *et al.*, 1969). When haemorrhage is severe enough to cause a fall in diastolic arterial blood pressure of about 20 mm Hg, the amounts of ADH released are greatly in excess of those required to produce maximal diuresis, so that an additional function of this release is doubtless to compensate for the fall in arterial blood pressure through the vasoconstrictive action of the vasopressin (Rocha e Silva and Rosenberg, 1969). We may assume that, just as volume-expansion activates receptors in the low-pressure vascular system, leading to inhibition of hormone release, so the fall in pressure in the same system during haemorrhage, although it may be very small, brings about reflex changes leading to hormone secretion.

The High-Pressure System. When haemorrhage is more severe, there will be changes in the high-pressure system, and there is little doubt that renin is released in response to altered arterial pressure; thus a decrease in renal perfusion-pressure stimulates renin release (Blair, 1971) whilst an increased blood-pressure inhibits the release of renin caused by clamping the ureter of the isolated kidney (Kaloyanides *et al.*, 1973). Arterial sensors are presumably present in the renal vasculature,* but the studies of Share and Levy (1966) indicate that baroreceptors and chemoreceptors of the carotid sinus are also capable of initiating reflex changes in ADH concentration. Moreover, the release of aldosterone during haemorrhage is biphasic, the initial release being apparently due to reduced blood-volume acting on the low-pressure system, and a later release operating through the arterial pressure in the high-pressure system (Fabre *et al.*, 1969).

Role of Sympathetic Activity. Stimulation of the atrial receptors causes increased sympathetic activity in the cardiac nerves (Chapter 2) but *decreased* activity in the renal nerves (Karim *et al.*, 1972); the diminished activity may result in increased blood-flow through the kidney, which might favour diuresis by abolishing osmolality gradients in the medulla (p. 420), but this is not an essential feature of the diuresis, since it occurs in the denervated kidney (Ledsome *et al.*, 1961).

---

* According to Blaine *et al.* (1971), renin is released from a non-filtering denervated kidney in response to haemorrhage in the adrenalectomized animal. Thus a vascular receptor, responsive to altered renal perfusion-pressure, is likely, possibly the afferent glomerular arteriole at the level of the granular juxtaglomerular cells (Tobian, 1964). Since the kidney was not filtering it is unlikely that the concentration of Na^+ in the tubule was the stimulus as postulated by Thurau (1966).

Expansion of the Blood-Volume

Infusions of isotonic saline solutions cause a diuresis; this is compounded of a water-diuresis, involving excretion of solute-free water, together with saluresis, i.e. increased excretion of salt (Fig. 5.14). The effects could be due to expansion of the interstitial fluid volume, rather than that of the circulating blood, but qualitatively similar

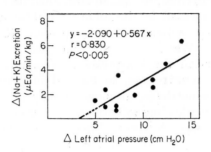

Fig. 5.14. Showing that expansion of blood-volume, simulated by dilatation of the left atrium with an inflated balloon, causes increased excretion of salt. The animals were infused with ADH, so that the renal effects could not have been due to liberation of this hormone. (Gillespie *et al., Amer. J. Physiol.*)

effects are obtained when the colloid osmotic pressure of the infused saline is raised to that of plasma, or alternatively when blood of exactly the same composition and haematocrit value is infused (Houttuin *et al.*, 1972), so that there is no doubt that expansion of blood-volume, *per se,* is the critical event.

Changed Blood-Hormone Levels. The expansion in blood-volume is associated with decreased ADH-, renin- and aldosterone-levels in the blood; and we may presume that the diuresis and saluresis are largely mediated through these hormones.

Changed C.O.P. When expansion is with saline alone, however, the reduction in the colloid osmotic pressure of the blood may well be the dominant factor, causing increased filtration with inadequate reabsorption in the proximal tubule and overloading of the distal tubular reabsorptive mechanism. As indicated, the decreased proximal tubular reabsorption could be due to the lowered colloid osmotic pressure in the peritubular blood. Thus in normal hydropenic rats, Brenner *et al.* (1971) found protein concentrations in efferent arteriolar and femoral arterial blood of 9·5 and 6·8 per cent. respectively. In volume-expanded rats the values were 7·0 and 5·0 per cent respectively. Increasing the concentration of protein experimentally, by infusion into the peritubular blood vessel directly, restored the fractional

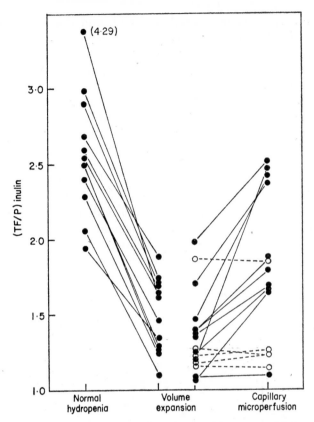

Fig. 5.15. Comparison of effects of volume expansion on proximal tubule fluid/ plasma inulin ratios in the presence and absence of reductions in postglomerular protein concentration. The solid circles joined by solid lines in the left-hand portion of the figure indicate the changes in TF/P inulin ratios induced by volume expansion in 12 proximal tubules. The solid lines in the right-hand portion of the figure join TF/P inulin values from 11 other proximal tubules (solid circles) studied initially during volume expansion and again during continuous microperfusion of an adjacent efferent arteriole and its branch peritubular capillaries with a Ringer's-bicarbonate solution containing 9–10g/100ml crystalline bovine serum albumin. The micro-perfusion control is indicated by five tubules (open circles and dashed lines) studied initially during volume expansion, and again during efferent arteriolar micro-perfusion with Ringer's-bicarbonate containing 6–7g/100ml albumin. (Brenner *et al.*, *J. clin. Invest.*)

reabsorption of salt to the original hydropenic value in the adjacent proximal tubules (Fig. 5.15).

Water-Immersion. A human assuming the recumbent position has temporarily an expanded blood-volume so far as the cardiovascular and renal systems are concerned, and this leads to diuresis associated with loss of plasma volume due to extra filtration into the tissue spaces. Immersion in water, in the erect position, has the same effect, since the gravitational pull on the blood, causing it to accumulate in the lower limbs, is no longer effective. It is interesting that prolonged immersion leads to diuresis and considerable changes in plasma volume (Graveline and Jackson, 1962; Behn *et al.*, 1969). It must be emphasized that the diuresis is not the main cause of the loss in blood-volume, which is due to a reflex change in the pre- and post-capillary resistances favouring filtration into the interstitial spaces.

The Sensory Mechanism

As indicated above, volume expansion without altering any of the parameters of the blood, such as its colloid osmotic pressure or its haematocrit, causes a natriuresis and diuresis; again, a diminution in blood-volume through haemorrhage, inadequate to affect the arterial pressure, causes antidiuresis and salt-retention. The obvious place for a sensor capable of responding to altered blood-volume is in the low-pressure part of the vascular system.

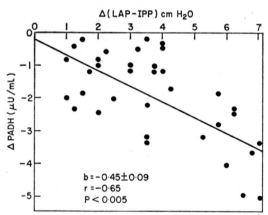

Fig. 5.16. The effect of distension of the left atrium on the blood ADH level. LAP, left atrial pressure; IPP, intrapleural pressure; $\triangle$PADH, change in plasma ADH level. $\triangle$(LAP–IPP) represents the change in left atrial transmural pressure. (Johnson *et al.*, *Amer. J. Physiol.*)

Atrial Distension. Artificial distension of the left atrium by inflation of a balloon causes a diuresis accompanied by diminished blood ADH and aldosterone concentrations (Fig. 5.16), effects that are blocked by section of the vagus, or injections of ADH. Since section of the vagus, or carotid sinus-nerve, causes increased secretion of

ADH and aldosterone, it would seem that the secretion of these hormones is normally held in check by afferent impulses from stretch- or other receptors. Distension of the atria, and probably of other parts of the low-pressure system, causes enhanced inhibition, whilst relaxation of these structures causes excretion of the hormones, presumably by nervous activation of the hypothalamus and, if aldosterone release is governed by the previous release of renin, by nervous activation of the juxtaglomerular apparatus by way of the sympathetic.

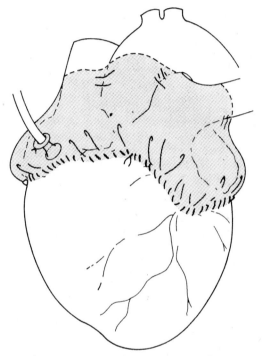

Fig. 5.17. Diagrammatic representation of atrial pericardial pouch with indwelling pericardial catheter. (Goetz *et al.*, *Amer. J. Physiol.*)

Atrial Transmural Pressure. The importance of *transmural* pressure in the atrium, rather than its absolute value, was demonstrated by Goetz *et al.* As illustrated by Fig. 5.17, the pericardium was cut around the level of the AV-groove and sewn to the upper edge of the heart making a pouch enclosing the atria. Into this pouch a tube is sewn and led off to the surface of the animal. The pouch is filled with saline and, by varying the pressure on this saline, we may prevent the atria from expanding, or cause them to expand. Goetz showed that the diuresis normally caused by expanding the plasma volume was inhibited if the pressure in the pouch was increased so that there was no change in transmural pressure, i.e. the pressure that tended to expand the atria. Alternatively, if the hydration of the animal was kept constant, and the pressure in the pouch was raised, so as to lower the transmural pressure by 4–8 mm Hg, then a reduction in the salt and water excretion was observed, with no measurable changes in haemodynamic parameters, such as arterial pressure.

Role of Renin in Autoregulation

It was argued by Guyton, Langston and Navar (1964), on the basis of considerable experimental evidence involving micropuncture, that the release of renin was controlled by the concentration of Na^+ in the distal tubule, and that this release operated in a feed-back mechanism that tended to maintain a constant blood-flow—*autoregulation*. Thus a high rate of filtration would, according to this argument, result in a higher-than-normal concentration of Na^+ in the distal tubule; this would cause secretion of renin, which would constrict the afferent arteriole and reduce filtration and blood-flow. Thus blood-flow would tend to be autoregulated, and also glomerulotubular balance would be achieved. The observation that autoregulation of blood-flow occurs when the kidney is perfused with oxygenated paraffin rules out the concentration of Na^+ in the tubules as a factor, and the finding that infusion of animals with angiotensin II in high concentration still permits autoregulation indicates that the renin system cannot be an important factor. Finally Bailie *et al.* (1972) found that the concentration of angiotensin II in renal lymph *increased* in response to a decrease in renal perfusion pressure, in association with autoregulation, and this showed that the autoregulation, which meant a decreased vascular resistance in the kidney, could not have been brought about by angiotensin II, which is a powerful vasoconstrictor.

Prostaglandins

These hormone-like substances are certainly produced by the kidney, and it is interesting that they are released by infusions of angiotensin II (Needleman *et al.*, 1973), an effect that is abolished by indomethacin, which blocks synthesis of PG's; other manoeuvres that cause release are noradrenaline, renal nervous stimulation, renal ischaemia, and bradykinin. Since prostaglandins are rapidly destroyed when they reach the general circulation, we must postulate a strictly local action, whatever this may be.

The "Natriuretic Hormone"

De Wardener among others has argued that the natriuresis, due to volume-expansion, may occur in the absence of altered aldosterone- or ADH-levels in the blood, and in the absence of any changes in the character of the blood, such as haematocrit or colloid osmotic pressure; and he postulated a "third hormone" that inhibited reabsorption of Na^+. The basic experiment consisted in cross-perfusing two dogs, expanding the blood-volume of the one by intravenous saline infusions and measuring the excretion of sodium by the other; both animals were given large doses of mineral corticoids so as to exclude the possibility that the effects were mediated by these. Expansion of the blood-volume of the one dog caused increased excretion of Na^+ by both, although the blood-volume of the non-infused dog was held constant. The natriuresis of the non-infused dog was smaller than that in the infused dog.

Exchange-Circulation. The main problem in this type of experiment is to ensure that expansion of blood-volume is not associated with variation in some other blood parameter that might influence renal function, e.g. a reduced haematocrit, other things being equal, would increase renal Na^+ excretion by virtue of the altered blood-viscosity (Houttuin *et al.*, 1972). By the process of "exchange-circulation" the animal's blood is fed into a reservoir containing an artificial blood, and the mixture is fed back into the animal; after a time the blood in the animal is in equilibrium with that in the reservoir and virtually identical with it. At this point, reservoir-fluid can be returned to the animal faster than it is taken away, thus causing expansion. Using this technique, Knox *et al.* (1968) showed, with the aid of micropuncture, that volume-expansion decreased proximal reabsorption of Na^+.

Perfused Kidney. More recently Bengele *et al.* (1972) have used the set-up illustrated by Fig. 5.18, using equilibrated blood and perfusing the denervated kidney separately, and ensuring that there was no change in renal vascular pressures. Natriuresis and diuresis were obtained on volume-expansion, and they concluded that some humoral factor was responsible, but not liberated from the kidney since the other kidney of the animal had been removed.

Kinin. Whether the "third hormone" is a kinin, as suggested by Marin-Grez *et al.* (1972), is not proved; sodium-loading of dogs causes an increase in the concentration of kinins in the vena caval blood, and this may have been due to the liberation of kallikrein, which was converted to a kinin (Vol. 2, Chapter 5). Certainly, as we have seen, vasodilators such as bradykinin promote natriuresis (p. 421).

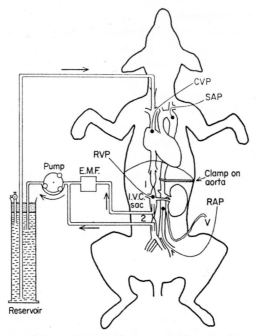

Fig. 5.18. Diagram of the method used to auto-perfuse the denervated dog kidney. The left kidney was exposed and all neural connections severed. The isolated kidney was perfused by its normal arterial supply but an adjustable clamp was placed on the aorta to control the renal arterial pressure. The blood supply to the gut and hind limb was also maintained as normal. Two ligatures (1 and 2) were placed around the inferior vena cava, and canulae inserted so that when the ligatures were closed blood from the hind-limb and gut was diverted into an external circuit via a sealed reservoir and then back into the external jugular vein. Blood from the perfused kidney passes into the section of inferior vena cava isolated by the ligatures and thence via a separate circuit to reservoir, the flow being monitored by an electromagnetic flowmeter (EMF). The blood in the reservoir was pumped back towards the heart at a rate to maintain the renal venous pressure at the same value as that prior to tying of the ligatures. The venous return could be suddenly increased by displacing blood from the sealed reservoir with air. Pressures were measured at points shown by the black dots. CVP and RVP, central and renal venous pressures; SAP and RAP, systemic and renal arterial pressures. (Bengele *et al.*, *Amer. J. Physiol.*)

Oedema

A generalized oedema, involving an expansion of the extracellular compartment of the body, is usually treated satisfactorily by diuretics (p. 503), which reduce the body-water until a steady state is achieved; the achievement of this steady state is due to the primary attack on the distal reabsorptive mechanism, so that excretion of Na^+ and water is the primary result; opposing this is the tendency for proximal reabsorption to increase in the face of the diminishing extracellular fluid volume, and finally a balance is struck, the patient achieving his so-called "dry-weight". If a diuretic acts on both proximal and distal sites, no such steady state may be achieved, and continued dosage may lead to severe Na^+-depletion.

Limits of Osmolality of Urine

The formation of a hypertonic urine requires the active transport of salt in a complicated counter-current manoeuvre that relies not only on the efficiency of the active transport process but on suitable permeability relations of water and solute in the loop of Henle and collecting duct. It would not be surprising to find limits to the degree of osmolality of the urine that may be established in different species and, in the same species, under different conditions. Thus, where the same species is concerned, factors favouring active transport of the Na^+ might be expected to increase concentrating ability, and in fact it is found that aldosterone, which increases active transport of Na^+, does permit a more concentrated urine when secreted or infused into the blood experimentally. Where different species are concerned, perhaps the most significant variable is the length of the loop of Henle; as Table I (p. 406) shows, there is, indeed, a very strong correlation between the relative thickness of the medulla and the maximum osmolality of the urine.

Drinking Sea-Water. It will be seen that, in man, the maximum depression of freezing-point is 2·6°C, corresponding to an osmolality of some 1400 milliosmoles per litre, compared with about 300 for blood; of the solutes, urea contributes materially so that urines with concentrations of salt greater than about 1000 milliosmoles/litre are rare. Since sea-water has an osmolality of about 1000 milliosmoles/litre, it is clear that it is useless as a source of water for man, the removal of the contained salt requiring more water than that actually imbibed. In species that have higher concentrating ability, however, drinking of sea-water is feasible, in fact the kangaroo rat may survive indefinitely without imbibing water at all, obtaining sufficient water from its diet and metabolism. Examination of its urine showed that it was twice as concentrated in respect to salts as that of white rats on a similar diet, whilst the concentration of urea was 1·6 times. Again, the harvest mouse, *Reithredontomys megalotis*, lives under arid conditions or in salt marshes where only sea-water is available; in the laboratory it will drink sea-water freely and survive. Maximum urinary osmolalities in the region of 4200 milliosmoles/litre were found, made up of 2600 milliosmolal urea and about 1000 milliosmolal electrolytes.

Stimulus to Water-Intake. Thirst

An animal, when short of water, develops a thirst and slakes it if water is available. The classical studies of Adolph on the pattern of water-intake in the dog showed that, under normal conditions, the intake was periodic and the periodicity was apparently governed by the water-loss; on the average the dog would not drink until its water-loss was 0·5 per cent of its body-weight (Robinson and Adolph, 1943). When the dog was deprived of water for a time, it drank rapidly and, what was remarkable, its intake almost exactly amounted to the deficit, there being a tendency to take water in excess by about 17 per cent (Adolph, 1939). The intake was too rapid for the ingested water to have been absorbed to any great extent during the whole period of drinking. When food was available, the pattern of food ingestion quite clearly affected the pattern of drinking, so that water-intake could be made almost continuous by appropriately feeding in small amounts.

Sham-Drinking

When the passage of water to the stomach was prevented by oesopha-gostomy—*sham-drinking*—the dog drank more than its requirements, indicating the importance of gastric distension as a clue to satiety; nevertheless, it did reach a point of satiety when some 250 per cent of the requirements had been taken in, so that oro-pharyngeal stimuli must contribute to the sensory mechanism that tells the animal when it has had enough. When water is given intragastrically to such a sham-drinking dog, it will drink to satisfy its true deficit, but now it drinks almost exactly the amount of its deficit; clearly, the gastric clue is now contributing. Furthermore, if a suitable delay intervenes between the intragastric loading, the animal exhibits satiety and does not sham-drink. Now a further clue has been provided; presumably the changed concentration of solutes in the blood (Bellows, 1939).

Gastric Balloon. To return to the gastric clue, Towbin (1949) showed that inflation of a balloon was an effective stimulus to satiety in the sham-drinking dog, so that now it tended only to satisfy its real requirements; the effect was abolished by vagotomy indicating this nerve as the probable afferent pathway in a reflex.

Oral, Gastric and Blood Factors

Thus these early classical studies emphasized the importance of three factors in determining the amount drunk by the water-deprived animal: *oral*, *gastric*, and finally, when the fluid had been absorbed, changed *concentration of solutes* in the blood.

Blood Changes

Before considering the oro-gastric factors further, let us examine the blood-changes; these could be twofold, namely a rise in osmolality of the blood and a diminution in blood- or extracellular fluid-volume. These might influence a "drinking centre" in the brain, either directly through stimulating osmoreceptive neurones, such as those concerned

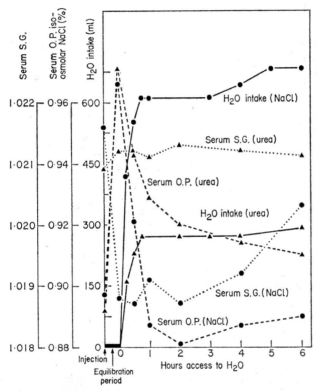

Fig. 5.19. The effect of intravenous injections of hypertonic sodium chloride and urea on voluntary water intake in dogs. The records show that 2·5 ml/kg of 20 per cent NaCl was more effective than 40 per cent urea in provoking voluntary water intake. S.G. = sp. gravity; O.P. = osmolality as equivalent NaCl solution. (Gilman, *Amer. J. Physiol.*)

with the release of ADH, or less directly through volume-receptors, e.g. the atrial receptors concerned in the release of renin and ADH.

Osmotic Stimulus. The importance of blood-osmolality was shown by Gilman (1937), who gave dogs hyperosmolal injections of NaCl or urea and observed large increases in voluntary water-intake; as Fig. 5.19 shows, urea was less effective in provoking drinking, and this is presumably because it penetrates most cells and so is less effective in causing shrinkage.

Hypovolaemic Stimulus. The importance of the blood-volume—the hypovolaemic stimulus—was suggested by the frequent observation that haemorrhage is accompanied by thirst, and experimentally,

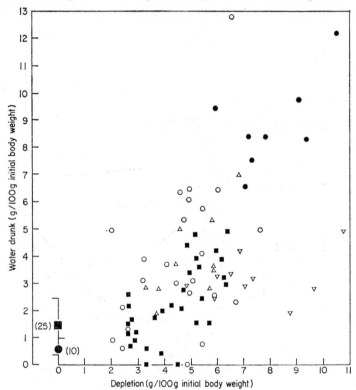

Fig. 5.20. The effect of reduced blood-volume, induced by intraperitoneal injections of colloid, on voluntary water intake in rats. Each point is one observation, except the controls (zero depletion) which are mean values with the numbers of observations in parentheses. The different symbols indicate different amounts of colloid injected. (Fitzsimons, *J. Physiol.*)

drinking in rats was provoked by causing the formation of excess extracellular fluid at the expense of the blood plasma by subcutaneous (Stricker, 1966), or intraperitoneal, injections of colloid, such as polyethylene glycol or gum-acacia. With such injections Fitzsimons (1961) was able to cause loss of body-water into the ascites up to 10 per cent of the body-weight; as Fig. 5.20 shows, the extra water-intake was proportional to the losses.

Additivity of Stimuli. According to Fitzsimons and Oatley (1968), the stimuli of hypovolaemia and hypertonicity are additive, and this accounts for the greater effectiveness of water-deprivation in inducing water-intake compared with hypovolaemia, since water-deprivation not only causes a rise in osmolality of the blood but also a decrease in blood-volume. This additivity is illustrated by Fig. 5.21 from a study by Stricker (1969), which shows the water-intake plotted against the concentration of colloid given subcutaneously (bottom curve). The intake increases with increased concentration, as we should expect. When the animal was previously injected with hypertonic NaCl,

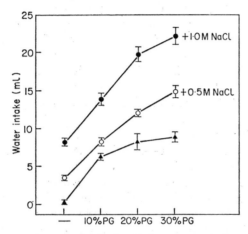

Fig. 5.21. The increase in water intake in rats in response to hypovolaemia induced by subcutaneous injections of polyethylene glycol (PG). The sensitivity of the above response is markedly increased if blood-hypertonicity is induced by the injection of 0·5 M and 1·0 M NaCl. Controls (bar) were sham-injected. (Stricker, *Amer. J. Physiol.*)

there was a further increase in water-intake at each level of colloid concentration, and the extra intakes were about equal to what would have been drunk if only hypertonic NaCl had been administered.

Hypovolaemic Satiety. As Stricker has emphasized, drinking alone is unlikely to satisfy the physiological requirement in hypovolaemic thirst, since expansion of blood-volume requires ingestion of salt as well; and it is therefore not surprising that, when an animal drinks in response to hypovolaemia, it exhibits satiety long before there has been adjustment of its plasma volume to normal, although, if allowed to drink isotonic NaCl, it now drinks sufficient to repair the deficit. We may ask: What stops the hypovolaemic animal from drinking? The answer is probably the lowered osmolality of the blood; and satiety must be regarded as a protective mechanism that overrides the hypovolaemic stimulus, preventing the excessive water-drinking that would otherwise occur. Thus a hypovolaemic animal will not drink if preloaded intragastrically with water, but it will do so if given hypertonic NaCl concurrently, the hypertonic NaCl preventing the fall in blood-osmolality that would have occurred had the dog drunk in response to hypovolaemia.

The Hypothalamic Centre

The presence of osmolality-sensitive* neurones in the hypothalamus has been described earlier; these respond to blood-hyperosomolality by liberating, or causing to be liberated, the neurohypophyseal hormone, vasopressin or ADH. Andersson et al. (1960) implanted electrodes into the lateral hypothalamus of goats and showed that electrical stimulation caused immediate drinking; this treatment also evokes the secretion of ADH, but Andersson considered that the osmoreceptors concerned with ADH secretion were not necessarily those concerned with drinking.

Adipsic Animals. Lesions in the lateral hypothalamus cause inhibition of spontaneous drinking—*adipsia*—and according to Andersson and McCann (1956) the sites of the lesions in their dogs that caused hypodipsia were the same as those that provoked drinking in goats in response to electrical stimulation. It will be recalled that lesions in this region also cause aphagia in rats, so that the animals are both adipsic and aphagic; it is difficult to say whether the "drinking centre" revealed by these lesions is separate from the "eating centre", as the lesions were insufficiently discrete, but Andersson's studies of electrical stimulation do suggest a separation. By appropriate feeding, these animals can be kept alive, and they eventually feed normally (Teitelbaum and Epstein, 1962), but their drinking is now unusual and is described as *prandial*, taking place only while eating. When made hypovolaemic or hyperosmolal, the rats do not respond by drinking (p. 449).

Possible Satiety Centre. Studies with lesions in the brain have failed to reveal a well defined "satiety centre" similar to that for eating (p. 281), and it may be that such a centre is not so physiologically necessary as one for food, since the effects of ingestion of water show up in the blood within an hour at least, and are well defined in terms of blood-osmolality, whereas the effects of feeding are slower to occur and are less simple. Nevertheless, Stricker's experiments showing the

* This sensitivity is probably due to the enhanced concentration of sodium in the blood rather than the hyperosmolality *per se*.

conflicting demands of hypovolaemia and blood-osmolality suggest a satiety-centre, responsive to dilution of the blood-plasma and opposing the activities of the thirst-centre, responding to hypovolaemic and hyperosmolal stimuli (Fig. 5.22).

Limbic System. In this connexion we must note that the lesions made in rats could well interfere with communications between the hypothalamus and other regions of the limbic system (Vol. 6) such as the amygdala. According to Grossman and Grossman (1963), the amygdala contains in its antero-ventral part a region that, when electrically stimulated, causes drinking and, when destroyed, causes

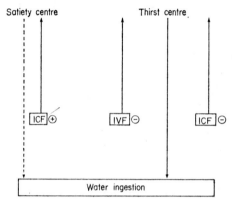

Fig. 5.22. Hypothetical activation of satiety and drinking centres. Full-line arrows indicate stimulation and broken arrow inhibition. + means increase and − means decrease in compartments. ICF = intracellular fluid; IVF = intravascular fluid. Thus from left to right, increased ICF excites the satiety centre which inhibits drinking; decreased IVF activates the thirst centre and stimulates drinking. Decreased ICF activates the thirst centre and stimulates drinking. (After Stricker, *Amer. J. Physiol.*)

hypodipsia; in addition, there is a more posterior region where stimulation causes hypodipsia and a lesion causes hyperdipsia. Again, Robinson and Mishkin (1968) stimulated at nearly 6000 loci in the monkey's forebrain and recorded the eating and drinking responses; drinking responses were by no means confined to the lateral hypothalamus or to the limbic area, the cingulate gyrus having a high concentration of responsive points.

Response to Electrical Stimulation. It is worth quoting a little from the authors' description of the response of the waking animal to stimulation. "One of the most notable features was the placidity which might accompany an intense drinking response . . . especially from the anterior cingulate region. The animal would give no visible sign at stimulus onset and then after the latency period would turn unhurriedly to the water spout and drink in a very natural fashion for the duration of the stimulus. At stimulus offset, the response would merely cease and there would be no rebound activity. . . . Another interesting aspect of evoked water drinking was the tendency of the animal to become 'glued' to the water spout and to drink continuously while simultaneously responding to environmental distractions with movements of the eyes, hands and body. At such times unusual amounts of water might be ingested, and on one occasion totalled about 400 cc in 10 min."

Adrenergic and Renin-Angiotensin Mechanisms

Lehr *et al.* (1967) observed that intravenous infusions of the β-adrenergic agonist, isoproterenol (isoprenaline), caused copious drinking in rats; this could be blocked by the β-antagonist propanolol. The drinking occurred for 3–4 hr, whilst increased urinary excretion only occurred by the 4th hour, and by the 6th hour all the extra water was eliminated. If the animal was previously given a large water-load, the drinking still occurred, whilst urine flow was inhibited. Thus increased drinking was accompanied by antidiuresis. The α-adrenergic agonist metaraminol caused increased urine-flow, but this was not accompanied by drinking. Epinephrine, with both α- and β-adrenergic activities, caused increased drinking and urinary flow. The authors suggested that the brain contained adrenergic neurones concerned in the drinking response, neurones that were activated by the intravenous infusions; α-adrenergic neurones were considered to be concerned in an inhibitory response, so that the α-blockers, phentolamine and phenoxybenzamine, caused excessive drinking through blocking of an inhibitory pathway.

Renal Dipsogen. However, the blood-brain barrier (p. 576) restricts the passage of such drugs into the central nervous system, and it is therefore unlikely that they could have been activating central neurones directly. The more likely explanation is based on the finding by Fitzsimons (1967) that the response to hypovolaemia was reduced if the animal's kidneys were removed, and by his demonstration that the "renal dipsogen" was renin, intravenous infusions of renin or angiotensin II causing increased drinking in normal and nephrectomized rats (Fitzsimons and Simons, 1969). The reasons why Lehr *et al.* obtained copious drinking with β-adrenergic agonists, such as isoproterenol, and with α-blockers such as phenoxybenzamine, was due to renin-releasing activity in consequence of the lowered arterial blood-pressure caused by these hypotensive drugs; all the effects of these drugs were blocked by removing the kidneys (Meyer *et al.*, 1971). Thus, if normal rats were given isoproterenol their mean water-intake was 14·6 ml/3 hr, compared with a negligible amount in its absence. In nephrectomized animals the water-intake was also negligible but, by giving these nephrectomized animals renin, the drinking was on average 16·8 ml/3 hr (Houpt and Epstein, 1971).

Intracerebral Angiotensin. When angiotensin was injected in small amounts into the brain, in the lateral preoptic area and the bed nucleus of the stria medullaris, Houpt and Epstein obtained drinking responses as effective as those of intravenous renin. Other studies on intracerebral injections of angiotensin have shown that the sensitive sites belong mainly to the limbic system, e.g. the nucleus accumbens septi, preoptic area, and anterolateral hypothalamus (Epstein *et al.*, 1970), and it was suggested by Fitzsimons that the renin-angiotensin system participated in normal thirst by sensitizing specific neuronal circuits in the brain that mediate drinking behaviour. According to Sharpe and Swanson (1974), angiotensin I is just as effective in the monkey, and its influence is not abolished by treatment of the animal with an inhibitor of the angiotensin I–angiotensin II converter enzyme (SQ 20,881). The question remaining, then, is how the renal renin, released in response to hypovolaemia, induces the formation of angio-tensin I or II within the brain.

Adrenergic inhibitors, such as haloperidol, did not influence the effects of localized application of angiotensin, so that it seems unlikely that an adrenergic circuit is important. Local injections of carbachol, the cholinomimetic drug, do activate the drinking centre, an effect that seems to be independent of any peripheral changes (Stricker and Miller, 1968).

Thermal Drinking

Hyperthermia, if maintained for any length of time, will provoke dehydration unless the animal drinks; it is reasonable to ask whether the raised temperature of the blood in the hypothalamus, which activates temperature-regulatory responses (Chapter 1), also activates the drinking mechanism. The results of an experiment by Andersson and Larsson (1961) on a goat with an implanted thermode are illus-trated in Fig. 5.23; warming the preoptic area caused a warming of the ear, this being the hypothalamic reaction of the heat-dissipation centre; at the same time the animal drank. The reciprocal responses of drinking and eating are well illustrated and demonstrate the strong relation between all three functions, namely thermoregulation, drinking and

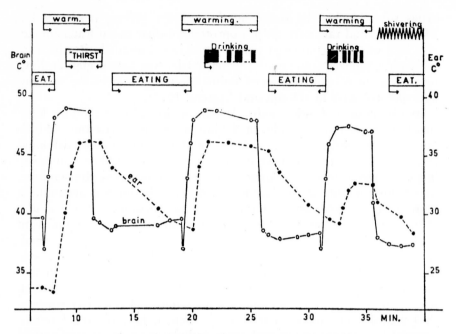

Fig. 5.23. Results of warming the preoptic area and rostral hypothalamus on drinking and eating in the previously hungry animal. The goat was fed hay at the beginning of the experiment and had free access to water except during the first period of central warming. During the periods of warming eating stopped simultaneously with the onset of peripheral vasodilatation (rise of ear-temperature), and started again when ear-temperature had begun to fall after discontinuation of central warming. The perfusion of the thermode with warm water induced a strong urge to drink. During the first period of central warming, when the water container was temporarily removed, it was evidenced by the animal's licking of the drops of water coming out of the outlet tubing of the thermode ("thirst") and later on by the repeated drinking of large amounts of water during the periods of central warming. (Andersson and Larsson, *Acta. physiol. scand.*)

eating, the desire to eat being suppressed when the animal is over-heated.

Importance of Water-Loss. In rats, however, there seems to be no such temperature-sensitive mechanism to activate drinking. Thus Hainsworth *et al.* (1968) showed that rats made hyperthermic would lick their fur to encourage cooling by evaporation; in this way they could lose some 14 per cent of their plasma volume, and they drank in order to maintain normal hydration. However, if the animals were desalivated and made to become hyperthermic they did not drink beyond their requirements; thus high blood-temperature *per se* is unable to provoke drinking unless it is accompanied by water-loss, as in salivation and licking the fur.

Oro-Gastric Stimuli

A dryness of the mouth is a symptom of thirst, but whether the reduced salivation that causes this is of importance as a factor governing water-intake is a matter of some doubt, although Cannon (1918) considered this as the main factor. On theoretical grounds it seems unlikely, since the role of the salivary glands is essentially digestive, their secretions being provoked in association with feeding, and their functions being to lubricate the mouth and initiate digestion.

Prandial Drinking. Removal of the salivary glands from rats—desalivation—does, indeed, cause excessive drinking (Kissileff, 1969), but the drinking under these conditions has a peculiar character and has been called by Teitelbaum and Epstein "prandial", in the sense that the animal clearly uses water as a means of lubricating the process of ingestion of dry food. Thus the desalivate animal does not go into negative water-balance, so that in the absence of food it drinks to maintain its requirements; however, when presented with dry food, it interrupts its eating with repeated drinks so that it is possible, experimentally, to make it go into water-imbalance, in the sense that, because of its prandial drinking, it drinks more than its requirements. Thus, if we may argue from rats to higher mammals including man, a dryness of the mouth may well provoke drinking, but it is by no means a primary stimulus; the dryness results from the lack of water with consequent inhibition of salivary secretion, but this is part of a generalized response to water-lack in which is included a drive to drink mediated by changes in blood-osmolality and/or changes in plasma-volume.

Food-Associated Drinking. Prandial drinking must be clearly differentiated from *food-associated drinking*, which is not related to salivary secretion. In general, as we have indicated earlier, an animal's intake of water is very strongly correlated with its intake of food; and both of these show a very strong diurnal rhythm, with most of the eating and drinking carried out during the night. This may be illustrated by the experiments of Fitzsimons and Le Magnen (1969); Fig. 5.24 illustrates the technique for automatically recording the intake of water, and Fig. 5.25 shows the association between food-intake and water-intake. At least 70 per cent of the rat's intake is drunk before, or immediately after, meals; and there is a strong positive correlation between the size of the meal and the water-intake associated with it. In prandial drinking, however, the character of the

18*

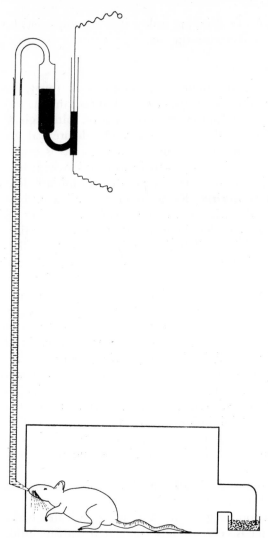

Fig. 5.24. Electromanometric method for making a continuous record of water consumption. (The pressure recorded by the manometer is proportional to the amount of water remaining in the drinking tube. The excursion of mercury is followed electrically by means of the resistance wire in the open limb of the manometer.) (Fitzsimons and Le Magnen, *J. comp. physiol. Psychol.*)

drinking changes; the amounts drunk are small—less than 0·5 ml compared with 0·5 to 2·5 ml. in food-associated drinking—and the draughts are taken immediately after ingestion of 45 mg pellets of dry food.

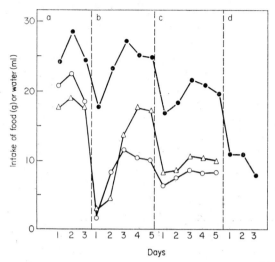

Fig. 5.25. The relation between food and water intake in the rat. Mean daily intake of food ($\triangle$), total water ($\bullet$), and water associated with meals ($\circ$) for six rats (a) with food and water *ad lib*, (b) during 5 days of a two meal/day schedule and (c) during 5 days of a one meal/day schedule; (d) total water intake during starvation. (Fitzsimons and Le Magnen, *J. comp. physiol. Psychol.*)

Predictive Control

Food-associated drinking in normal rats is of considerable interest since the amount of water drunk varies with the chemical composition of the diet; on a predominantly protein-diet rats drink some two grammes of water per gramme of food, but on a diet of mainly carbohydrate, or fat, the proportion falls to 1 : 1; and it seems from Radford's (1959) study that the intake of water is adjusted to the urinary and faecal requirements of the diet. Thus a high-protein diet requires the elimination of large amounts of urea, and therefore the formation of a more copious urine; a diet with large residue-bulk requires relatively more water for faeces; and so on. It seems, then, that the rat can assess, in some way, the character of its diet and adjust, by a "predictive control mechanism", the water-intake required. The effective stimulus is apparently not the systemic effects of the food, e.g. enhanced blood-urea or glucose, since the adjustment from, say, a high-protein to a high-lipid diet requires as long as 8 days (Le Magnen and Tallon, 1967); and it has been argued by Fitzsimons and Le Magnen (1969) that the oral, and perhaps gastric, stimuli act as cues that enable the animal to learn the water-intake necessary for a given diet.

Sensory Cue. Such a "predictive control" hypothesis begs the question of the sensory cues provided by the diet or its ingestion. The mere ingestion of food provokes the secretion of gastric juices and, according to Gregersen (1932), the volume of secretion can significantly affect the animal's water-balance, in the sense that temporarily, during digestion, the secretion of the juices is made at the expense of the blood and other extracellular fluids. Thus Pavlov measured a secretion of 20 ml of gastric juice in 5 min of sham-feeding in the dog, and it has been estimated that man secretes some 7·5–10 l of fluid daily in his digestive juices. Temporarily, then, a meal can provoke sufficient dehydration to stimulate drinking; and it could be that the greater secretion in response to a protein diet was the primary stimulus for increased drinking compared with that for a fatty diet. We may assume, then, that these primary stimuli, leading to drinking, act as conditioning stimuli that eventually allow the animal to predict its water requirements from its diet. Thus in the rat, and probably in other species, the intake of food is a powerful regulatory factor in the control of water-intake.

"Recovered Lateral" Rats. Teitelbaum and Epstein (1962) described the prandial drinking of rats whose lateral hypothalamic regions had been destroyed; this prandial drinking was different from that of desalivated animals in that these would maintain their water-

	Intact rats	Recovered lateral rats	Salivaless neurologically normal rats
Observation of Drinking patterns	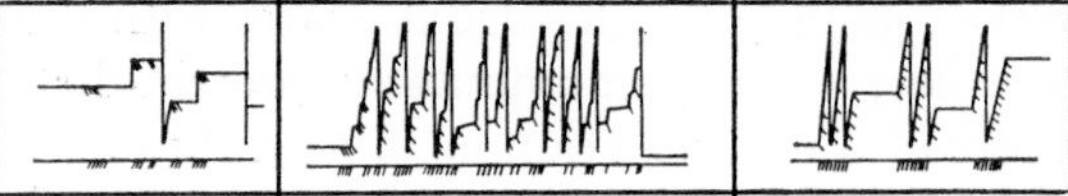		
Interruption of salivary flow	↑	↑	
Intra-oral water injection	↓	↓	↓
Intragastric water injection	↓	Unchanged	Unchanged

Fig. 5.26. Patterns of drinking in intact, recovered lateral, and desalivate rats. Arrows indicate change in water-intake. Recovered lateral and saliva-less rats have similar patterns, prandial drinking being common to both groups, and the pattern in these contrasting with the larger pre- and post-prandial draughts of intact animals (top line). Hatch-marks on the graphs indicate food-intake, so that prandial-type drinking is characterized by thickly hatched graphs. (Kissileff, *J. comp. physiol. Psychol.*)

balance, if not provided with food, whereas the "recovered laterals" would die of thirst under these conditions. In these animals, therefore, it is the difficulty of ingesting dry food that provokes drinking, as with the desalivate animal, but in the "recovered lateral" animal the drive of hyperosmolality of the blood, or hypovolaemia, is without effect, presumably because the afferent impulses fail to activate the drinking mechanism when the drinking centre is destroyed. This "crippling" of the drinking mechanism is revealed by loading a rat intragastrically with water; this has no influence on its drinking pattern, although in the normal animal this inhibits drinking. The same crippling can be demonstrated by removal of the salivary glands; in this case water-intake is decreased, the drinking being still entirely prandial, whereas all other manipulations, including alterations in body water-balance, would not elicit drinking (Kissileff and Epstein, 1969). The experiments on prandial drinking have been summarized in Fig. 5.26, where the patterns of drinking in relation to food-intake are shown in the top row, and the effects of various manoeuvres on water-intake are indicated in the lower rows.

Salt-Appetite

Since the maintenance of blood-volume depends not only on the water metabolism but also on the salt excretory and conservation mechanisms, we may expect the intake of salt to be controlled; this would have to be through the gustatory sense in the first place, the animal being able to recognize the taste of salt. We may assume, further, that the animal would respond to salt-deficiency by an increased appetite for salt. To some extent this latter prediction has been verified experimentally in man and lower animals, such as the rat. Thus in the Snowy Mountains of Australia, rabbits will gnaw at posts impregnated with salt in the spring, when they are salt-depleted, whilst farm animals will travel many miles to a salt-lick.

Salt-Deficient Rats

Experimentally various manoeuvres have been adopted to make animals salt-deficient, the commonest being *intraperitoneal dialysis*. A large volume of isotonic dextrose solution is injected into the peritoneal cavity; after a few hours the fluid will have exchanged its glucose for salt and, if the fluid is withdrawn, the animal becomes salt-deficient. Less acutely, the animal may be maintained on a salt-free diet and its preference for saline solutions estimated; and so on. When normal rats were kept on a salt-less diet and presented with 3 per cent NaCl as drinking water, as well as tap-water, it was found that the daily voluntary intake of salt was some 0·58 g/kg body-weight, approximately the same as that present in the balanced diet of McCollum, designed to meet the normal salt-requirements of the rat. Adrenalectomized rats, which, as we have seen, lose their salt-retaining capacity and have low blood-sodium, when fed a standard diet with tap-water survived some 17 days, but if given a salt-less diet plus 3 per cent NaCl they drank six times as much salt-water as normals on the same diet, and there was some 80 per cent survival (Richter, 1936).

Taste-Preference Threshold

Although man tends to prefer fresh water to a saline fluid to satisfy his normal thirst, there is no doubt that, where food is concerned, he shows a strong preference for food that has at least its normal salt-content, so that when potatoes, for example, have been boiled in salt-less water they become unpalatable through the leaching out of their normal salt-content; a baked potato, with its normal salt-content, is preferable but even then it is usually taken with salt. Experimentally we may measure a *taste-threshold*, defined by the smallest concentration that can be distinguished from distilled water; and this, on average, in man is 0·016 per cent NaCl; if the subject is asked to state at what concentration the solution *tastes* of salt, the threshold is much higher, namely about 0·09 per cent NaCl; this corresponds roughly to the rat's *taste-preference threshold*, which is measured by presenting two bottles, both containing originally water, and then the contents of one are changed to stronger and stronger solutions of NaCl; at a certain concentration the rat tends to drink more from the saline-containing bottle, and this concentration is called the taste-preference threshold. When the concentration is increased further, the rat shows a stronger preference, in that it tends to drink the saline to a greater extent and more rapidly; at a concentration of about 1 per cent NaCl the rat shows its maximum preference, and at still higher concentrations the intake declines. At the *aversion point*, namely about 1·5 per cent NaCl, the rat drinks more water than saline, and at 2·5 per cent, 3 per cent and 5 per cent nearly all the daily intake of fluid is from tap-water (Bare, 1949).

Salt-Greed. These points are illustrated by the study of Weiner and Stellar (1951); Fig. 5.27 shows the mean fluid-intake of rats permitted to drink for 1 hr during a day when presented with different solutions; the maximum at about 1 per cent NaCl is obvious. In these experiments the rats were presented with only a single solution, so that their fluid-intake is a measure of their salt-intake when allowance is

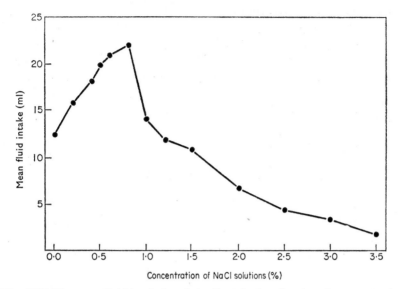

Fig. 5.27. The mean fluid intake in mls (ordinate) related to the salt concentration in drinking water of rats that were allowed to drink for only 1 hour per day. (Weiner and Stellar, *J. comp. physiol. Psychol.*)

made for the different concentrations. In Fig. 5.28 the computed salt-intakes have been plotted against concentration, and the important feature emerging is that the intake of salt is not constant, so that the animals are not satisfying a definite need governed by their state of salt-balance; they are rather showing a definite "greed" for salt-water, and this is manifest in untrained rats as well as trained ones, so that a tendency to prefer salt-water is an inborn characteristic. This might well have survival value against animals that only sought salt when they were salt-deficient.

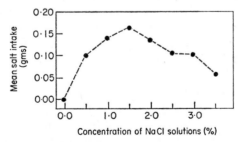

Fig. 5.28. Showing mean salt-intake of rats when presented with various salt-solutions for 1 hr per day and tap-water for 6 hr per day while on a water-deprivation schedule. (Weiner and Stellar, *J. comp. physiol. Psychol.*)

Salt-Deficiency and Threshold

The increased intake during salt-deficiency has been mentioned already; this occurs in experimental salt-deprivation and in adrenalectomized animals; it is accompanied by changes in the measured thresholds. Thus, in human subjects caused to sweat profusely on a salt-deficient diet, the threshold for salt-taste fell from 0·02 to 0·005 per cent NaCl; this was not due to just a sharpening of taste-acuity,

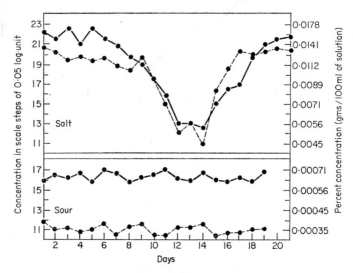

Fig. 5.29. The mean daily threshold for "salt" and "sour" taste in two subjects caused to sweat profusely on a salt deficient diet. (Yensen, *Quart J. exp. Psychol.*)

since the thresholds for bitter and sweet taste were unaffected (Fig. 5.29). Again, when de Wardener and Herxheimer (1957) caused humans to drink 10 litres of water a day, the threshold fell from 0.06 to 0·003 per cent NaCl; there was no consistent change in the salt-content of the saliva so that the suggestion that the increased acuity for salt-taste was due to a lower concentration of salt in the saliva bathing the taste-buds was not supported.

Adrenalectomy and Hypovolaemia

In adrenalectomized rats the taste preference threshold was reduced to about one tenth of its normal value, an effect that was reversed by treatment with mineral corticoid (DOCA). Hypovolaemia, induced by subcutaneous injections of colloid, also increased salt-appetite in rats.

Satiety

It would seem that, when a rat's appetite for salt has been increased, as after intraperitoneal dialysis, the consumption of extra salt does not lead to satiety; thus Falk and Lipton (1967) found that the salt-depleted rat continued to drink 3 per cent NaCl even though twice its salt-deficiency had been replaced by an intragastric load of saline.

Summary

To summarize, the most striking feature of salt-appetite is the inherent preference for a salt-containing food or water; superimposed on this is an increase in appetite, with lower thresholds, during salt-deficiency. The deficiency can convert an aversion, e.g. to 3 per cent NaCl, to a preference. Attempts to relate appetite quantitatively to changes in blood-salt concentration or volume have so far not been successful (Stricker and Wolf, 1966).

THE BLOOD pH

Normal Values

The pH of the arterial blood, i.e. the blood that has just left the aerating processes of the lungs, has a normal pH in the region of 7·40; the venous blood is more acid, and its actual pH depends to some extent on the degree of metabolic activity and the vascular supply of the organ from which it is derived. The mixed venous blood of the right ventricle or pulmonary artery has a pH of 7·376 (Comroe et al., 1962).

Range Compatible with Life. The range of blood-pH compatible with life in the mammal is quite restricted, the generally quoted limits being 6·9 to 7·8. This sensitivity is not a reflexion of the sensitivity of tissues and cells to pH, since they can be exposed to far greater extremes without damage; the sensitivity is rather the result of the development of highly reactive reflex mechanisms that tend to maintain the pH of the blood constant, so that death at the alkaline range might be essentially due to inhibition of respiration. However, the actual cause of death in, say, extreme acidosis is rather the result of the physiological adaptations to the acid-stress than of the specific effect of the acid pH on any parameter of the body. Thus, for a pH of, say, 6·9 to be reached, the buffering power of the whole body will have been strained to its limits, and by the time the acid pH has been achieved the blood-K^+ will have fallen, and the cause of death may well be ventricular fibrillation. Alterations in blood-Ca^{++}, associated with the pH changes, will further complicate the issue.

Buffering of Blood

Henderson-Hasselbalch Relation

The concept of the buffer, and the basic mechanisms of blood-buffering, have been dealt with in Vol. 1. Essentially, the primary defence of the blood against strong acid or alkali is through the carbonic acid-bicarbonate system, the pH of the blood being given by the Henderson-Hasselbalch relation:

$$pH = pK + \log_{10} \frac{[HCO_3{}^-]}{[CO_2 + H_2CO_3]}$$

$$= 6 \cdot 1 + \log_{10} \frac{[HCO_3{}^-]}{[0 \cdot 030 \times PCO_2]}$$

so that the determining factor is the ratio of concentrations of bicarbonate-ion to carbonic acid, the latter being taken, for practical purposes, as the sum of the carbonic acid plus dissolved CO_2, this sum being directly proportional to the partial pressure of $CO_2(PCO_2)$. When the ratio is about 20, the pH is in the normal range.

Importance of PCO_2. It is clear from the Henderson-Hasselbalch relation that the blood-pH will be directly dependent on the PCO_2 of the blood, which itself is closely related to respiratory activity; thus depressed respiration, leaving the lungs inadequately aerated, will cause an *acidosis*; whilst hyperventilation will cause an *alkalosis*; but, because of the additional buffering system provided by the haemoglobin within the erythrocyte, the changes in pH will be reduced in magnitude from those predicted by the Henderson-Hasselbalch relation.

Respiratory Acidosis

In general, a disturbance of blood-pH, caused by altered PCO_2, is called a *respiratory acidosis* or *alkalosis*, so that the acidosis due to breathing air containing a high PCO_2 is described as a respiratory acidosis, and the feature of the blood is the high PCO_2 associated with a normal* $HCO_3{}^-$-concentration. The defence of the organism against this high PCO_2 is twofold; first, as we have seen, is the buffering action of the haemoglobin in the cells through the Hamburger shift; and secondly, there is the adjustment of the ventilation of the blood in the lungs, reflexly controlled through the PCO_2 of the blood.

Exercise. The most common physiological occurrence of a heightened blood PCO_2 is that caused by exercise; the reflex increase

---

* Or greater than normal, as in pathological conditions.

in respiratory ventilation of the blood leads to a compensatory reduction in this parameter with the result that the ratio:

$$\frac{[HCO_3{}^-]}{[H_2CO_3 + CO_2]}$$

returns to its original value (Fig. 5.30a). If, in spite of the increased ventilation, the blood PCO_2 remains high, then the blood-pH can be returned to normal by an increase in the concentration of bicarbonate in the blood to bring the ratio back to 20; such an adaptation could be achieved through the kidney by retention of bicarbonate, i.e. by reduction in normal excretion (Fig. 5.30b).

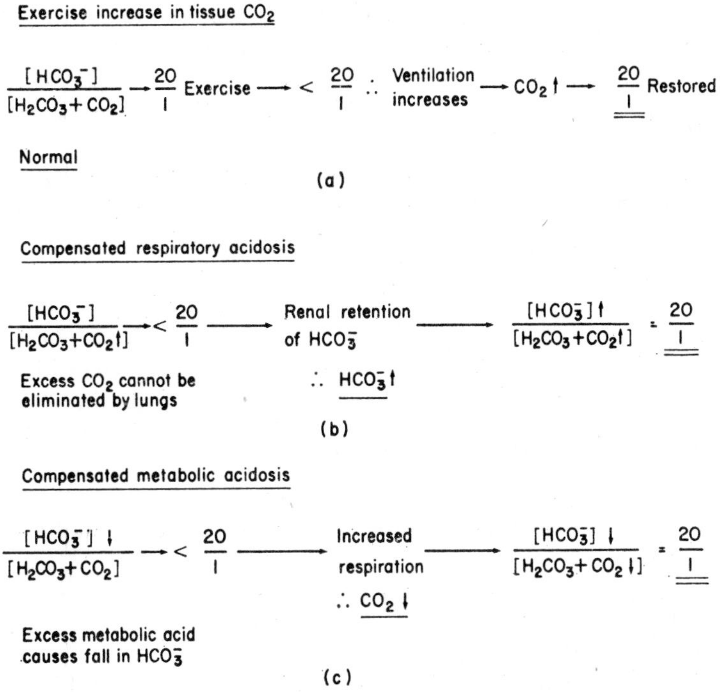

Exercise increase in tissue CO_2

$$\frac{[HCO_3^-]}{[H_2CO_3 + CO_2]} \rightarrow \frac{20}{1} \quad \text{Exercise} \longrightarrow < \frac{20}{1} \quad \therefore \quad \begin{array}{c}\text{Ventilation}\\ \text{increases}\end{array} \longrightarrow CO_2 \downarrow \longrightarrow \frac{20}{1} \text{ Restored}$$

Normal

(a)

Compensated respiratory acidosis

$$\frac{[HCO_3^-]}{[H_2CO_3 + CO_2\uparrow]} \rightarrow < \frac{20}{1} \longrightarrow \begin{array}{c}\text{Renal retention}\\ \text{of } HCO_3^-\end{array} \longrightarrow \frac{[HCO_3^-]\uparrow}{[H_2CO_3 + CO_2\uparrow]} \approx \frac{20}{1}$$

Excess CO_2 cannot be eliminated by lungs $\therefore HCO_3^- \uparrow$

(b)

Compensated metabolic acidosis

$$\frac{[HCO_3^-]\downarrow}{[H_2CO_3 + CO_2]} \rightarrow < \frac{20}{1} \longrightarrow \begin{array}{c}\text{Increased}\\ \text{respiration}\end{array} \longrightarrow \frac{[HCO_3^-]\downarrow}{[H_2CO_3 + CO_2\downarrow]} \approx \frac{20}{1}$$

Excess metabolic acid causes fall in HCO_3^- $\therefore CO_2 \downarrow$

(c)

Fig. 5.30. The effect of exercise on blood gas tension and the effect of respiratory and metabolic compensation.

Respiratory Alkalosis of High Altitude

At high altitude the important physiological variable is the decreased partial pressure of oxygen, PO_2, the altered PCO_2 being of little significance since this is so low in atmospheric air anyway. The physiological adaptation to the lowered PO_2 tends to conflict with the acid-base requirements; thus ventilation is increased, thereby improving oxygenation of the blood, but at the same time the PCO_2 of the blood is reduced so that a respiratory alkalosis occurs; this may be compensated by increased excretion of HCO_3^- so that the ratio returns to 20.

Metabolic Acidosis or Alkalosis

When the primary cause of the altered pH of the blood is the production or retention of extra strong acid, e.g. lactic acid, or of extra base, the change is described as *metabolic*; thus in *metabolic acidosis* the strong acid reacts with the bicarbonate system and is thereby buffered, but the result is a lowered concentration of HCO_3^- in the blood; the increased PCO_2 of the blood resulting from the reaction with the acid stimulates respiration, so that the PCO_2 falls, to give a compensated condition in which the pH is normal with the ratio $\dfrac{(HCO_3^-)}{(CO_2 + H_2CO_3)}$ back to 20 (Fig. 5.30c).

The condition would be described as a *compensated metabolic acidosis*, the pH being normal; however, the absolute concentration of HCO_3^- in the plasma is low, and this means that the buffering power is altered, since the capacity to buffer against acid relies on the magnitude of the bicarbonate concentration. Ultimately, then, further compensation is required, and this could be achieved through the kidney by retaining base, in which case the PCO_2 is allowed to rise. Similar considerations would apply to metabolic alkalosis, which may be produced experimentally, for example, by intravenous infusions of $NaHCO_3$. The immediate response is reduced ventilation leading to a higher-than-normal blood PCO_2, whilst the final compensation is achieved by increased renal excretion of base leading to a return to normal HCO_3^--concentration.

The Renal Mechanisms

H^+–Na^+ Exchange

In the long term, the kidneys control the pH of the blood, and thence of the body, by selective excretion of H^+-ions; in general, since there is a continuous production of acid by the body, there is a requirement for the continuous excretion of H^+-ions, although short-term variations might require retention of these, or the excretion of alkali, i.e. OH^--ions. It was suggested by Pitts and Alexander in 1945 that the basic mechanism for excretion of acid consisted in an exchange of H^+-ions in the interstitial fluid of the tubule with a cation, such as Na^+ or K^+. Such an exchange would, of course, make the tubular

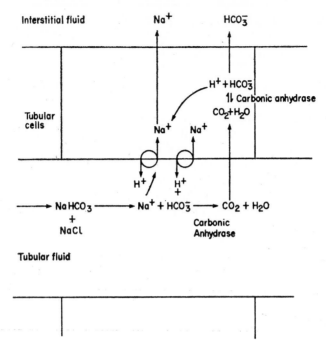

Fig. 5.31. The Pitts-Alexander hypothesis describing acidification of the fluid in the proximal tubule. Na^+ is reabsorbed from the tubular fluid in exchange for H^+, which reacts with HCO_3^-, a process that is catalysed by carbonic anhydrase.

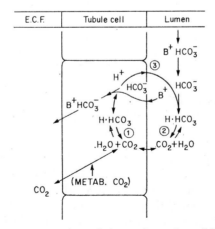

Fig. 5.32. Schematic representation of the reabsorption of $BHCO_3$ by H^+—B^+ exchange. (Brazeau and Gilman, *Amer. J. Physiol.*)

fluid more acid, but the degree of acidity would be largely masked by the reaction with bicarbonate (Fig. 5.31).

Reabsorption of Bicarbonate. The carbonic acid formed would be decomposed to CO_2 and H_2O, and the CO_2 would be reabsorbed into the blood to form HCO_3^-. Thus the H^+–Na^+-exchange would *effectively cause the reabsorption of the bicarbonate in the filtrate,* a process that should be inhibited by a carbonic-anhydrase inhibitor. In fact, treatment of the animal with Diamox, a specific inhibitor of the enzyme, does, in fact, cause a diuresis and natriuresis by virtue of a failure to reabsorb bicarbonate normally. As Fig. 5.32 shows, the source of H^+-ions involved in the primary exchange is postulated to be carbonic acid within the tubule-cell, a process that would likewise require catalysis by carbonic anhydrase.

Micropuncture Studies

Results of micropuncture studies involving measurement of pH are shown in Fig. 5.33; the change in pH in the proximal tubules is not

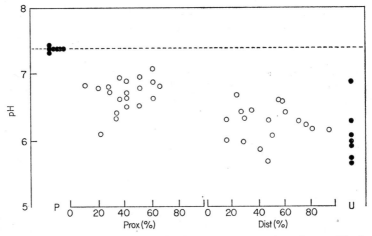

Fig. 5.33. The distribution of *in situ* pH values along the nephron in rats. The broken line corresponds to the mean blood-pH of this group. (Veira and Malnic, *Amer. J. Physiol.*)

large, but this is not because of a relatively small addition of H^+-ions here but because of the high amounts of HCO_3^-; the greater fall in pH in the distal nephron is due to the smaller volume and thus smaller amount of HCO_3^- remaining. In general, it seems that some 86·5 per cent of the bicarbonate in the filtrate is reabsorbed in the proximal tubule, 1·9 per cent in the loop of Henle, and 8·9 per cent in the distal tubule, the total reabsorption amounting to 99·7 per cent., i.e. it is

TABLE II

Percentage reabsorption of bicarbonate along the nephron
(After Malnic et al., 1972)

Group	Proximal	Loop	Distal	Total renal
Control	86·5	1·9	8·9	99·7
15% CO_2	72·7	20·7	4·1	98·8
Hyperventilation	61·0	17·3	11·4	98·1
Metabolic acidosis	85·5	5·3	4·1	99·6
Metabolic alkalosis	57·0	6·0	16·0	77·5
Diamox	41·0	0·04	34·0	92·6

normally virtually complete (Table II). The question arises, of course, as to whether the reabsorption of bicarbonate takes place in this manner, rather than by diffusion of bicarbonate-ions from tubular fluid into the blood. The weight of modern opinion is in favour of an almost exclusive reabsorption by the H^+-Cation$^+$ exchange mechanism taking place in proximal and distal tubules and, ultimately, in the collecting duct.

Disequilibrium pH

Walser and Mudge argued that, if H^+ were being added to the tubular fluid, the measured pH in the fluid would be more acid than if the same fluid were removed and equilibrated with a gas at a PCO_2 of some 40 mm Hg, i.e. that of the blood. This would be because the PCO_2 in the fluid would be effectively so much higher as a result of the addition of acid. In fact, Rector et al. (1965) found that there was no disequilibrium, the pH of the tubular fluid being what would be expected of the measured HCO_3^--concentration and blood PCO_2. If, however, the carbonic anhydrase of the renal tubules was blocked by the inhibitor CL 11,366, which did not affect the carbonic anhydrase of the blood and so left the blood-buffering system unaffected, then a disequilibrium of some 0·85 pH-units was observed. Thus the failure to observe any disequilibrium is due to the rapidity with which the secreted H^+-ions cause dissociation of the H_2CO_3 into CO_2 and H_2O.

Distal Tubule. In the distal tubule there was normally a dis-equilibrium pH of 0·85 units, suggesting secretion of H^+-ions into this part of the nephron, too; this was present whether the animal was treated with a carbonic anhydrase inhibitor or not, so that it seemed that, normally, the decomposition of HCO_3^- in the distal tubule was not accelerated by carbonic anhydrase, being, in consequence, sufficiently slow to create the disequilibrium. By an intravenous injection of carbonic anhydrase, Rector *et al.* caused the disequilibrium-pH to vanish, the enzyme presumably passing into the glomerular filtrate and thence into the tubular fluid. Thus, as we might expect, carbonic anhydrase is important for the dissociation of H_2CO_3 in the proximal tubular fluid, presumably being located in the membranes of the tubular cells. Complete inhibition of enzyme activity does not completely inhibit bicarbonate reabsorption, but only to the extent of 60 per cent.

Relation to Blood-K^+

Perhaps the most convincing evidence in favour of a H^+–Cation$^+$-exchange mechanism in the reabsorption of HCO_3^- is provided by the effects of altering the concentration of K^+ in the tubular filtrate. We shall see that the renal excretions of Na^+ and of K^+ are closely related, possibly through a Na^+–K^+-exchange mechanism. Changes in the K^+-balance of the animal have obvious effects on acid excretion; it appears that H^+ and K^+ have to compete for the Na^+-ions in an exchange mechanism, so that in K^+-deficiency (*hypokalaemia*) there is an acid urine, the competition from K^+-ions for Na^+ being less, permitting a greater-than-normal exchange of Na^+ with H^+. Conversely, administration of K^+-salts causes an alkaline urine.

Excretion of Ammonia

Besides employing the H^+-ion excretory mechanism, the kidney also removes acid continuously from the body by the expedient of excreting ammonia, synthesized within the tubular cells; the NH_4^+-ion formed in the tubule cells exchanges with Na^+ in the tubular fluid, thus producing a net gain of base (equivalent to a loss of H^+) by the body. Thus, just as the formation of non-volatile acids, such as lactic acid, from carbohydrate, etc. causes a net increase in H^+-ions in the body, so the formation of NH_3, which partly ionizes to NH_4^+ and OH^-, creates a net increase of alkali by the body (Fig. 5.34).

Synthesis of Ammonia. The ammonia is formed from glutamine and some amino acids. The reaction may be represented by:

$$\text{Glutamine} \rightarrow \text{Glutamate} + NH_3$$

being catalysed by the enzyme, *glutaminase*.

The glutamine is synthesized by most cells of the body, and it represents, in effect, the transport-form of ammonia, being carried to the kidney tubule cells in the glomerular filtrate. Such a transport form is necessary since appreciable concentrations of ammonia in the

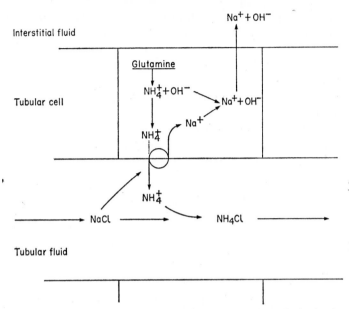

Fig. 5.34. The ammonium-mechanism for removal of acid from the body. Ammonium is produced from glutamine in the tubular cell; an exchange of an alkali metal cation, such as Na^+, leads to a net increase in the alkalinity of the blood, i.e. in an excretion of H^+-ion.

blood would interfere with the citric acid cycle in the brain and other tissues by removal of α-ketoglutarate by reductive amination (Lowenstein, 1972).*

Passage of Ammonia into Urine

The passage of the synthesized ammonia into the urine could be largely passive, since the greater acidity of this fluid necessarily means that it should accumulate here; in fact a dominant factor in the excretion of ammonia seems to be the acidity of the urine rather than the acid-base requirements of the whole body; for example, loading the animal with Na_2HPO_4 caused reduced excretion of ammonia to give

* The production of ammonia, especially by exercising muscle, has been reviewed by Lowenstein (1972); it is formed from AMP:

$$AMP + H_2O \rightarrow IMP + NH_3$$

where IMP is inosine monophosphate; the reaction is catalysed by *adenylate deaminase*. Reconversion of IMP to AMP involves the conversion of aspartate to fumarate, so that, in effect, the ammonia is derived from aspartate by what is called the *purine nucleotide cycle*. Other amino acids may substitute for aspartate.

an acid urine, in spite of the alkalinity of the load (Leonard and Orloff, 1955). However, a variable excretion of ammonia does constitute a mechanism for pH homeostasis; thus in chronic metabolic acidosis the kidney shows increased production of ammonia; this is because the concentration of glutamate in the blood falls; glutamate is an inhibitor of the enzyme glutaminase, and it seems that, in long-term adjustments, the concentration of glutamate determines the formation of ammonia, whilst in the short term, a change in pH of the urine alters the amount passing into the tubule, and this, on the basis of mass-action, favours increased or decreased synthesis.

Sites of Acidification and Ammonia Addition

Micropuncture studies have indicated a continuous addition of H^+-ions to the filtrate in its passage to the ureter; the main fall in pH is in the collecting ducts, but this is due to the small volume of fluid and its low bicarbonate concentration rather than to the actual amount of H^+-ion added (Gottschalk et al., 1960). Addition of ammonia was thought to be predominantly in the distal parts of the nephron but more recent work, e.g. that of Hayes et al. (1964), indicates that the proximal tubule is perhaps the main site.

Buffering the Urine

The phosphates in the glomerular filtrate constitute a buffer system and serve to prevent too large changes in pH of the tubular fluid resulting from the Na^+–H^+ exchange:

$$Na_2HPO_4 + H^+ \rightarrow NaH_2PO_4 + Na^+$$

The dietary intake of phosphate is sufficiently high to ensure a regular excretion of this ion in the urine.

Mechanisms of Adjustment of Plasma Bicarbonate

The variations in the extent of the Na^+–H^+-exchange, with its associated variations in ammonia transfer to the tubule, are sufficient to control the total acid-base balance of the body. The maintenance of the CO_2—HCO_3^- buffer system in the blood requires that when, say, too much acid has been formed in the body, and the plasma HCO_3^- has fallen below the optimal value for buffering power, the bicarbonate level should be restored. An ideal renal system would adjust the reabsorption of bicarbonate to meet the demands, making reabsorption more efficient in acidosis and allowing a urinary "spill over" in metabolic alkalosis. So far as alkalosis is concerned, the excretion of bicarbonate does, indeed, parallel the alkalosis, so that the kidney participates actively in correcting the high level of HCO_3^- in the blood. However, as we have seen (Table II, p. 459), at normal levels of plasma-HCO_3^-, tubular reabsorption is complete, so that a renal mechanism for correction of the imbalance of metabolic acidosis seems out of the question. Nevertheless, a tendency to eliminate extra H^+-ions during metabolic acidosis, through a Na^+–H^+ exchange, would operate to restore the concentration of bicarbonate in the plasma, the ion being synthesized from metabolic CO_2. In metabolic alkalosis, caused by infusions of $NaHCO_3$ solution, the high blood-bicarbonate results in a decreased reabsorption (Table II), so that there is little doubt that a variable reabsorption of this ion plays an important role in pH-homeostasis.

Adjustments to Raised PCO_2. An ideal renal system might also adjust the concentration of HCO_3^- in the plasma to the PCO_2, so that in respiratory acidosis, for example, when the aeration of the blood is defective, or the subject is exposed to air with a high PCO_2, the efficiency of the buffering system could be increased by retention of HCO_3^-. When animals are exposed to high PCO_2, the concentration of HCO_3^- in the blood increases; according to Polak et al. (1961), there is an initial acute response, as a result of which the rise achieves about half its final value, which is reached after some days. The initial response is not due to renal mechanisms, since it occurs in the nephrectomized animal; and it is due to the buffering of the tissues and erythrocytes, through the salts of weaker acids than carbonic acid. Examples of this buffering power of the erythrocytes have been discussed in detail in Vol. 1, and there is no doubt that most cells of the body can also buffer to some degree against H_2CO_3, causing the formation of $NaHCO_3$ in the plasma. After this initial rise, subsequent rises of plasma-bicarbonate, leading to compensation of the $[HCO_3^-]/PCO_2$ ratio, depend on increased reabsorption of HCO_3^-.

As Table II shows, the micropuncture studies of animals acutely exposed to high PCO_2 indicate complete reabsorption of bicarbonate, although there is some change in the regional distribution of the reabsorption.

Chloride-Bicarbonate

The renal handling of Cl^- is very closely linked with that of Na^+; and this is a necessary consequence of the demands for electrical neutrality of solutions, since Cl^- constitutes some two-thirds of the total plasma anions. To the extent that Cl^- may be replaced by HCO_3^-, which constitutes the other major anion, the handling of Cl^-

can exhibit some independence, so that it is more correct to say that the renal handling of Cl^- and HCO_3^-, on the one hand, is closely linked with that of Na^+ on the other. The separate regulation of the HCO_3^--concentration in the plasma, in the interests of acid-base homeostasis, means, moreover, that the renal excretion of Cl^- will be dependent on both the requirements for Na^+-homeostasis and of acid-base homeostasis, and should be largely predictable from these. This is not to imply, however, that the movements of Cl^- across the

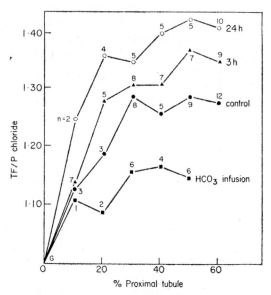

Fig. 5.35. TF/P ratios for Cl^- in the proximal tubular fluid under control and experimental conditions. Note that the ratio is in excess of unity. Top two curves represent animals breathing 12 per cent CO_2 for 24 and 3 hr respectively; bottom curve represents animals infused with sodium bicarbonate. Numbers on graphs indicate numbers of punctures of nephron at each point. (Warren *et al.*, *Clin. Sci.*)

nephron are entirely the passive consequences of movements of the other major ions; several experimental manoeuvres have demonstrated that—electrochemically speaking—the Cl^--ion may be actively transported across both proximal and distal tubule (Rector and Clapp, 1962; Malnic and Aires, 1970).

Relation to Reabsorption of Na^+. The iso-osmotic reabsorption of the filtrate in the proximal tubule is considered to be the result of a primary active transport of Na^+ associated with passive flow of Cl^- in the interests of neutrality; the flow of HCO_3^- is more complex but likewise related to active removal of Na^+ from the lumen in exchange for H^+ in the blood. On this basis, we might expect to find a TF/P-ratio for Cl^- of about unity along the length of the proximal tubule, i.e. the same as for Na^+. In general, this is normally greater, as indicated by Fig. 5.35, a discrepancy considered to be related to the complications introduced by the much greater reabsorption of HCO_3^- (some 86·5 per cent, Table II) compared with that of Cl^- (about 50 per cent, Table III). Certainly the TF/P ratio depends on the

TABLE III

Fractional reabsorption, expressed as percentage of filtered load, of chloride along the rat's nephron (Malnic *et al.*, 1970)

Group	Percent reabsorbed				
	Prox	Loop	Dist.	Collecting Duct	Urine
Control	49·4	43·5	5·7	1·26	99·86
NaHCO₃, 5%	43·2	50·4	3·3	1·10	97·90
NH₄Cl	43·1	51·9	3·6	3·6	98·50
Na₂SO₄, 0·4 M	42·0	53·1	2·7	1·67	99·47
Diamox	39·1	57·2	2·1	1·44	99·74

HCO_3^--concentration, so that when $NaHCO_3$ is infused, producing a high level in the filtrate, and therefore reducing fractional reabsorption, the TF/P for Cl^- becomes smaller (Fig. 5.35), whilst acute respiratory acidosis, demanding increased reabsorption of HCO_3^-, causes an increased TF/P. In the distal tubule most of the remainder of the filtered Na^+, Cl^- and HCO_3^- is normally reabsorbed; and, in general,

TABLE IV

Comparison of distal TF/P ratios for Cl^-, calculated by Nernst equation, with mean experimental values (Malnic *et al.*, 1970)

Group	Calculated TF/P	Observed TF/P
Control	0·17	0·30
NaHCO₃, 5%	0·14	0·19
NH₄Cl	0·13	0·34
Na₂SO₄, 0·4 M	0·16	0·13
Diamox	0·13	0·16

the concentrations of Cl^- are approximately equal to those of Na^+, since HCO_3^- is usually completely reabsorbed (Windhager and Giebisch, 1961). The corresponding TF/P-ratios for Na^+ are, of course, due to active transport, whilst calculations of the theoretical values of TF/P, having regard to the gradient of electrical potential, do not provide very strong evidence for active transport of Cl^- under several conditions, as illustrated in Table IV.

Possible T_m for Bicarbonate

Classical clearance studies failed to indicate a T_m for reabsorption of Cl^-, and this is what would be expected of a process largely dependent on Na^+. Similar studies on bicarbonate led to the conclusion that the excretion of this ion was governed by a process that gave complete reabsorption when the plasma level was less than 26 meq/litre; above this "renal threshold", excretion occurred because reabsorption,

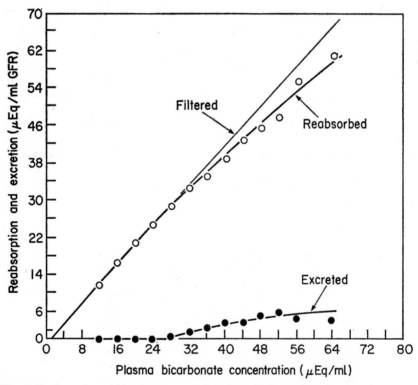

Fig. 5.36. Excretion of bicarbonate as a function of plasma bicarbonate concentration under conditions designed to hold expansion of extracellular fluid volume to a mimimum. There is no sign of a T_m. (Purkerson *et al.*, *J. clin. Invest.*)

although increasing with increasing plasma concentration, did not keep pace with filtration. When reabsorptive rate reached a T_m of 2·6 meq per 100 ml of glomerular filtrate, in the dog, total reabsorption remained constant as plasma bicarbonate was raised further (Pitts and Lotspeich, 1946).

Hypervolaemia. However, as Purkerson et al. (1969) point out, the experimental technique employed for varying the plasma concentration of HCO_3^- by infusions of $NaHCO_3$, tended to introduce a complicating factor, namely the effects of hypervolaemia, or extracellular volume expansion, on excretion of Na^+. Hypervolaemia is accompanied by natriuresis (p. 422) associated with reduced fractional reabsorption of Na^+ in the proximal tubule; such an inhibition of Na^+-reabsorption might be reflected in an inhibition of HCO_3^--reabsorption and give rise to an artefactual T_m. In fact, as Fig. 5.36 shows, when care is taken to minimize volume-expansion, reabsorption increases indefinitely, with no sign of a T_m. A similar study on the dog by Kurtzman (1970) yielded the same result, volume-expansion being prevented by simultaneous haemorrhage or constriction of the thoracic inferior vena cava.*

Reciprocal Handling of Cl^- and HCO_3^-

If the reabsorption of neither Cl^- nor HCO^- is subjected to a T_m-form of restraint, we may expect to see a well-defined reciprocity in the concentrations of these ions in tubular fluids and urine. Grossly, this may be observed by the increased concentration of Cl^- in urine when the animal is exposed to an increased PCO_2; and the changes in TF/P for Cl^-, indicated in Fig. 5.35 (p. 464), are clearly related to changed acid-base requirements. Again, inhibition of carbonic anhydrase with Diamox, by inhibiting bicarbonate reabsorption, tended to reduce TF/P for Cl^- in the proximal tubule (Malnic et al., 1970); and in the distal tubule very low values were obtained due to the failure to reabsorb all the bicarbonate in the filtrate.

Importance of Acid-Base Balance. To conclude, then, the renal excretion of anions is closely linked with that of Na^+, whilst the relative amounts of Cl^- and HCO_3^- excreted are determined by special factors governing either ion; physiologically the all-important special factor is the acid-base homeostasis of the animal, acting on the reabsorptive mechanism for HCO_3^-.

* Other examples of the influence of Na^+-excretion on that of HCO_3^- are given by the increased excretion of HCO_3^- during osmotic diuresis, the restraint on reabsorption of Na^+ influencing that of HCO_3^- (Stinebaugh et al., 1971). Infusion of the renal artery with acetylcholine causes natriuresis, and this is accompanied by increased excretion of HCO_3^- (Hebert et al., 1972).

The Intracellular pH

We may regard the buffering mechanisms of the blood, and the renal mechanisms that cooperate, as adaptations to ensure a relative constancy of the internal pH of the cells of the body; and it is therefore important that we examine the magnitude of the internal pH and its modifications through alterations in the blood. It must be appreciated at the outset, however, that each individual cell apparently has some internal buffering capacity, so that the maintenance of a stable blood-pH is to be looked on as a second line of defence in maintaining the internal milieu constant. Unfortunately the technical and theoretical difficulties in assessing the pH within the cell have resulted in this aspect of acid-base balance being relatively neglected.

Intracellular Electrode

In certain special cases the internal pH may be measured with a glass electrode inserted through the cell membrane; thus Caldwell, employing the large muscle cells of the crab, found an internal pH of 6·85, and this compared with the pH of 6·85 found with the same electrode in the minced tissue.

Weak Acid Distribution

However, the validity of the technique was questioned and there has been a tendency to rely more strongly on methods depending on the distribution of a weak acid between inside and outside of the cell. The basic principle on which the method is based is that the concentration of the ionized form of a weak acid in a solution depends on the pH of the solution; this is clear from the Henderson-Hasselbalch equation:

$$pH = pK' + \log \frac{[\text{Ionized acid}]}{[\text{Undissociated acid}]}$$

If the concentration of the weak acid, HA, in a cell, for example, is held constant, then the concentration of the ionized form, A^-, will increase with alkalinity and decrease with acidity; moreover, if we know the pK' of the acid, and the values of the concentrations of ionized (A^-) and unionized acid (HA) forms, clearly we may estimate the pH of the cell-contents. Cells are, in general, highly permeable to weak acids or bases in their unionized forms, and relatively impermeable to the ionized forms, so that if the weak acid is added to the extracellular medium, we may expect an equilibrium to be established with equal concentrations of the undissociated acid inside and outside, whilst the concentrations of the ionized form will be governed by the respective pH's of the inside and outside of the cell (Fig. 5.37).

DMO. A weak acid found ideal for studies on internal pH by Waddell and Butler is 5,5-dimethyl-2, 4-oxazolidenedione (DMO); this permeates the cell membrane readily in its unionized form, and it may be estimated chemically or, if labelled with ^{14}C, by radioactive techniques. Thus the tissue may be placed in a medium containing a known total concentration of DMO and, when equilibrium is achieved, the concentration in the medium, C_e, and the pH of the medium, pH_e,

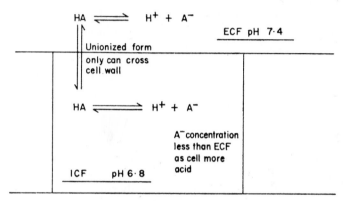

Fig. 5.37. The determination of intracellular pH with DMO. Only the unionized form of DMO can cross the cell wall and by determining the concentrations of ^{14}C-labelled DMO in the plasma and in a known weight of tissue, and knowing the extracellular space of that tissue, the experimenter can determine the intracellular pH.

may be measured. These are equivalent to the concentrations in the extracellular fluid surrounding the cells. The whole tissue is also analysed for the amount of DMO in unit weight, and the problem is simply to deduce from this measurement the proportions of ionized to unionized DMO within the cells. Clearly we must first know the volumes of the extracellular and intracellular spaces of the tissue, and these are obtained by the distribution of an extracellular marker, such as sucrose (Vol. 1).

Muscle

The classical determinations of the intracellular pH of muscle, carried out by Fenn and by Stella, relied on the carbonic acid-bicarbonate system, the total-CO_2 of the muscle being determined chemically and the H_2CO_3 deduced from the PCO_2 which, because of the high permeability of cell membranes to CO_2, may be treated as equal within and without the cells. On this basis, Fenn and Stella found an internal pH for muscle of 7·0, but the value was disputed later by Conway, who considered that the hydrogen-ion would be distributed across the cell membrane in accordance with the Gibbs-Donnan equilibrium. Thus we have seen that the ratio of $[K^+]_{In}/[K^+]_{Out}$ for the muscle fibre is about 50, and if the ratio for $[H^+]_{In}/[H^+]_{Out}$ were the same, this would require an internal pH of about 5·9, i.e. much more acid than found. However, the use of intracellular glass electrodes, and the application of the weak acid DMO, gave results agreeing with those derived from the CO_2 distribution, so that we must conclude that the H^+-ion is not at equilibrium between inside and outside of the cell but is maintained at a lower (more alkaline) value. In confirmation of this is the finding of Caldwell that the internal pH does not depend on the membrane potential, as would be expected were its distribution to be passively governed by electrochemical potential alone.*

Relation to External pH

The pH within the cell is not an equilibrium pH, so that it is not possible to predict, on simple thermodynamic grounds, the consequences of altering the external pH. It is necessary, therefore, to examine the situation empirically, remembering, moreover, that the cell is a composite structure with metabolism taking place not only in its cytoplasm but also within its mitochondria, which may well have an internal pH different from that of the cytoplasm, whilst the computed internal pH on the basis of DMO distribution may represent something between the cytoplasmic and mitochondrial pH's. The most striking feature of the relation between internal and external pH is the virtual independence of the internal pH of the external, when changes in the latter are brought about by adding strong acid or base, i.e. when a metabolic acidosis or alkalosis has been induced; in fact, it is quite possible to make the blood more alkaline, by infusion with $NaHCO_3$, and find the internal pH of muscle more acid, or *vice versa*. This is understandable in terms of the slow permeability of the cell membrane to bicarbonate-ion and its rapid permeability to CO_2. Thus, on infusing $NaHCO_3$ into the blood, the latter tends to become

---

* The failure of the H^+-ion to be at equilibrium between inside and outside of, say, a muscle cell means that the HCO_3^--distribution, unlike that of Cl^-, is not an equilibrium one. Benson *et al.* (1965) found a ratio

$$\frac{[HCO_3^-]_{out}}{[HCO_3^-]_{In}}$$

of approximately 1·5 at a PCO_2 of 40 mm Hg for cardiac muscle; this is very much less than the Cl^--ratio, which is of the order of 20 or more.

alkaline and, to compensate for this, the PCO_2 of the blood rises through inhibited respiration. The pH of the blood returns to normal, but the raised PCO_2 in the blood is reflected in a raised intracellular PCO_2, so that if the concentration of bicarbonate in the cells has not risen, they become more acid (Fig. 5.38).

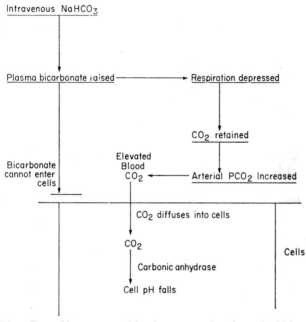

Fig. 5.38. The effect of intravenous bicarbonate on the plasma acid-base status and that within the cells. Although the pH of the plasma becomes alkaline that of the cells may become acid.

Metabolic Acidosis. Some experiments of Irvine and Dow (1966) are illustrative. They removed the kidneys of rats, and as a result, they developed a metabolic acidosis due to the accumulation of strong acids in the blood. The values for internal and external pH and the PCO_2 of the blood were as follows:

	Internal pH	External pH	PCO_2
Controls	6·92	7·49	23·7
Nephrectomized	6·90	7·29	23·9

Thus there has been virtually no change in internal pH in spite of a shift of 0·1 unit in external pH, and this is due to the unchanged PCO_2.

Metabolic Alkalosis. When an infusion of $NaHCO_3$ was given to the nephrectomized animals, their internal pH became *more acid*; and this was due to the fall in PCO_2 from 32·7 to 21·4 mm Hg with no change in internal bicarbonate concentration.

Excised Tissue

If excised tissue is studied, it is possible to examine the relation between internal and external pH at a given level of PCO_2, or alternatively we may use an altered PCO_2 to alter the internal and external pH. In Fig. 5.39 we see the effects of altered external pH on internal

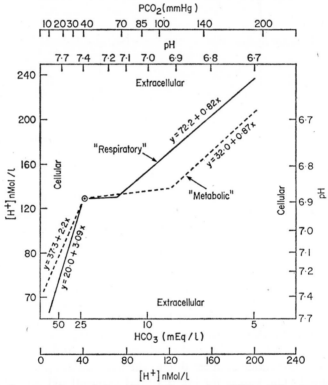

Fig. 5.39. A comparison of the effects of changing PCO_2 ("Respiratory") and external $[HCO_3]$ ("Metabolic") on cellular acidity. The PCO_2-scale at the top applies only to the respiratory curve, and the lower, $[HCO_3]$-scale only to the metabolic curve. (Adler *et al.*, *J. clin. Invest.*)

pH provoked by both situations, those provoked by altered PCO_2 being labelled "respiratory" and those by altered HCO_3^- as "metabolic". As we might expect, the changes provoked by altered HCO_3^--concentration at constant PCO_2 are small over a considerable range of external pH, namely from about 6·9 to 7·4. Where the changes are induced by altered PCO_2, and are therefore rapidly transmitted to the inside of the cell, the internal pH tends to follow the external pH more closely, the range of independence being only from about 7·1 to 7·4. It must be emphasized, however, that outside these ranges the internal pH of the cell does vary directly with the external pH whether produced by altered PCO_2 or HCO_3^--concentration

Intracellular Buffering. To the extent that the internal pH changes less than the external pH, we may speak of an internal buffering by the cell; and it is interesting that this occurs over the range of extracellular pH 6·9 to about 7·5, i.e. in a range compatible with life. Thus survival with a metabolic acidosis leading to a pH of 6·8 or 6·9 is rare and it is here that the cellular pH falls rapidly with external pH; in a similar way patients seem to endure a high PCO_2 (hypercapnia) until this rises above about 80 mm Hg; above this, disturbances of consciousness, etc. begin to appear, and it will be seen from Fig. 5.39 that it is at PCO_2 beyond about 80 mm Hg that cellular pH begins to fall sharply.

Tissue CO_2-Dissociation Curve. The curves of Fig. 5.39 demonstrate in no uncertain fashion that the internal pH of the cell does depend on the external pH, especially under extreme conditions. When we examined the effects of altered PCO_2 on the erythrocytes (Vol. 1), we found that the changes in internal and external pH were predictable from the known buffering characteristics of the CO_2–HCO_3^- and haemoglobin systems, on the assumption of rapid exchanges of anions between cells and plasma. Thus the CO_2-dissociation curve, obtained by plotting the total CO_2 (i.e. bicarbonate + dissolved CO_2) against the PCO_2 of the atmosphere with which blood came into equilibrium was a manifestation of these simple laws. When the medium outside

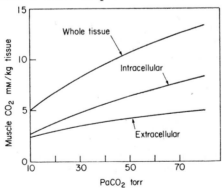

Fig. 5.40. Calculated CO_2-dissociation curves for muscle. Abscissae: arterial blood-PCO_2; ordinates: total CO_2 in tissue. The topmost curve, for the whole tissue, is given by the sum of the ordinates for the two lower curves indicating intra- and extra-cellular compartments. (Saborowski *et al.*, *Pflüg. Arch. ges. Physiol.*)

the muscle cell is made more acid or alkaline by varying the PCO_2 of the extracellular fluid, the concentration of bicarbonate within the cells varies, increasing with increased PCO_2 and decreasing with lowered PCO_2, in a rather similar manner to the behaviour of erythrocytes, so that we may obtain a "CO_2-dissociation curve" for the tissue comparable with that for blood (Fig. 5.40), and we may presume that the CO_2 reacts within the cell to form HCO_3^- when the PCO_2 is raised, and this is buffered by salts of weaker acids within the cell.

Metabolic Adaptations to Altered PCO_2. However, numerous studies indicate that the situation is much more complex than in the blood, where the effects are predictable from the known buffering power of the haemoglobin within the cell and the rapid exchanges of anions across the cell membrane. The complexity in the response of a tissue, such as muscle, is undoubtedly due to the metabolic adaptations of the cells to altered PCO_2 and bicarbonate concentration; these are such as to maintain the pH inside the cell much more alkaline than predicted from a Gibbs-Donnan equilibrium; and this is achieved by maintaining an internal HCO_3^- concentration much larger than predicted by this equilibrium; thus in skeletal muscle the internal concentration of Cl^- is only some 1/20 to 1/40 of the external concentration, corresponding to the internal negativity of the resting potential; the corresponding ratio for HCO_3^- is only about 1/4 or even less, and we may presume that the high internal HCO_3^- is maintained by a continued production of CO_2, which is converted to carbonic acid, a process accelerated by carbonic anhydrase within the cell. The conversion to HCO_3^- would require the continuous passage of OH^--ions into the cell from the blood or, what is equivalent, an active transport of H^+-ions outwards. A steady state would be achieved by a steady leak of HCO_3^- down its electrochemical gradient.

Changed HCO_3^- and PCO_2. In general, when both external PCO_2 and bicarbonate concentration are changed together, the effects on internal pH are by no means predictable from the separate effects of either, and this is because the effects of PCO_2 vary according to the concentration of bicarbonate and vice versa. In consequence, the cell may show signs of intracellular buffering against altered PCO_2, in the sense that the change in internal pH is smaller than the change in external pH, but this buffering may completely disappear when the bicarbonate concentrations are altered appropriately.

Relation of Intracellular pH to Intracellular K^+

Although the H^+-ion is not distributed in accordance with the Gibbs-Donnan equilibrium, the internal pH being remarkably resistant to changes in the membrane potential, there is a relation between cellular pH and K^+-concentration, such that a change in the ratio:

$$\frac{[H^+]_{In}}{[H^+]_{Out}}$$

is associated with a similar change in the ratio:

$$\frac{[K^+]_{In}}{[K^+]_{Out}}.$$

Such a relation was suspected because an acidity of the blood, which increased $[H^+]_{Out}$, was associated with an increase in plasma-$[K^+]$ (hyperkalaemia), i.e. with an increase in $[K^+]_{Out}$, presumably derived

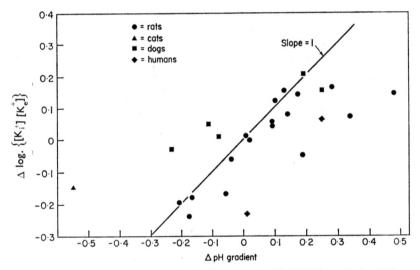

Fig. 5.41. Illustrating the linear relation between $\log[K^+_i]/[K^+_e]$ and the difference of pH between inside and outside of the cell. Values of the two parameters for experimental groups of animals were subtracted from those for the controls. (Waddell and Bates, *Physiol. Rev.*)

from the cells during an adjustment to make the change in the $[K^+]$-ratio correspond with the change in the $[H^+]$-ratio. Correspondingly, an alkalinity of the blood was associated with a hypokalaemia (Simmons and Avedon, 1959).

Experimentally, we may vary the plasma concentration of K^+ by appropriate dietary modification and measure the changes in internal H^+-and K^+-concentrations; as the cell's internal $[K^+]$ is reduced, the internal H^+-concentration is also reduced, and if we plot the changes in logarithm of $[K^+]_{In}/[K^+]_{Out}$ against the difference in pH, a straight line of slope equal to 1 is obtained, suggesting that, although the H^+-ion is definitely not in equilibrium between inside and outside of the cell, alterations in the steady-state relations are, in fact, predictable on considerations of shifts of equilibrium (Fig. 5.41). In a similar way, we may alter the plasma pH of a tissue by respiratory or metabolic acidosis and alkalosis, and measure the changes in plasma K^+ that

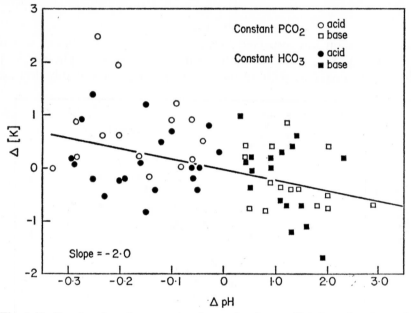

Fig. 5.42. Showing that, however the change in plasma-pH is brought about, the change in plasma-K^+ is the same. (Simmons and Avedon, *Amer. J. Physiol.*)

take place; as Fig. 5.42 shows, however the change of pH is brought about, the change of $[K^+]$, which is presumably due to loss from, or gain by, the cells, is governed only by the pH.

POTASSIUM

Normal Blood Concentration

The concentration of K^+ in mammalian blood is given as 3·5–5·0 meq/kgH$_2$O. Because of the large reservoir of K^+ in the cells, we may expect to find it difficult to create conditions of low blood-K^+—*hypo-kalaemia*—experimentally; nevertheless, maintaining animals on a K^+-free diet does lead to a fall in plasma-K^+, and, if continued, this leads to considerable replacement of intracellular K^+ by Na^+. Because of interchanges with the cells, the normal resting level is somewhat labile; thus anaesthesia is followed by a fall in plasma K^+ (see, for example, Bradbury and Davson, 1965) due apparently to mobilization of K^+ from the plasma by muscle cells and neurones as a result of the immobility caused by the anaesthesia. Thus, as we have seen, conduction of impulses along muscle and nerve is accompanied by losses of K^+, so that at any moment the concentration of K^+ in the extracellular fluid and blood plasma must be affected by this outflux.

Relation to Glucose Metabolism. Stimulation of glucose metabolism likewise causes movements of K^+ that may result in a reduced plasma-concentration temporarily. Thus injections of insulin or glucose stimulate synthesis of glycogen in liver and muscle; this is accompanied by increases in K^+-content of these tissues; according to Fenn (1939) the increase in uptake by the liver parallels the disappearance of glucose, and it appears that there is a formation of potassium phosphates intracellularly. A similar increase in internal K^+-concentration in response to insulin occurs in isolated rat muscle (Zierler, 1959).

Intestinal Absorption

Little or no evidence for active transport of this ion across the intestinal mucosa has been provided, so that it seems that absorption follows passively from the concentration gradients developed by the absorption of the Na^+ in the fluid-contents of the gut (Gilman *et al.*, 1963).

Renal Excretion

Reabsorption and Secretion

The mammalian diet contains an excess of K^+, so that the normal renal requirement consists in the excretion of some 10 per cent of the filtered load. This could be achieved by simply a failure to reabsorb the whole filtered load, but in fact the process of reabsorption, taking place predominantly in the proximal tubule, is associated with a process of tubular secretion, taking place predominantly in the distal tubule. In general, the clearance of K^+ is less than that of inulin, indicating that reabsorption predominates over secretion, but when the blood-level is raised by the intravenous infusion of potassium salts, the clearance may become greater than that of inulin, indicating net secretion.

Distal Nephron. Micropuncture studies of Malnic *et al.* (1966a,b) indicate that, in a variety of conditions, the fractional reabsorption in the proximal tubule remains fairly constant, so that adjustments of

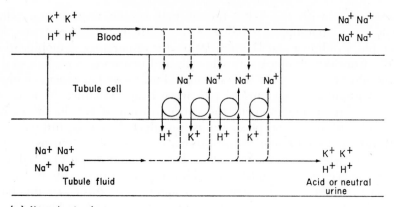

(a) Normal potassium

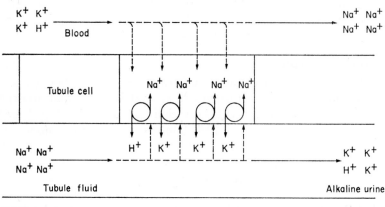

(b) High potassium

Fig. 5.43.

urinary excretion to the demands of the body, e.g. to low blood-K^+, are achieved by modifications in the amounts of K^+ added to, or extracted from the distal nephron. The distal tubule is the site at which secretion takes place predominantly, whilst the collecting duct is a region where reabsorption or secretion takes place according to the requirements of the animal (Diezi *et al.*, 1973). Thus in K^+-deficiency, secretion into the distal tubule is reduced, and reabsorption takes place in the collecting duct. In hyperkalaemia, increased secretion occurs in the distal tubule and the reabsorption occurring in the collecting duct is transformed into secretion.

Na^+-K^+ Exchange. In sodium-deficiency there is a retention of

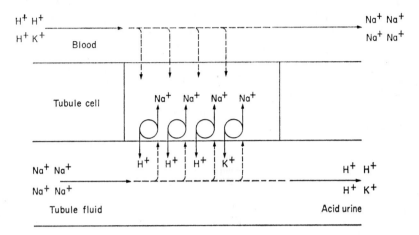

(c) Low Potassium

Fig. 5.43. The competition of potassium for hydrogen ions in exchange for sodium in the kidney.

K^+, as though the deficiency of Na^+, in the distal tubule were preventing the normal secretion of K^+. This, together with a number of other findings, suggested to Berliner *et al.* (1951) that secretion of K^+ into the distal tubule depended on an exchange with Na^+ within the tubule; shortage of Na^+, as in sodium-deficiency, would leave insufficient ions for the exchange. Support for this concept is the apparent competition of K^+- and H^+-ions for exchange with Na^+-ions in the tubule. Thus, if this competition occurred, we should expect that, when the blood contained a high concentration of K^+, some of its ions would substitute for H^+-ions in the exchange with Na^+, thus making the urine less acid (Fig. 5.43). This actually happens, so that injections of K^+-salts cause an alkaline urine and tend to leave the blood acid—*hyperkalaemic acidosis*. Conversely, depletion of the body-K^+ by dietary restrictions leads to a more acid urine and *hypokalaemic alkalosis*.

Na^+-Concentration in Tubule. Against the K^+–Na^+ exchange hypothesis is the micropuncture study of Malnic, Klose and Giebisch (1966a); according to this, the actual amount of Na^+ in the distal tubule and collecting duct is far in excess of the K^+ secreted, so that the concentration could in no way be the limiting factor governing secretion of K^+; this was also true in Na^+-depletion, when they calculated that the amount of Na^+ reaching the distal tubule was some 20 times the amount of secreted K^+.

Secretion and Electrochemical Potential. These experiments by no means rule out exchanges of cations of the type envisaged, i.e. Na^+–K^+, with H^+ competing for K^+, but they simply emphasize that the situation is more complex than hitherto thought. It appears that tubular secretion of K^+ is, in fact, passive, being governed by the electrical potential gradient as well as the concentration gradient. Thus Malnic *et al.* (1966b) measured the TF/P ratios for K^+ at different stages along the nephron when it was perfused with an artificial fluid. In the proximal tubule the ratio was 0·88; since the potential across

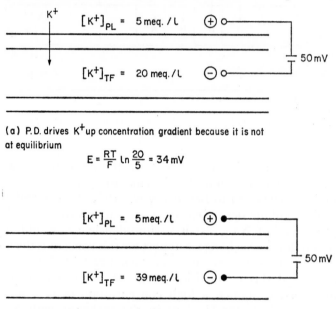

(a) P.D. drives K^+ up concentration gradient because it is not at equilibrium

$$E = \frac{RT}{F} \ln \frac{20}{5} = 34 \, mV$$

(b) P.D. no longer drives K^+ up concentration gradient

$$E = \frac{RT}{F} \ln \frac{39}{5} = 50 \, mV$$

Fig. 5.44. The potential across the renal distal tubule and the influence of this potential on potassium distribution.

the mammalian proximal tubule may be very small (Frömter *et al.*, 1967), and at any rate internally negative and thus favouring retention of K^+ in the lumen, the reabsorptive movement is against a gradient of electrochemical potential. In the early distal tubule the ratio was 0·85 and in the late distal tubule it was 2·32. The potential across the distal tubule under these experimental conditions was of the order of 50 mV, inside negative, so that passage of K^+ into the tubule from the blood could well have been passive since, on the basis of the Nernst equation, this potential could cause K^+ to move from blood to tubular fluid until the TF/P ratio was 6·6 (Fig. 5.44).

Active Reabsorption

Reabsorption of K^+ in the proximal tubule could be passive, and dependent on the reabsorption of Na^+ and water that leads to gradients of concentration favouring diffusion of K^+ from lumen to blood. However, Beck *et al.* (1973) were able to show that reabsorption of K^+ is not necessarily dependent on reabsorption of Na^+ in the proximal tubule; when reabsorption of Na^+ was inhibited, by treatment with Diamox (p. 458), that of K^+ was not affected.

Adrenal Hormonal Control

Adrenalectomy in animals, or Addison's disease in man, causes not only a fall in plasma-Na^+ but a rise in plasma-K^+, effects that can be reversed by administration of aldosterone or DOCA; thus, the adrenal cortical hormone appears to favour excretion of K^+ through an inhibition of the secretory process that adds K^+ to the distal fluid. Hierholzer *et al.* (1965) demonstrated this reduced capacity to secrete by measuring the accumulation of K^+ in a "split drop" in different parts of the nephron. The ratios were normal in the proximal and early distal tubules, but in the late distal fluid they were $2·3 \pm 1$ in normals and $0·93 \pm 0·1$ in adrenalectomized animals, indicating a significant decrease in the power of the distal tubule to secrete K^+.

Renin-Angiotensin. It will be recalled that the release of aldosterone in response to Na^+-deficiency is brought about through the renin-angiotensin system, rather than through the pituitary, the angiotensin acting as a secretogogue and causing the adrenal cortical cells to liberate their hormone. Thus, according to the study of Blair-West *et al.* (1962), infusion of ACTH into the arterial supply of the adrenal gland failed to stimulate aldosterone release, although it increased secretion of the glucocorticoids, cortisol and corticosterone, by five- to twenty-fold. When they raised the concentration of K^+ in the blood passing into the gland, there was an increase in the basal rate of secretion of aldosterone, so that a direct effect of high blood-K^+ seems to be the main mechanism for stimulating aldosterone release. There is little doubt that a rise in the level of plasma K^+ also alters the secretion of renin but this consists in an *inhibition* of secretion. This is demonstrated by Fig. 5.45, which shows the effects of infusion of K^+ into one of the renal arteries; there is a rapid fall in renin concentration in the renal vein, too rapid to have been brought about by a change in Na^+-balance. In man, Veyrat *et al.* (1967) showed that the

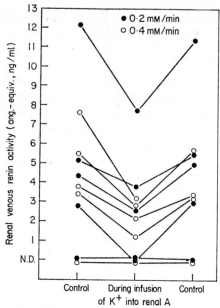

Fig. 5.45. The effects of renal intra-arterial infusion of potassium on the renal venous renin activity in the dog. N.D. signifies no detectable activity. Each plot is for one dog. (Vander, *Amer. J. Physiol.*)

increase in blood-renin caused by a restricted diet of Na$^+$ could be reduced by supplementing the diet with K$^+$; interestingly this was not accompanied by a change in the rate of excretion of aldosterone in the urine, so that it seems that the increased aldosterone secretion caused by K$^+$ occurred independently of the renin-angiotensin system, otherwise we should have expected the fall in renin secretion to have reduced aldosterone secretion.

MAGNESIUM

Physiological Importance

Functionally this divalent ion is of great importance since, as we have seen in Vol. 2, its concentration at both nerve-muscle and nerve-nerve synapses has a powerful influence on transmission; within the cells, moreover, it serves as an activator for the metabolically important ATPase as well as for the Na$^+$-K$^+$-activated enzyme. Surprisingly, therefore, there seems to be no well-defined central homeostatic mechanism responsive to the concentration of the ion in the blood.

Blood Concentration

The concentration in human blood plasma is given by Walser (1961) as 0.96 ± 0.06 mmoles/litre; if we make allowance for the plasma proteins (6·6 g/100 ml) and the specific gravity of plasma, the figure becomes 1·02 mmoles/kg H_2O. As with calcium, a portion of this Mg, some 32 per cent, is bound to plasma proteins so that when plasma is ultrafiltered the concentration in the ultrafiltrate is $0·66 \pm 0·05$ mmoles/kg H_2O. Not all of this filterable Mg is ionized, since some is complexed with phosphate ($MgHPO_4$), citrate, and other unidentified anions, so that of the total Mg in the plasma only 55 per cent consists of Mg^{++}-ions (Table V).

TABLE V

Fractions of magnesium in the normal plasma of humans
(Walser, 1961)

Species	Concn. in mmoles/litre	Per cent of total
Ionized	0·53	55
Protein-bound	0·30	32
$MgHPO_4$	0·03	3
MgCitrate	0·04	4
Unidentified complexes	0·06	6
Total	0·96	100 per cent

Balance

In human subjects the amount of Mg in the diet is more than adequate for the daily requirements, which may be as small as 1 meq. per day; moreover, it is difficult, experimentally, to alter the concentration of Mg in the plasma when the subject is maintained on a Mg-deficient diet, even though the subject may be in negative balance for some time. This is due mainly to a drastic reduction in excretion. Barnes *et al.* (1958) fed humans a milk-powder treated with a cation-exchange resin to reduce Mg to very low values. The total output of Mg fell from a normal 29·5 meq/day to 0·72, and this was compounded of a fall of urinary excretion from 6·9 to 0·70 meq/day and of faecal excretion of 22·6 to 0·02 meq/day. The authors computed that as little as 1 meq/day would be sufficient to maintain a human subject in normal balance.

Bone Mobilization. However, an important factor in maintaining stability of plasma Mg is probably mobilization from the bones, and if this was occurring in Barnes *et al.*'s experiments, mere replacement of the losses would not have been sufficient to keep the subjects in true balance. That bone mobilization can be important is shown by

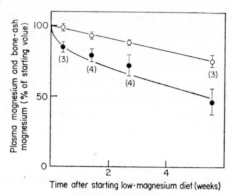

Fig. 5.46. Changes in bone (caudal vertebrae)- ash magnesium (○) and plasma magnesium (●) in young calves after an abrupt change from a magnesium-adequate diet to one of low-magnesium synthetic milk. (Smith, *Biochem. J.*)

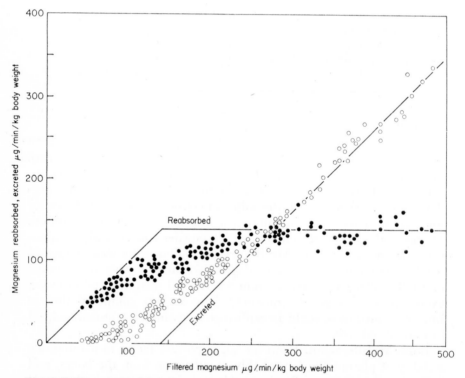

Fig. 5.47. The relationship between quantity of magnesium filtered and the quantities reabsorbed by the renal tubules, and excreted in the urine, in response to infusion of $MgCl_2$ in dogs. (Massry *et al.*, *Amer. J. Physiol.*)

Fig. 5.46, which gives the changes in plasma Mg concentration of calves maintained on a Mg-free diet; on the same graph is the percentage of Mg in the bone-ash of the animals, and it is seen that the two parameters are affected in parallel. It should be noted that this buffer-action of the bones is only one-way, an excess of Mg in the plasma not being reflected in increased uptake.

Renal Handling

The usual problem here will be to excrete the excess normally ingested. Employing classical clearance techniques, Massry *et al.* (1969) concluded that the basic mechanism consisted in a simple failure to reabsorb all the filtered load; when the load was increased by plasma infusions of $MgCl_2$ the absolute reabsorption increased, but the percentage of the filtered load absorbed decreased, the process indicating the existence of a T_m, as in Fig. 5.47. The clearance studies gave no evidence of a tubular secretory mechanism, in so far as the clearance was never greater than that of creatinine.

Reabsorption. With micropuncture techniques Brunette *et al.* (1969) found that, in the proximal tubule, the ratio: Concn. in Tubular Fluid/Concn. Plasma Filterable Mg^{++} was approximately unity suggesting that reabsorption followed passively the reabsorption of the filtrate as a whole; the ratio was independent of the TF/P ratio for inulin, and since this varies with position along the tubule, measuring as it does the fractional reabsorption of the filtrate, this independence

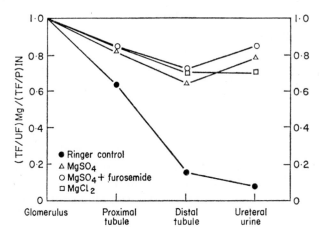

Fig. 5.48. The fraction of the filtered magnesium remaining in the nephron at various sites under normal conditions and during infusions of Mg salts to raise the blood-level. TF = tubular fluid; UF = ultrafiltrate of plasma; P = plasma. (Wen *et al.*, *Amer. J. Physiol.*)

means that the degree of reabsorption is independent of position in the tubule. Wen *et al.* (1970) micropunctured both proximal and distal tubules; the essentials of their results are summarized in Fig. 5.48, which shows the fractional absorption of the filtered Mg at various sites along the nephron under normal conditions and during infusions of Mg salts to raise the blood-level. Normally there is further reabsorption in the distal nephron, but with raised filtered load this tendency is reversed, so that the amount rejected, and therefore excreted, is increased.

Intestinal Absorption

Absorption from the intestine seems not to be complete, in view of the faecal excretion indicated earlier; *in vitro*, everted sac studies on the rat's intestine failed to indicate any active process, in the sense that concentration gradients were not established, but some saturation was revealed at a concentration of 4 meq/litre (Ross, 1962). Using an exteriorized loop of sheep intestine, Scott (1965) found that the amount absorbed from the jejunum was variable, but usually positive; ileal loops quite frequently showed no absorption. According to several studies, summarized by Walser (1967), absorption also takes place in the large intestine. In general, it would seem that the absorption is proportional to the intake, and is thus unrelated to the animal's needs (Chutgow, 1964).

CALCIUM

Physiological Roles

This ion plays a key role in a variety of physiological processes; thus its concentration in the extracellular fluid surrounding the cell influences its permeability characteristics, and through these the features of its activity that may be dependent on this, such as the excitability and conduction-velocity of nerve, the efficacy of the Na^+-pumps, and so on; in all types of muscle the internal concentration plays the critical role in excitation-contraction coupling; in secretory cells it plays an analogous role in excitation-secretion coupling, whilst the activities of many key enzymes are also governed by the internal concentration, e.g. that of phosphorylase-*b* kinase in glucose metabolism.

The Plasma Concentration

The total concentration of calcium in the blood plasma is given by Walser (1961) as $2 \cdot 48 \pm 0 \cdot 06$ mmoles/litre which, when corrected for plasma proteins, etc., comes out at 2·63 mmoles/kg H_2Q. A large fraction of the total calcium is in the form of unionized complexes, so that, as Table VI shows, the percentage of free ions is only 47·5; the great bulk of the complexing is done by the plasma proteins, so that the concentration in an ultrafiltrate of plasma, namely 1·36 $\pm$ 0·09 mmoles/litre, is a fairly close approximation to the concentration of ionized Ca^{2+}.

TABLE VI

Concentrations of the various fractions of calcium in the plasma and their percentages of the total (Walser, 1961)

Species	Mmoles/litre	Per cent of total
Free Ca^{2+}-ion	1·18	47·5
Protein-bound	1·14	46·0
$CaHPO_4$	0·04	1·6
CaCitrate	0·04	1·7
Unidentified compounds	0·08	3·2
Total	2·48	100 per cent

Balance

Some 99 per cent of the total body-calcium is in the bones, and this acts as a reservoir so that in calcium-deficiency the plasma concentration is buffered by this reserve, permitting a high degree of homeostasis. In general, the intake is more than adequate to maintain the total body-calcium, and thence the plasma level, constant. However, the role of calcium in building the skeleton means that, during lactation, the demands on the mother may be extreme; in the cow, for example, lactation, unaccompanied by dietary supplements can lead to hypocalcaemia resulting in tetany (Ramberg et al., 1967).

Faecal Excretion. Losses from the body are largely in the faeces, due mainly to secretory processes in the small intestine and probably connected with the formation of the digestive juices; thus failure to reabsorb all the calcium in these secretions would lead to a steady drain on the body's supply. The amount of calcium in the intestinal secretions seems to be independent of the intake, so that in calcium-deficiency this fraction of the excreted ion is relatively unaffected; at any rate when the dietary intake of a man was restricted to 100 mg/day, the faecal excretion remained at a high value of 300 mg/day, so that the subject was in negative balance. The faecal excretion in man is of the order,of 1 g per day; of this some 300 mg are endogenous, i.e. derived from the intestinal secretions, and the remaining 700 mg are exogenous, being derived from the diet.

Renal Excretion. Renal excretion accounts for a further drain, but this, unlike that in the faecal excretion, is controlled by the body's requirements.

Intake for Balance. It is not easy to determine the exact intake a man requires to maintain balance, but according to Nicolaysen *et al.* (1953) a man maintained on a daily intake of 910 mg Ca was in slight positive balance with a urinary excretion of some 430 mg/day; after 196 days he was transferred to a diet of 590 mg/day, and was now in slight negative balance, with a urinary excretion of 421 mg/day; after a further 184 days on this diet he came into balance with a urinary excretion of 391 mg/day. Under these conditions, then, the losses in the faeces, plus those in the urine, are approximately equal to the intake in the diet.

Homeostatic Mechanisms

The basic mechanisms through which a steady level of calcium in the blood is maintained consist of an intake in the diet accompanied by a fairly steady faecal and urinary excretion. Adjustments to altered conditions, e.g. dietary deficiency, are achieved by variations in the efficiency with which dietary intake is absorbed in the small intestine,

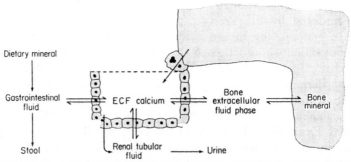

Fig. 5.49. Calcium homeostasis. The level of calcium in the extracellular fluids is normally regulated by controlling the exhange of calcium between the bulk extracellular fluids and three specialized extracellular fluid compartments: gastrointestinal fluids, renal tubular fluid, and bone extracellular fluid. Each of these specialized compartments is separated from the bulk phase by a functional membrane. In times of prolonged calcium deficiency osteoclast activity also contributes directly to mineral homeostasis. (Rasmussen and Tenenhouse, *Biochemical Actions of Hormones.*)

variations in urinary excretion, and finally exchanges with the bones, either mobilization, in the case of dietary deficiency, or sequestration, when the bones are deficient and this deficiency can be made up (Fig. 5.49).

Control

The controlling influences are exerted through (a) the *parathyroid gland,* whose secretions tend to raise the level of calcium in the blood; (b) through *vitamin D* whose most prominent influence is on absorption

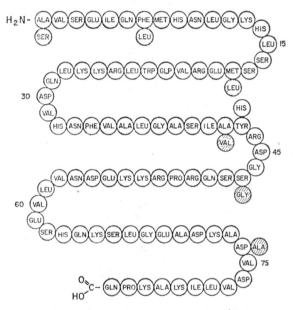

Fig. 5.50. Structures of bovine and porcine parathyroid hormones. The main structure represents the bovine hormone: the shaded residues represent the differences in amino acid sequence found in the porcine hormone. (Aurbach *et al., Rec. Prog. Hormone Res.*)

of calcium from the intestine, and (c) through *thyrocalcitonin,* which controls the resorption of calcium from bone and tends to reduce the concentration of calcium in the blood.

Parathyroid Hormone (PTH). This is secreted by two small glands closely associated with the thyroid; it consists of a single chain of 84 amino acids (Fig. 5.50) whose sequence has been determined; the first 34 amino acids may be broken off, leaving the remaining polypeptide as active as the parent molecule. The hormone causes a rise in plasma calcium when injected into the parathyroidectomized animal, whilst parathyroidectomy, itself, causes a fall in blood-calcium, which may be so severe as to lead to hyperexcitability of nerve and muscle giving the condition called *tetany*. The hormone acts on the reabsorptive process from bone, promoting this; in addition it exerts an action on the kidney, promoting reabsorption of calcium and Mg and promoting excretion of phosphate—*phosphaturia*.

Thyrocalcitonin. The hormone with opposite action to the parathyroid hormone is thyrocalcitonin, secreted by the thyroid gland; it

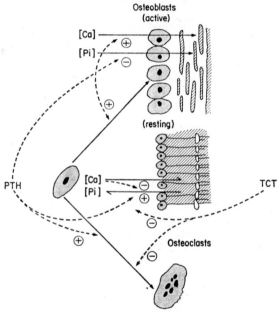

Fig. 5.51. The exchange of calcium and phosphates in bone cells with the bulk extracellular fluid. The actions of parathyroid hormone (PTH) and thyrocalcitonin (TCT) are shown by the broken lines. (Rasmussen and Tenenhouse, *Biochemical Actions of Hormones*. Academic Press.)

is a protein hormone that blocks resorption of calcium from bones, acting probably on the same bone target-cells as parathyroid hormone (Fig. 5.51).

Vitamin D. Vitamin D, produced in the animal body by the action of ultraviolet light on the sterol 7-dehydrocholesterol within the skin, and normally present in a properly balanced human diet, promotes the absorption of calcium from the intestine and its reabsorption from the renal tubule. Its deficiency, either through dietary failure or absence of sunlight, causes rickets in children, a condition described more generally as *osteomalacia*, with defective calcification of the bone-tissue, the fundamental defect being failure to mobilize calcium and phosphate at the bone-forming site through a primary defective absorption from the intestine.

Blood Calcium and Hormone Secretion. When rats are kept on a calcium-deficient diet, with adequate vitamin D, there is an increased bone-resorption. The effect is not a direct response to calcium-deficiency

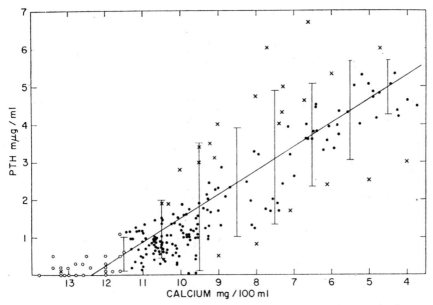

Fig. 5.52. Relationship between the plasma calcium concentrations and plasma parathyroid (PTH) hormone levels. × represents plasma samples from the early phases of EDTA infusion in a few animals and ○ represents plasma samples with calcium concentration greater than 11·5 mg/100ml. (Sherwood *et al.*, *Endocrinology*)

but due to an enhanced parathyroid activity, as indicated by a progressive increase in the weight of the glands (Stauffer *et al.*, 1973). The parathyroid hormone is a short-lived one, with a half-life of only 18 min, so that rapid responses of the level of the hormone in the blood to changes in the blood-calcium constitute a feasible means of controlling bone-resorption to compensate for these. As Fig. 5.52 shows, the concentration of PTH in the blood is an inverse linear function of the blood-concentration. Thyrocalcitonin, acting to promote calcium-deposition in the bones, may be expected to show the opposite relation to blood-calcium; and as Fig. 5.53 shows, this is generally true, but it appears that, below a set-point of some 6 mequiv/litre, i.e. considerably

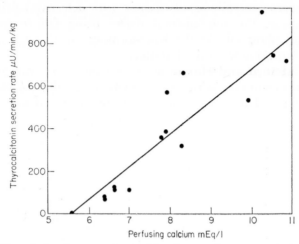

Fig. 5.53. The relation between thyrocalcitonin secretion rate and plasma calcium concentration of blood perfusing the thyroid in the pig. (Care *et al.*, *Endocrinol.*)

higher than the normal blood-level, the secretion ceases, so that it is only in hypercalcaemia that it is operative (Care *et al.* 1968).

Intestinal Absorption

Calcium is actively absorbed from the small intestine; this was demonstrated by Schachter and Rosen (1959), using the everted sac technique (Vol. 1) and measuring fluxes of $^{45}Ca^{2+}$; the degree of absorption was depressed by raising the concentration of calcium in the intestine, indicating a saturable mechanism; thus ingestion of large quantities of calcium would tend to promote excretion in the faeces through defective absorption. The absorption is governed, in addition, by the physiological requirements of the animal; thus in the normal animal active absorption against a concentration gradient is in the duodenum, but Kimberg *et al.* (1971) found that in calcium-deficiency active absorption, measured by the ability to establish concentration gradients, increased and now extended to the jejunal and ileal segments, but this adaptation was only possible with adequate vitamin D in the diet.

Pregnancy and Vitamin D. Everted sac preparations from pregnant and young animals show greater accumulation of calcium; vitamin D deficiency had the opposite effect, and according to Wasserman *et al.* (1966) this is due to an increase in passive permeability of the intestinal epithelium to the Ca^{2+}-ion, an increase that would militate against active absorption by favouring leakage of the ion back from the transported side. In this connexion, it must be emphasized that vitamin D-deficient rats, on an adequate calcium-diet, grow well, so that vitamin D-dependent active transport seems to be an adaptational functional response to low-calcium diets (Dowdle *et al.*, 1960).

Growth Hormone. Removal of the anterior pituitary diminished absorption, an effect that could be countered by administration of growth hormone (Finkelstein and Schachter, 1962).

Intestinal Secretion

As indicated above, the major loss of calcium from the animal is in the faeces; this is due partly to a failure to absorb dietary calcium, but also to a failure to reabsorb endogenous calcium derived from intestinal secretion. The importance of endogenous calcium is shown by the observation of Sernka and Borle (1969) that the concentration of calcium in the rat's ileal digestive contents was greater than in the duodenal. *In vitro* experiments, either employing an everted sac (Kimberg *et al.*, 1961) or portions of intestine stretched to form a membrane between two chambers (the Ussing-preparation), indicate that, when jejunal and ileal segments are used there is a net transport towards the mucosal side, i.e. towards the lumen, acting against a gradient of electrochemical potential (Walling and Kimberg, 1973). When these authors used duodenal pieces, they found a net flux in the opposite direction, indicating absorption. As to whether the active secretion in these *in vitro* preparations is directly across the unspecialized intestinal epithelium, or results from the action of intestinal glands, cannot be said; the amounts that could be excreted by this latter mechanism are certainly adequate to account for the actual excretion in the faeces.*

Renal Excretion

The results of a micropuncture study of reabsorption of calcium and inulin are shown in Table VII, the factor $\frac{\text{Calcium}}{\text{Inulin}} \times 100$ representing, in this case, the percentage unreabsorbed, since the concentrations in the tubular fluid (TF) are represented as fractions of the concentration in the glomerular fluid (GF). About 60 per cent of the filtered load is reabsorbed in the proximal tubule, and most of the remainder in the distal nephron, so that only 0·2 per cent is excreted.

---

* Thyrocalcitonin provoked a large increase in intestinal secretion of salts and water by the jejunum of human subjects; however, the secretion (or absorption) of calcium was unaffected (Gray *et al.*, 1973).

Parathormone. Parathormone decreased the clearance of calcium in dogs from 0·13 ml/min to 0·06 (Agus *et al.*, 1973), thus demonstrating one of its mechanisms for promoting retention of this ion; micropuncture studies indicate that the primary action is on reabsorption in the proximal tubule, the fractional reabsorption here falling from 0·25 to 0·15.

TABLE VII

Tubular reabsorption of calcium (Lassiter *et al.*, 1963)

Fluid	(TF)/(GF) Calcium	(TF)/(GF) Inulin	$\dfrac{\text{Calcium}}{\text{Inulin}} \times 100$
Early proximal	1·0	1·0	100
Late proximal	1·1	3·0	37
Early distal	0·7	5·0	14
Late distal	0·6	20	3
Ureteral urine	1·3	690	0·2

TF = Tubular fluid: GF = Glomerular fluid.

Relation to Na⁺. A striking feature of the urinary excretion of calcium is the strong parallelism between this and that of Na^+, as first emphasized by Walser (1961); thus in the proximal tubule the value of the TF/P ratio for Na^+ is unity throughout its length, because reabsorption is iso-osmotic, a given amount of reabsorption being accompanied by an appropriate amount of water, so that no appreciable differences of concentration are built up (p. 416). The same is true for the ionized Ca^{2+} in the tubular filtrate, so that the ratio: TF/UF, being the ratio of the tubular fluid concentration (TF) to that of an ultrafiltrate of plasma (UF), is approximately unity throughout the proximal tubule. A variety of other studies involving the effects of diuretics, acute and chronic volume expansion, and alterations in dietary sodium-intake often indicated parallel changes in excretion of Na^+ and Ca^{2+}, suggesting that the active transport of Na^+ is linked with that of Ca^{2+} (Walser, 1961). The similarity extends to the effects of PTH, since this apparently also reduces proximal reabsorption of Na^+, although subsequently the actions diverge, so that in the study of Agus *et al.* it caused an increased clearance of Na^+.

Cyclic AMP

We have seen that many hormones exert their influence through the second messenger, cyclic AMP, their initial action being to adsorb to a receptor site on the cell membrane of the target cell; their presence here activates adenylcyclase, a constituent of the cell membrane; this promotes the formation of cAMP within the cell and the heightened concentration is supposed to activate critical enzymes, e.g. phosphoryl kinases, that ultimately bring about the hormone's action. There is no doubt that parathyroid hormone acts through cAMP both in the kidney, where it causes increased renal excretion of cAMP, and in bone, where it causes increases in cAMP in foetal bone cultured *in vitro* (Fig. 5.54).

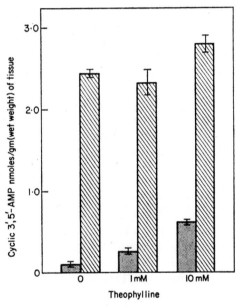

Fig. 5.54. The effect of parathyroid hormone on the accumulation of cyclic AMP in rat calvaria incubated in a medium without (O) and with (1 mM and 10 mM) theophylline. Vertical bars on left, without hormone; bars on right, with hormone. (Aurbach *et al.*, *Rec. Prog. Hormone Res.*)

Dibutyryl-cAMP. The effects of the hormone can be mimicked by the more lipid-soluble dibutyryl-cAMP causing a decrease in the fractional reabsorption of phosphate from the proximal tubule corresponding to a 30 per cent inhibition of reabsorption (Agus *et al.*, 1971). The second messenger also causes a rise in plasma-calcium in para-thyroidectomized rats and, if applied to explants of the foetal rat calvarium, it causes the formation of lacunae indicating localized reabsorption of bone; this is associated with loss of hydroxyproline, a typical collagen amino acid, as well as of Ca^{2+} and of phosphate. The increased renal excretion of cAMP induced by parathyroid hormone is not the result of an increased clearance from the blood, but is the consequence of the induced synthesis of cAMP by the tubular cells; this is demonstrated by taking a suspension of tubules, isolated by treating the kidney cortex with trypsin; PTH caused an increase in the cAMP in the suspension. We must assume, then, that the liberated cAMP finally activates the transport systems concerned with re-absorbing calcium and excreting phosphate.

The Intracellular Concentration

The internal concentration of Ca^{2+} in most cells is held at an extremely low level, of the order of 0·01 millimolar, if by this we mean the concentration of ionized Ca^{2+} in the cytoplasm; whilst the actual concentration of calcium is much higher, between 0·4 and 2·0 mM. Thus the bulk of the internal calcium is sequestered from the cyto-plasmic water, largely through incorporation within the endoplasmic reticulum and mitochondria, and also by the formation of unionized complexes.

Gradient of Electrochemical Potential

The concentration of ionized Ca^{2+} in the extracellular fluid is about 1 mM (Table VI), so that there is a large gradient of electrochemical potential between inside and outside of the cell, when we have regard to the ionized material in the internal and external fluids and the potential across the membrane (Fig. 5.55). Thus with a potential of

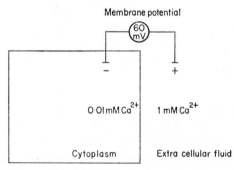

Fig. 5.55. The distribution of ionized Ca^{2+} between inside and outside of the cell illustrated in relation to the membrane potential. Both the concentration gradient and the electrical potential favour passage of Ca^{2+} into the cell.

60 mV, inside negative, the equilibrium distribution would require that the internal concentration be some 100 times the outside, but in fact it is about one hundredth, so that the system is very far from equilibrium, and a "calcium-pump" must be postulated to account for the low internal concentration within the cell; and it seems that a Ca^{2+}-sensitive ATPase is concerned with this, insensitive to ouabain and therefore operating independently of the Na^+-pump.

PHOSPHATE

There is no need to emphasize the role of phosphate in animal metabolism; the inorganic fraction, usually indicated by P_i, consists of a mixture mainly of Na_2HPO_4 and NaH_2PO_4, which at pH 7·4 would be present in the ratio: 1 : 0·2. Besides its involvement in inter-mediary metabolism, phosphate is an important constituent of bone, so we should not be surprised to find a close involvement of the hor-mones and vitamin controlling Ca^{2+} levels in the blood. The concen-tration in plasma given by Walser is 1·15 mmoles/litre, equivalent to 1·22 mmoles/kgH$_2$O; some 12 per cent of this is protein-bound. The computed fractions in plasma are shown in Table VIII.

TABLE VIII

Concentrations of the various fractions of phosphate in the plasma and their percentages of the total (Walser, 1961)

Species	mMoles/litre	Per cent of total
Free HPO_4^{--}	0·50	43
Free $H_2PO_4^-$	0·11	10
Protein-bound	0·14	12
$NaHPO_4^-$	0·33	29
$CaHPO_4$	0·04	3
$MgHPO_4$	0·03	3
Total	1·15	100 per cent

Intestinal Absorption

Phosphate is actively absorbed from the intestine; according to Harrison and Harrison (1961) the process is inhibited if Ca^{2+} is removed from the medium, whilst vitamin D enhances absorption.

Renal Excretion

Classical studies on renal excretion suggested an absence of any maximal reabsorptive capacity. According to the micropuncture study of Strickler *et al.* (1964), illustrated by Fig. 5.56, most reabsorption occurs in the proximal tubule; in the normal animal this amounts to about 76 per cent of the filtered load, and there is no evidence of secretion into the tubules. When the animal was loaded with an

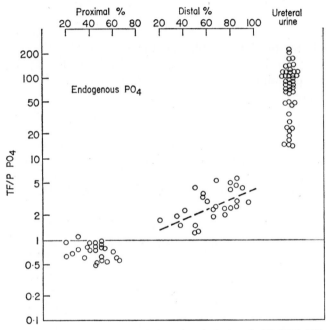

Fig. 5.56. The phosphate concentration ratios (tubular fluid (TF) / Plasma (P)) as a function of tubular length in the rat kidney. (Strickler *et al.*, *J. clin. Invest.*)

intravenous infusion of phosphate, the value of TF/P for the proximal tubule increased to about 2·0, indicating a failure of the reabsorptive process to keep pace with that of Na^+ and water; corresponding with this there was a diminished percentage reabsorption, falling from 76 to 22 per cent. Thus most of the "rejectate" from the proximal tubule, indicated by the high TF/P ratio, seems to be finally excreted.

Effect of PTH. Treatment with parathyroid hormone (PTH) decreased the fractional reabsorption of phosphate from the proximal tubule from 0·51 to 0·15, while the urinary clearance increased from 2·7 to 9·6 ml/min. Thus PTH has a marked *phosphaturic* effect. Brunette

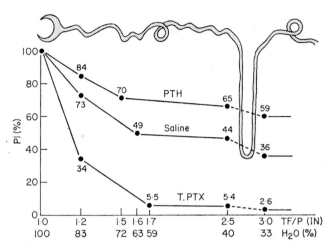

Fig. 5.57. The proportion of filtered phosphate (PI) that remains within the lumen at various levels in the rat nephron. PTH, parathyroid hormone loading; T.PTX, thyroparathyroidectomy. (Brunette *et al.*, *Amer. J. Physiol.*)

et al. (1973) studied the losses of ^{32}P-labelled phosphate from the nephron when it was injected at various sites, as measured by the recovery in the ureteral urine. The results of their study are summarized by Fig. 5.57, which shows the estimated percentage changes of concentration taking place when the filtrate passes along the nephron; in control animals infused with saline the main reabsorption was in the proximal tubule with a little more taking place between proximal and distal tubules. Parathyroid hormone treatment generally inhibited reabsorption, and is thus phosphaturic, whilst in thyroparathyroidectomy* (T.PTX) reabsorption was increased strikingly. Thus, so far as the kidney is concerned, PTH tends to conserve phosphate along with Ca^{2+}.

Bone and Calcium and Phosphate Metabolism

Growth

The histology of the bone is complex, and need not detain us here. Suffice it to say that the basic extracellular matrix in which the insoluble calcium phosphate is deposited consists of collagen; growth of such a solid structure requires not only laying down of more matrix,

---

* Amiel *et al.* (1970) noted a much smaller diminution in phosphate excretion in chronically parathyroidectomized rats than in acutely operated animals, excretion being some half normal in the former case and one-tenth normal in the latter.

with subsequent deposition of insoluble salt, but also a continuous process of remodelling, achieved by the resorption of already laid-down material, a process organized by the *osteoclasts*. This dynamic state of affairs persists into adulthood, in so far as breakdown and re-formation of bone are taking place continuously. The breakdown during bone resorption involves removal not only of Ca^{2+} and phosphate, but also of the collagen matrix, as revealed by loss of amino acids. It is considered that the region of calcification, or resorption, is covered by a screen of osteocytes, which behaves like an epithelium controlling the passage of Ca^{2+}, as indicated in Fig. 5.49, p. 488; and it is considered that the hormones influence this transport. It may well be, however, that the action of PTH is exerted on the great bulk of the bone cells.

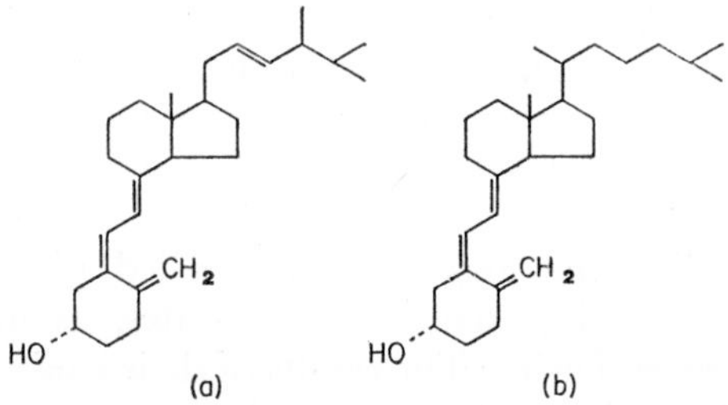

Fig. 5.58. The structures of (a)er gocalciferol (vitamin D_2) and (b) cholecalciferol (vitamin D_3)

Vitamin D

The disease of rickets may be prevented by dosing the growing child with vitamin D, the name given to a fat-soluble material which is especially concentrated in liver, but is also found in plant tissues. Exposure of the skin to adequate doses of ultraviolet light can substitute for vitamin D, and this is due to the conversion of 7-dehydrocalciferol, normally present in the skin, to vitamin D. Two dietary compounds corresponding with vitamin D have been isolated and synthesized, *ergocalciferol* (Fig. 5.58), or vitamin D_2, and *cholecalciferol*, or vitamin D_3; it is the latter that may be considered as the natural animal vitamin since it is this compound that is formed in the tissues by ultraviolet light from 7-dehydrocalciferol.

Intestinal Absorption of Ca^{2+}. The most prominent action of vitamin D is to increase absorption of Ca^{2+} from the intestine; this action requires a lag-period of some 10–12 hours, and this seems to be due to the requirement that the vitamin induce the synthesis of one or more proteins connected with the active transport of Ca^{2+}, since the effect of the vitamin may be blocked by previous administration of inhibitors of protein synthesis, such as actinomycin D. However, the delay may be considerably reduced if the hydroxylated vitamin, which is a normal metabolite, is given instead; thus vitamins D_2 and D_3 most probably act physiologically only after their metabolic conversion to 25-hydroxy-ergocalciferol, or 25-hydroxy-cholecalciferol respectively (Fig. 5.59), so that these latter compounds may be regarded as hormone- or transport-forms of the vitamin, by contrast with the storage-forms of the vitamins proper. This metabolic conversion takes place in the liver, and this explains why vitamin D is ineffective in promoting

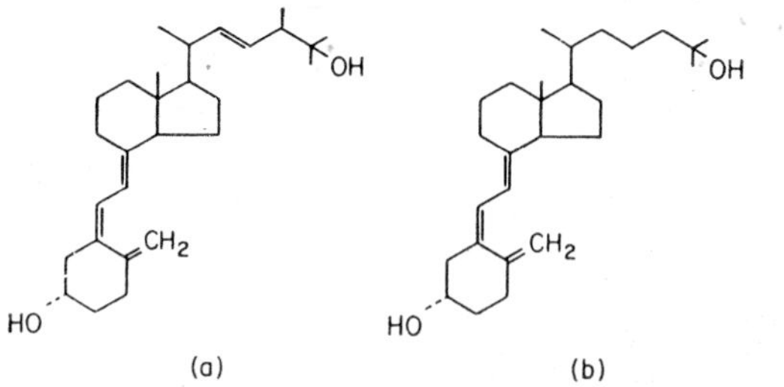

Fig. 5.59. The structures of (a) 25-hydroxy-ergocalciferol and (b) 25-hydroxy cholecalciferol.

active transport of Ca^{2+} by the isolated intestine, whereas the 25-hydroxy-derivatives are. It seems that an a_2-globulin of the plasma acts as carrier for the vitamins and their hydroxylated derivatives.

Rickets. The disease of rickets consists in the failure to supply adequate amounts of Ca^{2+} and phosphate to the bone-tissue; thus in the normal subject the plasma is super-saturated with respect to these two ions, whereas in the rickety child it is under-saturated; vitamin D brings the Ca^{2+}-level to saturation, primarily through increased absorption from the gut; however, it also behaves like parathyroid hormone in mobilizing bone-Ca^{2+}, in fact Rasmussen found that PTH will not mobilize Ca^{2+} from bone unless the animal is pre-treated with vitamin D.*

Mechanism of Action of Vitamin D. Actinomycin D, given prior to vitamin D, blocks completely both the intestinal and mineral-mobilization responses, indicating the prior necessity for protein

---

* Care must be taken in interpreting the interactions of vitamin D and the two hormones; thus in vitamin D-deficiency the low blood-calcium activates secretion of PTH, which may be thus acting maximally; in consequence, exogenous PTH may have no further effect. It would seem that the renal effects of PTH can take place independently of vitamin D.

synthesis; and this doubtless accounts for the 3-hour lag between giving hydroxylated vitamin D and its action. Thus the transcription of nuclear DNA to form a messenger RNA seems to be the first requirement in vitamin D action; and experiments with the RNA-precursor, tritium-labelled orotic acid, have shown that vitamin D accelerates the incorporation of radioactivity into nuclear RNA. When the DNA from intestinal nuclei was prepared at different times after administration of vitamin D, it was found that it acquired increased template activity in an artificial synthetic system containing an RNA polymerase, etc., at the time when a similar increase would have occurred *in vivo*. Thus vitamin D "unmasks", or "derepresses", the gene material

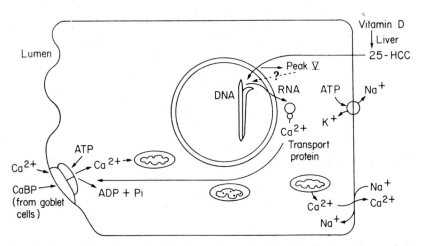

Fig. 5.60. A possible scheme for the absorption of calcium in the intestine and the influence of vitamin D on these processes. (De Luca and Melancon, *Biochemical Actions of Hormones*. Ed. Litwack, Academic Press.)

concerned in synthesis of one or more types of RNA that are subsequently employed in protein synthesis.

Carrier-Protein. Active transport of Ca^{2+} may presumably be favoured by the synthesis of some "carrier-protein", and it is interesting that Wasserman has isolated from homogenates of intestinal mucosa of chicks, given vitamin D, a protein that binds Ca^{2+} strongly; it has a molecular weight of 24,000–28,000, and binds one mole of Ca^{2+} per mole of protein. In addition Martin has found an ATPase, stimulated by Ca^{2+}, in the brush-borders of intestinal epithelium of rats given vitamin D. A possible scheme for intestinal absorption of Ca^{2+} and the influence of vitamin D is illustrated in Fig. 5.60; vitamin D_3 produces its hormone 25 hydroxy-cholecalciferol (25-HCC), and this induces the synthesis on the ribosomes of a transport-protein which migrates to the apical surface of the cell; Ca^{2+} is helped into the cytoplasm, a process involving ATP and the Ca^{2+}-activated ATPase which may, or may not, be the same as the synthesized transport protein. Ca^{2+} passes to the serosal side whence it leaves the cell probably in exchange for Na^+, whilst the extra Na^+, entering by this exchange, is extruded by the usual Na^+–K^+-pump.

DIURESIS AND SALURESIS

Diabetes

An abnormally large formation of urine—*diuresis*—may occur pathologically in diabetes insipidus owing to a failure of the concentrating mechanism through defective secretion of the antidiuretic hormone, vasopressin or ADH. Another pathological condition is that of diabetes mellitus, when the diuresis is called *osmotic*, and is due to overloading the glucose reabsorptive mechanism; the high concentration of glucose remaining in the proximal tubule impairs the reabsorption of Na^+, and an extra load is presented to the distal nephron.

Diuretics

Experimentally and therapeutically a diuresis may be caused by drugs—*diuretics*—that interfere with the reabsorptive mechanisms for water, but since the reabsorption of water is so closely linked with that of salt, both in the iso-osmotic reabsorption in the proximal tubule and in the establishment of gradients of osmolality in the loop of Henle, through active transport of salt out of the ascending limb (Vol. 1), the attack on the renal mechanism that causes diuresis consists in an attack primarily on the reabsorptive process for Na^+, so that the diuresis is accompanied, not only by excessive excretion of water—*water diuresis*—but also of salt—*saluresis* or *natriuresis*. We have already had an example of this in studying the effects of the carbonic anhydrase inhibitor, acetazoleamide or Diamox; this inhibits reabsorption of bicarbonate, and through this, of Na^+, and the results are a diuresis and saluresis; for this reason it has been employed therapeutically as a diuretic in the treatment of oedema.

General Considerations

C_{H_2O} and T_{H_2O}

Goldberg *et al.* (1964) have summarized the likely consequences of a diuretic according as it attacks the secretion of ADH by the pituitary,

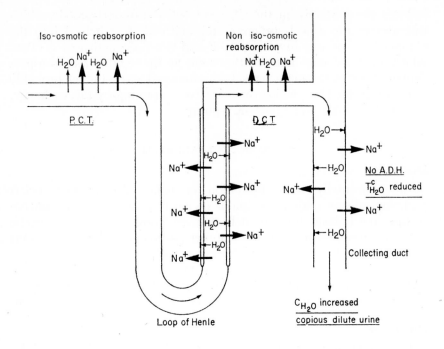

Iso-osmotic reabsorption

Non iso-osmotic reabsorption

P.C.T.

D C T

No A.D.H.

$T^c_{H_2O}$ reduced

Collecting duct

Loop of Henle

C_{H_2O} increased
copious dilute urine

←——— Passive water movement

←—— Active Na^+ transport

Fig. 5.61. The effect of antidiuretic hormone (ADH) insufficiency on the ability of the kidney to concentrate urine. ADH increases the permeability of the collecting duct epithelium and the absence of this hormone causes the duct wall to be relatively impermeable to water. The normal sodium reabsorption processes continue at the proximal tubule, loop of Henle and in the distal tubule, so the fluid passing into the collecting duct has a low sodium content and since the duct wall is impermeable, a copious dilute urine is produced. The clearance of free water (C_{H_2O}) is increased and the reabsorption of solute free water (Tc_{H_2O}) is reduced.

as with alcohol*; or as the reabsorptive mechanisms are impaired through an osmotic agent, such as mannitol; or through inhibition of reabsorption of Na^+ in the proximal tubule or in the distal segment, notably the ascending limb of the loop of Henle. Defective secretion of ADH would leave the proximal reabsorptive processes unaffected; the decreased permeability to water in the ascending limb would prevent any concentrative reabsorption of water, although active reabsorption of salt in the ascending limb, and later in the distal

---

* . . . drink, sir, is a great provoker of three things . . . nose-painting, sleep, and urine (Macbeth, II, (iii)).

tubule and collecting duct, would be unimpaired. Thus the copious urine would be "dilute" with a low concentration of salt (Fig. 5.61). Expressed technically, the *clearance of free water*, C_{H_2O}, i.e. of water in excess of that required to produce an isotonic urine, is increased, whilst the reabsorption of solute-free water, $T^C_{H_2O}$ (Vol. 1), is reduced.

Hydropenia and Water-Diuresis

In analysing the actions of other diuretics it is useful to examine these under two main conditions, namely during *antidiuresis*—or *hydropenia*—and during *water-diuresis*. During antidiuresis in the normal subject, water is being conserved, i.e. $T^c_{H_2O}$ is positive, due to the secretion of ADH, which allows rapid osmotic withdrawal of water into the collecting ducts. Any interference with the concentrative mechanism, i.e. the active transport of Na^+ out of the ascending limb of the loop of Henle, would be manifest during hydropenia as a reduction in $T^c_{H_2O}$. During water-diuresis, ADH secretion is suppressed, so that it would be useless to examine $T^c_{H_2O}$ to find any impairment of function created by the diuretic. Instead, because the kidney is occupied in excreting solute-free water, i.e. in making C_{H_2O} positive, we must examine any change in this caused by the diuretic. An attack on the active transport of Na^+, whether it occurs in the ascending limb or elsewhere in the "diluting segment" of the nephron, will now be manifest as a failure to reabsorb salt against gradients of concentration, and thus as a reduction in C_{H_2O}.

Attack on Proximal Tubule

A diuretic, acting solely on the proximal tubule, inhibiting re-absorption of the Na^+ salts, would enhance C_{H_2O}—free-water clearance —during water-diuresis because more sodium would be presented to both of the diluting sites, i.e. to the loop of Henle and the distal nephron, including the collecting duct, where reabsorption of Na^+ to establish high gradients of osmolality is possible. During hydropenia, or water-shortage, a proximally acting drug would increase reabsorption of solute-free water, $T^c_{H_2O}$, by the collecting duct in the concentrative mechanism, because of the availability of more osmotically active solute for transport into the medullary interstitium. This is demonstrated by the effects of the osmotic drugs, such as mannitol, which in fact increase C_{H_2O} during water diuresis and $T^c_{H_2O}$ during hydropenia. Thus during water shortage, unlike the situation created by ADH-insufficiency, the urine may be concentrated (Fig. 5.62).

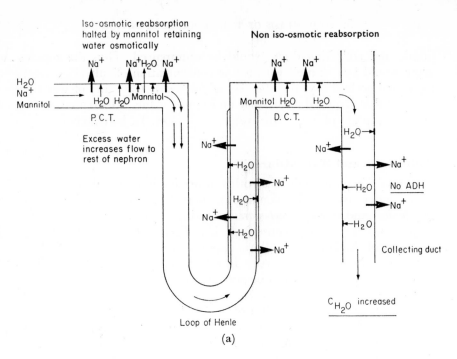

(a)

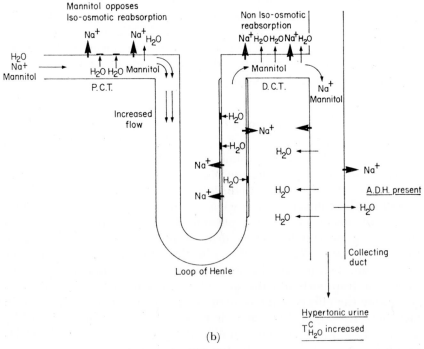

(b)

Fig. 5.62

Attack on Distal Nephron

Drugs acting on the distal nephron would have more variable effects, according as they attacked the ascending loop of Henle with or without an attack on the other diluting sites in the distal tubule and collecting duct. A drug acting predominantly on the ascending limb would lower the clearance of free water, C_{H_2O}, during water-diuresis, because the active transport of salt out of this limb would be inhibited, i.e. the selective reabsorption of solute, on which C_{H_2O} relies, would be reduced (Fig. 5.63a). During hydropenia, or water-shortage, the reabsorption of solute-free water, $T^c_{H_2O}$, would be impaired, due to failure of the concentrative mechanism, which is now manifest, since ADH is secreted. In both cases saluresis would occur due to failure to reabsorb salt (Fig. 5.63b). Thus a predominant attack on the ascending limb produces impairment of C_{H_2O} in water-diuresis and of $T^c_{H_2O}$ in hydropenia, and is therefore characteristically different in its effects from a proximal attack. If the drug acted predominantly at the second diluting site, i.e. the distal tubule and collecting duct, it should be possible to concentrate the urine, so that $T^c_{H_2O}$ would be normal in hydropenia, whilst in fully hydrated animals the clearance of free water, C_{H_2O}, brought about by the second diluting mechanism, would be impaired, and the copious urine would have a relatively high concentration of salt—saluresis.

Widespread Effects

Quite clearly, when we are dealing with drugs that inhibit the active transport of ions such as Na^+, it is probably too much to expect a unique site of attack, since the active transport takes place at the proximal tubule, the ascending limb of the loop, and in the distal nephron. Hower, in several instances, the effects are sufficiently characteristic to allow a statement as to the probable major site of action.

Fig. 5.62. The effect of osmotic diuretics on the kidney (a). In Water Diuresis. Osmotic diuretics, such as mannitol, are filtered by the kidney, but are not reabsorbed, so osmotically hold back some of the water and salt which are normally removed in the proximal tubule by the iso-osmotic reabsorption of salt and water. The excess water and salt pass to the loop of Henle and distal tubule where sodium can be removed against an osmotic gradient and a copious dilute urine is produced, i.e. C_{H_2O} is increased. (b) In Hydropenia. During water shortage the proximal osmotic retention of water and salts enables more sodium to be reabsorbed by the loop of Henle and the distal tubule so that the medullary osmotic gradient is increased. Since, in the hydropenic state, ADH is present, the collecting duct epithelium is permeable to water and the increased osmotic gradient increases the reabsorption of water so a concentrated urine is formed, i.e. $T^c_{H_2O}$ is increased.

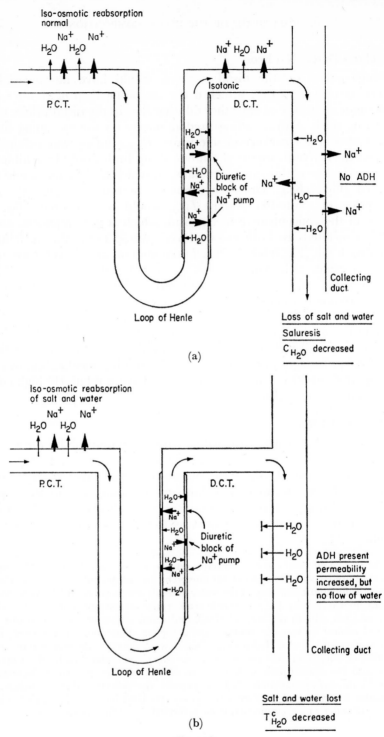

Fig. 5.63

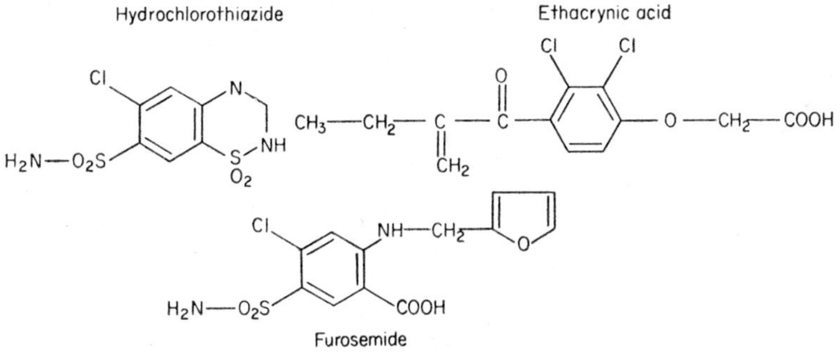

Fig. 5.64. Structural formulae of hydrochlorothiazide, ethacrynic acid and furosemide.

Ethacrynic Acid

The diuretic and saluretic effects of this substance, whose formula is illustrated in Fig. 5.64, were described by Baer *et al.* (1962); and the analysis of its actions by the classical clearance studies of salt and water, carried out by Goldberg *et al.*, illustrates some of the principles discussed above. These authors concluded that the attack was primarily on the ascending limb, so that C_{H_2O} was impaired during water-diuresis whilst the clearance of sodium increased—saluresis (Fig. 5.65) —but the urine remained hypotonic due to the heavy hydration of the subject. In hydropenia there was a precipitate fall in the urine osmolality, indicating a failure of the concentrating mechanism; $T^c_{H_2O}$ fell rapidly, and this fall was sustained whilst the solute clearance, C_{osm}, increased due to the great increase in Na^+ and Cl^- excretions (Fig. 5.66).

Fig. 5.63. The effect of inhibition of sodium transport in the ascending limb of the loop of Henle.

(a) In Water Diuresis.

Since the selective reabsorption of salt by the ascending limb of the loop of Henle is inhibited, excess salt and water pass through the distal tubule and into the collecting duct. In water diuresis there is an absence of ADH so that the collecting tubule is fairly impermeable to water and a loss of both salt and water occurs i.e. C_{H2O} is decreased.

(b) In Hydropenia.

In hydropenia ADH is present, but since the medullary osmotic gradient is destroyed by inhibition of sodium transport in the ascending limb, the increase in collecting duct permeability by ADH does not lead to water reabsorption so salt and water are lost and $T^c_{H_2O}$ is decreased.

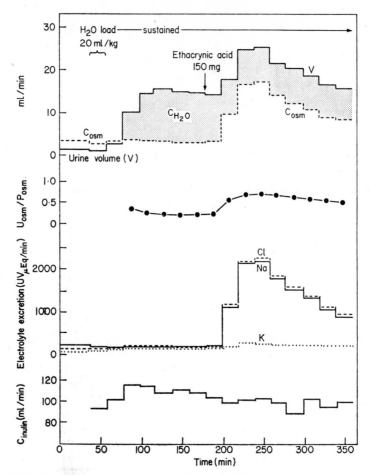

Fig. 5.65. The effect of ethacrynic acid on the kidney in a normal maximally hydrated subject. Effects on urine flow (V), free water clearance (C_{H_2O}), osmolar clearance (C_{osm}), electrolyte excretion (UV), and inulin clearance (C_{In}). Before administration of the drug, the control value for C_{H_2O} was 11·9 ml per min. At the peak of saluresis, C_{H_2O} fell to 8·2 ml per min and subsequently reached a minimal value of 7·29 ml per min. U/P_{osm} = urine osmolality/serum osmolality. (Goldberg *et al.*, *J. clin. Invest.*)

Micropuncture Studies

The interpretation of the actions of diuretics is always somewhat equivocal if based on the classical clearance studies illustrated by Figs. 5.65 and 5.66. Of more value are micropuncture studies, which are often able to identify much more accurately the main sites of action.

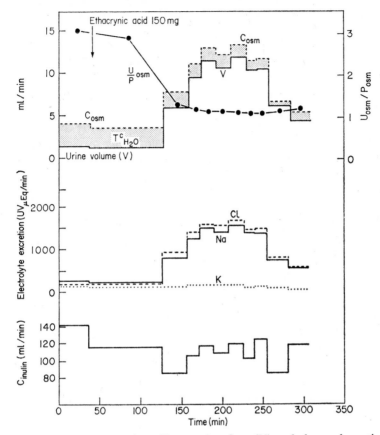

Fig. 5.66. Effects of ethacrynic acid on urine flow (V), tubular reabsorption of solute-free water ($T^c_{H_2O}$), osmolar clearance (C_{osm}), electrolyte excretion (UV), and inulin clearance (C_{In}) in a normal hydropenic subject. As C_{osm} increased, $T^c_{H_2O}$ progressively fell from a control value of 2·7 ml per minute to a mimimal value of 0·6 ml per minute. (Goldberg *et al.*, *J. clin. Invest.*)

Mercurials

Mercuric chloride, or organic compounds containing mercury, called *mercurials*, used to be employed commonly to induce diuresis; the organic compounds have the common structure:

$$XHg-\underset{\displaystyle H}{\overset{\displaystyle H}{C}}-\underset{\displaystyle OY}{\overset{\displaystyle H}{C}}-\underset{\displaystyle H}{\overset{\displaystyle H}{C}}-R$$

where X is usually a halogen, Y is not important, and R is important;

in *mersalyl* it is o-carbamyl-phenoxyacetic acid, and in *chloromeredrin* it is urea.

Attack on Ascending Limb. It was for a long time considered that their action was mainly to inhibit reabsorption of the filtrate in the proximal tubule, thus behaving like the osmotic diuretics. However, micropuncture studies by Dirks *et al.* (1966), and by Clapp and Robinson (1968), have identified the ascending limb of the loop of Henle as the main target for the mercurials and some other diuretics. Thus we have seen that the urinary concentrating mechanism depends on an active transport of salt from the ascending limb, so that normally the fluid entering the distal tubule is hyposomolal to the plasma; inhibition of this active transport process would necessarily prevent reabsorption of both salt and water, causing natriuresis and diuresis. In conformity with this viewpoint, Clapp and Robinson found that, when they punctured distal tubules in the dog, the osmolal TF/P-ratio for early distal fluid was raised by the mercurials. In a more recent study in which they measured actual Na^+ and K^+ concentrations, Evanson *et al.* (1972) found no significant effect on the TF/P for either Na^+ or K^+ in the proximal tubule; however, in the distal tubule, not only was TF/P for inulin lowered, indicating a defective concentrating mechanism, but also the TF/P for Na^+ rose, indicating defective reabsorption in the ascending limb. Chloromeredrin suppressed secretion of K^+, causing a large fall in the distal TF/P for this ion associated with increased excretion, so that the mercurial is a *kaliuretic*, and when used therapeutically in the control of oedema care must be taken not to lower the blood-K^+ too severely.

Carbonic Anhydrase Inhibitors

We have seen (Vol. 1) that a class of diuretics seems to work primarily through the inhibition of carbonic anhydrase, and this leads to failure to reabsorb Na^+ in both proximal and distal nephrons; the concentrating mechanism, indicated by $T_{H_2O}^c$, in the ascending limb is unaffected, since this is probably not a major site of bicarbonate reabsorption, the diuretic being both saluretic and water-diuretic. Other carbonic anhydrase inhibitors are often highly efficient diuretics, out of all relation to their inhibitory activity; of these are the thiazides, typically represented by hydrochlorothiazide (Fig. 5.64). On the basis of classical clearance studies, Goldberg *et al.* (1964) concluded that its action was distinct from that of ethacrynic acid since, although it decreased C_{H_2O} during water loading, indicating an attack on the distal diluting mechanism, it apparently did not affect $T_{H_2O}^c$ in hydropenia, suggesting an intact concentrating mechanism.

Furosemide

Furosemide (Fig. 5.64), a chemically related very powerful diuretic, has a large kaliuretic, as well as natriuretic, effect so that the clearance of K^+ can become greater than that of inulin (Dirks and Seely, 1970). According to a microperfusion study of Burg et al. (1973), employing isolated parts of the nephron, there is a defective reabsorption of salt by the ascending limb of the loop of Henle; this was reflected in a fall in the potential across the wall, a potential that they considered to be a reflexion of the active transport of Cl^- across the segment (Burg and Green, 1973), since, unlike the rest of the nephron, the potential is orientated with the inside of the limb positive. So far as the proximal tubule is concerned, furosemide definitely reduces its power of re-absorbing salt, as judged by the split-drop technique (Knox et al., 1969), and by microperfusion through isolated portions of the nephron, but the major effect revealed by these studies (Morgan et al., 1970) is an attack on the ability of the ascending loop to reabsorb Na^+. The effect on K^+ was to impair reabsorptive ability, so that, whereas normally the concentration in the early distal tubule is less than that of plasma, after treatment with furosemide it becomes greater.

Role of Ascending Limb. In general, as Dirks and Seely (1970) have emphasized, the failure to reabsorb filtrate in the proximal tubule is usually compensated by an increased reabsorption in the distal nephron, mainly in the ascending loop, so that unless a diuretic also attacked this portion of the nephron its effects might well be compensated adequately. Thus their micropuncture studies showed that furosemide caused a decrease in the TF/P for inulin in the distal tubule, i.e. after the fluid had passed through the ascending limb; and this indicated a failure of the reabsorbing mechanism which, as we have seen (Vol. 1, p. 516), leads to a hypotonic fluid (TF/P < 1) appearing in the early distal tubule. When animals were loaded with isotonic NaCl by intravenous infusions, the increased filtered load was not completely reabsorbed in the proximal tubule—the characteristic effect of volume-expansion (p. 422); in the normal animal this extra load passing to the distal nephron was reabsorbed on its way through the loop, indicating the compensatory mechanism just alluded to. However, when the animal was treated with furosemide, the increased load was not reabsorbed, as revealed, once again, by a rise in TF/P for inulin in the distal tubule. Thus this work on furosemide emphasizes the role of the ascending loop in restraining saluresis when proximal reabsorption is impaired, and hence its critical role in determining the final nature of the urine. A diuretic, attacking only the proximal nephron, would not be very effective; and it is for this reason that most chemical diuretics must attack the ascending limb too.

Tubular Secretion of the Diuretic

The effectiveness of the carbonic anhydrase inhibitor-type drugs, including the thiazides, depends on the ability of the kidney to secrete them into the proximal tubule, treating them as they would p-amino-hippurate; the high local concentration would be carried to the distal nephron and there be very effective. A competitive inhibitor of this tubular secretory process, such as probenecid, decreases the effectiveness of furosemide as a saluretic (Hook and Williamson, 1965).

Cardiac Glycosides

The cardiac glycosides inhibit active transport of Na^+ by blocking the membrane-bound enzyme that hydrolyses ATP, called $Na^+ + K^+$-ATPase. They have long been recognized as diuretics and saluretics; and there is little doubt that they act on the proximal tubule as well as more distal sites (Whittembury and Fishman, 1969). The enzyme ATPase contains SH-groups that are concerned in its catalytic activities, so that "sulphydryl reagents", i.e. substances that react primarily with SH-groups, are effective diuretics; and this may be the point of attack of the mercurials. In this connexion ethacrynic acid, which, as we have seen, is a potent diuretic and saluretic, acting mainly on the ascending limb, is also an SH-reagent, and inhibits a $Na^+ + K^+$-ATPase extracted from kidney cortex (Duggan and Noll, 1965). As with the cardiac glycosides, the action of ethacrynic acid is by no means limited to the kidney; thus it inhibits active transport of Na^+ from skeletal muscle (Erlij and Leblanc, 1971).

Phosphaturesis and Calciuresis

Phosphate

In so far as the renal treatment of Na^+ often parallels that of phosphate, at any rate in the proximal tubule, we may expect a phosphaturesis with some diuretics; according to Puschett and Goldberg (1968), the carbonic anhydrase inhibitors, such as Diamox, are, in fact, phosphaturics, whilst ethacrynic acid, presumably because of its mainly distal action, is not.

Calcium

So far as calcium is concerned, the parallel relation between excretion of this ion with sodium seems to be maintained with most diuretics except the thiazides; here there is a very pronounced dissociation, so that, whereas the fractional excretion of Na^+ could be increased threefold, that of Ca^{2+} was unaffected. Micropuncture studies indicated that chlorothiazide reduced reabsorption of Na^+ in the ascending limb of Henle whilst that of Ca^{++} was unaffected (Edwards et al., 1973).

THE BLOOD SUGAR

Normal Levels

The level of glucose in the blood—the "blood-sugar"—varies between 80 and 120 mg/100 ml*; after the ingestion of a carbohydrate meal it may rise to 120–130 mg/100 ml, whilst during fasting it may fall to around 60–70 mg/100 ml. Under normal conditions the blood-sugar is held within these limits which may be considered reasonably narrow when the large variations in supply from the intestine, on the one hand, and utilization by the tissues, on the other, are taken into account. Thus only during prolonged fast or severe exercise does the level fall below 60 mg/100 ml.

Supply to Tissues

Brain

The importance of maintaining a reasonably constant level will be appreciated when it is known that the brain has no reserves of metabolic glucose, whilst the neurones and glial cells are utilizing it continuously; all this utilized glucose must therefore be derived from the blood and, so far as can be discovered, this uptake occurs passively as a result of diffusion down concentration gradients between the plasma, on the one hand, and the extracellular fluid and intracellular fluid of the brain on the other. Thus the rate of uptake, and hence of utilization, depends on these concentration gradients, so that if the plasma level falls sufficiently, uptake is inadequate and the neurones suffer from glucose deficiency. This deficiency may become grossly manifest when an animal goes into hypoglycaemic convulsions on reducing its blood-sugar acutely with insulin. In humans, levels between 45 and 15 mg/100 ml plasma cause coma and sometimes convulsions.

* The important concentration, from the physiological point of view, is that in plasma, or plasma-water; unfortunately the values quoted in the literature, even to-day, often represent the amounts in unit volume of whole blood; the values so quoted are some 14–15 per cent lower than in plasma, owing to the smaller water-content of the whole-blood and the fact that the concentration within the blood cells is necessarily less than that in the plasma, owing to metabolism (McDonald et al., 1964).

Muscular

With the other tissues, too, utilization of glucose seems to be limited by the speed with which it can enter the cells, as with skeletal muscle, but here the tissue can utilize its sugar reserves, in the form of glycogen, directly, and so is not critically dependent for its activity on the level of glucose in the blood.

Role of the Liver

Storage and Release

In maintaining the homeostasis of the glucose concentration, the liver plays a dominant role, since it can vary the amount of glucose it pumps into the general circulation, or removes from it, in accordance with the requirements of the body, requirements that are transmitted by both neural and hormonal messengers, but which are sensed mainly through the actual concentration of glucose in the blood passing through the brain. Thus removal of the liver from a dog causes a progressive fall in the concentration of glucose in the blood until the animal goes into hypoglycaemic convulsions; and this can be avoided by infusion of glucose into the animal. The liver is able to exert this role primarily because it acts as a storage-site for glucose in the form of glycogen, and it can draw from this store by *glycogenolysis*,* i.e. the breakdown of the polysaccharide (Vol. 1), and can add to it by *glycogenesis*, the synthesis of glycogen from glucose.

Glycogenesis

The basic steps in glycogenesis are the conversion of glucose to glucose-6-phosphate (the first step in glycolysis); this is converted to glucose-1-phosphate, which reacts with uridine triphosphate (UTP) to form uridine diphosphate-glucose (UDPG; Fig. 5.67). By the action of the enzyme *glycogen synthetase*, the glucose units are joined through glucosidic linkages between the first and fourth C-atoms of adjacent glucose residues. When a chain has been lengthened to eight glucose residues, a second enzyme comes into play causing branching—the "branching enzyme"—by transferring a part of the 1–4 chain to a neighbouring chain through a 1–6 linkage, thereby establishing a branch-point in the molecule. The types of linkage leading to straight chain or branching have already been shown in Vol. 1 (Fig. 9.2).

---

* Liver glycogen is synthesized largely from lactates and other non-carbohydrate sources rather than from blood-glucose, so that it is only when blood-sugar is very high that formation from glucose becomes significant. Thus the process of *gluconeogenesis*—the formation of glucose from glycine, fatty acids, amino acids, etc.—usually precedes glycogenesis.

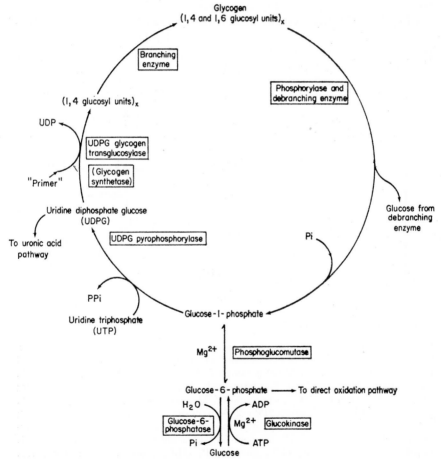

Fig. 5.67. The structural formula of uridine diphosphate glucose (UDPG). (Harper, *Review of Physiological Chemistry*.)

Glycogen
(1,4 and 1,6 glucosyl units)$_x$

Branching enzyme

Phosphorylase and debranching enzyme

(1,4 glucosyl units)$_x$

UDP

UDPG glycogen transglucosylase

(Glycogen synthetase)

"Primer"

Glucose from debranching enzyme

Uridine diphosphate glucose (UDPG)

Pi

To uronic acid pathway

UDPG pyrophosphorylase

PPi

Uridine triphosphate (UTP)

Glucose-1-phosphate

Mg^{2+} Phosphoglucomutase

Glucose-6-phosphate ⟶ To direct oxidation pathway

H$_2$O   ADP

Glucose-6-phosphatase   Mg^{2+} Glucokinase

Pi   ATP

Glucose

Fig. 5.68. Pathway of glycogenesis and of glycogenolysis in the liver. (Harper, *Review of Physiological Chemistry*.)

Glycogenolysis and Gluconeogenesis

The breakdown of glycogen to glucose—*glycogenolysis*—is catalysed by the enzyme *phosphorylase*, which breaks the chains at the 1–4 linkages; the breakage of the 1–6 linkages requires the action of a "debranching enzyme". As a result of these activities glycogen becomes glucose-1-phosphate, which is converted to glucose-6-phosphate, and this, through the enzyme *glucose-6-phosphatase*, present in liver and kidney (but not in muscle), is converted into free glucose which may pass into the blood. The pathways are illustrated in Fig. 5.68. In addition, the liver can synthesize glucose from non-carbohydrate sources, such as lactic and amino acids, and the products of fat hydrolysis and metabolism, a process given the general name of *gluconeogenesis*.

Metabolic Pathways for Gluconeogenesis. The metabolic pathways are indicated in Fig. 5.69. Thus, under fasting conditions, the liver obtains the glucose that it pumps into the blood by glycogenolysis

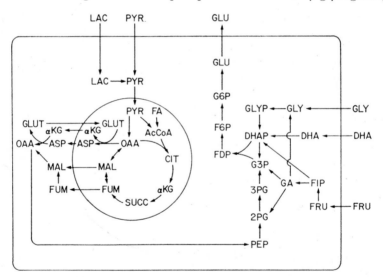

Fig. 5.69. Diagram of the pathways of gluconeogenesis from lactate, pyruvate, fructose, dihydroxyacetone in the rat liver. The rectangle represents a liver cell and the circle a mitochondrion. Abbreviations are: LAC, lactate; PYR, pyruvate; OAA, oxaloacetate; MAL, malate; FA, fatty acid; AcCoA, acetyl-CoA; CIT, citrate; αKG, α-ketoglutarate; SUCC, succinate; FUM, fumarate; ASP, aspartate; GLUT, glutamate; PEP, P-pyruvate; 2PG, 2-P-glycerate; DHAP, dihydroxyacetone-P; G3P, glyceraldehyde-3-P; GLYP, glycerol-1-P; GLY, glycerol; DHA, dihydroxyacetone; FRU, fructose; F1P, fructose-1-P; GA, glyceric acid; FDP, fructose-1, 6-di-P; F6P, fructose-6-P; G6P, glucose-6-P; GLU, glucose. Exton *et al.*, *Rec. Prog. Hormone Res.*)

and gluconeogenesis. Glycogenolysis may be regarded as an emergency response to meet rapid demands, as in muscular exercise, but it must be emphasized that the muscles of the body have their own glycogen stores, their glycogen being broken down to glucose-1-phosphate which then enters directly into the exergonic reactions required to sustain muscular contraction. The lactate formed during severe exercise is converted by the liver into glycogen, which is ultimately returned to the muscles in the form of glucose, to give the so-called *Cori cycle* (Fig. 5.70). In general, at blood-levels of glucose between 80–100 mg/100 ml, the liver is a nett producer of glucose, and as the concentration rises the production falls so that, in the rat, at a level of about 135 mg/100 ml production and utilization are equal. Gluconeogenesis, being dependent on non-carbohydrate materials, relies largely on the breakdown of tissue stores, such as proteins to amino

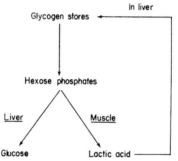

Fig. 5.70. The Cori cycle. (Clegg and Clegg, *Hormones, Cells and Organisms*. Heinemann)

acids, and fats to fatty acids and glycerol; this latter process of breakdown of fat is given the name *lipolysis*, and represents a principal mechanism for maintaining the blood-sugar during fasting.

Control Mechanisms

Adrenal Action

Glycogenolysis, the breakdown of glycogen to glucose, may be regarded as an emergency reaction to meet the extra metabolic requirements of the tissues during stress, and it is not surprising, therefore, that the sympathetic branch of the autonomic nervous system, and the hormones of the adrenal gland, exert a prominent action on this process. Thus sympathetic stimulation causes the liberation of adrenaline from the adrenal medulla and this activates glycogenolysis in such tissues as skeletal muscle leading to a rapid rise in the blood-sugar; in addition, there is a direct action of the sympathetic nerves on the liver cells. The breakdown of fat—*lipolysis*—is an accessory process to meet metabolic demands during stress and this, likewise, is promoted by adrenaline.

Glucocorticoids. Gluconeogenesis, like glycogenolysis, occurs continuously in the resting state, and it, too, is increased during emergencies, but the mechanisms controlling this are slower-acting, primarily through the corticosteroid hormones, the "glucocorticoids", so that it becomes a significant reaction only in severe stress, as in prolonged fasting or the hypoglycaemia of severe exercise. Thus the adrenaline secreted during conditions of stress not only activates glyogenolysis in liver and muscle but also, by its action on the pituitary, stimulates the release of ACTH which causes the adrenal cortex to liberate the glucocorticoids that stimulate gluconeogenesis by the liver.

The Adrenergic Receptors. There is little doubt that the metabolic actions of adrenaline are brought about through a β-receptor, these actions being blocked by propanolol. So far as the action on the liver is concerned, the picture is obscured by the tendency to use the hyperglycaemic response as an index to action; this can arise not only from hepatic glycogenolysis but also from the synthesis of glucose from lactate, whilst the release of insulin is affected by the catecholamines through their influence on adenylcyclase (p. 526). According to Hornbrook (1970), the weight of evidence favours a β-action in the liver too.

Insulin and Glucagon

Insulin

In addition to these hormones, which trigger off the responses to hypoglycaemia or other stress signals, we have the two pancreatic hormones, *glucagon* and *insulin*. Insulin has a variety of actions, as we shall see, but their features may be summarized by stating that it is an *anabolic hormone*, promoting the usage of glucose; it does this through accelerating the passage of glucose into all cells of the body, except those of the brain and the liver, the permeability of the latter cells being so high as not to require any assistance whilst the access to the brain is governed primarily by the blood-brain barrier (p. 576) which is, apparently, not insulin-sensitive. The effect of its multifarious activities is to reduce the level of sugar in the blood, and a powerful factor activating the release of the hormone into the blood is a rise in the concentration of glucose in the plasma—the *hyperglycaemic stimulus*. Another anabolic action is the promotion of protein synthesis, achieved once again by favouring passage of the primary metabolites, amino acids, into cells. So far as liver is concerned, insulin promotes glycogen synthesis—glycogenesis—and in fatty tissue it promotes fat synthesis—lipogenesis. In general, since all these processes involve utilization of glucose, the powerful hypoglycaemic action of insulin is understandable, whilst the raised blood-sugar in diabetes mellitus is likewise comprehensible.

Glucagon

Glucagon is the "opposite number" of insulin, promoting catabolic events leading to the breakdown of glycogen—glycogenolysis—and the synthesis of glucose from non-glycogen sources—gluconeogenesis—and the breakdown of fat to fatty acids and glycerol—lipolysis. Thus glucagon antagonizes the action of insulin, its effect being to raise the blood-sugar; as we shall see, however, it also has a direct action on the β-cells of the pancreas, causing them to release insulin, a form of negative feedback.

General Control Scheme

Response to Hyperglycaemia

The general scheme for maintenance of a constant blood-sugar or, what is more correct, for ensuring that the cells, especially of the brain, have an adequate supply to meet their varying requirements under varying conditions of nutritional state, is indicated in Fig. 5.71. In (a) we envisage a condition in which the blood-sugar has risen, through absorption of a meal; insulin is released through a direct response of the β-cells of the pancreas and reflexly through the brain, and it promotes the passage of glucose into, say, muscle cells where it is converted to glycogen, and into fat cells where fat is synthesized. In the liver it inhibits gluconeogenesis and stimulates synthesis of glycogen. The secretion of glucagon by the a-cells of the pancreas is inhibited by hyperglycaemia. Hyperglycaemia acts on the brain to produce, not only a hormonal response, but also a direct neural action on the liver, evoking a parasympathetically mediated inhibition of any existing adrenergic liver activity (p. 527).

Response to Hypoglycaemia

In Fig. 5.71b the response to hypoglycaemia is shown. During prolonged fasting the corticosteroids exert a prominent influence, diverting energy-metabolism to the utilization of non-glucose substrates, whilst the supply of glucose is sustained by gluconeogenesis, made possible by the breakdown of muscle proteins and fats to provide substrate for the synthesis (Fig. 5.71c). The secretion of insulin is suppressed, both

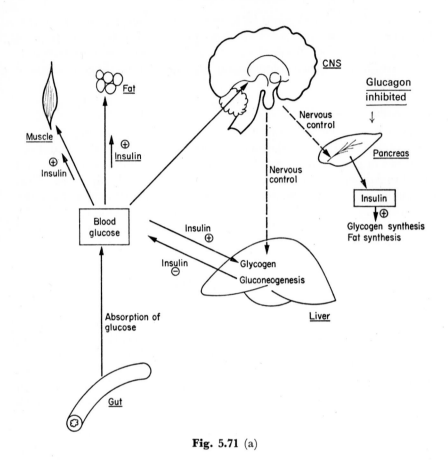

Fig. 5.71 (a)

by central nervous action and direct action on the β-cells of the pancreas, and the dominant hormones now become adrenaline and glucagon acting synergistically at the various sites.

Insulin Excess and Deficiency

In Fig. 5.72 the main consequences of insulin excess and insulin deficiency are summarized. It will be deduced from the category of effects of insulin-deficiency, as in diabetes, that not only will blood-sugar rise through excessive gluconeogenesis and defective cellular utilization, but also the formation of the ketone-bodies, such as acetone, is promoted, leading to their accumulation in the blood, whilst the accelerated breakdown of protein, in gluconeogenesis, can lead to wasting and defective growth.

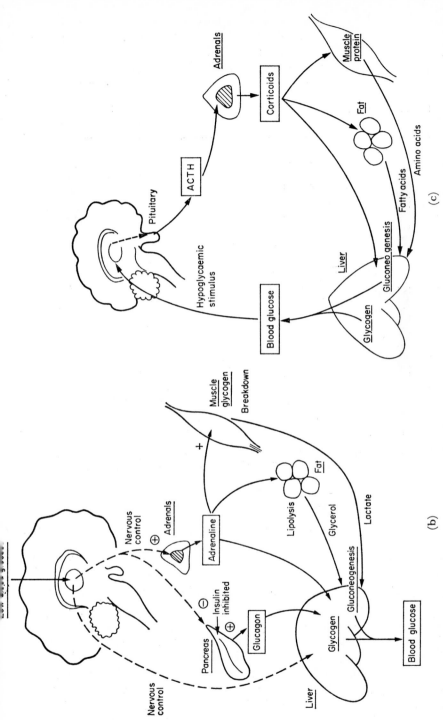

Fig. 5.71. The endocrine control of glucose metabolism. (a) The response to excess carbohydrate intake after a meal showing the formation of glycogen. (b) The response to hypoglycaemia when the blood sugar is low. (c) The response to prolonged fasting showing the alternative sources of carbohydrate from fats and proteins. (After Clegg and Clegg, *Hormones, Cells and Organisms*. Heinemann.)

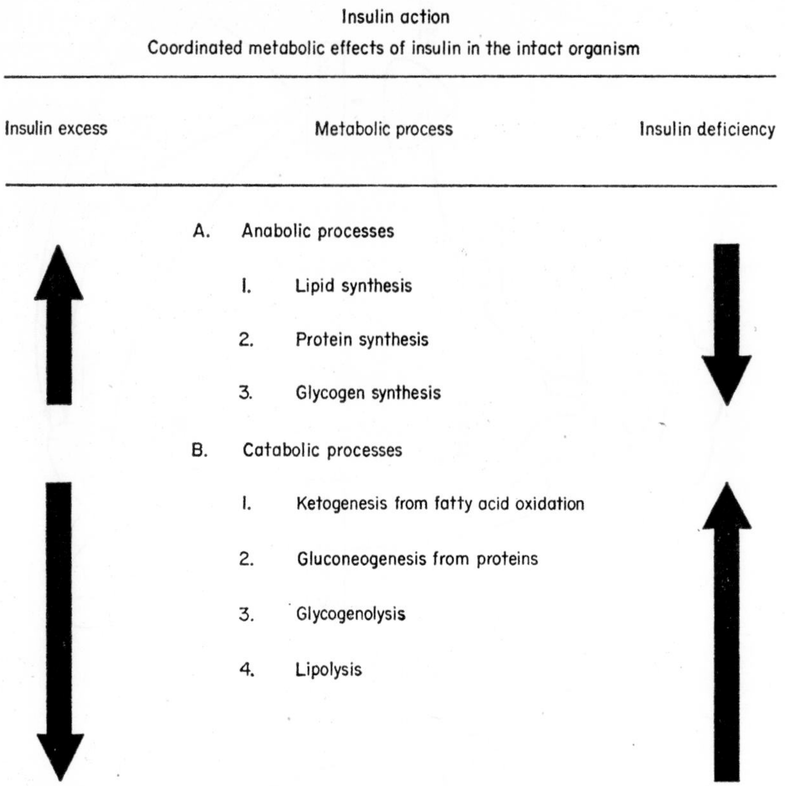

Insulin action

Coordinated metabolic effects of insulin in the intact organism

Insulin excess	Metabolic process	Insulin deficiency

A. Anabolic processes

    I.   Lipid synthesis

    2.   Protein synthesis

    3.   Glycogen synthesis

B. Catabolic processes

    I.   Ketogenesis from fatty acid oxidation

    2.   Gluconeogenesis from proteins

    3.   Glycogenolysis

    4.   Lipolysis

Fig. 5.72. A summary of the main consequences of insulin excess and deficiency. (Fritz, In *Insulin Action*. Academic Press.)

Some Experimental Studies

Let us now proceed to fill out this general scheme by examining some of the experimental findings in detail.

Perfused Liver

The processes of glycogenolysis and gluconeogenesis may be studied experimentally by perfusing the rat's liver *in situ* by a technique developed by Mortimore (1961). Blood from a reservoir is pumped into the animal's portal vein and collected from a cannula inserted into the vena cava from an opening in the right atrium, retrograde leakage of this artificial supply of blood being prevented by ligaturing the inferior vena cava between the kidney and the liver. The inflowing blood can be supplied with ^{14}C-labelled lactate, or amino acid, and

the process of gluconeogenesis may be measured by the amount of
^{14}C-glucose produced, whilst glycogenolysis is measured by the total
output of glucose.

Availability of Substrate. Figure 5.73 shows that the rate of
gluconeogenesis is affected by the availability of substrate, in this case
of amino acid. The fact that availability of substrate is a critical factor
means that any influence that alters the concentrations of amino acids,
glycerol, etc. in the blood will influence hepatic gluconeogenesis; thus
the glucocorticoids of the adrenal cortex increase release of amino

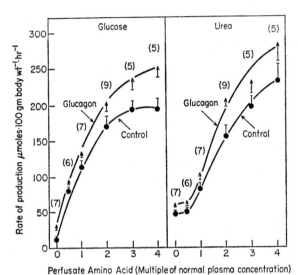

Fig. 5.73. The glucose and urea production of the perfused rat liver, as a function of
the amino acid concentration in the perfusate. The effect of 4×10^{-9} M glucagon
on these processes is shown by the upper curves. The livers were from fasted rats.
(Exton *et al.*, *Rec. Prog. Hormone Res.*)

acids from tissues, and thereby favour gluconeogenesis; insulin, which
favours uptake of amino acids from blood and incorporation into
tissue proteins (Wool and Krahl, 1959), thus antagonizes gluconeogenesis through this mechanism, in addition to its direct action on the
hepatic cells. In the early phases of starvation the level of amino acids
in the blood rises, and this activates gluconeogenesis.

Hormonal Effects. As indicated above, the hormones acting
directly on the liver are glucagon, insulin, catecholamines and corticosteroids. The figure shows the accelerating effects of glucagon on the
rate of gluconeogenesis. The level of glucagon in hepatic portal blood
increases during hypoglycaemia and decreases with hyperglycaemia,

so that glucagon represents the hormone of "glucose need", and its action, as studied in the perfused liver preparation, is twofold, increasing both gluconeogenesis and glycogenolysis. The relative effects of glucagon, adrenaline and noradrenaline are shown in Table IX, the glucose output by the perfused liver representing, essentially, glycogenolysis, and the ^{14}C-labelled glucose representing gluconeogenesis.

TABLE IX

Effects of hormones on glucose output, glucose synthesis and cAMP level of perfused rat liver (Exton *et al.*, 1970)

	Glucose output (μmoles/g/hr)	Glucose synthesis (Arbitrary units)	Cyclic AMP (μmoles/g)
Control	69	20	0·5
5.10^{-10} Glucagon	147	34	1·3
1.10^{-8} Glucagon	162	41	18·0
1.10^{-7} Adrenaline	110	34	1·1
2.10^{-8} Noradrenaline	196	29	0·6

Cyclic AMP. It will be recalled that the actions of many hormones are brought about through the intervention of the "second messenger", cyclic adenosine monophosphate (cAMP). Table IX shows that the level of cAMP in the perfused liver increased strikingly with glucagon. In order to achieve a significant effect of adrenaline on glucose synthesis and cAMP level, unphysiological levels had to be employed, the concentrations in blood following adrenergic stimulation being of the order of 10^{-9} to 10^{-8} M and thus too low to affect gluconeogenesis by an action of the catecholamine on the liver directly.

Adrenaline and Liver. The significance of adrenaline in the normal control of liver glycogenolysis was also examined by Sokal *et al.* (1964) and they showed that in the perfused isolated liver glucagon was active at a concentration of 0·4 μg/litre compared with 140 μg/litre for adrenaline, this latter concentration being far greater than natural levels. Thus the effects of adrenaline on glycogenolysis are limited to peripheral tissues, such as skeletal muscle, where it is a potent glycogenolytic agent (Sokal and Sarcione, 1959).

Insulin. The opposite effects of insulin on the liver may be demonstrated best in a negative fashion, i.e. by reducing the level of insulin by treatment with insulin-antibody, or by treatment of the animal with alloxan, which specifically destroys the β-cells of the pancreas. Under these conditions there is an increase in glycogenolysis and gluconeogenesis, and these are accompanied by a high cAMP which returns to normal on administration of insulin. Thus glucose production seems to be controlled by a continuous interaction between insulin, on the one hand, and glucagon and adrenaline on the other, acting on the systems synthesizing and degrading cAMP in the liver.

Central Control of Liver

In 1854 Claude Bernard discovered that puncture of the floor of the IVth ventricle caused hyperglycaemia, with excretion of glucose in the urine. Subsequent studies have shown that the critical sites in the brain exerting an influence over the blood-glucose are in the hypothalamus; thus Shimazu *et al.* (1966) showed that, when the ventromedial hypothalamus was stimulated, the concentration of glucose in the blood rose by some 60 per cent, with a fall in the liver-glycogen content; stimulation of the lateral hypothalamus caused a fall of some 20 per cent in blood-glucose. The ventromedial hypothalamus may be regarded as a sympathetic centre, and the lateral region a parasympathetic centre, so that when the splanchnic nerve was stimulated the same effects on liver activity were obtained, as those of ventromedial stimulation. This was shown by an increase in activity of key enzymes in glycogenolysis and gluconeogenesis, such as glycogen phosphorylase and glucose-6-phosphatase. Figure 5.74 shows the large increase in phosphorylase activity and the absence of effect of vagal stimulation; however, when both nerves were stimulated together, the effects of sympathetic stimulation were inhibited. The phosphorylase of liver is partly in an active and partly in an inactive form; adrenergic stimulation did not affect the total content, so that its effect was

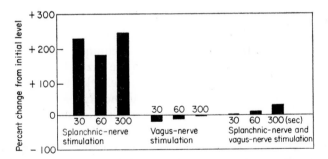

Fig. 5.74. Effect of electrical stimulation of the splanchnic nerve, the vagus nerve, or both nerves simultaneously on the activity of phosphorylase in rabbit liver. In each animal, portions of the liver were removed serially, 30 sec, 1 min and 5 min after the onset of nerve stimulation (Shimazu and Amakawa, *Biochim. biophys. Acta*)

exerted by converting the inactive to the active form, presumably by activation of a specific kinase (Vol. 2). That the effects were not exerted through the adrenal or pancreatic hormones was shown by the failure of adrenalectomy and pancreatectomy to influence the result.

Adipose Tissue

Control by Insulin

The utilization of fat is a vital element in homeostasis of the blood-sugar in animals that normally eat irregularly, as with the carnivores and with man before agriculture was developed. Insulin plays a dominant role in controlling the fat reserves, ensuring that, when the animal is replete, the glucose ingested is stored. It does this by stimulating the appropriate enzymes for glycogenesis and inhibiting the mobilization of glucose through lipolysis, an inhibition that is released during the hypoglycaemia of starvation. It is probable that there is another balance, involving mainly catecholamines and insulin, controlling the cAMP content of adipose tissue, and through that, the lipase activity and output of free fatty acids.

Isolated Fat-Pad. Experimentally fatty tissue is commonly studied in the form of the isolated epididymal fat-pad of the rat; this is a thin piece of tissue, and so adequate oxygenation in an artificial medium is practicable, whilst diffusion into and out of the cells from the medium may be measured quantitatively by assessments of the extracellular space and alterations in the total content of the tissue. Using this technique, Crofford and Renold (1965) showed that the fat-cell was an "insulin responsive cell", in the sense that insulin promoted the influx of glucose. Its metabolic effects on the adipose tissue included increased utilization of glucose, with increased conversion to glyceride glycerol, total fatty acids and glycogen; increased protein synthesis, and inhibition of lipolysis activated by adrenaline and other agents.

Isolated Fat Cells. An alternative technique was developed by Rodbell (1964) who treated fat tissue with the enzyme collagenase, which disrupts the connective tissue linking the cells to each other; the individual fat cells, of some 50–100 μ diameter, could be prepared as a suspension in a nutrient medium and their synthetic and lipolytic activities studied. In this way it was shown that adrenaline was lipolytic, causing fatty acids and glycerol to be released into the suspending medium, whilst insulin favoured the synthesis of fat from glucose.

ACTH. It is interesting that the adrenocorticotrophic hormone, whose primary physiological function is to cause release of steroid hormones from the adrenal cortex, had a direct action on the fat cells,

promoting breakdown of fat, and the same was true of thyroid stimulating hormone, TSH. As we shall see, ACTH also stimulates insulin
release, acting probably on the adenylcyclase system (p. 544), so that
injections of ACTH lower the blood-sugar in both intact and adrenalectomized animals (Genuth and Lebovitz, 1965).

Accumulation of cAMP

When the adenylcyclase activities of the fat cells were studied it was
clear that the lipolytic hormones, adrenaline, ACTH, glucagon, LH
and prolactin, all increased accumulation of cAMP (Butcher *et al.*,
1968), whilst the cell membranes prepared after disruption of the cells,
exhibited cyclase activity that was favoured by these hormones (Birnbaumer and Rodbell, 1969). Figure 5.75 shows the importance of
inhibiting the breakdown of cAMP by phosphodiesterase when
assessing the effects of a hormone; it will be seen that adrenaline
produces, by itself, a very small increase in cAMP in isolated liver
cells, whilst in the presence of caffeine the accumulation is some
tenfold.

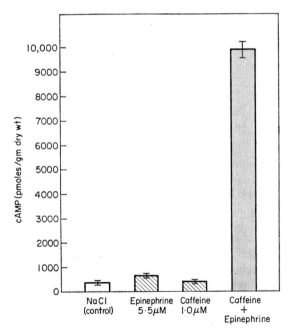

Fig. 5.75. Illustrating the importance of inhibiting phodiesterase with caffeine
for demonstrating increased cAMP synthesis by isolated fat cells in response to
epinephrine (adrenaline). (Butcher *et al.*, *J. biol. Chem.*)

Insulin-Glucagon Antagonism. Insulin has the opposite effects of glucagon and catecholamines, inhibiting lipolysis; according to Butcher *et al.* (1968), when isolated adipose cells were incubated with adrenaline, or adrenaline plus caffeine, there was an increase in cAMP accumulation (Fig. 5.76), and this was decreased when insulin was added; this was not due to an increased escape of cAMP into the medium, so that it seemed that the suppression of the lipolytic action of epinephrine was associated with a suppression of the formation of cAMP. This concept of glucagon, on the one hand, and insulin, on

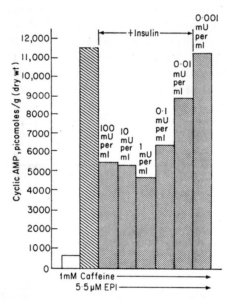

Fig. 5.76. Effect of various concentrations of insulin on cylic AMP concentration in fat cells from the rat. Cells were incubated with 1 mM caffeine with no adrenaline (EPI) in the first clear column and then with 5·5 μM adrenaline for the remaining columns, with variable amounts of insulin, as indicated. (Butcher *et al.*, *J. biol. Chem.*)

the other, controlling metabolic activity through the level of cAMP in the effector cells is well illustrated by Fig. 5.77 which shows the output of glucose (upper curve) and cAMP (lower curve) from a perfused liver, using a re-circulating medium. Glucagon infusion was maintained throughout, and gave rise to steadily increasing outputs of cAMP and glucose; when insulin was added to the circulating medium the concentration of glucose in the effluent fell together with that of cAMP.

Insulin and Adenylcyclase. The question arises as to whether insulin has a direct inhibitory action on the adenylcyclase activity of

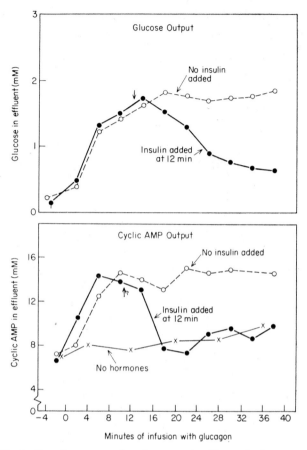

Fig. 5.77. Illustrating the antagonism between insulin and glucagon when their effects on output of glucose and CAMP from the perfused liver are studied. Infusion of glucagon was maintained, as indicated on the abscissa. Note the pronounced fall in output when insulin infusion was imposed on the glucagon infusion. (Park *et al.*, *Diabetes*).

the target-tissue cell membrane, or whether its effects are less direct, preventing, say, the activation due to glucagon and other activators. It is not possible yet to give an unequivocal answer to these questions, but recent work of Cuatrecasas (1969, 1972) suggests that the actions of insulin may well be closely linked with its antagonism to the stimulating activities of glucagon and adrenaline on the adenylcyclase of the cell membrane. Thus, when liver and fat-cell membranes were prepared from tissue-homogenates, their basal adenylcyclase activity was unaffected by insulin, but when this was accelerated by adrenaline, glucagon or ACTH, insulin, in concentrations that fell within the physiological range $(3.10^{-11}$ M), reversed these actions. If this is, indeed, the manner in which insulin competes with glucagon, etc., then the action of cAMP or of its more lipid soluble analogue, DBcAMP (added to the fat cells), should not be affected by insulin; and this is, indeed, what Hepp *et al.* (1969) found.

Endogenous vs. Exogenous cAMP. The situation is confused, however, by the finding of Solomon *et al.* (1970) that, when low concentrations of insulin are employed $(1\cdot7 \times 10^{-11}$ M), the lipolysis of isolated fat cells, induced by caffeine, was blocked by insulin, although much higher concentrations did not. These authors emphasized the very great effectiveness of caffeine in promoting lipolysis; this inhibits the enzyme phosphodiesterase that normally destroys cAMP in the cell (Vol. 2), so that it was suggested that the cAMP produced by the fat cell might be more effective than extraneous cAMP.

Facilitation of Phosphodiesterase. An alternate hypothesis is that insulin prevents the accumulation of cAMP in the effector cells, not by inhibiting adenylcyclase but by facilitating the action of phosphodiesterase, thereby increasing the rate of destruction. Evidence in favour of this was provided by Loten and Sneyd (1970) who made homogenates of fat-pads and isolated fat cells after they had been incubated with insulin; a significant increase in phosphodiesterase activity was observed, although there was no effect if insulin was added directly to the homogenate so that, as in other experiments involving cAMP, the agents must act on the intact cell, or at any rate the cell with its membrane reasonably whole.* The effect was not large, but as the formation of cAMP is slow whilst diesterase activity is rapid, a small slowing of the latter could have a large effect.

Effects of Hormones on Glucose and Amino Acid Transport

Facilitation by Insulin

The pioneering studies of Levine and Goldstein and of Park and his collaborators indicated that, in the presence of insulin, the rate of penetration of glucose into the cells of such tissues as skeletal muscle was so rapid that it was governed by the rate of utilization; this, rate, moreover, is sufficiently high that the concentration of glucose in most cells is very small. In the absence of insulin the penetration is

---

* Rodbell (1967) described many hormonal effects on the fat cell ghost, i.e. on the cell that had lost most of its contents but retained a virtually intact membrane, incorporated in which is the adenylcyclase of the cell (Vol. 2).

much slower so that it was concluded that at least one factor in the hypoglycaemia of insulin action was the accelerated penetration of glucose into the cells of the body. As indicated earlier, the liver and the brain, however, were unaffected; in the former case penetration is very rapid indeed (Cahill *et al.*, 1958) whilst in the latter, access to the metabolizing cells is governed by two barriers, the blood-brain barrier and the cell membranes of the metabolizing cells (Ch. 6).

Anaerobiosis. Besides insulin, anaerobiosis and muscular activity will increase cellular uptake of glucose. This is physiologically signifi- cant since, in anaerobiosis the uptake of sugar by the cell becomes more important and it is found that the effectiveness of a given dose of insulin is enhanced, thereby favouring uptake of glucose by the cells that require it, while avoiding useless consumption by well oxygenated or quiescent tissue. The effects of muscular activity were shown by Park *et al.*, who produced a fivefold increase in rate of uptake by increasing the work-load of a perfused heart.

Amino Acids. The rate of uptake of amino acids is also increased; thus Wool *et al.* (1965) were able to show that insulin increased the accumulation of amino acids in the rat heart. They inhibited incor- poration of the amino acids into protein with puromycin, so that the effect of insulin was not to promote incorporation into the cell proteins, an effect that would accelerate penetration by promoting a large con- centration gradient across the cell membrane. When protein synthesis is allowed to proceed, insulin has, indeed, a direct action on this, in addition to its accelerating action on transport (Manchester, 1972).

Fat Cells. Like the muscle cell, the fat cell has a very low internal concentration of glucose, and the rate-limiting factor for utilization seems to be the rate of transport into the cell, which is reduced in the absence of insulin and favoured by adding the hormone (Crofford and Renold, 1965). Using isolated fat cell ghosts, Rodbell (1967) showed that the acceleration of penetration of sugars into the cell caused by insulin was independent of any action on the adenylcyclase system, or accumu- lation of cAMP.

Adrenaline

This hormone generally has opposite effects to those of insulin, and it seems that a factor in the *adrenaline hyperglycaemia*, provoked by infusions of this hormone, is an inhibition of uptake by skeletal muscle, although, according to Brody and McNeill (1970) the effect is complex, depending on the level of glycogen in the cells and the rate of glycogen synthesis.

Proinsulin

Steiner and Oyer (1967) extracted an insulin with a higher molecular weight than that which had previously been called insulin, and called it proinsulin, considering it to represent a precursor-form to insulin proper. Amino-acid sequence analysis showed it to contain an extra chain of 33 amino acids joining the terminal free carboxy-group of alanine of the B-chain with the terminal free amino-group of glycine on the A-chain (Fig. 5.78), this chain being called the *connecting peptide*. Amino acids were incorporated into the proinsulin before insulin, suggesting its precursor status. There is not agreement as to whether the insulin, determined in blood by radioimmunoassay, contains any proinsulin (Meade *et al.*, 1965) nor yet whether proinsulin can exert a direct action on a tissue before the tissue has split off the connecting peptide to produce "single component insulin" (Shaw and Chance, 1968).

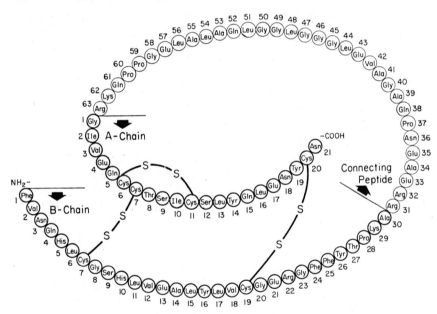

Fig. 5.78. The amino-acid sequence of porcine proinsulin. (Chance, *Diabetes.*)

Glucocorticoid Hormones

The cortical steroid hormones influencing carbohydrate and fat metabolism, notably cortisol and corticosterone, are described as glucocorticoids. They are secreted during prolonged stress, such as in fasting, and their effect is to provoke breakdown of protein and fat to metabolites that can be utilized in gluconeogenesis; this process of gluconeogenesis is promoted by a direct facilitatory action of the hormone on the hepatic synthesis of glucose (Long *et al.*, 1940), and also by an inhibition of the utilization of glucose (Ingle, 1942) which manifests itself as an inhibition of phosphorylation of glucose within the cell. The increased glucose production evoked by corticosteroids was accounted for approximately by the concomitant production of urea, i.e. it was from amino acids, and these last were derived mainly from the non-hepatic tissues.

Effect on Uptake of Glucose

The inhibition of utilization of glucose could be the result of a direct inhibitory action of the hormones on some stage in the metabolic conversion of glucose, e.g. phosphorylation to glucose-6-phosphate; alternatively, it could result from a failure of glucose to penetrate the metabolizing cells. This latter hypothesis has been supported by the arguments and experimental studies of Munck (see, e.g. Munck, 1971). The difficulty in accepting the hypothesis lay in the failure to observe any significant inhibition of penetration of glucose into muscle cells, and this seems to be well established; nevertheless, in some other tissues, such as thymus, and adipose tissue, uptake of glucose is inhibited by cortical hormones, either *in vivo* or *in vitro*, the effects being delayed by one to two hours. Similar effects were found in skin (Overell *et al.*, 1960). The inhibition of glucose-uptake occurs in intact cells, but not in damaged, so that the idea that inhibition of uptake was the consequence of an inhibition of the metabolic process of utilization is incorrect. (Thus it could be argued that the rate of uptake was governed by the rate of utilization, which created the necessary concentration gradient.)

Inhibition of Protein Synthesis

Accompanying the inhibition of the uptake and utilization of glucose, there is a decrease in protein synthesis (Morita and Munck, 1964). If this inhibition of protein synthesis is a consequence of the fall in glucose utilization, then we have a unifying hypothesis with which to describe many of the diverse actions of the corticosteroids. Thus the primary attack is on glucose utilization; the consequence is the failure to synthesize protein together with the breakdown of protein within the responsive cells. Thus the breakdown of protein—catabolism—can be viewed as the consequence of the attack on glucose-entry into many cells of the body, the amino acids made available being carried to the liver to be converted to glucose. The action of corticoids is not a straightforward inhibition, or antagonism, of insulin action, since their effects, say, on glucose-uptake by adipose tissue are demonstrable in tissue from alloxan-diabetic animals; furthermore, insulin apparently does not favour penetration of glucose into thymus cells, whilst corticoids inhibit this.

Production of a Specific Protein

Studies on RNA and protein synthesis indicate that the mode of action of the corticoids, as in other target organs (Vol. 2), is through binding to a receptor and passage into the nucleus where a specific protein is synthesized that causes decreased glucose transport. The processes leading to the synthesis of the specific protein take probably about 15 min, and the greater time-lag required to measure the catabolic effects, i.e. breakdown of protein and fat, is presumably due to the necessity for the glucose-lack within the cell to manifest itself.

Triggering Action

As Munck emphasizes, the amounts of glucose spared to the fasting animal by this inhibition in certain restricted tissues is small, and their significance is in the secondary effects of the glucose-lack, namely breakdown of protein and fat to give amino acids and other substrates that can be used by the liver and kidneys in gluconeogenesis. The fatty acids, moreover, may well inhibit uptake of glucose by muscle (Randle *et al.* 1963). Thus the peripheral effects of the corticoids are *triggering* actions, their consequences being the important feature. Undoubtedly the liver itself is a primary target for the hormones, but the stimulation of gluconeogenesis is facilitated by the availability of substrate resulting from the peripheral actions.

Glucocorticoid and Glucagon

Although glucagon stimulates gluconeogenesis by the livers of normal rats, it does not do so in starved adrenalectomized animals, presumably because the cooperation or "permission" of adrenal corticoids is necessary; Friedman *et al.* (1967) showed that the formation of glucose from lactate in such rats could be restored by treatment with dexamethasone 30 min before killing. Since glucagon acts through adenylcyclase, whilst it is very doubtful whether the cortical hormones do, it is likely that the glucocorticoids reduce, in some way, the sensitivity of the cell to cAMP.

Glucagon Secretion. Treatment of human subjects with dexamethasone, a synthetic glucocorticoid, caused a 40 per cent rise in the basal level of glucagon in the blood; this was probably the result of a direct action on the α-cells of the pancreas, since the corticoid also increased the maximal response to infusions of the amino acid, alanine, which, like some other amino acids, stimulates secretion of glucagon (Wise *et al.*, 1973).

The Stimuli to Hormonal Release

The three hormones that dominate the situation with respect to the homeostasis of the blood-sugar are insulin, on the one hand, and glucagon and adrenaline on the other. Stimuli, such as hyperglycaemia, that evoke the secretion of insulin from the β-cells may be expected to inhibit the secretion of glucagon from the a-cells of the pancreas, and of adrenaline from the chromaffine cells of the adrenal cortex. The adrenocorticotrophic hormone, ACTH, and through this the glucocorticoid hormones, apparently play a permissive role, favouring the gluconeogenetic mechanism. Because insulin, in man and carnivores, occupies a dominant role in this homeostasis, we shall emphasize the effects of various changes in the animal's blood composition on the secretion of this hormone, remembering, however, that there is usually a reciprocal arrangement of activation and inhibition of release of the individual hormones.

The Glycaemic Stimulus to Insulin Release

The threshold level for activating insulin secretion is, according to Dean and Matthews, about 4 mM, or some 72 mg/100 ml plasma, the stimulus for half-maximal effect being 9 mM or 162 mg/100 ml. We have seen (Vol. 2) that the effects are accompanied by a depolarization of the β-cells. It is doubtful whether glucose, itself, constitutes the stimulus for activating secretion, since this may be blocked by mannoheptulose, which interferes with the phosphorylation of glucose within the cell (Coore *et al.*, 1963); thus an intermediate in glucose metabolism is probably the stimulus.*

Hypoglycaemic Stimulus to Glucagon Release

Hypoglycaemia causes release of glucagon; this is best demonstrated by analysis of the venous effluent from the pancreas, rather than by analysing the blood from a peripheral vein, owing to the technical difficulties of estimating the hormone. The upper curve of Fig. 5.79, from the work of Ohneda *et al.* (1969), shows the rise in the blood

---

* Mannoheptulose causes a diabetic response, in the sense that blood-sugar is raised; the rise in blood-glucose is not due to glycogenolysis but to increased gluconeogenesis, presumably through diminished secretion of insulin. Adrenalectomy prevents the hyperglycaemic response, which is restored by hydrocortisone, a hormone that favours gluconeogenesis (Simon *et al.*, 1962).

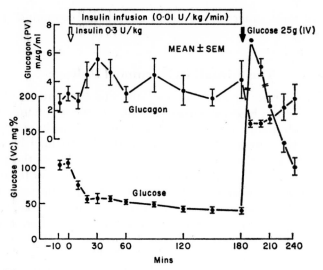

Fig. 5.79. The upper curve shows the rise in the concentration of glucagon in the pancreatic venous blood of conscious dogs in response to hypoglycaemia induced by insulin. The lower curve shows the plasma glucose level in the inferior vena cava. (Ohneda *et al.*, *Diabetes*.)

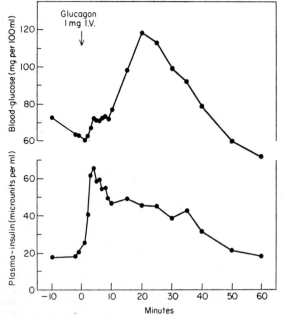

Fig. 5.80. Effect of 1 mg glucagon intravenously on venous glucose and insulin concentrations in a healthy young adult. (Samols *et al.*, *Lancet*.)

concentration of glucagon during the hypoglycaemia induced by insulin, and the fall when hyperglycaemia was induced by an intravenous dose of glucose.

Effect of Glucagon on Insulin Secretion

The hyperglycaemia, due to an injection of glucagon, acts as a stimulus to insulin secretion; nevertheless, glucagon, itself, appears to act directly on the β-cells; thus, Fig. 5.80 shows that the concentration of insulin in the blood rises rapidly on injecting glucagon in man, the maximum being reached within 10 min, whereas the maximum blood-concentration of glucose is reached much later; in fact, the rise in insulin occurs before there has been a significant hyperglycaemia.*

Effect of Adrenaline

Adrenaline is liberated during hypoglycaemia (p. 546) and stimulates glycogenolysis in liver and peripheral tissues; we might expect an inhibitory action of this hormone on insulin secretion, and in fact Porte et al. (1966) found that infusion of adrenaline into man did not raise the insulin level, although the concomitant hyperglycaemia, alone, would certainly have done so. When hyperglycaemia was induced by exogenous glucose, or glucagon, the expected secretion of insulin was inhibited by adrenaline.

Other Hormones

The digestive hormones secretin, cholecystokinin-pancreozymin (CCK-PZ), and gastrin, share with glucagon the power to stimulate the β-cells of the pancreas to secrete insulin. When injected into the portal blood they give rise to a brief but rapid rise in concentration of insulin in the pancreaticoduodenal venous plasma. The sharing of the action of glucagon by secretin is understandable in view of the similar amino-acid sequences of these polypeptide hormones (p. 345), and like glucagon, secretin has a lipolytic action on the epididymal fat-pad (Lazarus et al., 1968). Interestingly CCK-PZ also provokes the secretion of glucagon; this is illustrated by Fig. 5.81, which shows the rises in glucose, insulin and glucagon concentrations in the blood following an injection of CCK-PZ. It will be seen that the secretion of glucagon precedes the hyperglycaemia, and is probably the cause of this; the effect on insulin secretion is probably not through the secretion of glucagon (Allan and Tepperman, 1969).

* The release of insulin from the perfused liver in response to glucagon requires the potentiating effect of glucose, so that if this is removed from the medium in the perfused liver, there is no secretion. Tolbutamide (p. 545) will also act as the potentiator (Curry, 1970).

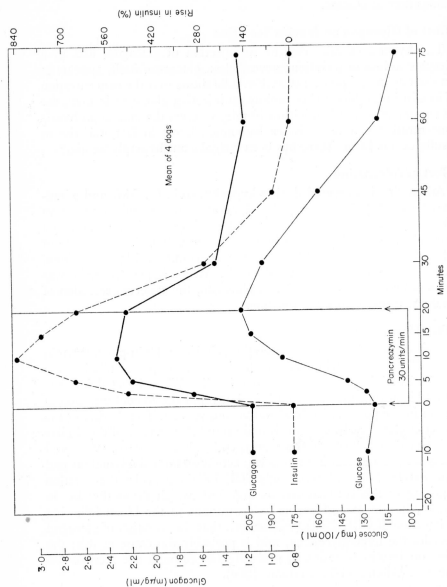

Fig. 5.81. The effect of endoportal infusion of pancreozymin (CCK—PZ) on the levels of insulin and glucagon in pancreatic venous plasma and on the arterial plasma levels of glucose. Note that secretion of glucagon precedes the hyperglycaemia. (Unger *et al.*, *J. clin. Invest.*)

The "Entero-Insular Axis". It would seem that the three en-zymes, glucagon, secretin and CCK-PZ act by stimulating adenyl cyclase in the β-cells of the pancreas, since their effects are potentiated by the inhibitor of phosphodiesterase, aminophylline (the ethylenedi-amine derivative of theophylline). According to Unger *et al.* (1967), this manifestation of an "entero-insular axis" is a development that prevents the high substrate concentrations that would appear in the blood following the ingestion of large meals, were the insulin res-ponse entirely a function of the arterial substrate concentration; thus potent stimulators for CCK-PZ secretion are amino acids, which also stimulate insulin and glucagon secretion (Boyns *et al.*, 1966).

Gastric Secretion

A further example of the close relation between metabolism, as affected by insulin, and digestion, is shown by the well known gastric response to hypoglycaemia; thus injection of insulin to give hypoglycae-mia causes secretion of acid and pepsin by the stomach and an increased flow of bile, effects that are abolished by cutting the vagi and are medi-ated by the hypoglycaemia. Insulin will also directly inhibit gastric acid secretion and gastric motility by an action on the target organs (Herrera *et al.*, 1967; Tsukamoto *et al.*, 1967). Glucagon will also inhibit gastric secretion and motility, an effect not due to the accompanying hyper-glycaemia.*

Amino Acids

The effect of amino acids is to promote secretion of insulin; the most effective stimulus, according to Fajans *et al.* (1967), is a mixture of ten essential amino acids, although arginine alone is highly effective; the effect may be obtained experimentally by intravenous infusions of amino acids or by feeding a heavy meat meal. The significance of this secretion is evident when it is appreciated that insulin promotes protein synthesis (Sinex *et al.*, 1952; Manchester, 1972), acting directly on the protein synthetic machinery (Wool and Munro, 1963) and also favouring transport into the cell (Scharff and Wool, 1965); thus the response is part of the anabolic or storage syndrome. At the same time, insulin suppresses gluconeogenesis, an important element of which is the conversion of amino acids, principally alanine, into

---

* The physiological significance of the actions of these digestive hormones on release of insulin may be questioned; thus Boyns *et al.* (1966) found that, in humans, intraduodenal injections of acid, which provoke the secretion of secretin, failed to cause secretion of insulin. Rehfeld and Stadel (1973) obtained a rise in blood-insulin on giving a heavy protein meal, the rise being preceded by a rise in blood-gastrin; these authors think that the effects of gastrin on insulin secretion might be significant after a heavy protein meal.

glucose. The efficacy of a reduced supply of amino acids to the liver, through the promotion of protein synthesis, combined with inhibition of amino-acid gluconeogenesis, makes the anti-gluconeogenetic action of insulin very powerful.

Glucose and Amino Acids Compared. The analogy between glucose and amino acids, as stimulants and inhibitors of release of insulin, is illustrated by Fig. 5.82. According to Fajans *et al.* the amino-acid phenomena may have preceded those of glucose in man, before the development of agriculture, some 8–10,000 years ago, when he was mainly a hunter and fisher living principally on protein and fat with little carbohydrate. Whether the fact that the toadfish releases insulin only in response to amino acids, and not to glucose, is of evolutionary significance remains to be shown.

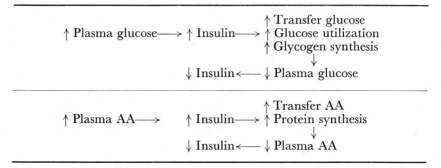

Fig. 5.82. A comparison of the ability of glucose and amino acids to stimulate or inhibit the release of insulin. (Fajans *et al.*, *Rec. Prog. Hormone Res.*)

Glucagon and Amino Acids. Glucagon is involved in amino acid homeostasis, causing a fall in the level in the blood (Curry and Beaton, 1958), mainly through promoting uptake and conversion to glucose by the liver (Shoemaker, 1969). Thus Mallette *et al.* (1967) perfused the fasted rat's liver with an artificial fluid containing serum albumin; the production of glucose was 67 μmoles/100 g.wt/hr; when amino acids were added this rose to 163 μmoles, and if glucagon was added this rose to 200 μmoles/hr; the production of urea showed parallel changes. Labelling of the amino acid, e.g. alanine, with ^{14}C, showed that the carbon-skeleton of the amino acid was being utilized in the gluconeogenesis. The release of glucagon from the pancreas in response to the amino-acid stimulus was demonstrated by Ohneda *et al.* (1968), who estimated the concentration of the hormone in the pancreatico-duodenal vein and demonstrated an increase in response to the infusion of a mixture of ten amino acids; the concentrations of insulin and

CCK-PZ also rose. They concluded that an important function of glucagon might be to prevent the hypoglycaemia that could otherwise result when large amounts of amino acids were absorbed, a hypo-glycaemia that would be provoked by the secretion of insulin in response to the same stimulus. The very close relations between glucose and amino acid metabolism are emphasized by the fact that intravenous glucose inhibited the secretion of glucagon provoked by amino acids (Ohneda *et al.*, 1969).

Fatty Acids

The effects of fatty acids in the blood are to stimulate lipogenesis, and thus to provoke secretion of insulin. As in so many experimental studies, of course, the problem is to separate a direct action of the

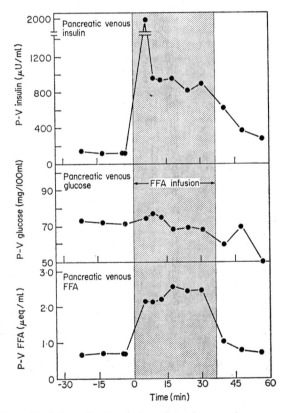

Fig. 5.83. Effect of infusion of sodium oleate into the superior pancreaticoduodenal artery on pacreatic venous free fatty acids (FFA), glucose and insulin. (Crespin *et al.*, *J. clin. Invest.*)

metabolite from that of the consequent hyperglycaemia that occurs during conversion to glucose; this, of course, causes insulin secretion. Seyffert and Madison (1967) described a decrease in hepatic glucose output and peripheral utilization during infusion of fatty acids in dogs, and this could be attributed to an increased insulin secretion. To avoid this difficulty, Crespin *et al.* (1973) injected the fatty acids directly into the pancreatic artery at rates that gave no increase in the level in the general circulation; as Fig. 5.83 shows, the rise in pancreatic

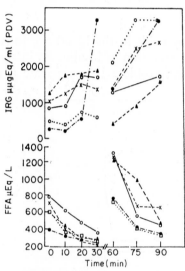

Fig. 5.84. Changes in pancreatic duodenal venous (PDV) plasma glucagon concentrations (IRG) and arterial plasma free fatty acid levels (FFA). On the left the fall in FFA was induced by injection/infusion of nicotinic acid; on the right the fall in plasma FFA followed cessation of triglyceride emulsion–heparin infusion. (Luyckx and Lefebvre, *Proc. Soc. exp Biol. Med. N.Y.*)

fatty acids is accompanied by a sharp rise in pancreatic venous insulin. The secretion of insulin, like so many of the responses to alterations in blood-parameters, was accompanied by an opposite effect on secretion of glucagon, a high level of fatty acids suppressing the secretion of the catabolic hormone in the same way that a hyperglycaemia does (Edwards and Taylor, 1970), whilst a diminution of the fatty acid content of blood-plasma, induced by nicotinic acid, caused an increase in the blood-glucagon (Fig. 5.84).

Adrenocorticotrophic Hormone

It has been known for over forty years that extracts of pituitary cause hypoglycaemia, and later studies have indicated that pure

ACTH, injected into animals, will lower the blood-sugar; this occurs in the intact and also the adrenalectomized animal (Genuth and Lebovitz, 1965), but not in animals made alloxan-diabetic (Miller and Krake, 1963). ACTH also causes a copious release of insulin from the isolated pancreas.

This effect of ACTH is potentiated by puromycin, the inhibitor of protein synthesis. Lebovitz and Poolen (1967) considered that the action of puromycin was the result of an accumulation of cAMP in the pancreatic cells, this being one of its effects (Appleman and Kemp, 1966), and this suggested that the release of insulin in response to ACTH was mediated by cAMP. They showed that aminophylline, an inhibitor of phosphodiesterase, potentiated the action of ACTH, increasing the amount of insulin released in response to a given dose of the hormone. It also augmented the release in response to glucagon and to glucose, so that it appears that the liberation of insulin from the β-cell is, indeed, mediated through the second messenger. Whether this release by ACTH has any physiological significance has been questioned, and it may simply reflect the fact that ACTH promotes synthesis of cAMP in a variety of cells, so that its effect is not confined to the adrenal cortex. According to Genuth and Lebovitz, the concentrations of ACTH required to elicit these extra-adrenal effects are higher than would be encountered normally.

Sulphonylureas

The number of the different chemical agents that will cause the β-cells of the pancreas to release insulin is remarkable, including as it does glucose, amino acids, fatty acids, and several polypeptide hormones; an additional class of compounds, quite unrelated chemically, is given by the sulphonylureas, characterized by tolbutamide

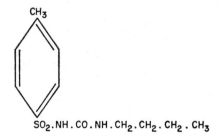

Tolbutamide

(N–p–tolyl sulphonyl)–N'– butyl carbamide)

Fig. 5.85. The structural formula of tolbutamide.

(Fig. 5.85). This causes the β-cells to release insulin and so, in the presence of an intact pancreas, it causes hypoglycaemia, without, however, affecting the responsiveness of the gland to the glycaemic stimulus (Seltzer *et al.*, 1965). In diabetes, when the pancreatic islets are degenerate, tolbutamide, by stimulating the residual β-cells to release insulin, can be an effective therapeutic agent.

The Response to Acute Hypoglycaemia

Secretion of Adrenaline

Cannon *et al.* (1924) showed that the adrenal medulla apparently secreted adrenaline in response to hypoglycaemia, an effect that was abolished by cutting the splanchnic nerves. That adrenaline was the agent liberated was proved conclusively by Armin and Grant (1959) who used, as a measure of adrenaline release, the cooling of the denervated rabbit's ear. Figure 5.86 shows the falls in ear-temperature and blood-sugar following injection of insulin (Curves a); the

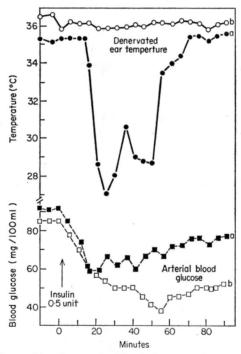

Fig. 5.86. The effects of insulin on the blood-glucose and on the denervated ear-temperature in the conscious rabbit. (a) Filled symbols, intact animals; (b) open symbols, 8 days after excision of the left adrenal and denervation of the right adrenal. (Armin and Grant, *J. Physiol.*)

blood sugar returns towards normal in association with the fall in ear-temperature, i.e. with the secretion of adrenaline. In the adrenal-ectomized animal (Curves b) ear-temperature is unaffected by the injection of insulin, whilst the blood-sugar falls to very low levels. The critical level for release of adrenaline was, in this case, some 70 mg/100 ml, whilst convulsions occurred when it had fallen to 10 mg/100 ml.

Emergency Reactions. This is an emergency reaction to hypo-glycaemia, and is not to be regarded as a part of the normal homeo-static mechanisms that hold the blood-sugar reasonably level; thus the response ceases well before the blood-sugar has returned to normal, and also it requires an unusual degree of hypoglycaemia to be evoked, being as low as 40 mg/100 ml in the animals studied by Himsworth (1968).

Hypothalamic Glucose-Lack

This central response to hypoglycaemia is probably due to lack of metabolizable sugar available to sensitive hypothalamic neurones, an effect that may be mimicked by loading an animal with a non-meta-bolizable sugar, such as 3-methylglucose. This sugar actually causes an increased concentration of glucose in the blood, as shown by Fig. 5.87, and this is partly due to the ability of 3-methylglucose to compete with glucose for entry into the cells of the tissue, so that utilization is decreased and the concentration rises. Under these conditions, however, the adrenal glands secrete adrenaline—an effect that is once again abolished by separating the glands from their nervous supply—and this secretion contributes to the hyperglycaemia. The effect of 3-methyl-glucose is presumably to block passage of glucose across the blood-brain barrier which, as we shall see, is of the facilitated carrier-mediated type. Thus, in spite of the hyperglycaemia, the brain is short of glucose and responds by activating the adrenal medulla.

2-Deoxyglucose. Associated with the activation of the adrenals is an inhibition of insulin release, presumably acting through adrenaline. Thus Smith *et al.* (1973) used the glucose analogue, 2-deoxyglucose (2-DG), which, like 3-methylglucose, competes with glucose for transport into cells and into the brain. When injected into the blood it raises the blood-glucose; a normally induced rise in blood-sugar would provoke the secretion of insulin; however this does not occur appreciably, suggesting that insulin-secretion is being suppressed by the cerebral hypoglycaemia induced by 2-deoxyglucose (2-DG). When the same experiment was carried out on an adrenalectomized monkey, there was no response, indicating the involvement of adrena-line, although it could have been argued that the 2-DG was having a direct effect on the insulin-secreting β-cells of the pancreas. However, Smith *et al.* showed that the sugar was not affecting the power of the pancreas to release insulin in response to a changed blood-sugar. Thus Fig. 5.88 shows the simultaneously measured concentrations of glucose and insulin in the blood of a monkey. Injection of 2-DG raised the

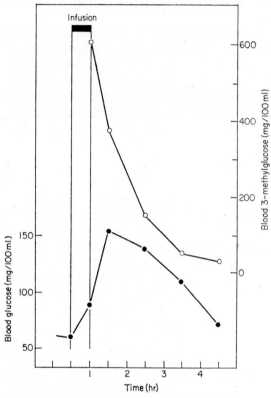

Fig. 5.87. The effect of an intravenous infusion of 3-methylglucose upon the blood glucose (filled circles) of a fasted rat. (Himsworth, *J. Physiol.*)

blood-sugar and lowered the blood-insulin, as before; now, an intravenous injection of glucose was given, causing a further rise in blood-sugar but only a small rise in blood-insulin. When the same experiment was repeated in the adrenalectomized animal (Fig. 5.88), there was a large insulin-secretion in response to the injected glucose. Thus the cerebral response to cerebral hypoglycaemia consists in a primary secretion from the adrenal glands; the adrenaline provokes a hyperglycaemia by its direct action on the liver, a reaction that is supported by the inhibition of insulin-release.

Hypothalamic Glucose-Sensitive Neurones. The actual site of

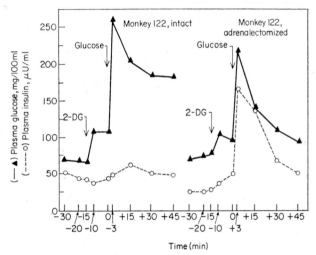

Fig. 5.88. Plasma glucose and insulin levels after 2-deoxyglucose (2-DG) at 0 min in the monkey before and after bilateral adrenalectomy. There was no significant insulin response to glucose when the monkey was intact. After bilateral adrenalectomy there was a large insulin response to glucose despite pretreatment with the same dose of 2-DG. (Smith, *Endocrinology*.)

the glucose-sensitive neurones is in the hypothalamus, as shown for example by Colin-Jones and Himsworth (1970) when they injected 2-DG directly into the lateral hypothalamic area of rats. This time they used, as their index of the hypoglycaemic response, the secretion of acid by the stomach, mediated through the vagus. Injections into the lateral hypothalamic area, and only here, caused copious acid secretion in rats, comparable with that obtained with insulin hypoglycaemia. Injection of a local anaesthetic into the same region abolished the response to 2-DG given by intravenous injection.

The Efferent Nervous Pathways

The sympathetic activation of the liver has already been indicated; this is antagonized by the parasympathetic. The release of insulin and that of glucagon are both under autonomic nervous control, as manifest through stimulation of the mixed nerve that runs along the superior pancreatico-duodenal artery. In general, the outputs of insulin and glucagon show a reciprocal arrangement, so that, whereas the sympathetic causes inhibition of insulin secretion, it causes secretion of glucagon; the parasympathetic stimulus has inverse effects. Thus Porte *et al.* (1973) obtained a 40 per cent reduction in the release of insulin in response to a hyperglycaemic stimulus when the mixed nerve was stimulated in atropinized animals; in the absence of atropine the output was increased.

α- and β-Receptors. The sympathetic inhibition is an α-effect; β-receptors on the insulin-secreting cells cause secretion of insulin. For example, Porte (1967) noticed that if he infused both adrenaline and a β-blocker he obtained unexpectedly low values of insulin-release, as though adrenaline had been having a dual effect, inhibiting secretion through its action on α-receptors and activating secretion through the β-receptors; thus a β-inhibitor, such as propanolol, would accentuate the inhibitory action of adrenaline by preventing the concurrent β-activation of secretion. Using the β-mimicker, isoproterenol, be obtained, with low doses, a rise in blood free fatty acids in humans, together with a rise in concentration of insulin in the blood without any rise in blood-glucose, effects that were blocked by propanolol.

Secretion of Glucagon. When release of glucagon was studied, Martins *et al.* (1973) found that stimulation of the mixed nerve caused a release of the hormone which was not inhibited by atropine; the effect seemed to be one of sensitization of the gland to the stimulating action of hypoglycaemia, since the higher the actual glucagon output the greater was the effect of stimulation. Iversen (1973) found that secretion was evoked by adrenaline, noradrenaline and isoproterenol, even in the presence of a blood-sugar of 150 mg/100 ml, which normally inhibits secretion. The effects were blocked by propanolol, the β-blocker whilst the α-blocker phentolamine had no effect. Thus the release of insulin is *inhibited* through α-action and that of glucagon is *stimulated* through β-action; β-action also stimulates insulin release, so that isoproterenol provokes secretion of both hormones.

The Shunt of Glucose to the Brain

The various reactions leading to the secretion, or inhibition of secretion, of insulin not only tend to stabilize the level of glucose in the blood but also to favour uptake by the brain preferentially. This is achieved by the differential sensitivities of the brain and the rest of the body (except the liver) to insulin so far as favouring increased uptake by the cells is concerned. When the brain needs glucose, secretion of insulin is inhibited; this, by reducing cellular uptake, tends to make the blood-concentration rise, and the brain can profit by this because it does not depend on insulin for its own uptake of glucose. The liver, too, does not depend on insulin for the transport of glucose across its cells, so that inhibited insulin secretion, whilst it favours production of glucose by liver cells, does not slow down the escape of the newly formed glucose into the blood. Thus, during starvation, the brain acquires adequate glucose, and the other tissues tend to make use of fatty acids, etc. for their energy-giving reactions (Fritz, 1972).

Renal Excretion and Intestinal Absorption of Glucose

The T_m Mechanism

Renal excretion of glucose plays a relatively unimportant role in glucose homeostasis, since the proximal tubular reabsorptive process is geared to ensure that the normal filtered load is completely reabsorbed and the urine is free from glucose. During the hyperglycaemia of diabetes, the maximal reabsorptive capacity, T_m, is exceeded and glucose is excreted in the urine. Thus the urinary excretory mechanism is essentially an overflow device, metabolically expensive, that limits the degree of hyperglycaemia arising from unusual causes.

Intestinal Absorption

The intestinal absorption has been discussed in detail in Vol. 1; clearly the special mechanisms that are necessary to provide rapid reabsorption in the kidney tubule are also necessary to ensure rapid and complete absorption from the gut; and we find similar active transport processes favouring, especially, the metabolically important sugars, glucose and galactose. The highly efficient absorptive mechanism means that, during a carbohydrate meal, the concentration in the blood rises, but the intervention of the liver in the portal circulation ensures that this hyperglycaemia is held within reasonable limits, usually insufficient to bring about excretion in the urine.

Evolutionary Aspects

Islets and Acinar Cells

Fritz (1972) has discussed in some detail the evolutionary significance of the development of the endocrine secretory system of the pancreas in close relation with its exocrine—digestive—secretions. In all vertebrates the acinar cells involved in exocrine digestive secretions are present alongside the endocrine islet-type of cells; and it may be that the various agents that were evolved for the control of the secretions of the acinar cells were also employed for the control of secretion of insulin by the β-cells of the islets. In all species higher, phylogenetically, than the teleosts, discrete islets are in close association with the acinar cells.

Carnivores. This close relationship between digestion and the hormones concerned in disposing of the products of digestion—sugars, fatty and amino acids—is teleologically reasonable. Thus, to consider the wild carnivores, they eat irregularly, periods of hunger alternating with satiety; clearly an "anabolic hormone" that prevents the absorbed products of food from being wasted during satiety, by causing them to be stored in readily available forms such as glycogen fat and protein.

is of enormous value. In addition, if it helps the animal to survive during long periods of fasting, its value is correspondingly extended; the shunting of the glucose to the brain is an example, whilst the parallel development of hormones that serve to increase the supply of glucose in an emergency, completes the picture.

Islet Cells as Sensors. The sensors to the metabolic state of the animal are, according to Fritz, primarily the β-cells of the pancreas; these have a very high sensitivity to the level of glucose in the blood, but also respond to a variety of other blood-components including the hormones glucagon, secretin, pancreozymin, gastrin, and (inhibiting) adrenaline, leucine and other amino acids, and short-chain fatty acids. Vagal influences on insulin secretory mechanisms also suggest a tonic neural control. The secretion of the β-cell, insulin, thus acts as the messenger that rapidly initiates changes in the metabolic patterns of the tissues. If these arguments are correct, we may expect that animals with regular eating habits, such as ruminants, will be less dependent on insulin; and this is true, so that extirpation of the pancreas produces only a mild form of diabetes compared with that in carnivores including man (Young, 1963), whilst the glucose metabolism of their adipose tissue is less sensitive to insulin (Hanson and Ballard, 1967).

Ruminants. In the adult ruminant the main absorptive products from the ingested cellulose are fatty acids, such as acetic, propionic and butyric acids; infusion of these into a sheep, say, causes a rapid rise in blood-glucose, due to synthesis from the fatty acids; a secretion of insulin is provoked under these conditions, but the stimulus seems to be the concentration of fatty acid in the blood rather than the hyperglycaemia since the output of insulin was greater with butyrate than with propionate although the hyperglycaemias were about the same (Manns and Boda, 1967). Interestingly, young lambs, which are essentially monogastric, are sensitive to hyperglycaemia, as such, but as they develop into ruminants their β-cell sensitivity changes to one for fatty acids.

Growth Hormone

Pituitary deficiencies may be manifest as dwarfism, and the hormone responsible for this particular manifestation is secreted by acidophilic cells of the anterior pituitary, or adenohypophysis, and given the name of growth hormone (GH) or somatotrophin. It is a single-chain polypeptide containing some 200 amino-acid residues, and no carbohydrate (Niall et al., 1973), and is released into the blood in response to the secretion by the hypothalamus of a releasing factor, whose isolation and synthesis have not yet been achieved.

Somatostatin

A factor secreted by the hypothalamus causing inhibition of secretion
—*somatostatin* or *SRIF*—has been isolated; it is a tetradecapeptide:

$$\text{H-Ala-Gly-Cys-Lys-Asp-Phe-Phe-Trp-Lys-Thr-Phe-Thr-Ser-CysOH}$$

(Brazeau *et al.*, 1973), and when administered to rats it inhibits the
secretion of growth hormone evoked by electrical stimulation of the
ventromedial hypothalamus (Martin, 1974).

Acromegaly

The condition of *acromegaly*, i.e. an enlargement of the extremities,
is characteristic of human subjects that have tumours of the acidophilic
cells, leading to hypersecretion of the hormone.

Long- and Short-Term Influences

A hormone exercising control over growth must exert a long-term
influence over metabolism in which the control of glucose, fat and
amino acid utilization and synthesis will doubtless play a part, so that
it might be thought that its involvement in day-to-day, or hour-to-
hour, blood homeostasis would be of little account; the interesting
feature of the hormone, therefore, is that it does play a role in short-
term homeostasis, its secretion being activated and inhibited by
fluctuations in the concentrations of glucose, fatty acids and amino
acids in the blood.

Hypophysectomy and Diabetes. This was first revealed by
Houssay's studies (see, for example, Urgoiti *et al.*, 1963), showing that
the diabetic condition, caused by removing the dog's pancreas, could
be ameliorated by removal of the anterior pituitary, a finding that
suggested that the pituitary was contributing to the hyperglycaemia
and ketogenesis that appear in the absence of insulin secretion; in
other words, insulin and pituitary hormone might be exerting antagonistic actions, insulin being the *anabolic hormone,* causing synthesis of
fat and storage of glucose in the form of carbohydrate, and the pituitary
hormone having the catabolic effect, causing fat mobilization and
synthesis of glucose from amino acids, etc.

Diabetes Provoked by Growth Hormone. Thus during a period
of plentiful nutrition, as indicated earlier, the hormone insulin would
prevent waste by promoting storage, whilst in starvation growth
hormone would take over as the dominant hormone, promoting

mobilization of fat and inhibiting usage of glucose.* This view was fortified by Young's discovery (1945) that a form of diabetes mellitus could be induced in dogs and cats by injections of pituitary extracts containing growth hormone. In these animals, repeated treatment was associated with degeneration of the β-cells of the pancreas, and the diabetic condition was thus similar to the human disease; in other species, less severe effects are obtained, which are nevertheless to be classed as anti-insulin in their nature.

Effects of Injections of Growth Hormone

Repeated injections of growth hormone over a period of days into animals, including man, cause an increase in the concentration of free fatty acids in the plasma, due to increased lipolysis—fat mobilization— and this is accompanied by an increase in the blood-sugar. The hyperglycaemia is associated with an increased secretion of insulin. Some results on the dog are illustrated in Fig. 5.89, and it will be seen that the rise in blood-sugar is sufficient to cause urinary excretion.

Increased Insulin Secretion. The high blood-sugar is present in the face of a considerably increased secretion of insulin; and the evidence suggests that growth hormone not only increases the sensitivity of the β-cells of the pancreas to glucose, but it also prevents the secreted insulin from exerting its hypoglycaemic effects. Thus Campbell and Rostogi (1966) sampled portal vein blood from dogs with indwelling catheters, and found, first, that the level of insulin in the fasting blood was some 10 times greater after a daily dosage of GH for 6–13 days, whilst the insulin-response to infused glucose was also increased. The concentration of free fatty acids (FFA) in the blood rose, as well as that of glucose, whilst the insulin/glucose ratio increased. In effect, then, the growth hormone had readjusted the insulin-response, so that at any given level of blood-glucose, insulin was secreted at a higher rate.

Increased Responsiveness of Pancreas. The effect of the growth hormone is to potentiate the secretion of insulin by the pancreas, increasing its responsiveness to the natural—hyperglycaemic—stimulus. This was shown by Martin and Gagliardino's (1967) study on isolated rat pancreatic islets *in vitro*; addition of glucose to the medium increased the amount of insulin released, and this must have been due to provoked synthesis since the amount remaining in the tissue was unchanged Tissue from hypophysectomized rats was resistant to the glucose-

* The adrenal hormone, adrenaline, also works in opposition to insulin, and so might contribute, by its lipolytic action, to the diabetic condition of the pancreatectomized animal; according to Houssay *et al.* (1967), thoracolumbar sympathectomy, as well as adrenalectomy, reduces the level of free fatty acids, and the ketonuria, of pancreatectomized dogs.

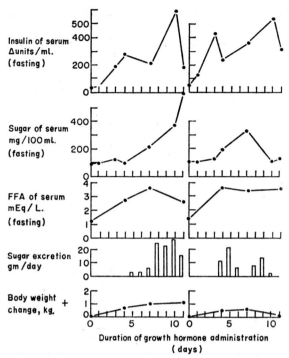

Fig. 5.89. The effects of daily injections of growth hormone on serum insulin, sugar and free fatty acid (FFA) levels, sugar excretion, and body-weight in fed dogs. (Campbell and Rastogi, *Diabetes.*)

stimulus, so that a concentration of 300 mg/100 ml failed to stimulate release or synthesis; if the animals were treated for three days with bovine growth hormone, however, their isolated islet tissue responded to the glucose-stimulus normally.

Acromegalic Subjects. This increased sensitivity to blood-glucose can be demonstrated in acromegalic human subjects; this is illustrated by Fig. 5.90. The upper curves show the normal and acromegalic glucose-tolerance tests, i.e. the blood-sugar responses to oral ingestion of 100 g of glucose; the tolerance is lower, in the sense that the blood-sugar rises to greater-than-normal heights, suggesting a deficiency of insulin, but in fact the lower curves show that the insulin response is *very much greater* in the acromegalics, proving that the diabetic condition that accompanies acromegaly, or hypersecretion of growth hormone, is not due to defective insulin secretion but rather to reduced effectiveness of the insulin.

Insulin Antagonism

It seems, then, that growth hormone either directly inhibits the action of insulin on its target tissues, or does this through some inter-

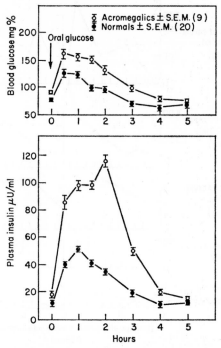

Fig. 5.90. Blood-sugar and plasma-insulin following ingestion of 100 gm of glucose by nine acromegalic patients as compared to results obtained with 20 normal subjects. (Daughaday and Kipnis, from Beek *et al.*, *Rec. Prog. Hormone Res.*)

mediate inhibitory substance. There is no doubt that growth hormone inhibits some of the actions of insulin; thus the facilitated uptake of glucose by skeletal muscle (p. 532) is antagonized, and this presumably contributes to the rise in blood-sugar caused by the hormone.

Common Actions

However, insulin and growth hormone do share some actions in common; thus they both facilitate amino acid transport and its incorporation into proteins, although the facilitated amino acids are different. Thus insulin facilitates transport of methionine, say, whereas growth hormone, whilst facilitating transport of say, alanine, does not facilitate that of methionine (see, for example, Matsuzaki & Raben, 1965).

Growth Hormone Components

The situation is complex, since it may be that growth hormone, as originally synthesized, is subsequently split into two peptides of opposing function; thus Bornstein *et al.* (1968) described two fractions prepared from human growth hormone, the one indicated by AcG and the other, inhibitory, by InG (somantin and cataglykin respectively; Zimmet *et al.*, 1972). AcG accelerates the synthesis of free fatty acids from acetate, whilst InG inhibits this process; also InG inhibits two important enzymes in carbohydrate metabolism, namely glyceraldehyde-3-phosphate dehydrogenase and α-glycerophosphate dehydrogenase. Bornstein considered that the two factors normally opposed each other, and that the predominance of the inhibitory factor, InG, with its inhibition of glycolysis and fatty acid synthesis, could account for the diabetogenic action of pituitary extracts. In fact, it has been suggested (Krahl, 1974) that human diabetes might arise from some genetically determined alteration in the balance between these two fractions; at any rate, the plasma levels of growth hormone are raised in human juvenile diabetes (Hagen *et al.*, 1971); and the InG concentration is greater than normal; it is absent from hypophysectomized diabetic humans and is highest on insulin therapy (Zimmet *et al.*, 1971).

Natural Peptides. The fractions studied by Bornstein *et al.* were artificially derived from the larger molecule by acid hydrolysis; Louis and Conn (1969) have described a peptide isolated from the urine of proteinuric diabetic patients, and a similarly acting peptide extracted from the pituitary gland itself (Louis *et al.*, 1971). In dogs, the pituitary extract had the characteristic actions of raising the glucose and insulin levels in the blood, but there was no significant growth-promoting activity, as determined by the tibia test. Again Miller and Larner (1972) showed that a similar peptide, of molecular weight about 26,000, from bovine pituitary depressed the insulin-mediated glucose-uptake by diaphragm muscle and inhibited the insulin-mediated glycogen-synthesis mechanisms, i.e. inhibited the activation of glycogen synthetase brought about by insulin.*

The Stimulus to Secrete Growth Hormone

If growth hormone (GH) acts as a physiological antagonist to insulin we may expect its secretion to be evoked by the opposite stimuli to those evoking insulin secretion, namely a lowered level of sugar and fatty acids, and a raised level of amino acids, in the blood. Alternatively its secretion should be suppressed by raised sugar and free fatty acid levels in the blood.

---

* The growth hormones of the ox, pig, sheep, etc., are ineffective in man, so that it is common to refer to *human growth hormone, HGH,* in studies applied to man. The need for a cheap supply of hormone has prompted the study of the effects of tryptic digests of bovine hormone in the hope that an active portion, with the required amino-acid sequence, can be split off. Sonenberg *et al.* (1965) have obtained a number of HGH-effects in humans with tryptic digests, including hyperglycaemia.

Hypoglycaemia. The hypoglycaemic stimulus is usually demonstrated by an injection of insulin. Thus the normal level of GH in fasting human subjects is 0–3 mμg/ml; with an insulin-induced fall in blood-sugar to 50 per cent of normal, the concentration rises by a factor of 5 or more (Glick *et al.*, 1965). This is shown in Fig. 5.91. If glucose was administered after the fall in blood-sugar, the release of growth hormone was suppressed (Fig. 5.91b) even though this was administered some 25 min after the hypoglycaemia had occurred. This emphasizes that the secretion in response to hypoglycaemia requires time to develop. Roth *et al.* (1963) have shown that the hypoglycaemia

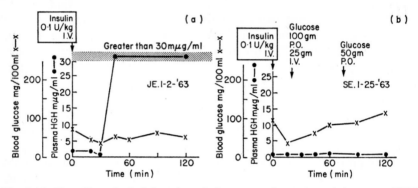

Fig. 5.91. The effect of administration of glucose on plasma growth hormone (GH) during insulin tolerance tests in normal subjects. (a) Unmodified insulin tolerance test. (b) Insulin tolerance test with termination of hypoglycaemia 20 minutes after the administration of insulin. (Glick *et al.*, *Rec. Prog. Hormone Res.*)

induced by feeding fructose to sensitive subjects, where the insulin concentration was normal, also caused increased GH-secretion, an effect that could be suppressed by intravenous glucose. It will be recalled that the secretion of insulin may be suppressed by injections of 2-deoxyglucose which, because it prevents utilization of glucose by the brain, has all the effects of hypoglycaemia (p. 547); in a similar way 2-deoxyglucose *provokes* secretion of growth hormone.

Rebound Rise. Perhaps more important than the absolute level of the glucose in the blood is the direction of change, so that after ingestion of glucose the secretion is first suppressed, as the blood-sugar rises, but it starts again at a higher-than-normal level when the blood-sugar is on the wane, although the absolute concentration is still higher than normal—this is called the "rebound rise" in growth hormone level late during an oral glucose-tolerance test. This is shown by Fig. 5.92; curve (a) shows the characteristic rise and fall of the blood-glucose after ingestion of glucose; curve (b) shows the rise and fall in insulin level, and curve (c) shows the sudden rise in growth hormone secretion associated with the decline in blood-sugar; the high level is sustained, however, so that if the same subject is given a second test, his blood-sugar exhibits a much higher rise due to the antagonistic action of the remaining growth hormone in the blood.

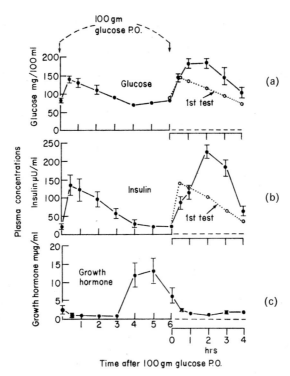

Fig. 5.92. Changes in blood-glucose (a), insulin (b) and growth-hormone (c) following ingestion of 100 g of glucose at zero time, and again some 6 hr later. Note the large rise in blood-glucose after the second dose of glucose, which is due to the relatively high concentration of growth hormone remaining in the blood. The rise in concentration of insulin, at the second test, is also very high but it fails to suppress the rise in blood-glucose. The open circles and dotted lines recapitulate the changes induced during the first test. (Yalow *et al.*, *Diabetes.*)

Fat and Growth Hormone

Growth hormone tends to mobilize the breakdown of fat—lipolysis —switching metabolism to the fat-consuming, or diabetic, type, with ketonuria. Raising the level of free fatty acids in the blood by ingestion of corn-oil, while administering intravenous heparin, inhibits the secretion induced by insulin or arginine (Fig. 5.93). Alternatively, reducing the normal level of fatty acids in sheep, by treatment with inhibitors of lipolysis, caused an increased secretion of growth hormone.

It will be recalled that, in the ruminant, it is the fatty acids produced by breakdown of cellulose that constitute an important normal source of energy metabolism, so that a sensitivity to reduced fatty acid levels in the blood is to be sought in the ruminant rather than in mono-gastric animals (Hertelendy and Kipnis, 1973).

Raising the Level of FFA in Blood. In general it is the conditions in which the level of free fatty acids in the blood requires to be raised

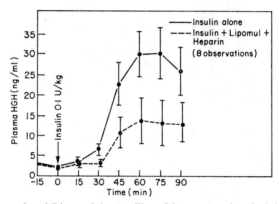

Fig. 5.93. Effect of oral Lipomul (corn oil) and intravenously administered heparin on insulin-induced plasma growth hormone (HGH) elevations in humans. The subjects ingested Lipomul 3 hr before the first blood sample and intravenous heparin was administered at zero time. (Blackard *et al.*, *J. clin. Invest.*)

that are accompanied by secretion of growth hormone. This happens in hypoglycaemia, during severe exercise, during prolonged fasting and with interferences with glucose metabolism, as with feeding 2-deoxy-glucose. All these conditions provoke secretion of growth hormone whose prominent metabolic action seems to be the raising of the blood free-fatty acid levels. It may be that obesity, which represents an abnormal tendency to synthesize and store fat, is associated with a defective response of the pituitary to normal physiological stimuli (Roth *et al.*, 1963).

Evolutionary Significance

The evolutionary significance of the diabetogenic action of growth hormone has been discussed by Young (1971); like insulin it is an important hormone for carnivores and other animals feeding at irregular intervals; during starvation it tends to maintain the glucose-level in the blood at a value consistent with survival of the brain, so that animals with more active pituitaries might well have greater survival potentiality than those with less. Thus evolution would provide a drive towards the diabetic type of animal,* a condition that would be held in check by the periods of starvation that caused its development. For civilized man, however, with a too plentiful supply of food, it may be that the active pituitary, valuable to uncivilized man, has become a positive evil, through imposing an excessive strain on the islets of Langerhans, leading ultimately to diabetes mellitus, if we assume that the hypertrophy of the tissue, resulting from repeated doses of the hormone, leads ultimately to atrophy. It is certainly true that in developed countries diabetes has become commoner.

REFERENCES

Adler, S., Roy, A. and Relman, A. S. (1965). Intracellular acid-base regulation I. The response of muscle cells to changes in CO_2 tension or extracellular bicarbonate concentration. *J. Clin. Invest.*, **44**, 8–21.

Adolph, E. F. (1939). Measurements of water drinking in dogs. *Amer. J. Physiol.*, **125**, 75–86.

Agus, Z. S., Gardner, L. B., Beck, L. H. and Goldberg, M. (1973). Effects of parathyroid hormone on renal tubular reabsorption of calcium, sodium and phosphate. *Amer. J. Physiol.*, **224**, 1143–1148.

Agus, Z. S. and Goldberg, M. (1970). Renal mechanisms of the natriuretic and antiphosphaturic effects of triflocin—a new diuretic. *J. lab. clin. Med.*, **76**, 281–292.

Agus, Z. S., Puschett, J. B., Senesky, D. and Goldberg, M. (1971). Mode of action of parathyroid hormone and cyclic adenosine 3′,5′-monophosphate on renal tubular phosphate reabsorption in the dog. *J. clin. Invest.*, **50**, 617–626.

Allan, W. and Tepperman, H. M. (1969). Stimulation of insulin secretion in the rat by glucagon, secretin and pancreozymin: Effect of aminophylline. *Life Sci.*, **8**, 307–317.

Amiel, C., Kuntziger, H. and Richet, G. (1970). Micropuncture study of handling of phosphate by proximal and distal nephron in normal and parathyroidectomized rat. Evidence for distal reabsorption. *Pflüg. Arch. ges. Physiol.*, **317**, 93–109.

Andersson, B. and Larsson, B. (1961). Influence of local temperature changes on the preoptic area and rostral hypothalamus on the regulation of food and water intake. *Acta physiol. scand.*, **52**, 75–89.

Andersson, B., Larsson, S. and Persson, N. (1960). Some characteristics of the hypothalamic "drinking centre" in the goat as shown by the use of permanent electrodes. *Acta physiol. scand.*, **50**, 140–152.

Andersson, B. and McCann, S. M. (1956). The effect of hypothalamic lesions on the water intake of the dog. *Acta physiol. scand.*, **35**, 312–320.

Appleman, M. M. and Kemp. R. G. (1966). Puromycin: a potent metabolic effect independent of protein synthesis. *Biochem. Biophys. Res. Comm.*, **24**, 564–568.

Armin, J. and Grant, R. T. (1959). Adrenaline release during insulin hypoglycaemia in the rabbit. *J. Physiol.*, **149**, 228–249.

Aurbach, D. G. *et al.* (1972). Structure, synthesis and mechanism of action of parathyroid hormone. *Rec. Prog. Hormone Res.*, **28**, 353–392.

Baer, J. E., Russo, H. F., Michaelson, J. K. and Beyer, K. H. (1962). A new class of diuretic-saliuretic agents—the α, β-unsaturated ketone derivatives of aryloxyacetic acids. *The Pharmacologist*, **4**, 158.

---

* It would have this drive through its action on the islets of Langerhans described by Young, its stimulating action eventually leading to dystrophy.

Bailie, M. D., Loutzenheiser, R. and Moyer, S. (1972). Relation of renal hemodynamics to angiotensin II in renal hilar lymph of the dog. *Amer. J. Physiol.*, **222,**
1075–1078.

Bare, J. K. (1942). The specific hunger for sodium chloride in normal and adrenalectomized rats. *J. comp. physiol. Psychol.*, **42,** 242–253.

Barnes, B. A., Cope, O. and Harrison, T. (1958). Magnesium conservation in the
human being on a low magnesium diet. *J. clin. Invest.*, **37,** 430–440.

Barraclough, M. A. and Jones, N. F. (1970). The effect of vasopressin on the reabsorption of sodium potassium and urea by the renal tubules in man. *Clin. Sci.*,
39, 517–527.

Beck, L. H., Senesky, D. and Goldberg, M. (1973). Sodium independent active
potassium reabsorbtion in proximal tubule of the dog. *J. clin. Invest.*, **52,** 2641–
2645.

Behn, C., Gauer, O. H., Kirsch, K. and Eckert, P. (1969). Effects of sustained
intrathoracic vascular distension on body fluid distribution and renal excretion in
man. *Pflüg. Arch. ges. Physiol.*, **313,** 123–135.

Bellows, R. T. (1939). Time factors in water drinking in dogs. *Amer. J. Physiol.*, **125,**
87–97.

Bengele, H. H., Houttin, E. and Pearce, J. W. (1972). Volume natriuresis without
renal nerves and renal vascular pressure rise in the dog. *Amer. J. Physiol.*, **223,**
68–73.

Benson, E. S., Freier, E. F. and Vijums, R. (1965). Carbon dioxide dissociation
curve and buffer capacity of dog heart muscle. *Amer. J. Physiol.*, **209,** 941–944.

Berliner, R. W., Kennedy, T. J. and Orloff, J. (1951). Relationship between acidification of the urine and potassium metabolism. Effect of carbonic anhydrase
inhibition on potassium excretion. *Amer. J. Med.*, **11,** 274–282.

Binnion, P. F. *et al.* (1965) Mechanisms regulating aldosterone secretion during
sodium depletion. *Amer. J. Physiol.*, **208,** 655–661.

Birnbaumer, L. and Rodbell, M. (1969). Adenyl cyclase in fat cells. II. Hormone
receptors. *J. biol. Chem.*, **244,** 3477–3482.

Blackard, W. G., Hull, E. W. and Lopez-S., A. (1971). Effect of lipids on growth
hormone secretion in humans. *J. clin. Invest.*, **50,** 1439–1443.

Blaine, E. H., Davis, J. O. and Prewitt, R. L. (1971). Evidence for a renal vascular
receptor in control of renin secretion. *Amer. J. Physiol.*, **220,** 1593–1597.

Blair-West, J. R. *et al.* (1962). Humoral stimulation of adrenal cortical secretion. *J.
clin. Invest.*, **41,** 1606–1627.

Bornstein, J. *et al.* (1968). Pituitary peptides with direct action on the metabolism
of carbohydrate and fatty acids. *Biochim. biophys. Acta*, **156,** 31–37.

Bornstein, J., Armstrong, J. McD. and Jones, M. D. (1968). The effect of a growth
hormone fraction on the activity of glyceraldehyde-3-phosphate dehydrogenase.
Biochim. biophys. Acta, **156,** 38–43.

Boyns, D. R., Jarrett, R. J. and Keen, H. (1966). Intestinal hormones and plasma
insulin. *Lancet*, **i,** 409–410.

Bradbury, M. W. B. and Davson, H. (1965). The transport of potassium between
blood, cerebrospinal fluid and brain. *J. Physiol.*, **181,** 151–174.

Braverman, B. and Davis, J. O. (1973). Adrenal steroid secretion in the rabbit:
sodium depletion, angiotensin II and ACTH. *Amer. J. Physiol.*, **225,** 1306–1310.

Brazeau, P. *et al.* (1973). Hypothalamic polypeptide that inhibits the secretion of
immuno-reactive pituitary growth hormone. *Science*, **179,** 77–79.

Brenner, B. M., Bennett, C. M. and Berliner, R. W. (1968). The relationship
between glomerular filtration rate and sodium reabsorption by the proximal
tubule of the rat nephron. *J. clin. Invest.*, **47,** 1358–1374.

Brenner, B. M. and Galla, J. H. (1971). Influence of postglomerular hematocrit and protein concentration on rat nephron fluid transfer. *Amer. J. Physiol.*, **220**, 148–161.

Brenner, B. M. and Troy, J. L. (1971). Postglomerular vascular protein concentration: Evidence for a causal role in governing fluid reabsorption and glomerulotubular balance by the renal proximal tubule. *J. clin. Invest.*, **50**, 336–349.

Brenner, B. M. *et al.* (1972). Dynamics of glomerular ultrafiltration in the rat. II. Plasma-flow dependence of GFR. *Amer. J. Physiol.*, **223**, 1184–1190.

Brody, T. M. and McNeill, J. H. (1970). Adrenergic receptors for metabolic responses in skeletal and smooth muscles. *Fed. Proc.*, **29**, 1375–1378.

Brubacher, E. S. and Vander, A. J. (1968). Sodium deprivation and renin secretion in unanaesthetized dogs. *Amer. J. Physiol.*, **214**, 15–21.

Brunette, M. G., Taler, L. and Carriere, S. (1973). Effect of parathyroid hormone on phosphate reabsorption along the nephron of the rat. *Amer. J. Physiol.*, **225**, 1076–1081.

Brunette, M., Wen, S.-F., Evanson, R. L. and Dirks, J. H. (1969). Micropuncture study of magnesium reabsorption in the proximal tubule of the dog. *Amer. J. Physiol.*, **216**, 1510–1516.

Burg, M. B. and Green, N. (1973). Function of the thick ascending limb of Henle's loop. *Amer. J. Physiol.*, **224**, 659–668.

Burg, M. B. and Orloff, J. (1968). Control of fluid absorption in the renal proximal tubule. *J. clin. Invest.*, **47**, 2016–2024.

Burg, M., Stoner, L., Cardinal, J. and Green, N. (1973). Furosemide effect on isolated perfused tubules. *Amer. J. Physiol.*, **225**, 119–124.

Butcher, R. W., Baird, C. E. and Sutherland, E. W. (1968). Effects of lipolytic and antilipolytic substances on adenosine 3'-5'-monophosphate levels in isolated fat cells. *J. biol. Chem.*, **243**, 1705–1712.

Cahill, G. F., Ashmore, J., Earle, A. S. and Zottu, S. (1958). Glucose penetration into liver. *Amer. J. Physiol.* **192**, 491–496.

Caldwell, P. C. (1958). Studies on the internal pH of large muscle and nerve fibres. *J. Physiol.*, **142**, 22–62.

Campbell, J. and Rastogi, K. S. (1966). Growth-hormone induced diabetes and high levels of serum insulin in dogs. *Diabetes*, **15**, 30–43.

Cannon, W. B. (1918). The physiological basis of thirst. *Proc. Roy. Soc.*, B, **90**, 283–301.

Cannon, W. B., Iver, M. A. Mc. and Bliss, S. W. (1924). A sympathetic and adrenal mechanism for mobilizing sugar in hypoglycemia. *Amer. J. Physiol.*, **69**, 46–66.

Care, A. D. *et al.* (1968). A study of thyrocalcitonin secretion by direct measurement of in vivo secretion rates in pigs. *Endocrinology*, **83**, 161–169.

Care, A. D. *et al.* (1971). Role of pancreozymin-cholecystokinin and structurally related compounds as calcitonin secretogogues. *Endocrinology*, **89**, 262–271.

Chance, R. E. (1972). Amino acid sequence of proinsulins and intermediates. *Diabetes*, **21**, 461–467.

Chutgow, J. G. (1964). Metabolism of magnesium in the normal rat. *J. lab. clin. Med.*, **63**, 80–99.

Clapp, J. R. and Robinson, R. R. (1968). Distal sites of action of diuretic drugs in the dog. *Amer. J. Physiol.*, **215**, 228–235.

Clark, B. J. and Rocha e Silva, M. (1967). An afferent pathway for the selective release of vasopressin in response to carotid occlusion and haemorrhage in the cat. *J. Physiol.*, **191**, 529–542.

Claybaugh, J. R. and Share, L. (1973). Vasopressin, renin and cardiovascular responses to continuous slow hemorrhage. *Amer. J. Physiol.*, **224**, 519–523.

Colin-Jones, D. G. and Himsworth, R. L. (1969). The secretion of gastric acid in response to a lack of metabolizable glucose. *J. Physiol.*, **202**, 97–109.

Colin-Jones, D. G. and Himsworth, R. L. (1970). The location of the chemoreceptor controlling gastric acid secretion during hypoglycaemia. *J. Physiol.*, **206**, 397–409.

Comroe, J. H. *et al.* (1962). *The Lung: Clinical Physiology and Pulmonary Function Tests.* 2nd Ed. Year Book Med. Publ. Co., Chicago.

Coore, H. G. *et al.* (1963). Block of insulin secretion from the pancreas by D-manno-heptulose. *Nature*, **197**, 1264–1266.

Crespin, S. R., Greenough, W. B. and Steinberg, D. (1973). Stimulation of insulin secretion by long-chain free fatty acids. *J. clin. Invest.*, **52**, 1979–1984.

Crofford, O. B. and Renold, A. E. (1965). Glucose uptake by incubated rat epididymal adipose tissue. *J. biol. Chem.*, **240**, 14–21.

Cuatrecasas, P. (1969). Interaction of insulin with the cell membrane. The primary action of insulin. *Proc. Nat. Acad. Sci. Wash.*, **63**, 450–451.

Cuatrecasas, P. (1972). The insulin receptor. *Diabetes*, **21**, 396–402.

Curry, D. M. (1970). Glucagon potentiation of insulin secretion by the perfused rat pancreas. *Diabetes*, **19**, 420–428.

Curry, D. M. and Beaton, G. H. (1958). Glucagon administration in pregnant rats. *Endocrinology*, **63**, 252–254.

Daughaday, W. H. and Kipnis, D. M. (1966). The growth-promoting and anti-insulin action of somatotropin. *Rec. Prog. Hormone Res.*, **22**, 49–99.

Dean, P. M. and Matthews, E. K. (1970). Glucose-induced electrical activity in pancreatic islet cells. *J. Physiol.*, **210**, 255–264.

Dean, P. M. and Matthews. E. K. (1970). Electrical activity in pancreatic islet cells: effects of ions. *J. Physiol.*, **210**, 265–275.

Dean, P. M. and Matthews, E. K. (1972). Pancreatic acinar cells: measurement of membrane potential and miniature depolarization potentials. *J. Physiol.*, **225**, 1–13.

Deen, W. M., Robertson, C. R. and Brenner, B. M. (1972). A model of glomerular ultrafiltration in the rat. *Amer. J. Physiol.*, **223**, 1178–1183.

De Luca, M. H. and Melancon, M. J. (1972). Hydroxycholecalciferol, a hormonal form of vitamin D. In *Biochemical Action of Hormones* (Ed. W. Litwak), Vol. II, pp. 365–415. Academic Press, New York.

Denton, D. A. (1967). Salt appetite. *Hdb. Physiol.*, Sect. VI, Vol. 1, pp. 453–459.

Diezi, J., Michoud, P., Aceves, J. and Giebisch, G. (1973). Micropuncture study of electrolyte transport across papillary collecting duct of the rat. *Amer. J. Physiol.*, **224**, 623–634.

Dirks, J. H., Cirksena, W. J. and Berliner, R. W. (1966). Micropuncture studies on diuretics in dogs. *Proc. 3rd. Int. Congr. Nephrol.*, **1**, 260–268.

Dirks, J. H. and Seely, J. F. (1970). Effect of saline infusions and furosemide on the dog distal nephron. *Amer. J. Physiol.*, **219**, 114–121.

Dowdle, E. B., Schachter, D. and Schenker, H. (1960). Requirement for vitamin D for the active transport of calcium by the intestine. *Amer. J. Physiol.*, **198**, 269–274.

Duggan, D. E. and Noll, R. M. (1965). Effects of ethacrynic acid and cardiac glycosides upon a membrane adenosine-triphosphatase of renal cortex. *Arch. Biochem. Biophys.*, **109**, 388–396.

Dunn, F. L., Brennan, T. J., Nelson, A. E. and Robertson, G. L. (1973). The role of blood osmolality and volume in regulating vasopressin secretion in the rat. *J. clin. Invest.*, **52**, 3212–3219.

Edwards, B. R., Baer, P. G., Sutton, R. A. L. and Dirks, J. H. (1973). Micropuncture study of diuretic effects on sodium and calcium reabsorption in the dog nephron. *J. clin. Invest.*, **52**, 2418–2427.

Edwards, J. C. and Taylor, K. W. (1970). Fatty acids and the release of glucagon from isolated guinea-pig islets of Langerhans incubated in vitro. *Biochim. biophys. Acta.*, **215**, 310–315.

Epstein, A. N., Fitzsimons, J. T. and Rolls, B. J. (1970). Drinking induced by injection of angiotensin into the brain of the rat. *J. Physiol.*, **210**, 457–474.

Erlij, D. and Leblanc, G. (1971). The effects of ethacrynic acid and other sulphydryl reagents on sodium fluxes in frog muscle. *J. Physiol.*, **214**, 327–342.

Evanson, R. L., Lockhart, E. A. and Dirks, J. H. (1972). Effect of mercurial diuretics on tubular sodium and potassium transport in the dog. *Amer. J. Physiol.*, **222**, 282–289.

Exton, J. H. *et al.* (1970). The hormonal control of hepatic gluconeogenesis. *Rec. Prog. Hormone Res.*, **26**, 411–457.

Fabre, L. F. *et al.* (1969). Biphasic stimulation of aldosterone secretion during hemorrhage in dogs. *Circulation Res.*, **24**, 893–900.

Fajans, C. S. *et al.* (1967). Effect of amino acids and proteins on insulin secretion in man. *Rec. Prog. Hormone Res.*, **23**, 617–656.

Falchuk, K. H., Brenner, B. M., Tadokoro, M. and Berliner, R. W. (1971). Oncotic and hydrostatic pressures in peritubular capillaries and fluid reabsorption by proximal tubule. *Amer. J. Physiol.*, **220**, 1427–1433.

Falk, J. L. and Lipton, J. M. (1967). Temporal factors in the genesis of NaCl appetite by intraperitoneal dialysis. *J. comp. physiol. Psychol.*, **63**, 247–251.

Fenn, W. O. (1939). The deposition of potassium and phosphate with glycogen in rat liver. *J. biol. Chem.*, **128**, 297–307.

Fenn, W. O. (1961). Carbon dioxide and intracellular homeostasis. *Ann. N.Y. Acad. Sci.*, **92**, 547–555.

Finkelstein, J. D. and Schachter, D. (1962). Active transport of calcium by intestine: effects of hypophysectomy and growth hormone. *Amer. J. Physiol.*, **203**, 873–880.

Fischer-Ferraro, C., Nahmod, V. E., Goldstein, D. J. and Finkielman, S. (1971). Angiotensin and renin in rat and dog brain. *J. exp. Med.*, **133**, 353–361.

Fitzsimons, J. T. (1961). Drinking by rats depleted of body fluid without increase in osmotic pressure. *J. Physiol.*, **159**, 297–309.

Fitzsimons, J. T. (1967). The kidney as a thirst receptor. *J. Physiol.*, **191**, 128–129.

Fitzsimons, J. T. (1972). Thirst. *Physiol. Rev.*, **52**, 468–561.

Fitzsimons, J. T. and Le Magnen, J. (1969). Eating as a regulatory control of drinking in the rat. *J. comp. physiol. Psychol.*, **67**, 273–283.

Fitzsimons, J. T. and Oatley, K. (1968). Additivity of stimuli for drinking in rats. *J. comp. physiol. Psychol.*, **66**, 450–455.

Fitzsimons, J. T. and Simons, B. J. (1969). The effect on drinking in the rat of intravenous infusion of angiotensin, given alone or in combination with other stimuli of thirst. *J. Physiol.*, **203**, 45–57.

Friedmann, N., Exton, J. H. and Park, C. R. (1967). Interaction of adrenal steroids and glucagon on gluconeogenesis in perfused rat liver. *Biochem. Biophys. Res. Comm.*, **29**, 113–119.

Fritz, I. B. (1972). *Insulin Actions.* Academic Press, New York.

Frömter, E., Wick, T. and Hegel, U. (1967). Untersuchungen uber die Ausspritz-methode zur Lokalisation der Mikroelektrodenspitze bei Potentialmessungen am proximalen Konvolut der Rattenniere. *Pflüg. Arch. ges. Physiol.*, **294**, 265–273.

Genuth, S. and Lebovitz, H. E. (1965). Stimulation of insulin release by corticotropin. *Endocrinology*, **76**, 1093–1099.

Gertz, K. H. *et al.* (1965). On the glomerular tubular balance in the rat kidney. *Pflüg. Arch. ges. Physiol.*, **285**, 360–372.

Gill, J. R. and Casper, A. G. T. (1971). Renal effects of adenosine-3′,5′-cyclic monophosphate and dibutyryl adenosine 3′,5′-cyclic monophosphate. *J. clin. Invest.*, **50**, 1231–1240.

Gillespie, D. J., Sandberg, R. L. and Koike, T. I. (1973). Dual effect of left-atrial receptors on excretion of sodium and water in the dog. *Amer. J. Physiol.*, **225**, 706–710.

Gilman, A. (1937). The relation between blood osmotic pressure, fluid distribution and voluntary water intake. *Amer. J. Physiol.*, **120**, 323–328.

Gilman, A., Koelle, E. and Ritchie, J. M. (1963). Transport of potassium ions in the rat's intestine. *Nature*, **197**, 1210–1211.

Glabman, S., Aynedjian, H. S. and Bank, N. (1965). Micropuncture study of the effect of acute reductions in glomerular filtration rate on sodium and water reabsorption by the proximal tubules of the rat. *J. clin. Invest.*, **44**, 1410–1416.

Glick, S. M., Roth, J., Yalow, R. S. and Berson, S. A. (1965). The regulation of growth hormone secretion. *Rec. Prog. Hormone Res.*, **21**, 241–270.

Goetz, K. L., Bond, G. C., Hermreck, A. S. and Trank, J. W. (1970). Plasma ADH levels following a decrease in mean atrial transmural pressure in dogs. *Amer. J. Physiol.*, **219**, 1424–1428.

Goetz, K. L., Hermreck, A. S., Slick, G. L. and Starke, H. S. (1970). Atrial receptors and renal function in conscious dogs. *Amer. J. Physiol.*, **219**, 1417–1423.

Goldberg, M., McCurdy, D. K., Foltz, E. L. and Bluembe, L. W. (1964). Effects of ethacrynic acid (a new saluretic agent) on renal diluting and concentrating mechanisms: evidence for site of action in the loop of Henle. *J. clin. Invest.*, **43**, 201–216.

Gottschalk, C. W., Lassiter, W. E. and Mylle, M. (1960). Localization of urine acidification in the mammalian kidney. *Amer. J. Physiol.*, **198**, 581–585.

Gotshall, R. W. and Davis, J. O. (1973). Mineralocorticoid activity of 18-hydroxycorticosterone in the dog. *Amer. J. Physiol.*, **224**, 1116–1118.

Graveline, D. E. and Jackson, M. M. (1962). Diuresis associated with prolonged water immersion. *J. appl. Physiol.*, **17**, 519–524.

Gray, T. K., Bieberdorf, F. A. and Fordtran, J. S. (1973). Thyrocalcitonin and the jejunal absorption of calcium, water and electrolytes in normal subjects. *J. clin. Invest.*, **52**, 3084–3088.

Gregersen, M. I. (1932). Studies on the regulation of water intake. *Amer. J. Physiol.*, **102**, 344–349.

Grossman, S. P. and Grossman, L. (1963). Food and water intake following lesions or electrical stimulation of the amygdala. *Amer. J. Physiol.*, **205**, 761–765.

Grundy, H. M., Simpson, S. A. and Tait, J. F. (1952). Isolation of a highly active mineralocorticoid from beef adrenal extract. *Nature, Lond.*, **169**, 795–796.

Guyton, A. C., Langston, J. B. and Navar, G. (1964). Theory for renal autoregulation by feedback at the juxtaglomerular apparatus. *Circ. Res.*, **15**, 187–197.

Hagen, T. C., Laurence, A. M. and Kirsteins, L. (1971). Abnormal growth hormone (GH) secretion in ketosis-prone diabetes. *J. lab. clin. Med.*, **78**, 993–994.

Hainsworth, F. R., Stricker, E. M. and Epstein, A. N. (1968). Water metabolism of rats in the heat: dehydration and drinking. *Amer. J. Physiol.*, **214**, 983–989.

Hanson, R. W. and Ballard, F. J. (1967). The relative significance of acetate and glucose as precursors for lipid synthesis in liver and adipose tissue from ruminants. *Biochem. J.*, **105**, 529–536.

Harrison, H. E. and Harrison, H. C. (1961). Intestinal transport of phosphate: action of vitamin D, calcium and potassium. *Amer. J. Physiol.*, **201**, 1007–1012.

Hayes, C. P., Mayson, J. S., Owen, E. E. and Robinson, R. R. (1964). A micropuncture evaluation of renal ammonia excretion in the rat. *Amer. J. Physiol.*, **207**, 77–83.

Hayward, J. N. and Vincent, J. D. (1970). Osmosensitive single neurones in the hypothalamus of unanaesthetized monkeys. *J. Physiol.*, **210**, 947–972.

Hebert, C. S., Martinez-Maldonado, M., Eknoyan, G. and Suki, W. N. (1972). Relation of bicarbonate to sodium reabsorption in dog kidney. *Amer. J. Physiol.*, **222**, 1014–1020.

Hepp, K. D., Menahan, L. A., Wieland, O. and Williams, R. H. (1969). Studies on the action of insulin in isolated adipose tissue cells. II. *Biochim. biophys. Acta*, **184**, 554–565.

Herrera, F., Kemp, D. R., Tsukamoto, M. and Eisenberg, M. M. (1967). Insulin inhibition of gastric-secretion and motility: the potassium reversal effect. *Surg. Forum*, **18**, 300–303.

Herrera-Acosta, J. *et al.* (1972) Effect of expansion of extracellular volume on single-nephron filtration rates in the rat. *Amer. J. Physiol.*, **222**, 938–944.

Hertelendy, F. and Kipnis, D. M. (1973). Studies on growth hormone secretion. V. *Endocrinology*, **92**, 402–410.

Hierholzer, K. *et al.* (1965). Micropuncture study of renal transtubular concentration gradients of sodium and potassium in adrenalectomized rats. *Pflüg. Arch. ges. Physiol.*, **285**, 193–210.

Himsworth, R. L. (1968). Compensatory reactions to a lack of metabolizable glucose. *J. Physiol.*, **198**, 451–465.

Himsworth, R. L. (1968). Interference with the metabolism of glucose by a non-metabolizable hexose (3-methylglucose). *J. Physiol.*, **198**, 467–477.

Hodge, R. L., Lowe, R. D. and Vane, J. R. (1966). The effects of alteration of blood-volume on the concentration of circulating angiotensin in anaesthetized dogs. *J. Physiol.*, **185**, 613–626.

Hook, J. B. and Williamson, H. E. (1965). Influence of probenecid and alterations in acid-base balance on the saluretic activity of furosemide. *J. Pharmacol.*, **149**, 404–408.

Hornbrook, K. R. (1970). Adrenergic receptors for metabolic response in the liver. *Fed. Proc.*, **29**, 1381–1385.

Houpt, K. A. and Epstein, A. N. (1971). The complete dependence of beta-adrenergic drinking on the renal dipsogen. *Physiol. Behav.*, **7**, 897–902.

Houssay, B. A. (1963). Hormonal factors of diabetic ketosis. *Diabetes*, **12**, 481–489.

Houssay, B. A. *et al.* (1967). Fatty metabolism and ketogenesis after liver denervation or bilateral thorocolumbar sympathectomy in pancreatectomized dogs. *Diabetes*, **16**, 259–263.

Houttuin, E., Bengele, H. H. and Pearce, J. W. (1972). Effect of altered initial haemotocrit on the renal response to blood volume expansion. *Amer. J. Physiol.*, **223**, 63–67.

Ingle, D. J. (1942). Problems relating to the adrenal cortex. *Endocrinology*, **31**, 419–438.

Irvine, R. O. H. and Dow, J. (1966). Intracellular pH and electrolyte content of voluntary muscle in renal acidosis. *Clin. Sci.*, **31**, 317–324.

Iversen, J. (1973). Adrenergic receptors and the secretion of glucagon and insulin from the isolated perfused canine pancreas. *J. clin. Invest.*, **52**, 2102–2116.

Johnson, J. A., Moore, W. W. and Segar, W. E. (1969). Small changes in left atrial pressure and plasma antidiuretic hormone titer in dogs. *Amer. J. Physiol.*, **217**, 211–214.

Kaloyanides, J. G., Bastron, R. D. and Di Bona, G. F. (1973). Effect of ureteral clamping and increased renal arterial pressure on renin release. *Amer. J. Physiol.*, **225**, 95–99.

Karim, F., Kidd, C., Malpus, C. M. and Penna, P. E. (1972). The effects of stimulation of the left atrial receptors on sympathetic efferent nerve activity. *J. Physiol.*, **227**, 243–260.

Kimberg, D. V., Schachter, D. and Schenker, H. (1961). Active transport of calcium by intestine: effects of dietary calcium. *Amer. J. Physiol.*, **200**, 1256–1262.

Kissileff, H. R. (1969). Oropharyngeal control of prandial drinking. *J. comp. physiol. Psychol.*, **67**, 309–319.

Kissileff, H. R. and Epstein, A. N. (1969). Exaggerated prandial drinking in the "recovered lateral" rat without saliva. *J. comp. physiol. Psychol.*, **67**, 301–308.

Knox, F. G. *et al.* (1968). Effect of dilution and expansion of blood volume on proximal sodium reabsorption. *Amer. J. Physiol.*, **215**, 1041–1048.

Knox, F. G., Wright, F. S., Howards, S. S. and Berliner, R. W. (1969). Effect of furosemide on sodium reabsorption by proximal tubule *Amer. J. Physiol.*, **217**, 192–198.

Knox, F. G. *et al.* (1972). Role of peritubule Starling forces in proximal reabsorption following albumin infusion. *Amer. J. Physiol.*, **223**, 741–749.

Knox, F. G. *et al.* (1973). Effect of volume expansion on sodium excretion in the presence and absence of increased delivery from superficial proximal tubules. *J. clin. Invest.*, **52**, 1642–1646.

Krahl, M. E. (1974). Endocrine functions of the pancreas. *Ann. Rev. Physiol.*, **36**, 331–360.

Kurtzman, N. A. (1970). Regulation of renal bicarbonate reabsorption by extracellular volume. *J. clin. Invest.*. **48**, 586–595.

Lassiter, W. E., Gottschalk, C. W. and Mylle, M. (1963). Micropuncture study of renal tubular reabsorption of calcium in normal rodents. *Amer. J. Physiol.*, **204**, 771–775.

Lazarus, N. R. *et al.* (1968). Extra-gastrointestinal effects of secretin, gastrin and pancreozymin. *Lancet*, **ii**, 248–250.

Lebovitz, H. E. and Poolen, K. (1967). ACTH-mediated insulin secretion: effect of aminophylline. *Endocrinology*, **81**, 558–564.

Ledsome, J. R., Linden, R. J. and O'Connor, W. J. (1961). The mechanism by which distension of the left atrium produces diuresis in anaesthetized dogs. *J. Physiol.*, **159**, 87–100.

Lehr, D., Mallow, J. and Krukowski, M. (1967). Copious drinking and simultaneous inhibition of urine flow elicited by beta-adrenergic stimulation and contrary effect of alpha-adrenergic stimulation. *J. Pharmacol.*, **158**, 150–163.

Le Magnen, J. and Tallon, S. (1967). Les déterminants de la prise hydrique dans ses relations avec la prise d'aliments chez le rat. *C. r. Soc. Biol. Paris*, **161**, 1243–1246.

Leonard, E. and Orloff, J. (1955). Regulation of ammonia excretion in the rat. *Amer. J. Physiol.*, **182**, 131–138.

Levine, R. and Goldstein, M. (1955). On the mechanism of action of insulin. *Rec. Prog. Hormone Res.*, **11**, 343–380.

Lewy, J. E. and Windhager, E. E. (1968). Peritubular control of proximal tubular fluid reabsorption in the rat kidney. *Amer. J. Physiol.*, **214**, 943–945.

Leyssac, P. P. (1963). Dependence of glomerular filtration rate on proximal reabsorption of salt. *Acta. physiol. scand.*, **58**, 236–242.

Long, C. N. H., Katzin, B. and Fry, E. G. (1940). The adrenal cortex and carbo-hydrate metabolism. *Endocrinology*, **26**, 309–344.

Loten, E. G. and Sneyd, J. G. T. (1970). An effect of insulin on adipose-tissue adenosine 3′,5′ cyclic monophosphate diesterase. *Biochem. J.* **120**, 187–193.

Louis, L. H. and Conn, J. W. (1969). A urinary diabetogenic peptide in proteinuric diabetic patients. *Metabolism*, **18**, 556–563.

Louis, L. H., Conn, J. W. and Appelt, M. M. (1971). Induction of hyperinsulin-emia and hyperglycaemia in dogs by administration of diabetogenic bovine pituitary peptide. *Metabolism*, **20**, 326–330.

Lowenstein, J. M. (1972). Ammonia production in muscle and other tissues: the nucleotide cycle. *Physiol. Rev.*, **52**, 383–414.

Luyckx, A. S. and Lefebvre, P. J. (1970). Arguments for a regulation of pancreatic glucagon secretion by circulating plasma free fatty acids. *Proc. Soc. exp. Biol. N.Y.*, **133**, 524–528.

Lynch, R. E., Schneider, E. G., Willis, L. R. and Knox, F. G. (1972). Absence of mineral-corticoid-dependent sodium reabsorption in dog proximal tubule. *Amer. J. Physiol.*, **223**, 40–45.

Mallette, L. E., Exton, J. H. and Park, C. R. (1967). Glucagon stimulation of amino acid gluconeogenesis. *Fed. Proc.*, **26**, 563.

Malnic, G. and Aires, M. M. (1970). Microperfusion study of anion transfer in proximal tubules of rat kidney. *Amer. J. Physiol.*, **218**, 27–32.

Malnic, G., Aires, M. M. and Veira, F. L. (1970). Chloride excretion in nephrons of rat kidney during alteration of acid-base equilibrium. *Amer. J. Physiol.*, **218**, 20–26.

Malnic, G., Klose, R. M. and Giebisch, G. (1964). Micropuncture study of renal potassium excretion in the rat. *Amer. J. Physiol.*, **206**, 674–686.

Malnic, G., Klose, R. M. and Giebisch, G. (1966a). Micropuncture study of distal tubular potassium and sodium transport in rat nephron. *Amer. J. Physiol.*, **211**, 529–547.

Malnic, G., Klose, R. M. and Giebisch, G. (1966b). Microperfusion study of distal tubular potassium and sodium transfer in the rat kidney. *Amer. J. Physiol.*, **211**, 548–559.

Malnic, G., de Mello Aires, M. and Giebisch, G. (1972). Micropuncture study of renal tubular hydrogen ion transport in the rat. *Amer. J. Physiol.*, **222**, 147–158.

Manchester, K. L. (1972). Effect of insulin on protein synthesis. *Diabetes*, **21**, 447–452.

Manns, J. G. and Boda, J. M. (1967). Insulin release by acetate, propionate, butyrate and glucose in lambs and adult sheep. *Amer. J. Physiol.*, **212**, 747–755.

Marin-Grez, M., Cottone, P. and Carretero, O. A. (1972). Evidence for an involve-ment of kinins in regulation of sodium excretion. *Amer. J. Physiol.*, **223**, 794–796.

Martin, J. B. (1974). Inhibitory effect of somatostatin (SRIF) on the release of growth hormone (GH) induced in the rat by electrical stimulation. *Endo-crinology*, **94**, 497–502.

Martin, J. M. and Gagliardino, J. J. (1967). Effect of growth hormone on the isolated pancreatic islets of rat *in vitro*. *Nature*, **213**, 630–631.

Martin, D. L., Melancon, M. J. and deLuca, H. F. (1969). Vitamin D stimulated calcium-dependent adenosine triphosphatase from brush borders of rat small intestine. *Biochem. Biophys. Res. Comm.*, **35**, 819–823.

Massry, S. G., Coburn, J. N. and Kleeman, C. R. (1969). Renal handling of mag-nesium in the dog. *Amer. J. Physiol.*, **216**, 1460–1467.

Matsuzaki, F. and Raben, M. S. (1965). Growth hormone. *Annu. Rev. Pharmacol.*, **5**, 137–150.

McCance, R. A. (1936). Experimental sodium chloride deficiency in man. *Proc. Roy. Soc. B*, **119**, 245–268.

McDonald, G. W., Fisher, G. F. and Burnham, C. E. (1964). Differences in glucose determinations obtained from plasma or whole blood. *Publ. Health Rpts.*, **79**, 515–521.

Meade, R. C. *et al.* (1965). The state of pancreatic and serum insulin. *Diabetes*, **14**, 387–391.

Menninger, R. P. and Frazier, D. T. (1972). Effects of blood volume and atrial stretch on hypothalamic single-unit activity. *Amer. J. Physiol.*, **223**, 288–293.

Merrill, J. E., Peach, M. J. and Gilmore, J. P. (1973). Angiotensin I conversion in the kidney and its modulation by sodium balance. *Amer. J. Physiol.*, **224**, 1104–1108.

Meyer, D. K., Peskar, B. and Hertting, G. H. (1971). Hemmung des durch blutsenkende Pharmaka bei Ratten ausgelösten Trinkens durch Nephrektomie. *Experientia*, **27**, 65–66.

Miller, T. B. and Larner, J. (1972). Anti-insulin actions of a bovine pituitary diabetogenic peptide on glycogen synthesis. *Proc. Nat. Acad. Sci. Wash.*, **69**, 2774–2777.

Miller, W. L. and Krake, J. J. (1963). Effect of corticotropin on exhaled carbon-dioxide of mice. *Endocrinology*, **72**, 518–522.

Milton, A. S. and Paterson, A. T. (1974). A microinjection study of the control of antidiuretic hormone release by the supraoptic nucleus of the hypothalamus in the cat. *J. Physiol.*, **241**, 607–628.

Morgan, T., Tadokoro, M., Martin, D. and Berliner, R. W. (1970). Effect of furosemide on Na^+ and K^+ transport studied by microperfusion of the rat nephron. *Amer. J. Physiol.*, **218**, 292–297.

Morita, Y. and Munck, A. (1964). Effect of glucocorticoids *in vivo* and *in vitro* on net glucose uptake and amino acid incorporation by rat thymus cells. *Biochim. biophys. Acta*, **93**, 150–157.

Mortimore, G. E. (1961). Effects of insulin on potassium transfer in isolated rat liver. *Amer. J. Physiol.*, **200**, 1315–1319.

Munck, A. (1971). Glucocorticoid inhibition of glucose uptake by peripheral tissue: old and new evidence, molecular mechanisms, and physiological significance. *Persp. Biol. Med.*, **14**, 265–289.

Needleman, P. *et al.* (1973). Specific stimulation and inhibition of renal prostaglandin release by angiotensin analogs. *Amer. J. Physiol.*, **224**, 1415–1419.

Niall, H. D. *et al.* (1973). The chemistry of growth hormone and the lactogenic hormones. *Rec. Prog. Hormone Res.*, **29**, 387–404.

Nicolaysen, R., Eeg-Larsen, N. and Malm, O. J. (1953). Physiology of calcium metabolism. *Physiol. Rev.*, **33**, 424–444.

Ohneda, A., Aguilar-Parada, E., Eisentraut, A. M. and Unger, R. H. (1969). Control of pancreatic glucagon secretion by glucose. *Diabetes*, **18**, 1–10.

Ohneda, A., Parada, E., Eisentraut, A. M. and Unger, R. H. (1968). Characterization of response of circulating glucagon to intraduodenal and intravenous administration of amino acids. *J. clin. Invest.*, **47**, 2305–2322.

Overell, B. G., Condon, S. E. and Petrow, V. (1960). The effect of hormones and their analogues upon the uptake of glucose by mouse skin *in vitro*. *J. Pharm. Pharmacol.*, **12**, 150–153.

Park, C. R. *et al.* (1959). The action of insulin on the transport of glucose through the cell membrane. *Amer. J. Med.*, **26**, 674–684.

Park, C. R., Lewis, S. B. and Exton, J. H. (1972). Relationship of some hepatic actions of insulin to the intracellular level of cyclic adenylate. *Diabetes*, **21**, 439–446.

Pitts, R. F. and Alexander, R. S. (1945). The nature of the renal tubular mechanism for acidifying the urine. *Amer. J. Physiol.*, **144**, 239–254.

Pitts, R. F. and Lotspeich, W. D. (1946). Bicarbonate and the renal regulation of acid base balance. *Amer. J. Physiol.*, **147**, 138–154.

Polak, A., Haynic, G. D., Hays, R. M. and Schwartz, W. B. (1961). Effects of chronic hypercapnia on electrolyte and acid base-equilibrium. I. Adaptation. *J. clin. Invest.*, **40**, 1223–1237.

Porte, D. (1967). Beta adrenergic stimulation of insulin release in man. *Diabetes*, **16**, 150–155.

Porte, D. *et al.* (1973). Neural regulation of insulin secretion in the dog. *J. clin. Invest.*, **52**, 210–214.

Porte, D., Graber, A. L., Kuzuya, T. and Williams, R. H. (1966). The effect of epinephrine on immunoreactive insulin levels in man. *J. clin. Invest.*, **45**, 228–276.

Purkerson, M. L., Lubowitz, H., White, R. W. and Bricker, N. S. (1969). On the influence of extracellular fluid volume on bicarbonate reabsorption in the rat. *J. clin. Invest.*, **48**, 1754–1760.

Puschett, J. B. and Goldberg, M. (1968). The acute effects of furosemide on acid and electrolyte excretion in man. *J. lab. clin. Med.*, **71**, 666–677.

Radford, E. P. (1959). Factors modifying water metabolism in rats fed dry diets. *Amer. J. Physiol.*, **196**, 1098–1108.

Ramberg, C. F. *et al.* (1967). Plasma calcium and parathyroid hormone responses to EDTA infusion in the cow. *Amer. J. Physiol.*, **213**, 878–882.

Randle, P. J., Garland, P. B., Hales, C. N. and Newsholme, E. A. (1963). The glucose fatty-acid cycle: its role in insulin sensitivity and the metabolic disturbances of diabetes mellitus. *Lancet*, **i**, 785–789.

Rasmussen, H. and Tenenhouse, A. (1970). Parathyroid hormone and calcitonin. In *Biochemical Action of Hormones* (Ed. G. Litwack), Vol. I, pp. 365–415. Academic Press, New York.

Rector, F. C., Carter, N. W. and Seldin, D. W. (1965). The mechanism of bicarbonate reabsorption in the proximal and distal tubules of the kidney. *J. clin. Invest.*, **44**, 278–290.

Rector, F. C. and Clapp, J. R. (1962). Evidence for active chloride reabsorption in the rat. *J. clin. Invest.*, **41**, 101–107.

Rector, J. B. *et al.* (1972). Effect of hemorrhage and vasopressor agents on distribution of renal blood flow. *Amer. J. Physiol.*, **222**, 1125–1131.

Rehfeld, J. F. and Stadel, F. (1973). The effect of gastrin on basal- and glucose-stimulated insulin secretion in man. *J. clin. Invest.*, **52**, 1415–1426.

Richter, C. P. (1936). Increased salt appetite in adrenalectomized rats. *Amer. J. Physiol.*, **115**, 155–161.

Robinson, B. W. and Mishkin, M. (1968). Alimentary responses to forebrain stimulation in monkeys. *Exp. Brain Res.*, **4**, 330–366.

Robinson, E. A. and Adolph, E. F. (1943). Pattern of normal water drinking in dogs. *Amer. J. Physiol.*, **139**, 39–45.

Robison, G. A., Butcher, R. W. and Sutherland, E. W. (1972). The catecholamines. In *Biochemical Actions of Hormones* (Ed. G. Litwack), Vol. II, pp. 81-111. Academic Press, New York.

Rocha e Silva, M. and Rosenberg, M. (1969). The release of vasopressin in response to haemorrhage and its role in the mechanism of blood pressure regulation. *J. Physiol.*, **202**, 535–557.

Rodbell, M. (1964). Metabolism of isolated fat cells. *J. biol. Chem.*, **239**, 375–380.

Rodbell, M. (1967). Metabolism of fat cells. VI. The effects of insulin, lipolytic hormones, and theophyllin in glucose transport and metabolism in "ghosts". *J. biol. Chem.*, **242**, 5751–5756.

Ross, D. B. (1962). *In vitro* studies on the transport of magnesium across the intestinal wall of the rat. *J. Physiol.*, **160**, 417–428.

Roth, J., Glick, S. M., Yalow, R. S. and Berson, S. A. (1963). Secretion of human growth hormone: physiologic and experimental modification. *Metabolism*, **12**, 577–579.

Saborowiski, F., Usinger, W. and Albers, C. (1971). pH und CO_2-Bindungskurve im Intracellularraum der Skelet-Muskulatur beim Hund. *Pflug. Arch.*, **328**, 121–134.

Samols, E., Marri, G. and Marks, V. (1965). Promotion of insulin secretion by glucagon. *Lancet*, **ii**, 415–416.

Schachter, D. and Rosen, S. M. (1959). Active transport of Ca^{45} by the small intestine and its dependence on vitamin D. *Amer. J. Physiol.*, **196**, 357–362.

Scharff, R. and Wool, I. G. (1965). Accumulation of amino acids in muscle of perfused rat heart. *Biochem. J.*, **97**, 272–276.

Schmidt-Nielsen, B. and O'Dell, R. (1961). Structure and concentrating mechanism in the mammalian kidney. *Amer. J. Physiol.*, **200**, 1119–1124.

Scott, D. (1965). Factors influencing the secretion and absorption of calcium and magnesium in the small intestine of the sheep. *Quart. J. exp. Physiol.*, **50**, 312–329.

Seltzer, H. S., Allen, E. W. and Brennan, M. T. (1965). Failure of prolonged sulfoxyl- urea administration to enhance response to glycemic stimulus. *Diabetes*, **14**, 392–395.

Sernka, T. J. and Borle, A. B. (1969). Calcium in the intestinal contents on different calcium diets. *Proc. Soc. exp. Biol. N.Y.*, **131**, 1420–1423.

Seyffert, W. A. and Madison, L. L. (1967). Acute effect of elevation of plasma fatty acids on hepatic glucose output, peripheral glucose utilization, serum insulin, and plasma glucagon levels. *Diabetes*, **16**, 765–776.

Share, L. and Levy, M. N. (1966). Effect of carotid chemoreceptor stimulation on plasma antidiuretic hormone titer. *Amer. J. Physiol.*, **210**, 157–161.

Sharma, K. N. (1967). Receptor mechanisms in the alimentary tract: their excitation and functions. *Hdb. Physiol.*, Sect. VI, Vol. 1, pp. 225–237.

Sharpe, L. G. and Swanson, L. W. (1974). Drinking induced by injections of angio- tensin into forebrain and mid-brain sites of the monkey. *J. Physiol.*, **239**, 595–622.

Shaw, W. N. and Chance, R. E. (1968). Effect of porcine proinsulin *in vitro* on adipose tissue and diaphragm of the normal rat. *Diabetes*, **17**, 737–745.

Sherwood, L. M. *et al.* (1968). Regulation of parathyroid hormone secretion: proportional control by calcium, lack of effect of phosphate. *Endocrinology*, **83**, 1043–1051.

Shimazu, T. and Amakawa, A. (1968). Regulation of glycogen metabolism in liver by the autonomic nervous system. II. Neural control of glycogenolytic enzymes. *Biochim. biophys. Acta*, **165**, 335–348.

Shimazu, T., Fukuda, A. and Ban, T. (1966). Reciprocal influences of the ventro- medial and lateral hypothalamic nuclei on blood glucose level and liver glycogen content. *Nature*, **210**, 1178–1179.

Shoemaker, W. C. and Van Itallie, T. B. (1960). The hepatic response to glucagon in the unanaesthetized dog. *Endocrinology*, **66**, 260–268.

Shoemaker, W. C. and Elwynn, D. H. (1969). Liver: Functional interactions within the intact animal. *Ann. Rev. Physiol.*, **31**, 227–268.

Simmons, D. H. and Avedon, M. (1959). Acid-base alterations and plasma potassium concentration. *Amer. J. Physiol.*, **197**, 319–326.

Simon, E., Kraicer, P. F. and Shelesnyak, M. C. (1962). Physiologic response to D-mannoheptulose: gluconeogenesis. *Endocrinology*, **71**, 83–89.

Sinex, F. M., MacMullen, J. and Hastings, A. B. (1952). The effect of insulin on the incorporation of C^{14} into the protein of rat diaphragm. *J. biol. Chem.*, **198**, 615–619.

Smith, G. P. *et al.* (1973). Effect of 2-deoxy-D-glucose on insulin response to glucose in intact and adrenalectomized monkeys. *Endocrinology*, **92**, 750–754.

Smith, R. H. (1959). Calcium and magnesium metabolism in calves. 4. *Biochem. J.* **71**, 609–614.

Sokal, J. E. and Sarcione, E. J. (1959). Effect of epinephrine on glycogen stores. *Amer. J. Physiol.*, **196**, 1253–1257.

Sokal, J. E., Sarcione, E. J. and Henderson, A. M. (1964). Relative potency of glucagon and epinephrine as hepatic glycogenolytic agents: studies with the isolated perfused rat liver. *Endocrinology*, **74**, 930–938.

Solomon, S. S., Brush, J. S. and Kitabchi, A. E. (1970). Antilipolytic activity of insulin and proinsulin on ACTH and cyclic nucleotide-induced lipolysis in the isolated adipose cell of the rat. *Biochim. biophys. Acta*, **218**, 167–169.

Sonenberg, M. *et al.* (1965). The metabolic effects in man of growth hormone digested with trypsin. *Metabolism*, **14**, 1189–1213.

Stauffer, M., Baylink, D., Wergedal, J. and Rich, C. (1973). Decreased bone formation, mineralization, and enhanced resorption in calcium-deficient rats. *Amer. J. Physiol.*, **225**, 269–276.

Stein, J. H., Osgood, R. W. and Ferris, T. F. (1972). Effect of volume expansion on distribution of glomerular filtrate and renal cortical blood flow in the dog. *Amer. J. Physiol.*, **223**, 984–990.

Stein, J. H. *et al.* (1971). Effect of renal vasodilation on the distribution of cortical blood flow in the kidney of the dog. *J. clin. Invest.*, **50**, 1429–1438.

Steiner, D. F. and Oyer, P. E. (1967). The biosynthesis of insulin and a probable precursor of insulin by a human islet cell adenoma. *Proc. Nat. Acad. Sci. Wash.*, **57**, 473–480.

Stella, G. (1929). The combination of carbon dioxide with muscles: its heat of neutralization and its dissociation curve. *J. Physiol.*, **68**, 49–66.

Stinebaugh, B. J. *et al.* (1971). Renal handling of bicarbonate: effect of mannitol diuresis. *Amer. J. Physiol.*, **220**, 1271–1274.

Stricker, E. M. (1966). Extracellular fluid volume and thirst. *Amer. J. Physiol.*, **211**, 232–238.

Stricker, E. M. (1969). Osmoregulation and volume regulation in rats: inhibition of hypovolemic thirst by water. *Amer. J. Physiol.*, **217**, 98–105.

Stricker, E. M. and Miller, N. E. (1968). Saline preference and body fluid analyses in rats after intrahypothalamic injections of carbachol. *Physiol. Behav.*, **3**, 471–475.

Stricker, E. M. and Wolf, G. (1966). Blood volume and tonicity in relation to sodium appetite. *J. comp. physiol. Psychol.*, **62**, 275–279.

Strickler, J. C., Thompson, D. D., Klose, R. M. and Giebisch, G. (1964). Micropuncture study of inorganic phosphate excretion in the rat. *J. clin. Invest.*, **43**, 1596–1607.

Teitelbaum, P. and Epstein, A. N. (1962). The lateral hypothalamic syndrome. *Psychol. Rev.*, **69**, 74–90.

Thurau, K. (1966). Nature of autoregulation of renal blood flow. *Proc. III. Int. Congr. Nephrol.*, **1**, 162–173.

Tobian, L. (1964). Sodium, renal arterial distension and the juxtaglomerular apparatus. *Can. Med. Ass. J.*, **90**, 160–162.

Towbin, E. J. (1949). Gastric distention as a factor in the satisfaction of thirst in esophagostomized dogs. *Amer. J. Physiol.*, **159**, 533–541.

Tsukamoto, M. *et al.* (1967). Effect of vagal stimulation by 2-deoxy-D-glucose and insulin on gastric motility in dogs. *Ann. Surgery*, **165**, 605–608.

Unger, R. H., Ketterer, H., Dupré, J. and Eisentraut, A. M. (1967). The effects of secretin, pancreozymin and gastrin on insulin and glucagon secretion in unanaesthetized dogs. *J. clin. Invest.*, **46**, 630–645.

Urgoiti, E. J., Houssay, B. A. and Rietti, C. T. (1963). Hypophyseal and adrenal factors essential for ketoacidosis of pancreatectomized dogs. *Diabetes*, **12**, 301–307.

Vander, A. J. (1965). Effect of catecholamines and the renal nerves on renin secretion in anesthetized dogs. *Amer. J. Physiol.*, **209**, 659–662.

Vander, A. J. (1970). Direct effects of potassium on renin secretion and renal function. *Amer. J. Physiol.*, **219**, 455–459.

Verney, E. B. (1947). The antidiuretic hormone and the factors which determine its release. *Proc. Roy. Soc.*, **135**, 25–106.

Veyrat, R., Brunner, H. R., Grandchamp, A. and Muller, A. F. (1967). Inhibition of renin by potassium in man. *Acta. endocrin.*, Suppl. **119**, 86.

Waddell, W. J. and Bates, R. G. (1969). Intracellular pH. *Physiol. Rev.*, **49**, 285–329.

Waddell, W. J. and Butler, T. C. (1959). Calculation of intracellular pH from the distribution of 5,5-dimethyl-2,4-oxazolidinedione (DMO). *J. clin. Invest.*, **38**, 720–729.

Walling, M. W. and Kimberg, D. V. (1973). Active secretion of calcium by adult rat ileum and jejunum *in vitro*. *Amer. J. Physiol.*, **225**, 415–422.

Walser, M. (1961). Calcium clearance as a function of sodium clearance in the dog. *Amer. J. Physiol.*, **200**, 1099–1104.

Walser, M. (1961). Ion association. VI. *J. clin. Invest.*, **40**, 723–730.

Walser, M. (1967). Magnesium metabolism. *Ergeb. Physiol.*, **59**, 185–296.

Walser, M. and Mudge, G. H. (1960). Renal excretory mechanisms. In *Mineral Metabolism* (Ed. C. L. Comar and F. Bronner), Vol. I, p. 288. Academic Press, New York.

de Wardener, H. E. (1969). Control of sodium reabsorption. *Brit. med. Bull.*, **3**, 611–616; 676–683.

de Wardener, H. E. and Herxheimer, A. (1957). The effect of a high water intake on salt consumption, taste thresholds and salivary secretion in man. *J. Physiol.*, **139**, 53–63

Warren, Y., Luke, R. G., Kashgarian, M. and Levitin, H. (1970). Micropuncture studies of chloride and bicarbonate absorption in the proximal renal tubule of the rat in respiratory acidosis and in chloride depletion. *Clin. Sci.*, **38**, 375–383.

Wasserman, R. H. and Taylor, A. N. (1968). Vitamin D-dependent calcium-binding protein. *J. biol. Chem.*, **243**, 3987–3993; 3978–3986.

Weber, M. A., Thornell, I. R. and Stokes, G. S. (1973). Effect of hemorrhage with and without fluid replacement on plasma renin activity. *Amer. J. Physiol.*, **225**, 1161–1164.

Weiner, I. H. and Stellar, E. (1951). Salt preference of the rat determined by a single-stimulus method. *J. comp. physiol. Psychol.*, **44**, 394–401.

Wen, S.-F., Evanson, R. L. and Dirks, J. H. (1970). Micropuncture study of renal magnesium transport in proximal and distal tubule of the dog. *Amer. J. Physiol.*, **219**, 570–576.

Whittembury, G. and Fishman, J. (1969). Relation between cell Na extrusion and transtubular absorption in the perfused toad kidney: the effect of K, ouabain and ethacrynic acid. *Pflüg. Arch. ges. Physiol.*, **307**, 138–153.

Wiederholt, M., Stolte, H., Brecht, J. P. and Hierholzer, K. (1966). Mikropunktions untersuchungen uber den Einfluss von Aldosteron, Cortison und Dexamethason auf die renale Natrium resorption adrenalektomierter Ratten. *Pflüg. Arch. ges. Physiol.*, **292**, 316–333.

Willis, L. R., Ludens, J. H., Hook, J. B. and Williamson, H. E. (1969). Mechanism of natriuretic action of bradykinin. *Amer. J. Physiol.*, **217**, 1–5.

Windhager, E. E. and Geibisch, G. (1961). Micropuncture study of renal tubular transfer of sodium chloride in the rat. *Amer. J. Physiol.*, **200**, 581–590.

Wise, J. K., Hendler, R. and Felig, P. (1973). Influence of glucocorticoids on glucagon secretion and plasma amino acid concentrations in man. *J. clin. Invest.*, **52**, 2774–2782.

Wool, I. G., Castles, J. J. and Moyer, A. N. (1965). Regulation of amino acid accumulation in isolated rat diaphragm: effect of puromycin and insulin. *Biochim. biophys. Acta*, **107**, 333–345.

Wool, I. G. and Krahl, M. E. (1959). Incorporation of C^{14}-amino acids into protein of isolated diaphragm: an effect of insulin independent of glucose entry. *Amer. J. Physiol.*, **196**, 961–964.

Wool, I. G. and Munro, A. J. (1963). An influence of insulin on the synthesis of a rapidly labelled RNA by isolated rat diaphragm. *Proc. Nat. Acad. Sci. Wash.*, **50**, 918–923.

Yalow, R. S., Goldsmith, S. J. and Berson, S. A. (1969). Influence of physiologic fluctuations in plasma growth hormone on glucose tolerance. *Diabetes*, **18**, 402–408.

Yensen, R. (1959). Some factors affecting taste sensitivity in man. II. Depletion of body salt. *Quart. J. exp. Psychol.*, **11**, 230–238.

Young, F. G. (1945). Growth and diabetes in normal animals treated with pituitary (anterior lobe) diabetogenic extract. *Biochem. J.*, **39**, 515–536.

Young, F. G. (1963). In *Comparative Endocrinology* (Ed. U.S. von Euler and H. Heller), Vol. I, p. 371. Academic Press, New York. (Quoted by Fritz, 1972).

Young, F. G. (1971). Diabetes, diet and biochemistry. *Conquest*, No. **162**, 3–9.

Zierler, K. L. (1959). Effect of insulin on membrane potential and potassium content of rat muscle. *Amer. J. Physiol.*, **197**, 515–523.

Zimmet, P., Ng, F. M., Bornstein, J., Armstrong, J. McD. and Taft, H. P. (1971) Insulin antagonist of pituitary origin in plasma of normal and diabetogenic subjects. *Brit. med. J.*, (**1**), 203–204.

Zimmet, P., Ng, F., Bornstein, J. and Taft, P. (1972). Somantin (In-G), Cataglykin (AcG), and glucose homeostasis in man. *Horm. Metab. Res.*, **4**, 309–310.

CHAPTER 6

Homeostasis in the Nervous System

THE CEREBROSPINAL FLUID AND BLOOD-BRAIN BARRIER

Second Line of Defence

The brain* is supplied with a vascular system that grossly and microscopically appears similar to that in other parts of the body such as skeletal muscle, so that we might expect that the neurones and glial cells of the brain would be subject to the same environmental influences, exerted through the blood-plasma, as in other parts of the body, so that the relative constancy of the cellular environment would be determined by the relative constancy of the composition of the blood plasma. Thus a rise in blood-glucose, for example, would be rapidly reflected in a rise in the concentration in the extracellular fluid surrounding the brain cells. In fact, however, the brain cells are doubly protected from fluctuations in their environment; they share with the rest of the body the primary defence, through the homeostatic mechanisms that we have so far described, which achieve a reasonable constancy of composition of the blood-plasma, but their second line of defence insulates them against the naturally occurring fluctuation in the composition of the plasma. This insulation is achieved primarily by what has been called the *blood-brain barrier*, a restraint on the passage of substances from the blood plasma into the extracellular fluid of brain that differs radically from the negligible restraint imposed by the blood capillaries in, say, skeletal muscle, a restraint that only shows itself where obviously large molecules, such as serum proteins, are concerned.

Blood-Brain Barrier

Vital Staining

Ehrlich and Goldmann, in their classical studies on the passage of a variety of dyestuffs from the blood into the tissues, noticed that,

* In this discussion the term brain includes the spinal cord.

with many of their dyes, the brain remained uncoloured although the remaining tissues of the body were heavily stained; typical of the dye-stuffs employed was trypan blue; this stained the dura of the brain and spinal cord but left the nervous tissue uncoloured, except for a few highly localized spots; the rest of the tissues of the body were heavily stained.

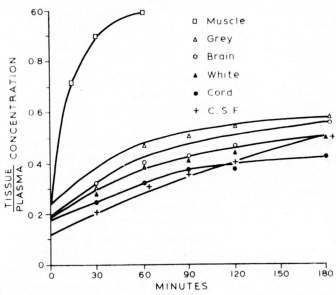

Fig. 6.1. Penetration of urea into muscle, cerebrospinal fluid and various tissues of the central nervous system. (Kleeman, Davson and Levin, *Amer. J. Physiol.*)

Quantitative Studies

Subsequent work of a more quantitative kind has firmly established this concept of a blood-brain barrier; thus Fig. 6.1 shows the penetration of the simple molecule urea into the muscle and nervous tissue of the rabbit; skeletal muscle comes into complete equilibrium with the blood-plasma in less than an hour whereas the brain and cord are by no means at equilibrium in 3 hr.

Extraction-Coefficient. By analysing the blood flowing into and out of the brain, it is possible to measure an "extraction coefficient" and from this to deduce a permeability coefficient for the brain capillaries; some figures from Crone's (1965) study are given in Table I and compared with estimates of muscle capillary derived by the quantitative studies of Landis and Pappenheimer (1963) and Alvarez and Yudilevich (1969).

TABLE I

Permeability coefficients (cm/sec 10^5) for blood-brain barrier
and skeletal muscle

Substance	Brain	Muscle
Fructose	0·16	—
Glucose	—	6·0
Urea	0·44	14·0
Glycerol	0·21	1·5
Antipyrine	3·3	—
Ethanol	10·0	—
Sucrose	Very small	4·0
Inulin	Very small	0·3

Lipid-Solubility. An important feature of the blood-brain barrier is its similarity to the restraint on penetration into the single cell, so that when substances of different lipid-solubility are compared, it is found that the greater the lipid-solubility the more rapid the penetration. In fact, therefore, the blood-brain barrier is by no means an absolute barrier to penetration from blood to brain, but, where highly lipid-soluble substances are concerned, it offers little or no restraint to equilibration between blood and brain. Practically, this difference is revealed by the relative effectiveness of anaesthetics when given intravenously; it has been known for a long time that some, such as Nembutal, will cause anaesthesia as soon as the animal is injected, whereas others, such as phenobarbitone, may take over half an hour to induce anaesthesia after an intravenous dose. Mark *et al.* (1957, 1958) analysed the brain after injecting different anaesthetics, and showed that thiopental penetrated much more rapidly into the brain than its analogue pentothal; similarly, thiobarbital and thiophenobarbital penetrated more rapidly than their analogues barbital and phenobarbital; and these differences in rate of uptake correlated well with the speed with which the anaesthetics would affect the electroencephalogram (EEG).

Transmitters. Thus, if we may think of the blood-brain barrier as being protective, in that it slows down the rate of penetration of material from blood into the brain, then this protection is only seriously manifest where relatively water-soluble substances are concerned. Physiologically and pharmacologically this protection is manifest by the relative immunity of the brain from the actions of such transmitters, and their analogues, as acetylcholine, noradrenaline, dopamine, carbachol, and so on; these, when given intravenously, will act peripherally, e.g. on muscles, but have negligible effects in the brain in spite of the fact that, when they do gain access, either pathologically or experimentally, their effects may be profound. We have already seen examples of this in the excitation of localized regions of the hypothalamus by microinjections of 5-HT, acetylcholine, noradrenaline, and so on.

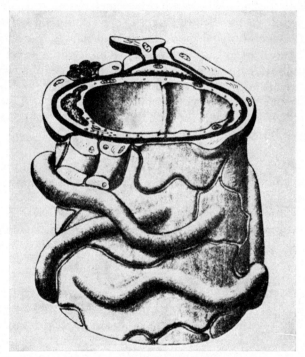

Fig. 6.2. A three dimensional drawing of a cerebral capillary. The astrocytic processes are shown terminating in flat "end feet" which envelop the capillary endothelium in a complete sheath. (Wolff, *Z. Zellforsch.*)

The Ultrastructure of the Blood-Brain Barrier

The only obvious microscopical difference between a capillary of skeletal muscle and that of the brain or spinal cord is the presence of a layer of astrocytes that appear, by apposing their end-feet to the capillary basement membrane, to ensheathe the vessel completely, as illustrated by Fig. 6.2. For a long time the functional difference between the brain and muscle capillary was attributed to this feature, the glial sheath acting as a permeability barrier. For such a barrier to be highly effective in restraining the passage of, say sucrose, out of the plasma, the junctions between the protoplasmic processes would have to be sealed to give the so-called tight junctions or zonulae occludentes (Vol. 1), but, in fact, the electron microscopical studies of Brightman (1968) failed to reveal any such occlusive barriers, so that the astroglial covering, or sheath, has been rejected as the site of the barrier.

Endothelial Tight Junctions. With the development of the horseradish peroxidase technique, whereby the relatively small molecule (by capillary permeability standards), horseradish peroxidase, could be made visible in the electron microscope, a fundamental difference in capillary structure between the brain and muscle was demonstrated by Reese and Karnovsky (1967). This molecule escapes from the muscle capillary readily and may be seen filling the junctions between endothelial cells and within the basement membrane; by contrast the tracer molecule was confined to the capillaries of the brain, and at localized regions its passage through the intercellular clefts was blocked, so that none appeared in the clefts distal to this blockade and none appeared in the basement membrane and interstitial space. Thus the brain capillary membrane shares with the epithelia the selective permeability that restrains most lipid-insoluble molecules but permits the passage of lipid-soluble molecules; and it also shares the ultrastructural feature that seems to be responsible for these phenomena, namely the tight junction. Thus permeability through these membranes is equivalent to permeability through individual plasma membranes.

Facilitated Transfer

We have seen that single cells do have a relatively high permeability to some lipid-insoluble molecules, notably those that are important metabolically such as some hexoses and amino acids; this facilitated diffusion is shared also with certain epithelia and permits the rapid absorption through the intestinal wall, for example, or the reabsorption through the renal tubule, processes that are accelerated by active transport as well. It is reasonable to expect the brain capillaries to have a similar specialization, and this is true so that the metabolically important D-glucose or D-galactose penetrate rapidly, whereas substances of comparable lipid-solubility and molecular size, such as mannitol, penetrate so slowly into the brain that it is difficult to make quantitative measurements.

Sugars and Amino Acids. The characteristics of the blood-brain barrier with respect to sugars and amino acids have been examined in a semiquantitative manner by Oldendorf (1971, 1973). In these studies he injected a single "bolus" of the solute, e.g. glycine, into the carotid artery of the rat and, after some 15 sec, the animal was decapitated and the brain removed for analysis. In the same bolus there was contained a known quantity of tritiated water, which penetrates very rapidly into brain, its actual rate being governed by the rate of blood-flow. Thus the uptake of the tritiated water acted as a standard of reference, or comparison, for each solute that was injected with it, and in this way allowances were automatically made for variations in blood-flow and speed of injection. The measure of permeability of the blood-brain barrier to the various solutes was taken as the ratio of the extractions of the given substance to that of tritiated water, and this could vary from zero to unity or greater.

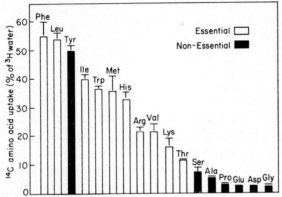

Fig. 6.3. The uptake of amino acids across the blood-brain barrier as indicated by single pass studies of radioactive labelled compounds. Note the essential amino acids show a greater uptake than non-essential. It is probable that tyrosine is an essential amino acid for the rat. (Oldendorf, *Amer. J. Physiol.*)

Competition. It will be recalled that the carrier-mediated type of permeability is revealed by the effects of adding non-radioactive solute to the radioactive solute; if the non-radioactive material competes for the radioactive material, it is deduced that the permeability depends on some sort of carrier system. Furthermore, where sugars and amino acids are concerned, competition between different solutes for transport will be measured, so that adding alanine, for example, to glycine, inhibits the passage of glycine, and *vice versa*.

Amino Acids. Oldendorf's studies fully confirmed earlier and less exhaustive studies (Crone, 1965; Yudilevich and De Rose, 1971; Bidder, 1968, etc.) indicating the carrier-mediated type of permeability across the blood-brain barrier. Figure 6.3 shows the results of a study on a series of amino acids, the relative rates of penetration being indicated by the heights of the bars. There are large differences, and the interesting feature emerging is that the amino acids exhibiting high permeability are essential amino acids. Comparable studies on some sugars are shown in Table II, where it will be seen that D-glucose, for example, penetrates some twenty times as rapidly as L-glucose or D-fructose.

TABLE II

Uptake of labelled hexoses by the rat's brain as fraction of the uptake of tritiated water (Oldendorf, *Amer. J. Physiol.*)

Hexose	Brain uptake index
Tritiated water reference	100
2-Deoxy-D-glucose	46
D-Glucose	33
3-O-Methyl + D-glucose	29
D-Mannose	21
D-Galactose	14
D-Fructose	1·75
L-Glucose	1·63

Transmitter Precursors. Another interesting finding is that solutes that are required for synthesis of transmitters within the brain, such as choline (for acetylcholine) histidine (for histamine), dopa (for dopamine), glucose (for glycine) enter the brain rapidly, although, as indicated earlier, the transmitters themselves are virtually excluded from the brain when injected intravenously.

Heroin and Morphine. Of considerable interest is the opium alkaloid heroin; this has always been recognized clinically as more effective than morphia, and this is because of its more rapid penetration into the brain, through greater lipid-solubility; within the brain it is transformed into morphine which does not penetrate the barrier so easily, and so it tends to be trapped within the brain and thus remains effective for some time.

The Cerebrospinal Fluid

Anatomical Location

No study of the relations between blood and brain is complete without a corresponding study between blood and the cerebrospinal fluid (CSF), and a study of the relations between CSF and the brain, since the CSF comes into close relations with the brain, on the one hand, and the blood on the other. The location of the cerebrospinal fluid is indicated schematically in Figs. 6.4 and 6.5; it occupies the cavities within the brain, namely the *ventricles*, and also it occupies spaces surrounding the brain, the *subarachnoid space* including the *cisterns*, which are essentially localized expansions of the space. Thus the brain is bathed on its internal and external aspects by this fluid. The two compartments, namely the *internal*, or ventricular fluid and the *external*, or subarachnoid fluid, are in communication through certain foramina that connect the fourth ventricle with the adjacent subarachnoid fluid in the cisterna magna, the *foramen of Magendie* and

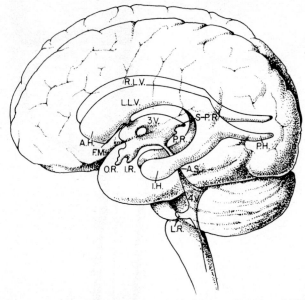

Fig. 6.4. A schematic diagram of the ventricles in man. LLV and RLV, left and right lateral ventricles; 3V, third ventricle; FM, foramen of Monro ; AS, Aqueduct of Sylvius; 4V, fourth ventricle; LR, lateral recess; AH, PH, IH, anterior, posterior, and inferior horns of LV; SPR, supraspinal recess; OR, optic recess; IR, infundibular recess; PR, pineal recess. (Netter, *Nervous System*, Ciba.)

the *foramina of Luschka*. The fluid flows out of the ventricles through these foramina into the subarachnoid spaces and is ultimately drained into the blood.

Drainage

In man and higher mammals the drainage takes place into the large venous sinus—the superior sagittal sinus—that carries much of the venous supply of the brain out of the skull. The mode of drainage is illustrated by Fig. 6.6; projecting through the wall of the venous sinus, or the adjacent lacunae laterales, there are the arachnoid villi or

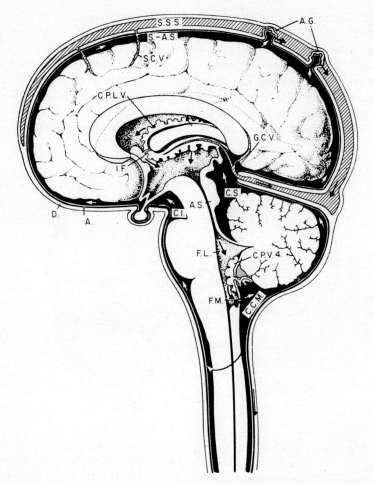

Fig. 6.5. A schematic diagram showing the route of drainage of the cerebrospinal fluid. A, arachnoid; AG, arachnoid granulation; AS, aqueduct of Sylvius; CC-M, cisterna cerebello-medullaris; CI, cisterna interpeduncularis; CPLV, CPV4, choroid plexuses of lateral ventricle and fourth ventricle; CS, cisterna superior; D, dura mater; FL, foramen of Luschka; FM, foramen of Magendie; GCV, great cerebral vein; IF, intraventricular foramen (Monro); SAS, subarachnoid space; SCV, superior cerebral vein; SSS, superior sagittal sinus. (Netter, *Nervous System*, Ciba.)

granulations, finger-like evaginations that penetrate the limiting endothelium of the venous sinus and thus project into the blood-stream. The limiting membrane covering the villus is highly porous, as demonstrated by the fact that large water-soluble molecules, including the plasma proteins, will pass out without serious restraint (Davson,

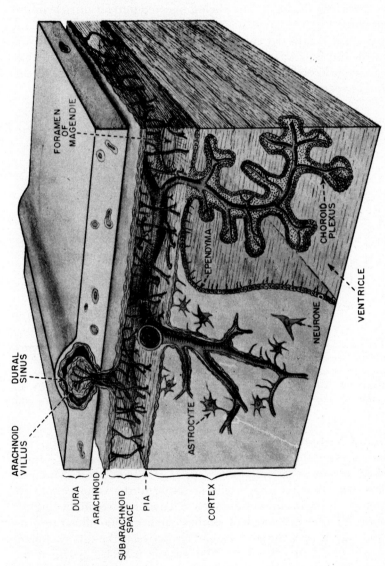

Fig. 6.6. A section of the brain and the investing membranes. Cerebrospinal fluid (CSF) is formed by the choroid plexuses, passes through the ventricular system and out on to the surface of the brain into the subarachnoid space. Drainage of CSF into the venous system occurs at arachnoid villi, one of which is shown in section in the upper part of the figure. (Tschirgi, *Handbook of Physiology*, Amer. Physiol. Soc.)

Domer and Hollingsworth, 1973) and even labelled erythrocytes will pass into the blood from the cerebrospinal fluid (Simmonds, 1953).

Figure 6.7 illustrates the relative ease with which radioactive serum-albumin passes into the blood after being injected into a ventricle of the brain; the same Figure shows the rise in blood concentration of serum albumin when it is injected continuously intravenously at a rate comparable with the flow of cerebrospinal fluid, and it will be seen that there is a remarkable parallelism suggesting a free flow out of the subarachnoid spaces into the blood.

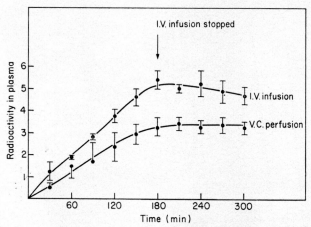

ig. 6.7. The course of development of radioactivity in plasma with time. The lower curve shows the escape into the blood of RIHSA from a bilateral ventricular perfusion of RIHSA in a mock CSF. The upper curve shows the result of a similar quantity of RIHSA given via an intravenous infusion. Ordinate: plasma radioactivity in arbitrary units; Abscissa: time after beginning of infusion. (Davson, Domer and Hollingsworth, *Brain*.)

Arachnoid Villus Pores. The actual nature of the pores in the membrane covering the villus is of some interest and has until recently puzzled the electron microscopists, such as Shabo and Maxwell (1968), who described an intact cellular lining to the villus composed of cells joined by tight-junctions. Such a covering would be highly selective, yet all the physiological studies, such as that illustrated in Fig. 6.7, indicate a very unselective barrier between the subarachnoid fluid and the blood in the villus. The answer may be provided by Tripathi and Tripathi's (1974) description of giant vacuoles that are present in many of the cells covering the villus; when examined in serial section these were often seen to be, in effect, large open channels between the inside and outside of the cell; in other words, the vacuole had actually cloven the cell to form a wide channel (Fig. 6.8). Tripathi, in discussing a similar problem concerned with drainage of aqueous humour from the eye, suggested that this process of vacuolization was cyclical, so that at any given moment a certain number of cells would be providing open channels to permit flow of fluid into the blood, as in Fig. 6.9.

Pressure-Flow. The force favouring flow of fluid from subarachnoid space into the blood is given by the difference of hydrostatic pressures between the cerebrospinal fluid and the blood; this is in favour of flow, the pressure in the cerebrospinal fluid being some 150 mm H_2O in man, whereas the pressure in the dural sinus is very much less. Changes in posture alter the absolute values, but leave the differential about the same.

Chemical Composition

The cerebrospinal fluid is very similar in composition to an ultrafiltrate of blood plasma, having a very low concentration of proteins, and the high concentration of Na^+ and the low concentration of K^+ characteristic of plasma. Careful examination of the composition, however, reveals some significant differences (Table III); thus the concentration of K^+ is significantly lower whilst that of Mg^{++} is higher; the concentration of Cl^- is higher, whilst the pH is more acid than that of plasma and the concentration of bicarbonate less. Since the PCO_2 is probably the same as that in venous blood, the lower pH is what would be expected of the lower concentration of bicarbonate. These differences of composition suggest that the fluid is formed by a process of secretion rather than as a simple filtrate from the blood.

TABLE III

Concentrations (meq/kg H_2O) of some solutes in human cerebrospinal fluid and plasma. (After Davson, *Physiology of the Cerebrospinal Fluid.*)

Substance	Plasma	CSF	Plasma filtrate
Na	150	147	142
K	4·6	2·9	4·4
Mg	1·6	2·2	1·3
Ca	4·7	2·3	3·1
Cl	99	113	104
HCO₃	26·8	23·3	28
Osmolality	289	289	289
pH	7·397	7·307	—
Glucose (mg/100 ml)	100	53	100

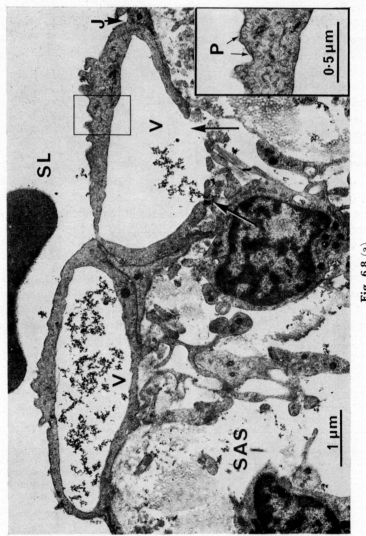

Fig. 6.8 (a)

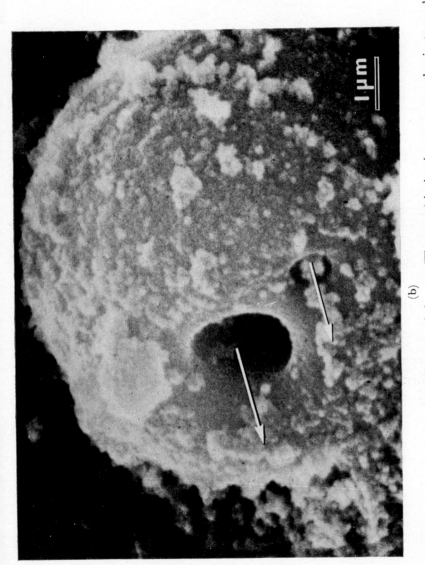

(b)

Fig. 6.8. (a) Following an injection of a colloidally suspended tracer (Thorotrast) in the cisterna magna, the giant vacuoles (V) in the mesothelial lining of the arachnoid villus are readily filled with the tracer material. (At this level of section, basal openings (arrows) are seen in the vacuole on the right but not in the vacuole on the left.) In contrast, the micropinocytotic vesicles (P) are essentially devoid of the tracer element and no leakage is seen through the cell junction (J). SAS, subarachnoid space; SL, sinus lacuna. (b) Scanning electron micrograph of a giant vacuole in the mesothelial cell lining the arachnoid villus seen from the apical (dural) aspect. A leakage of the tracer material (colloidally suspended Thorotrast) is seen here through the natural openings (arrows) on the apical surface of the vacuole. (Tripathi, *Brain Res.*)

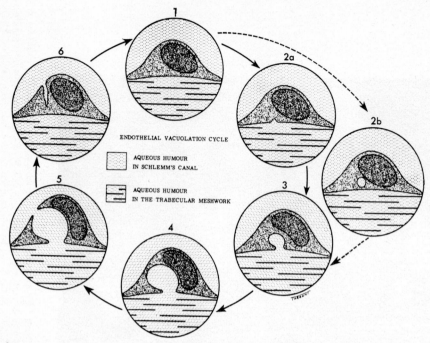

Fig. 6.9. Hypothetical cycle of vacuolation in an endothelial cell of Schlemm's canal resulting in the creation of a temporary channel communicating between the canal and the trabecular mesh-work. (Tripathi, *Exp. Eye Res.*)

Source of the Fluid

When the channel communicating between the third and fourth ventricles is blocked, either experimentally or pathologically by a tumour, the lateral ventricles enlarge—*hydrocephalus*—indicating that a main source of fluid is in the ventricles; and a large amount of experimental work (e.g. Welch, 1963; Rougemont *et al.*, 1960) has left little doubt that the origin of the fluid is the *choroid plexuses*, vascular outpouchings into the ventricles that are covered by the choroidal epithelium, which is continuous with the cellular lining of the ventricle called the *ependyma*. Although continuous with it, and derived embryologically from the same source, the choroidal epithelium is fundamentally different; its cells are sealed together by tight junctions whereas those of the ependyma are not.

Rate of Secretion

The actual rate of production of the fluid may be measured by perfusing the ventricles with an artificial CSF, the inflow cannulae being in the lateral ventricles and an outflow cannula in the cisterna magna; if the fluid contains a substance that cannot diffuse into the adjacent brain-tissue or into the choroid plexuses, any change in its concentration will indicate the dilution due to addition of new fluid (Pappenheimer *et al.*, 1962); a suitable substance is a coloured dextran of molecular weight about 2 million, its concentration being measured colorimetrically. When different species are compared the results shown in Table IV are obtained; in general, although the absolute rates vary, the rate, expressed as a percentage of the whole, except, perhaps, for the rat, is reasonably constant at about 0·4 per cent. This means that the fluid has a half-life of some 3 hr, in the sense that half of it is renewed in this time. If inhibitors of active transport are incorporated into the perfusion fluid, such as ouabain, acetazolamide,

TABLE IV

Rates of secretion of cerebrospinal fluid
(After Davson, *Physiology of the Cerebrospinal Fluid*)

Species	Rate	
	(µl/min	%/min
Man	520	0·37
Dog	50	0·40
Cat	20	0·45
Rabbit	10	0·63
Rat	2·2	1·4*

* On assumption of a total volume of 150 µl of CSF.

etc., there are quite large inhibitions of secretion (see, e.g. Davson and Segal, 1970). It has been argued that, in addition to the choroid plexuses, the adjacent brain-tissue produces fluid, which is added to that in the ventricles (Bering and Sato, 1963; Pollay and Curl, 1967; Milhorat *et al.*, 1971), but the evidence is not overwhelming for such extra-plexus sources. Nevertheless, the relations between the CSF and the adjacent brain tissue are of utmost importance.

The Blood-CSF Barrier

When the passage of different substances from blood to the CSF is studied, an essentially similar "barrier phenomenon" is found, so that lipid-soluble molecules, for example, show increasing rates of penetration in accordance with their lipid-solubility (Fig. 6.10), whilst the passage of lipid-insoluble substances is usually highly restricted unless the phenomenon of facilitated or carrier-mediated transport intervenes, as with glucose, for example. The existence of this barrier is physiologically intelligible, since to exclude, say, glycine, from passage across the blood-brain barrier but not to exclude it from passage into the CSF would mean that glycine would have access to the brain by first passing into the CSF and then from this fluid into the adjacent tissue.

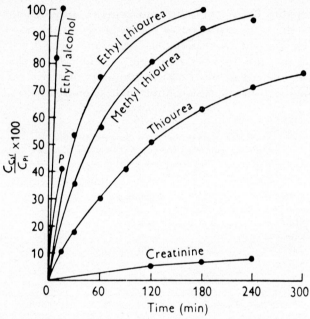

Fig. 6.10. The penetration of different substances of increasing lipid-solubility into the rabbit's cerebrospinal fluid. P = propyl thiourea. A steady level of the penetrating solute (100) was maintained in the plasma and the animal was anaesthetized at a given time and its CSF removed for analysis. (Davson, *Physiology of the Cerebrospinal Fluid*, Churchill.)

CSF-Brain Relations

Trans-Ependymal Flux

Thus, when substances such as glycine or sucrose that do not cross the blood-brain barrier easily are perfused through the ventricles, they penetrate readily into the brain-tissue; this is illustrated by Fig. 6.11, which shows the uptake of the rabbit's brain, when a sucrose-containing solution is perfused through the ventricles (curve A) and when the sucrose is in the blood and has to cross the blood-brain barrier (curve B). Studies with many substances all lead to the conclusion that there is no significant barrier between the CSF and the brain, either across the ventricular wall or across the pia mater in the subarachnoid space.

Application of Drugs

Experimentally, the pharmacologist has profited by this feature when he has wished to apply drugs to specific sites; thus addition of 5-HT to the fluid in the lateral ventricle brings it into close apposition with the hypothalamus when it passes into the third ventricle; and it exerts its effects on the thermoregulatory centre for this reason (Chapter 1).

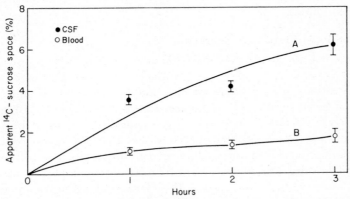

Fig. 6.11. The uptake of the ^{14}C-labelled sucrose by the rabbit's brain when the isotope is given (A) by a ventriculo-cisternal perfusion and (B) by an intravenous infusion. (After Oldendorf and Davson, *Arch. Neurol.*)

Brain Extracellular Fluid

If there is such a ready interchange between CSF and brain, this suggests that the extracellular fluid of brain is similar in composition to the CSF; if it were not, we should certainly find differences in composition according as the fluid was taken from the ventricles or from the cortical subarachnoid space. Thus we can imagine that the extracellular space has a concentration of glucose similar to that in plasma; the concentration in CSF is much less, about 50 mg/100 ml compared with 100 mg/100 ml (Table III). Clearly, if the fluid starts off with a low value when formed in the ventricles, the concentration should rise as the fluid passes through the system, exchanging with the high-glucose extracellular fluid of the brain on its way, so that the cortical subarachnoid fluid should have a much higher concentration than the ventricular fluid. The same argument should apply to K^+; however, the concentrations of the various constituents of the CSF are remarkably uniform (Davson, 1958; Bito and Davson, 1966), so that it is difficult to escape the conclusion that the CSF is a good index to the character of the fluid bathing the cells of the brain.

Glial Resting Potentials. An excellent confirmation of this viewpoint was provided by Cohen *et al.* (1968), who showed that glial cells of the brain had resting potentials that were dependent on the concentration of K^+ outside them; when the blood level of K^+ was raised some fivefold, the rise in the level of K^+ in the CSF was much smaller, and the resting potential behaved as though the cell were bathed by CSF rather than blood-plasma, i.e. the extracellular fluid surrounding the glial cell had the characteristics of CSF rather than of an ultrafiltrate of plasma.

Extracellular Fluid as a Secretion

There is little doubt that the CSF may be described as a secretion, formed by a variety of active transport processes that control the concentrations of its constituent ions, and perhaps glucose and amino acids, at levels significantly different from those in blood plasma or its ultrafiltrate. If this is true, then the extracellular fluid of brain is a secretion too, since it is most unlikely that the CSF could control its composition, by diffusional exchanges, and impose its own composition on it. Thus if this were so, i.e. if the CSF were controlling the composition of the extracellular fluid and if the extracellular fluid were formed passively as a filtrate from the blood capillaries of the brain, then, in order that its composition should approach that of CSF, K^+ and glucose, for example, would have to diffuse out of the extracellular fluid into the CSF, as it flows through the ventricular-subarachnoid system; in this case the concentration would be least in the ventricles and greatest in the cortical subarachnoid CSF, but in fact, as we have already seen, the concentrations throughout the system are remarkably uniform.

Site of Active Transport. We must assume, then, either that the blood capillaries of the brain are capable of actively transporting solutes to or from the extracellular space, or that such active processes are brought about by the glial cells covering the capillaries. These cells could conceivably absorb salts and water from the capillaries, and secrete them at their more distal regions into the surrounding extracellular spaces. In this way there would be a certain "turnover" of the extracellular fluid, and some would be carried into the adjacent ventricles and subarachnoid spaces and contribute to the total production of fluid, as postulated by Pollay and Curl. Such a flow would have to be very slow, as there is no evidence for a bulk flow of fluid through the tissue, although recently Cserr (1975) has provided some evidence for a flow around the larger blood vessels of the brain, as indicated by a preferential diffusion of dyes.

Active Transport out of CSF

Iodide and Thiocyanate

Up to this point, we have considered the choroid plexuses entirely as sources of CSF, producing it continuously by active transport processes across the choroidal epithelium. Studies on the removal of substances injected into the cerebral ventricles, e.g. those of Wallace and Brodie (1939, 1940) and Davson (1955b, 1956) indicated that certain substances were removed very rapidly although, when their passage from blood into CSF was measured, there was negligible penetration; particularly striking were the anions, I^- and CNS^- and the synthetic compound p-aminohippurate (PAH) which, as we have seen, is rapidly eliminated from blood by the kidney tubule. It was postulated that some metabolic event was involved that allowed these substances to pass out of the CSF easily but prevented their passage into it from blood; and the study of Pappenheimer et al. (1961), on the perfused ventricles of the goat, showed that, so far as Diodrast and phenol red were concerned, the choroid plexuses did, in fact, actively transport these substances out of the CSF into the blood. Later studies have shown that iodide, thiocyanate PAH, acetylcholine, and many other substances are actively transported from CSF into blood. In consequence, it is found with all these substances that, whereas penetration from blood into CSF is very slow, the escape from CSF into blood is very rapid.

Physiological Importance

It is not, at first sight, easy to provide a physiological explanation for these active transport processes; however, there is no doubt that the thiocyanate ion, for example, is toxic to the brain neurones, and a mechanism for its removal from the CSF, and thence from the environment of the neurones, is of obvious value. Of great interest is the finding that prostaglandins are removed from the CSF by a carrier-mediated process. These local hormones are liberated by neurones within the brain during activity, and appear in the CSF; and it may well be that the basic mechanism for their removal from this fluid consists in an active transport outwards across the choroid plexuses into the blood. Once brought into the general circulation they are promptly metabolized by the lung.

Prostaglandins. This active removal is illustrated by Fig. 6.12 which shows the changes in concentration of ^{3}H-labelled $PGF_{2\alpha}$ when perfused through the ventricles of the rabbit. An artificial CSF containing the labelled PG was injected continuously into the lateral ventricles and drained away from the cisterna magna; and the curve shows the concentration in the emerging fluid, as a percentage of the ingoing concentration, after it has passed through the ventricular system. At the beginning of the experiment, the fluid withdrawn consists of the animal's own CSF and thus contains no labelled PG;

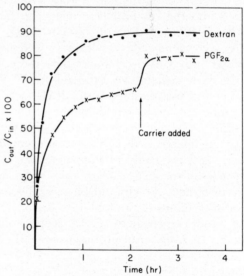

Fig. 6.12. Effects of adding carrier amounts of $PGF_{2\alpha}$ (arrow) on absorption of [^{3}H]-$PGF_{2\alpha}$ from the perfused ventricle. Filled circles: dextran dilution indicating secretion of CSF. Crosses: PGF_2. Ordinate: (out-flowing concn.)/(inflowing concn.) × 100. Abscissa: time in hr. after beginning perfusion. (Bito and Davson, *J. Physiol*).

as perfusion proceeds the animal's CSF is replaced by the artificial CSF containing the labelled PG, and the concentration eventually reaches a steady state, which is some 65 per cent of the incoming fluid; thus the absorption of the PG by the choroid plexuses causes the concentration of the outgoing fluid to be considerably less than that of the ingoing fluid. At the point marked by the arrow, the perfusion fluid was replaced by one containing exactly the same concentration of radioactive PG, but to this has been added some 0·5 μg/ml of inactive $PGF2_{\alpha}$. It will be seen that the activity in the emerging fluid immediately rises and levels out at a new steady state, indicating a considerable reduction in the absorption by the choroid plexuses.

Thus the absorption belongs to the carrier-mediated type, very similar to that found with iodide and thiocyanate. Studies on the isolated choroid plexus indicate, moreover that these organs are able to accumulate prostaglandins to a large extent, suggesting that not only is the transport carrier-mediated but that it is an active process capable of moving the prostaglandins against concentration gradients (Bito *et al.*, 1975).

Dextran Concentrations. To return to Fig. 6.12, the upper curve represents the changes in concentration of dextran incorporated in the artificial CSF with the prostaglandin. As indicated earlier, this cannot escape across the choroid plexuses, and its diffusion into the adjacent brain-tissue is very small, so that changes in its concentration are due almost exclusively to the addition of new CSF to the perfusion fluid as it is secreted by the choroid plexuses. It will be seen that a steady state is reached with the emerging fluid having a concentration some 90 per cent of the ingoing fluid. From this change in concentration we may compute the rate of secretion of CSF. The curve is useful, moreover, in showing what the steady-state level of prostaglandin would have been were there no absorption by the choroid plexuses; it will be seen that, although the inactive $PGF2_\alpha$ reduced absorption, it did not suppress it completely since the steady-state level is below that for dextran.

Homeostasis of the Extracellular Fluid

We must now come back to the blood-brain barrier concept; we saw this as a restraint on the movement of many molecules, and thus it acts as a passive barrier to the foreign molecules, to "unwanted" molecules, such as neurotransmitters after they have been released. The barrier also damps down the effects of fluctuations in the plasma concentrations of important ions and metabolites.

Glucose

Thus the rate of utilization of glucose by the brain-cells is governed by the amount penetrating them in unit time, and this is governed by the concentration in their extracellular fluid.

Large fluctuations in the concentration of glucose in the extracellular fluid of the brain are very considerably damped by the special carrier-mediated features of the blood-brain barrier to this solute. Thus at low concentrations of glucose, permeability from blood to the brain is favoured, since the carrier-mechanism is not saturated; at high levels, the saturation effect, whereby permeability is suppressed, reduces the penetration across the barrier, and so prevents wasteful usage of glucose by the brain cells. An interesting feature of transport of sugar across the blood-brain barrier, and its further transport into the brain cells, is that these parameters are unaffected by insulin, in marked contrast to the situation in skeletal muscle where uptake is "insulin sensitive". Thus in a hyperglycaemic state the glucose-sensitive centre in the brain reflexly causes the release of insulin, which favours passage into the cells and synthesis of glycogen, but the brain itself is immune from this increased transport into its tissue, an increased transport that would serve no useful function but lead to wasteful consumption since the brain is not a glycogen synthesis site. During hypoglycaemia, release of insulin is inhibited so that transport into muscle and other insulin-sensitive cells is reduced, but the availability of glucose to the brain is not impaired because of this insulin-insensitivity of the blood-brain barrier; in fact, as we have indicated earlier (p. 550), the homeostatic mechanisms that tend to maintain the blood-glucose constant serve as a shunting mechanism that favours transport specifically to the brain.

Amino Acids

It is likely that a similar basic mechanism operates in the control of transport of amino acids, although there is no doubt from the basic studies of Lajtha and of Oldendorf, that each acid must be considered separately, especially when involvement in transmitter activity is concerned. Thus access of glycine to the brain is strongly limited, in fact there is strong reason to believe that this amino acid is actively removed from the cerebrospinal fluid (Davson, 1976).

Active Processes

These restraints on penetration could be achieved by a purely passive barrier; however, some blood changes can persist for long periods, so that it would be insufficient merely to slow down exchanges between blood and extracellular fluid, and some more active process must intervene to prevent the equalization. Thus experimentally or pathologically the blood-K^+ may be raised for weeks on end; if the barrier to exchange of K^+ were merely passive, we know from isotope-exchange studies that the concentrations in CSF and brain extracellular fluid would equalize with those in the plasma within say, four or five hours. In fact, the studies of Bekaert and Demeester (1951) and Bradbury and Kleeman (1967) have shown that the CSF and brain maintain nearly normal concentrations of K^+ in the face of chronically maintained high or low concentrations of this ion in the plasma, and the same is true for Mg^{2+} and Ca^{2+} (Bradbury, 1965) and chloride (Abbott *et al.*, 1971). Thus the homeostasis of the brain cell's environment is achieved by more than a passive barrier; so far as the ionic milieu is concerned, active secretory processes, controlling the concentrations of these ions, are able to resist any fluctuations in the plasma levels indefinitely. The value of this homeostasis for K^+ for example is revealed by the experiments of Zuckermann and Glaser (1968) who injected small amounts of K^+ into the ventricle of the cat leading to epileptiform discharges.

Homeostasis of K^+

As to the detailed mechanism whereby the concentration of K^+ in the brain fluids is maintained at a nearly constant level in the face of large fluctuations in plasma concentration, some studies by Bradbury (Bradbury and Kleeman, 1967; Bradbury and Stulcova, 1970; Bradbury *et al.*, 1972) have contributed greatly to our understanding. Bradbury's work has shown that, so far as the CSF is concerned, the passage of K^+ from blood into the fluid tends to be inhibited by raising the concentration in the plasma, i.e. the inward flux tends to become saturated at normal plasma levels, so that the net inward movement is much smaller than would be expected of a non-carrier mediated system. In a converse way, when the concentration of K in the cerebrospinal fluid is *increased*, the efflux of K^+ tends to be accelerated, i.e. the carrier system tends to be desaturated with increasing concentration of K^+, as though the presence of one ion on it favoured the chances of another ion being attached. This is illustrated by Fig. 6.13, which shows the efflux of K^+ introduced artificially into the cerebrospinal fluid, by ventriculo-cisternal perfusion. As the concentration of K^+ is increased, the flux increases linearly until at about $2 \cdot 5 - 3 \cdot 0$ mequiv/litre there is a steep change of slope indicating a facilitation of efflux by the increased concentration; the point of inflexion comes at about the normal concentration in the CSF.

Dual Carrier Mechanism. Thus, by a combination of two mechanisms, the concentration of K^+ in the CSF is kept remarkably constant; the first mechanism is through a carrier operating from blood into CSF whose efficiency, measured in terms of the fraction of the plasma concentration carried in unit time, decreases with plasma concentration, and the second mechanism that operates from CSF to blood whose efficiency increases with increasing concentration of K^+ when this has reached a certain critical value. It must be appreciated, of course, that the mechanism begs the question as to how a carrier, passing from blood to CSF, can have one characteristic and an opposite one when moving in the opposite direction. On thermodynamic grounds this demands the expenditure of energy, which would be provided by metabolism; it is, in fact, the energy required for the active transport process that maintains the difference of electro-chemical potential between plasma and cerebrospinal fluid.

Active Transport Across Blood-Brain Barrier. In view of the similarity in transport processes across the blood-brain and blood-CSF barriers, we may presume that a similar homeostatic mechanism serves to keep the concentration of K^+ in the extracellular fluid of the brain constant, and a study of Bradbury *et al.* (1972) in which exchanges

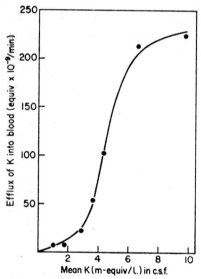

Fig. 6.13. The relation of the efflux of potassium from the cerebrospinal fluid to the mean concentration in this fluid during ventriculo-cisternal perfusion. (Bradbury and Stulcova, *J. Physiol.*)

between the brain-tissue and a solution flowing over it, in the subarach-noid space, were measured, showed a dependence of uptake of K^+ on the actual concentration that was compatible with a similar mechanism, flux of K^+ from extracellular fluid to blood being inhibited by low concentrations, and favoured by high concentrations.

CSF and Respiration

The close relations between the CSF and the nervous tissue mean that the neurones of the respiratory centres, sensitive to changes in local pH and PCO_2, will be influenced by changes in these parameters taking place in the CSF as well as in the blood. This point has been

discussed earlier (Chapter 3), and it will be recalled that it was concluded that the local pH and PCO_2 would, indeed, be a complex
function of the pH and PCO_2 of both blood and CSF, the drive to
respiration, in consequence, not being easily predictable from a
knowledge of these.

The Topography of the Blood-Brain Barrier

The main site of the blood-brain barrier is the capillary, with its
low permeability. It must be appreciated, however, that if substances
pass easily into the CSF from the blood, they can pass easily into the
brain from the CSF because the ependymal and pial membranes are
highly permeable. As we have seen, the choroid plexuses act as a
barrier, restraining those substances that are restrained at the blood
capillaries of the brain. A further site requiring restraint is at the
arachnoid membrane; this lies closely apposed to the dura, and the
subarachnoid space is the space between the arachnoid membrane and
the pia. The dural blood capillaries probably have high permeability,
characteristic of those in muscle and connective tissue; hence the
arachnoid membrane must act as a significant barrier between the
dura and the CSF. Electron microscopical studies indicate that the
epithelial type of cell constituting this membrane joins with its neigh-
bours to form tight junctions (Brightman, 1975).

Special Regions

There are certain regions of the brain, notably the area postrema,
the posterior lobe of the hypophysis, the pineal body, and eminentia
saccularis of the hypophyseal stem, that exhibit high permeability to
trypan blue, so that in these very limited regions more rapid exchanges
between blood and brain can take place.

Peripheral Nerve

We have seen how nerve fibres are grouped together into bundles,
a given bundle being surrounded by a membranous sheath called the
perineurium. This acts as a barrier to diffusion of substances from
outside the nerve bundle, so that when, experimentally, a nerve is
exposed to an altered medium, it requires some time for its effects to
show up (see, for example, Krnjevic, 1954). This layer is analogous
with the arachnoid membrane lining the dura, which acts as a barrier
to materials passing out of the dural capillaries, slowing their
passage into the CSF (Shanthaveerappa and Bourne, 1962). Within

the bundle the individual fibres are embedded in what has been called endoneurium (Fig. 1.5, Vol. 2), and these receive a blood supply through vessels that penetrate the perineurium and break into capillary networks within the endoneurium. These capillaries exhibit blood-brain barrier characteristics, in so far as they restrain the passage of fluorescent albumin out of the blood, by contrast with neighbouring epineurial and perineurial vessels; and an electron-microscopical study of these capillaries by Olsson and Reese (1971), using the peroxidase technique, has shown that they are analogous with those in the brain, the peroxidase being held up at tight junctions sealing the endothelial intercellular clefts.

CEREBRAL BLOOD-FLOW

We have seen how the flow of blood to a tissue, such as skeletal muscle, can alter over a wide range in accordance with the metabolic demands; these demands are transmitted reflexly to the central co-ordinating centres in the brain—notably the medulla and hypo-thalamus—and the more general readjustments that permit, say, an increased flow to the limbs without prejudicing the arterial pressure are brought about through appropriate cardiovascular reflexes. The circulation to the brain must take precedence of all other demands, for the simple fact that cutting off the blood-supply for just a few seconds causes loss of consciousness. The tissue of the brain consumes O_2 at a remarkably constant rate, so that although there are local variations, according to the relative amounts of grey and white matter, the supply of blood to the brain as a whole requires very little variation according to the activity of the animal as a whole; and it is not surprising, there-fore, to find that the most striking feature of the cerebral circulation is its relative constancy over a wide range of arterial pressures.

Autoregulation

This is revealed by Fig. 6.14 from Lassen's study of human subjects; so long as the mean arterial pressure remains above a critical value of some 60 mm Hg, the blood-flow is independent of this variable. This constancy of blood-flow with variable arterial pressure has been encountered earlier, and has been given the name of *autoregulation*, since it apparently depends on an intrinsic feature of the tissue, be it muscle, kidney, or brain, that permits the vascular resistance to adjust itself automatically to altered perfusion-pressure, i.e. the difference between arterial and venous pressures.

Myogenic Theory. Bayliss' (1902) original observation of an expansion of the denervated limb when blood-pressure was reduced

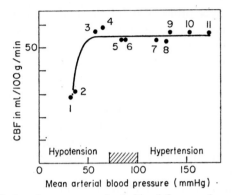

Fig. 6.14. The relation between cerebral blood-flow and mean arterial blood pressure in man. Mean values for 11 groups of subjects. Various chronic and acute conditions have been selected characterised by a change in blood pressure. 1 and 2, drug-induced hypotension; 3 and 4, drug-induced moderate hypotension; 5 and 6, normal pregnant women and normal young men; 7, drug-induced hypertension and hypertension of toxaemic pregnancy. (Lassen, *Physiol. Rev.*)

was considered to be the result of an inherent tendency of the smooth muscle of blood vessels to contract when pressure rose, and to dilate when it fell, so that resistance tended to balance alterations in pressure. This *myogenic theory* of autoregulation has received fairly general support, and has been applied especially to the brain, since in this tissue it is possible to study, visually, changes in the calibre of the arteries supplying the cortex—the pial arteries—by making a "window" in the skull (Forbes, 1928). According to the now classical studies of Forbes and Wolff (1928) and of Fog (1937, 1939), the adjustments of vascular resistance in the brain that apparently maintain a constant blood-flow are accompanied by variations in the calibre of the pial arteries. In this connexion we must note that the drop of pressure along the arteries of the brain is large; according to Betz (1972), some 42 per cent of the total flow-resistance is caused by vessels down to pial arteries of 30–40 μ diameter, so that fluctuations in the diameter of these vessels could certainly contribute materially to maintenance of a constancy in flow. Furthermore, these arteries are capable of marked variations in calibre, in fact local stimulation may cause complete obliteration of the lumen (Echlin, 1942).

Some General Considerations

Brain Precedence

At this point we may pause to consider what to expect of cerebral blood-flow; clearly, because of its importance, we may expect it to take precedence over other parts of the body, but this precedence, if the word is to have meaning, must involve an active control of its own circulation by the brain, through its vasomotor centres. Thus, if the brain is to take precedence, it must initiate reflex changes in the cardiovascular system to ensure that its supply of blood is maintained.

Buffer Reflexes. The first defence against a fall in the arterial pressure might then be the well known reflex adjustments, through the buffer nerves, to bring the arterial pressure back to its original value; if this took place rapidly and accurately the blood-flow to the brain would suffer only temporarily, but it would suffer, and a second line of defence is necessary.

Autoregulation. This is given by the phenomenon of autoregulation, an adjustment of the vascular resistance to the altered arterial pressure. It is hard to believe, however, that the central autonomic vasomotor control system would not be involved in bringing about this adjustment, i.e. as Ponte and Purves (1974) have emphasized, it is unlikely that the blood vessels would dilate passively to allow them to carry more blood at the lower pressure. It seems far more logical to expect that the adjustments of cerebral vascular resistance would be part of a series of reflex adjustments in all the vascular beds; in this case the dilatation of the cerebral arteries, and presumably smaller vessels, would result from nervous vasodilator stimuli brought into action by the primary lowering of arterial pressure. Similarly, the increased resistance associated with raised arterial pressure would be the result of vasoconstrictor activity. Before considering the modern experimental work that supports this point of view, let us examine some of the basic phenomena, and see to what extent a constancy of blood-flow is maintained.

The Vascular Anatomy

Arterial System

In man the arterial supply to the brain is through the pairs of internal carotid and vertebral arteries; at the base of the brain these anastomose to form the *circle of Willis* (Fig. 6.15), and it is from this arterial circle that large arteries supplying the brain, namely the anterior, middle and posterior cerebral arteries, arise. Over the surface of the brain they run in the pia-arachnoid, giving off branches that plunge into the underlying tissue.

Venous System

The venous system is rather more complex and is not easily illustrated; suffice it to say that the veins draining the various parts finally

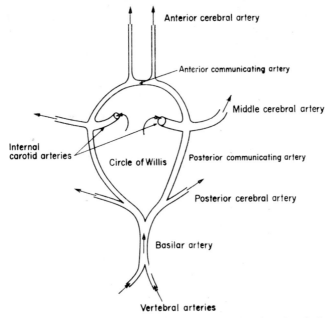

Fig. 6.15. A diagram of the arterial supply to the brain showing the circle of Willis.

empty into large dural sinuses, i.e. large veins embedded in the substance of the dura. Within this tough tissue they are reasonably immune from the pressure exerted by the cerebrospinal fluid, and for this reason they are a valuable site for the drainage of this fluid. It will be recalled (p. 583) that the arachnoid villi project into the sinus or adjacent lacunae laterales. Thus a rise in CSF-pressure will not cause the sinus to collapse and hence drainage of CSF can proceed. Blood from the choroid plexuses drains into the torcular, rather than into the superior sagittal sinus, so that in studies requiring a knowledge of extraction of substances from the blood flowing through the choroid plexuses, it is necessary to tap the torcular.

Measurement and Values

Wash-Out Curves

A method of measuring cerebral blood-flow based on the washing out of a radioactive tracer has been indicated in Vol. 1; the wash-out curves can be analysed into a fast and slow component, probably indicating the blood-flow through grey and white matter respectively. In man values ranging from 80 to 51 ml 100 g^{-1} min^{-1} for grey matter and 21 to 9·1 for white matter, with means for the whole brain

23*

TABLE V

Local cerebral blood flow in the unanaesthetized cat
(Landau *et al.*, 1955)

	Blood flow ($ml\ g^{-1}\ min^{-1} \pm$ S.E.)
Superficial cerebral structures:	
Cortex:	
Sensory motor	1.38 ± 0.12
Auditory	1.30 ± 0.05
Visual	1.25 ± 0.06
Miscellaneous-association	0.88 ± 0.04
Olfactory	0.77 ± 0.06
White matter	0.23 ± 0.02
Deep cerebral structures:	
Medial geniculate ganglion	1.22 ± 0.04
Lateral geniculate ganglion	1.21 ± 0.08
Caudate nucleus	1.10 ± 0.08
Thalamus	1.03 ± 0.05
Hypothalamus	0.84 ± 0.05
Basal ganglia and amygdala	0.75 ± 0.03
Hippocampus	0.61 ± 0.03
Optic tract	0.27 ± 0.02
Cerebellum, medulla and spinal cord:	
Cerebellum:	
Nuclei	0.79 ± 0.05
Cortex	0.69 ± 0.04
White matter	0.24 ± 0.01
Medulla:	
Vestibular nuclei	0.91 ± 0.04
Cochlear nuclei	0.87 ± 0.07
Pyramids	0.26 ± 0.02
Spinal cord:	
Grey matter	0.63 ± 0.04
White matter	0.14 ± 0.02

of 50 to 31 ml 100 g^{-1} min^{-1} have been given. If we take the higher value of about 50 ml 100 g^{-1} min^{-1}, this means a total flow of some 750 ml/min for a human brain of average weight, and represents some 15 per cent of the total cardiac output. The O_2-uptake by the brain is some 3.5 ml. 100 g^{-1} min^{-1}, corresponding to some 50 ml min^{-1} for the whole brain and some 20 per cent of the total O_2-consumption of the body.

Local Variations. Because of the variations in the proportions of grey to white matter in different parts of the brain, and because of variations in capillary density, we may expect to find corresponding differences in flow-rate in the brain. Local differences may be mapped out by injecting a radioactive isotope into the blood and rapidly removing the brain, which is then sectioned and examined auto-radiographically, the greater the radioactivity in any part the greater the vascularity and thus the blood-flow. Some figures obtained by Landau *et al.* (1955) are shown in Table V.

Changes with Activity. Although the mean blood-flow and O_2-consumption remain constant under a variety of conditions, it is likely that local changes take place in accordance with neuronal activity; thus Ingvar (1955) observed a dilatation of the cerebral capillaries, converting the colour of the brain from a rather pale colour to a flush, with obvious increases in flow-rate of individual blood-cells, when the reticular ascending system was stimulated, a stimulus that evoked activity in the EEG (Vol. 6). When blood-flow of human subjects was measured before and during sleep there was a pronounced increase, in spite of the fall in arterial blood pressure; thus the blood vessels relax during sleep, leading to an increased blood-flow. This is not associated with any increase in metabolism.

Effects of Blood Gas Tensions

It is well known that inhalation of air with a high PCO_2 causes increased blood-flow with lowered intracranial vascular resistance, associated with dilatation of the large arteries. Thus inhalation of 5 per cent CO_2 by man causes a 50 per cent increase in blood-flow, and 7 per cent CO_2 causes a 100 per cent increase. Since these large changes in blood-flow are not accompanied by corresponding increases in arterial pressure, we may say that, under these conditions, the "autoregulatory mechanism" is over-ridden, in the sense that cerebral blood-flow has changed. Figure 6.16 shows changes in blood-flow with arterial PCO_2 in dogs, the arterial pressure not having varied significantly. Again, when a low blood-pressure was induced in hyper-capnic animals, there was no regulation of blood-flow. Under these conditions we may assume that the hypercapnia had brought about maximal vasodilatation, and further dilatation, due to lowered arterial pressure, could not now manifest itself.

Hypercapnic Response

The increased blood-flow through the brain with raised $PaCO_2$ is understandable telelogically, since its result is to prevent, or reduce,

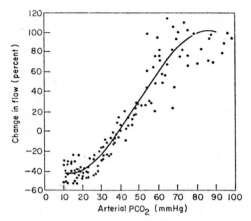

Fig. 6.16. The variation in cerebral blood flow with arterial PCO_2 in dogs. (Harper, *Acta neurol. scand.*)

the accumulation of CO_2 and acid in the neighbourhood of the brain cells; under natural conditions a raised PCO_2 in the brain would be due to defective local blood-flow, or perhaps to asphyxia, as during diving. The increased blood-flow in response to a rise in $PaCO_2$ could be the result of a local action of the PCO_2 or pH on the blood vessels; and certainly there is no doubt that the pial arteries show high reactivity to locally applied CO_2 (Shalit *et al.*, 1967); but the dilatation could also be the result of vasodilator nerves activated reflexly by the high blood PCO_2 (p. 129.)

Hypoxia

Lowering the blood PO_2 also increases cerebral blood-flow, but the effect is not so striking as that of altered PCO_2 since, as Fig. 6.17

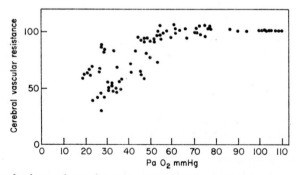

Fig. 6.17. Cerebral vascular resistance, as percentage of normal, plotted against the arterial oxygen tension (PaO_2). (Kogure *et al.*, *J. appl. Physiol.*)

shows, the blood-flow, or vascular resistance, remains constant down to a threshold of about 50 mm Hg; in these dogs the respiration was controlled artificially so that the $PaCO_2$ did not vary appreciably. It seems unlikely, therefore, that the degree of oxygenation of brain tissue, as such, acts as an important control mechanism for maintaining constancy of blood-flow. Thus it has been argued that the basic mechanism for autoregulation consists in the adjustment of vascular resistance to altered local pCO_2 and PO_2; a rise in PCO_2 and fall in PO_2 would be a reflection of insufficient blood-flow, and the intrinsic

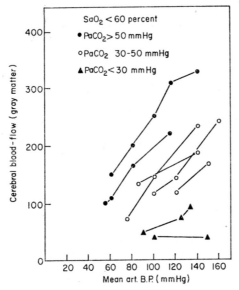

Fig. 6.18. Pressure-flow relationship in animals with arterial oxygen saturation below 60 per cent at different levels of arterial carbon dioxide tension. Most animals show a passive pressure-flow relationship. (Häggendal, *Acta neurol. scand.*)

response to these, namely vasodilatation, would compensate and bring blood-flow back to normal. Such a mechanism, although it undoubtedly operates, would, of itself, lack the sensitivity required for adequate homeostasis of blood-flow.

Local pH. The importance of local brain changes was shown by Kogure *et al.* (1970) in their cross-circulation experiments; thus the blood from a hypoxic animal was transfused into a normoxic animal, and although the blood of the hypoxic animal had a high concentration of lactate, it had no effect on the recipient's cerebral blood-flow. Again, they pointed out that lowering the blood-sugar impaired the response to lowered PO_2, presumably by reducing the available glucose for the anaerobic glycolysis and increased lactate production that are probably at the basis of the response to lowered PO_2. Thus measurements of the local pH on the surface of the cortex showed that, when the PO_2 fell to less than 50 mm Hg, there was an increased acidity, and in fact the blood-flow and local pH varied inversely.

Failure of Autoregulation. When PaO_2 was lowered to give an arterial saturation of less than 60 per cent, Häggendal (1965) found that autoregulation failed, in the sense that now the cerebral blood-flow varied linearly with arterial pressure (Fig. 6.18).

Cerebrospinal Fluid and Extracellular Fluid

Respiratory Responses

The role of the cerebrospinal fluid in maintaining homeostasis of the environment of the cells of the brain has been discussed earlier; and it will be recalled that the respiratory response to altered $PaCO_2$ is probably governed mainly by the changes in pH of the CSF, as well as those in the extracellular fluid in the immediate neighbourhood of the CO_2-sensitive neurones. To the extent that the composition of the CSF reflects the composition of the extracellular fluid of the neurones, we may expect to find correlations between CSF parameters and respiration. When, for example, pH of the CSF and blood plasma alter in opposite directions (p. 232), we may expect respiration to follow the pH of the CSF. In fact, as we have seen, the respiratory response seems to be the result of a compromise between the stimuli deriving from altered CSF- and blood-compositions.

Circulatory Responses

A similar problem arises with the influence of altered PCO_2 and pH of the blood and CSF on cerebral circulation. Thus we have seen that we may make blood alkaline by intravenous infusion of $NaHCO_3$; because of the rise in arterial PCO_2 that follows, due to reduced ventilation in the lungs, the pH of the CSF actually falls, i.e. becomes more acid, since the rise in blood-bicarbonate is not reflected in a rise in CSF-bicarbonate. As a result the cerebral blood-flow is increased. This is illustrated by Fig. 6.19, which shows the fall in cortical vascular resistance (equivalent to increased blood-flow) on injecting $NaHCO_3$ into the cat.

pH of Cortex. The pH was recorded from an electrode applied to the surface of the cortex and was presumed to represent the pH of the extracellular fluid of the brain. During acute hypoxia, induced by breathing N_2, the flow increases although the PCO_2 of the tissue falls,

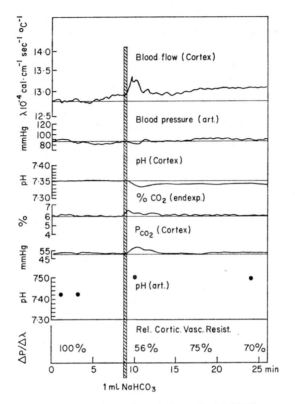

Fig. 1.19. Effect of intravenous injection of 40 mg/kg $NaHCO_3$ on cortical blood-flow, mean arterial blood-pressure, cortical pH, end-expiratory CO_2-content, cortical PCO_2, arterial pH, and cortical vascular resistance (initial value = 100 per cent). (Betz and Heuser, *J. appl. Physiol.*)

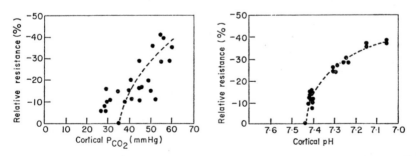

Fig. 6.20. Cortical vascular resistance as a function of PCO_2 and pH. (Betz and Kozak, *Pflüg. Arch. ges. Physiol.*)

due to hyperventilation. The pH of the cortex at first rises and later falls due, presumably, to the accumulation of lactic acid. In general, when studying the effects of several parameters on cerebral blood-flow, Betz and Kozak (1967) found a better correlation between cortical pH and blood-flow than between blood-flow and cortical PCO_2 (Fig. 6.20).

Reactive Hyperaemia. The return of the blood PO_2 to normal after a period of anoxia is associated with a sustained increase in cerebral blood-flow, in spite of the return to normal tissue PO_2; this *reactive hyperaemia* is not due to an elevated PCO_2 since this may be low; however, the cortical pH, measured with a surface-electrode, is acid and presumably accounts for the increased blood-flow.

Tissue PCO_2 vs Arterial PCO_2

According to Severinghaus and Lassen (1967) the response of the cerebral blood-flow to a lowered PCO_2 in the blood occurs very rapidly, and follows the changes in PCO_2 of the arterial blood (Fig. 6.21; the PCO_2 of the tissue, measured by that in the venous blood, falls much more slowly owing to the time required to wash CO_2 from the tissue. Thus it is the tension of CO_2 in the arterial blood vessels that seems to govern their calibre.

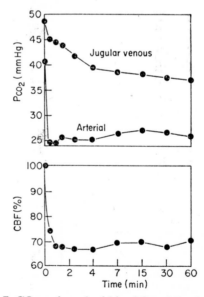

Fig. 6.21. Changes in $PaCO_2$ and cerebral blood-flow following a step reduction in alveolar PCO_2. Cerebral blood-flow closely followed the arterial PCO_2 rather than the jugular venous blood-PCO_2 wash-out curve. (Severinghaus and Lassen, *Circ. Res.*)

Hyperventilation. Prolonged hyperventilation occurs at high altitudes, with a consequent lowering of the $PaCO_2$; during this reaction the CSF tends to become acid owing to the accumulation of lactic acid (Plum and Posner, 1967). According to McDowall and Harper (1968), the cerebral blood-flow does not increase, in spite of the fall in CSF-pH, so that under these conditions of hypocapnia the relation between blood-flow and CSF-pH seems to fail.

Neural Basis of Autoregulation

By definition, the term autoregulation implies mechanisms of adjusting flow to pressure intrinsic to the tissue, and thus independent of extrinsic reflexes. If, therefore, the regulation is achieved by the help of extrinsic mechanisms, and is mediated by nervous influences originating in the autonomic control centres, we should drop the term "auto-regulation", and refer simply to "regulation".

Autonomic Innervation

There is no doubt that the blood vessels of the brain are innervated by both sympathetic and parasympathetic divisions; furthermore, the classical studies of Hurthle (1889) showed that stimulation of the cervical sympathetic trunk caused a reduction in cerebral blood-flow; this is associated with a reduction in calibre of the larger pial arteries (Forbes and Wolff, 1928) and may be mimicked by direct application of adrenaline to the brain (Fog, 1939). Again Cobb and Finesinger (1932) showed that stimulation of NVII caused dilatation of pial arteries, and the pathway for the parasympathetic innervation of the arteries was described by Chorobski and Penfield (1932).

Nervous Influences on Pial Arteries

The involvement of these nervous mechanisms in the regulation of blood-flow was questioned, however, by failure to observe serious interference with regulation on cutting the sympathetic supply. However, evidence in favour of neural mechanisms in the autoregulatory control over the diameters of pial arteries was provided by Mchedlish-vili and Nikolaishvili (1970), who found, in the rabbit, that a brief period of cerebral ischaemia, caused by dropping the arterial pressure transiently to zero, prevented the autoregulatory responses. It was argued that the ischaemia had put the neural mechanisms out of action permanently. Again, intravenous atropine blocked the pial dilatation that normally resulted from lowered arterial pressure, leaving the constrictor response to raised arterial pressure unaffected.

Earlier Yoshida *et al.* (1966), in a study on monkeys, had shown that autoregulation in response to an acute rise in arterial pressure was by no means perfect, there being an initial steep rise in blood-flow, which later slowed down but failed to achieve its original value after 3 min; correspondingly there was a rise in vascular resistance, as in Fig. 6.22. After sympathectomy the acute rise in resistance was abolished, so that the initial increase in blood-flow was rather larger than before.

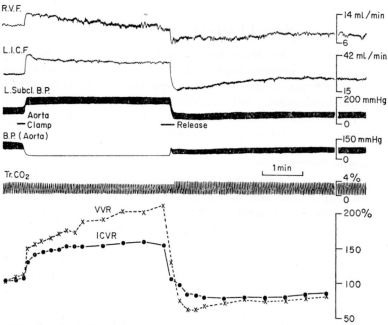

Fig. 6.22. Showing changes in right vertebral flow (RVF), left internal carotid flow (LICF), left subclavian blood pressure (L Sublc. BP), blood pressure of abdominal aorta (BP aorta), end-tidal CO_2 concentration (Tr. CO_2), vertebral vascular resistance (VVR), and internal carotid vascular resistance (ICVR) during and after induced acute hypertension. Note that "autoregulation" is by no means perfect. (Yoshida *et al.*, *Circ. Res.*)

Experiments on Baboons

Some elaborate studies on the baboon by Purves (James, Millar and Purves, 1969; Ponte and Purves, 1974) have made it very likely, indeed, that reflex vasodilator activity, mediated through the facial nerve (NVII), plays an important role in the adjustment of the cerebral vascular resistance to a rise in arterial pressure, a reflex control activated by receptors in the carotid bodies and baroreceptors of the sinus and aortic arch.

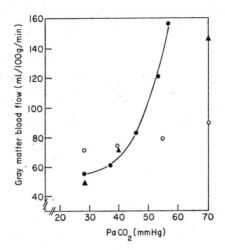

Fig. 6.23. Relation between cortical blood-flow and $PaCO_2$ with vagus intact (solid circles), following section of the vagus (open circles) and during stimulation of central end of cut vagus (triangles). (James, Millar and Purves, *Circ. Res.*)

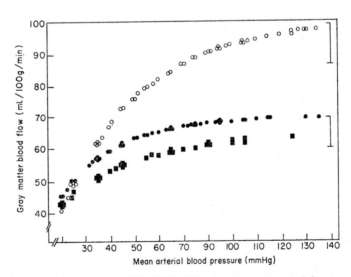

Fig. 6.24. Relation between cortical blood-flow and mean arterial pressure with nerves intact (solid circles), following sympathectomy (open circles), and during sympathetic stimulation (squares). Average curves derived from 13 baboons. Vertical lines at right represent 95% confidence limits for values of asymptotes toward which the upper curves tend. (James, Millar and Purves, *Circ. Res.*)

Vagotomy and Sympathotomy. James *et al.* (1969) showed that the response to altered PaCO$_2$ was very considerably modified by cutting the vagus, and sinus-nerve, thereby reducing the reflex afferent discharges from the carotid sinus and aortic arch (Fig. 6.23), so that responses to high PaCO$_2$ were virtually abolished. When the vagus was stimulated, the response to high PaCO$_2$ was restored (triangle in Fig. 6.23). Cutting the sympathetic supply caused an increase in blood-flow, suggesting the operation of a tonic vasoconstrictor tone; the effect was most marked at high PaCO$_2$ (Fig. 6.24); sympathetic stimulation caused a reduction in blood-flow.

Importance of Vasodilatation. In general, the authors concluded that the predominant contribution to regulation made by these reflex mechanisms was through vasodilatation, and they considered that vasoconstriction came into play merely as a fine control over the vasodilator responses to hypoxia and hypercapnia; thus the net effects of these changes in gas tension is one of vasodilatation, although vaso-constrictor activity is, in fact, evoked in the sympathetic system.

Carotid Sinus Perfusion. In a later study Ponte and Purves (1974) perfused the carotid sinus of one side independently of the cerebral circulation, which was maintained also by an artificial pump-oxygenator. Perfusing the carotid sinus with venous blood with low PaCO$_2$ and high PaCO$_2$, while the head was perfused with normal arterial blood, caused an immediate increase in cerebral blood-flow (Fig. 6.25, points 1 and 2). Raising the PaCO$_2$ from 39 to 58 mm Hg likewise caused an increase in blood-flow (points 3 and 4); if, now, the remaining carotid sinus nerve was cut, the same change in PaCO$_2$ produced a much larger effect, because there was an accompanying rise in arterial pressure to greater than 200 mm Hg (points 5 and 6). The effects of changed pressure in the carotid sinus, i.e. of stimulating *baroreceptors*, were also investigated. Thus, when the inflow-pressure to the brain was held constant at 125–140 mm Hg and the carotid sinus pressure was raised to 160–180 mm Hg, there was a fall in blood-flow amounting to 28 per cent of the control value; similarly, a reduction in carotid sinus pressure to 45–65 mm Hg caused an increase in cerebral blood-flow.

Response to Hypoxia. Ponte and Purves concluded from their studies that the vascular response to hypoxia was largely reflexly regulated, the vasodilatation being mediated by NVII, with the sympathetic probably acting as a fine control. The result is the maintenance of adequate oxygenation of the tissue in spite of the lowered PO$_2$ of the arterial blood.

Response to Hypercapnia. The response to hypercapnia contains both an intrinsic and reflex component; the former (intrinsic) component is manifest by the observation of a constriction of the pial arteries when CO_2 is added to the cerebrospinal fluid (Shalit *et al.*, 1967) or an acid solution is injected locally by micropuncture (Wahl *et al.*, 1970), and the strong correlation between surface-pH and blood-flow already described. Some two-thirds of the response, however, is reflex, and mediated primarily by the dilator action of NVII, with

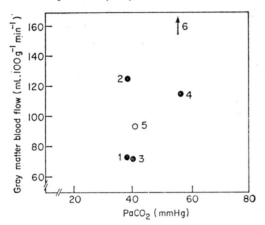

Fig. 6.25. The effect of altering PCO_2 of blood by various means upon the gray matter blood-flow in one baboon. The sequence of measurements is shown by the figures. 1 and 2, gray matter blood-flow when the left carotid sinus was perfused naturally with arterial blood ($PaCO_2$ 38 mmHg) and artificially with venous blood at systemic pressure (PaO_2 45 mmHg, $PaCO_2$ 48 mmHg and pH 7·29 units) respectively. 3 and 4, blood-flow when the sinus nerve was still intact and the left carotid sinus and cerebral vessels were naturally perfused with arterial blood at PCO_2 39 and 58 mmHg respectively. 5, blood-flow when the remaining (left) sinus-nerve had been cut and the head perfused naturally with arterial blood ($PaCO_2$ 39 mmHg) and 6, when $PaCO_2$ had been raised to 57 mmHg with an accompanying rise in mean pressure to > 200 mmHg. (Ponte and Purves, *J. Physiol.*)

the sympathetic exerting a fine control, i.e. tending to oppose the vasodilator action.

Response to Raised Arterial Pressure. The actual mechanism of the vasoconstriction in response to raised arterial pressure remains to be elucidated; it is a reflex response, since it is impaired by denervation of the carotid sinus, but the motor effect is not known, i.e. whether it involves only abolition of tonic vasodilatation or also active vasoconstriction.

Analogy with Coronary Circulation. In general, then, it seems that it is by possessing a powerful vasodilator reflex control that the cerebral circulation distinguishes itself from most other vascular beds, where vasoconstriction is usually the most powerful reflex response. It shares this characteristic with the coronary circulation; and it may be because most investigators into the nervous control over the cerebral circulation have concentrated on the sympathetic vasoconstrictor component that they have denied to the cerebral circulation any significant nervous control.

REFERENCES

Abbott, J., Davson, H., Glen, I. and Grant, N. (1971). Chloride transport and potential across the blood-CSF barrier. *Brain Res.*, **29**, 185–193.

Alvarez, O. A. and Yudilevich, D. L. (1969). Heart capillary permeability to lipid-insoluble molecules. *J. Physiol.*, **202**, 45–58.

Bayliss, W. M. (1902). On the local reactions of the arterial wall to changes of internal pressure. *J. Physiol.*, **28**, 220–231.

Bekaert, J. and Demeester, G. (1951). The influence of glucose and insulin upon the potassium concentration of serum and cerebrospinal fluid. *Arch. int. Physiol.*, **59**, 262–264.

Bering, E. A. and Sato, O. (1963). Hydrocephalus: changes in formation and absorption of cerebrospinal fluid within the cerebral ventricles. *J. Neurosurg.*, **20**, 1050–1063.

Betz, E. (1972). Cerebral blood flow: its measurement and regulation. *Physiol. Rev.*, **52**, 595–630.

Betz, E. and Heuser, D. (1967). Cerebral cortical blood flow during changes of acid-base equilibrium of the brain. *J. appl. Physiol.*, **23**, 726–733.

Betz, E. and Kozak, R. (1967). Der Einfluss der Wasserstoffionenkonzentration der Gehirnrinde auf die Regulation der corticalen Durchblutung. *Pflüg. Arch. ges. Physiol.*, **293**, 56–67.

Bidder, T. G. (1968). Hexose translocation across the blood-brain interface: configurational aspects. *J. Neurochem.*, **15**, 867–874.

Bito, L. Z. and Davson, H. (1966). Local variations in cerebrospinal fluid composition and its relationship to the composition of the extracellular fluid of the cortex. *Exp. Neurol.*, **14**, 264–280.

Bito, L. Z. and Davson, H. (1974). Carrier-mediated removal of prostaglandins from cerebrospinal fluid. *J. Physiol.*, **236**, 39–40P.

Bito, L. Z., Davson, H. and Salvador, E. V. (1975). Inhibition of the *in vitro* concentrative tritium-labelled prostaglandin accumulation by prostaglandins, prostaglandin analogues and by some inhibitors of organic anion transport. *J. Physiol.* (in the press).

Bradbury, M. W. B. (1965). Magnesium and calcium in cerebrospinal fluid and in the extracellular fluid of the brain. *J. Physiol.*, **179**, 67–68P.

Bradbury, M. W. B. and Kleeman, C. R. (1967). Stability of the potassium content of cerebrospinal fluid and brain. *Amer. J. Physiol.*, **213**, 519–528.

Bradbury, M. W. B., Segal, M. B. and Wilson, J. (1972). Transport of potassium at the blood-brain barrier. *J. Physiol.*, **221**, 617–632.

Bradbury, M. W. B. and Stulcova, B. (1970). Efflux mechanism contributing to the stability of the potassium concentration in cerebrospinal fluid. *J. Physiol.*, **208**, 415–430.

Brightman, M. W. (1968). The intracerebral movement of protein injected into blood and cerebrospinal fluid of mice. *Progr. Brain Res.*, **29**, 19–37.

Brightman, M. W., Shivers, R. R. and Prescott, L. (1975). Morphology of the walls around fluid compartments in nervous tissue. In *Fluid Environment of the Brain* (Ed. Cserr, H. F., Fenstermacher, J. D. and Fencl, V.). Academic Press, N.Y.

Chorobski, J. and Penfield, W. (1932). Cerebral vasodilator nerves and their pathway from the medulla oblongata. With observations on the pial and intracranial vascular plexus. *Arch. Neurol. Psychiat.*, *Chicago*, **28**, 1257–1289.

Cobb, S. and Finesinger, J. E. (1932). The vagal pathway of the vasodilator impulses. *Arch. Neurol. Psychiat.*, *Chicago*, **28**, 1243–1256.

Cohen, M. W., Gerschenfeld, H. M. and Kuffler, S. W. (1968). Ionic environment of neurones and glial cells in the brain of an amphibian. *J. Physiol.*, **197**, 363–380.

Crone, C. (1965). The permeability of brain capillaries to non-electrolytes. *J. Physiol.*, **181**, 103–113.

Cserr, H. F. (1975). Bulk flow of cerebral extracellular fluid as a possible mechanism of CSF-brain exchange. In *Fluid Environment of the Brain* (Ed. Cserr, H. F., Fenstermacher, J. D. and Fencl, V.). Academic Press, N.Y.

Davson, H. (1955a). A comparative study of the aqueous humour and cerebrospinal fluid in the rabbit. *J. Physiol.*, **129**, 111–133.

Davson, H. (1955b). The rates of disappearance of substances injected into the subarachnoid space of rabbits. *J. Physiol.*, **128**, 52–53 P.

Davson, H. (1956). *Physiology of the Ocular and Cerebrospinal Fluids*. Churchill, London.

Davson, H. (1958). Some aspects of the relationship between the cerebrospinal fluid and the nervous system. In *The Cerebrospinal Fluid*, Ciba Foundn. Symp., pp. 189–203. Churchill, London.

Davson, H. (1967). *Physiology of the Cerebrospinal Fluid*. Churchill, London.

Davson, H., Domer, F. R. and Hollingsworth, J. R. (1973). The mechanism of drainage of the cerebrospinal fluid. *Brain*, **96**, 329–336.

Davson, H. and Segal, M. B. (1970). The effects of some inhibitors and accelerators of sodium transport on the turnover of ^{22}Na in the cerebrospinal fluid and the brain. *J. Physiol.*, **209**, 131–153.

Echlin, F. A. (1942). Vasospasm and focal cerebral ischemia. *Arch. Neurol. Psychiat.*, **47**, 77–96.

Fog, M. (1937). Cerebral circulation. The reaction of pial arteries to a fall in blood pressure. *Arch. Neurol. Psychiat.*, *Chicago*, **37**, 351–364.

Fog. M. (1939). Reaction of pial arteries to epinephrine by direct application and by intravenous injection. *Arch. Neurol. Psychiat.*, *Chicago*, **41**, 109–118.

Forbes, H. S. (1928). The cerebral circulation. I. Observation and measurement of pial vessels. *Arch. Neurol. Psychiat.*, *Chicago*, **19**, 751–761.

Forbes, H. S. and Wolff, H. G. (1928). The vasomotor control of cerebral vessels. *Arch. Neurol. Psychiat.*, *Chicago*, **19**, 1057–1086.

Goldmann, E. E. (1909). Die äussere und innere Sekretion des gesunden und kranken Organismus im Lichte der "Vitalfärbung". *Bietr. klin. Chir.*, **64**, 192–265.

Goldmann, E. E. (1913). Vitalfärbung am Zentralnervensystem. *Abh. preuss. Akad. Wiss. Phys.-Math. Kl.*, No. 11 pp. 1–60.

Häggendal, E. (1965). Blood flow autoregulation of the cerebral grey matter with comments on its mechanism. *Acta. neurol. scand.*, Suppl. **14**, 104–110.

Harper, A. M. (1965). The inter-relationship between PCO_2 and blood pressure in the regulation of blood flow through the cerebral cortex. *Acta. neurol. scand.*, Suppl. **14**, 94–103.

Hürthle, K. (1889). Untersuchungen uber die Innervation der Hirngefasse. *Pflüg. Arch. ges. Physiol.*, **44**, 561–618.

Ingvar, D. H. (1955). Extraneuronal influences upon the electrical activity of isolated cortex following stimulation of the reticular activating system. *Acta physiol. scand.*, **33**, 169–193.

Ingvar, D. H. *et al.* (1968). CBF and CSF. IIIrd Int. Symp. on Cerebral Blood Flow. *Scand. J. Lab. Invest.* **22**, Suppl. 102.

James, I. M., Millar, R. A. and Purves, M. J. (1969). Observations on the extrinsic neural control of cerebral blood flow in the baboon. *Circ. Res.*, **25**, 77–93.

Kleeman, C. R., Davson, H. and Levin, E. (1962). Urea transport in the central nervous system. *Amer. J. Physiol.*, **203**, 739–747.

Kogure, K. *et al.* (1970). Mechanisms of cerebral vasodilatation in hypoxia. *J. appl. Physiol.*, **29**, 223–229.

Krnjevic, K. (1954). The connective tissue of the frog sciatic nerve. *Quart. J. exp. Physiol.*, **39**, 55–71.

Lajtha, A. (1968). Transport as control mechanism of cerebral metabolite levels. *Prog. Brain Res.*, **29**, 201–216.

Landau, W. H. *et al.* (1955). Local circulation of the living brain: values in the unanesthetized and anesthetized cat. *Trans. Amer. Neurol. Assoc.*, **80**, 125.

Landis, E. M. and Pappenheimer, J. R. (1963). Exchange of substances through capillary walls. *Hdb. Physiol.*, Sect. 2, Vol. 11, pp. 961–1034.

Lassen, N. A. (1959). Cerebral blood flow and oxygen consumption in man. *Physiol. Rev.*, **39**, 183–238.

Mark, L. C. *et al.* (1957). The passage of thiopental into brain. *J. Pharmacol.*, **119**, 35–38.

Mark, L. C. *et al.* (1958). The passage of thiobarbiturates and their oxygen analogs into brain. *J. Pharmacol.* **123**, 70–73.

McDowall, D. G. and Harper, A. M. (1968). CBF and CSF pH in the monkey during prolonged hypocapnia. *Scand. J. Lab. &. clin Invest.*, Suppl. **102**, VIII. E.

Mchedlishvili, G. I. (1964). Vascular mechanisms pertaining to the intrinsic regulation of the cerebral circulation. *Circulation*, **30**, 597–610.

Mchedlishvili, G. I. and Nikolaishvili, L. S. (1970). Evidence of a cholinergic nervous mechanism mediating the autoregulatory dilatation of the cerebral vessels. *Pflüg. Arch. ges. Physiol.*, **315**, 27–37.

Milhorat, T. H., Hammock, M. K., Fenstermacher, J. D. and Levin, V. A. (1971). Cerebrospinal fluid production by the choroid plexus and brain. *Science*, **173**, 330–332.

Oldendorf, W. H. (1971). Brain uptake of radiolabeled amino acids, amines and hexoses after arterial injection. *Amer. J. Physiol.*, **221**, 1629–1639.

Oldendorf, W. H. (1973). Stereospecificity of blood-brain barrier permeability to amino acids. *Amer. J. Physiol.*, **224**, 967–969.

Oldendorf, W. H. and Davson, H. (1967). Brain extracellular space and the sink action of cerebrospinal fluid. *Arch. Neurol.*, **17**, 196–205.

Oldenford, W. H. (1973). Carrier-mediated blood-brain barrier transport of short-chain monocarboxylic organic acids. *Amer. J. Physiol.*, **224**, 1450–1453.

Olsson, Y. and Reese, T. S. (1971). Permeability of vasa nervorum and perineurium in mouse sciatic nerve studied by fluorescence and electron microscopy. *J. Neuropath. exp. Neurol.*, **30**, 105–119.

Pappenheimer, J. R., Heisey, S. R. and Jordan, E. F. (1961). Active transport of Diodrast and phenosulphonphthalein from cerebrospinal fluid to blood. *Amer. J. Physiol.*, **200**, 1–10.

Pappenheimer, J. R., Heisey, S. R., Jordan, E. F. and Downer, J. de C. (1962). Perfusion of the ventricular system in unanaesthetized goats. *Amer. J. Physiol.*, **203**, 763–774.

Plum, F. and Posner, J. B. (1967). Blood and cerebrospinal fluid lactate during hyperventilation. *Amer. J. Physiol.*, **212**, 864–870.

Pollay, M. and Curl, F. (1967). Secretion of cerebrospinal fluid by the ventricular ependyma of the rabbit. *Amer. J. Physiol.*, **213**, 1031–1038.

Ponte, J. and Purves, M. J. (1974). The role of the carotid body chemoreceptors and carotid sinus baroreceptors in the control of cerebral blood vessels. *J. Physiol.*, **237**, 315–340.

Purves, M. J. (1972). *The Physiology of the Cerebral Circulation.* C.U.P.

Rougemont, J. De, Ames, A., Nesbitt, F. B. and Hofmann, H. F. (1960). Fluid formed by choroid plexus. *J. Neurophysiol.*, **23**, 485–495.

Reese, T. S. and Karnovsky, M. J. (1967). Fine structural localization of a blood-brain barrier to exogenous peroxidase. *J. Cell Biol.*, **34**, 207–217.

Severinghaus, J. W. and Lassen, N. (1967). Step hypocapnia to separate arterial from tissue PCO_2 in the regulation of cerebral blood flow. *Circulation Res.*, **20**, 272–278.

Shabo, A. L. and Maxwell, D. S. (1968). Electron microscopic observations on the fate of particulate matter in the cerebrospinal fluid. *J. Neurosurg.*, **29**, 464–474.

Shalit, M. N., Shimojyo, S. and Scheinberg, P. (1967). Carbon dioxide and cerebral circulatory control. I. *Arch. Neurol. Psychiat., Chicago*, **17**, 298–303.

Shanthaveerappa, T. R. and Bourne, G. H. (1962). The "perineurial epithelium", a metabolically active, continuous, protoplasmic cell barrier surrounding peripheral nerve fasciculi. *J. Anat.*, **96**, 527–537.

Simmonds, W. J. (1953). The absorption of labelled erythrocytes from the subarachnoid space in rabbits. *Austr. J. exp. Biol. med. Sci.*, **31**, 77–83.

Tripathi, R. C. (1971). Mechanism of the aqueous outflow across the tubular wall of Schlemm's canal. *Exp. Eye Res.*, **11**, 116–121.

Tripathi, R. (1974). Tracing the bulk outflow route of cerebrospinal fluid by transmission and scanning electron microscopy. *Brain Res.*, **80**, 503–506.

Tripathi, B. J. and Tripathi, R. C. (1974). Vacuolar transcellular channels as a drainage pathway for cerebrospinal fluid. *J. Physiol.*, **239**, 195–206.

Tschirgi, R. D. (1960). Chemical environment of the central nervous system. *Handbook of Physiology.* The American Physiological Society, Section 1, 1865–1890.

Wahl, M. *et al.* (1970). Micropuncture evaluation of the importance of perivascular pH for the arteriolar diameter of the brain surface. *Pflüg. Arch. ges. Physiol.*, **316**, 378–382.

Wallace, G. B. and Brodie, B. B. (1939). The distribution of iodide, thiocyanate, bromide and chloride in the central nervous system and spinal fluid. *J. Pharmacol.*, **65**, 220–226.

Wallace, G. B. and Brodie, B. B. (1940). The passage of bromide, iodide and thiocyanate into and out of the cerebrospinal fluid. *J. Pharmacol.*, **68**, 50–55.

Welch, K. (1963). Secretion of cerebrospinal fluid by choroid plexus of the rabbit. *Amer. J. Physiol.*, **205**, 617–624.

Wolff, J. (1963). Beitrag zur Ultrastruktur der Kapillaren in der normalen Grosshirnrinde. *Z. Zellforsch.*, **60**, 409–431.

Yoshida, K., Meyer, J. S., Sakamoto, K. and Handa, J. (1966). Autoregulation of cerebral blood flow. *Circ. Res.*, **19**, 726–738.

Yudilevich, D. L. and De Rose, N. (1971). Blood-brain transfer of glucose and other molecules measured by rapid indicator dilution. *Amer. J. Physiol.*, **220**, 841–846.

Zuckermann, E. C. and Glaser, G. H. (1968). Hippocampal epileptic activity induced by localized ventricular perfusion with high-potassium cerebrospinal fluid. *Exp. Neurol.*, **20**, 87–110.

SUBJECT INDEX

A

α receptors
  food intake control, 285
  gut, 296–298, 302
  insulin inhibition, 550
  phenoxybenzamine, 138
  pulmonary circulation, 187–188
  salivary glands, 318
α_2 globulin, angiotensin, 141, 412
Acclimatization, 20–22
Accommodation, bladder, 370
Acetazoleamide, (Diamox)
  CSF secretion, 591
  renal bicarbonate, 457–460
Acetyl β-methylcholine, 301
Acetycholine, 140–141
  bronchoconstriction, 221
  food intake control, 285
  gastric acid secretion, 326–333
  gut, 295–296
  gut, peristalsis, 309
  pulmonary artery, 183–185
  salivary secretion, 317–318
Acidity, binding and release of hormones, 334–335
Acidosis, 230, 320, 454
Acid secretion, stomach, 324–342
Acromegaly, 553, 555–556
ACTH (adreno corticotrophic hormone) 528–545
  blood sugar lowering, 544–545
  cAMP and insulin, 545
  fat, actions on, 528–529
  gluconeogenesis, 520
  insulin release, 528–529
  mineralocorticoid stimulation, lack of 412–413
Actinomycin D, vitamin D inhibition, 501–503
Addison's disease, 411
  potassium, 481

Adenosine
  aminophylline, potentiation by, 177
  coronary vasodilation, 176–177
  lidoflazine, potentiation by, 177
  purinergic transmission, 298
  stomach, vagal stimulation, 298
Adenylcyclase, 529
  insulin and catecholamines, 520
  insulin and fat cells, 530–532
ADH (antidiuretic hormone), 408–411, 503–505
  atrial distension, 411
  blood levels, 408–409
  blood volume, 137
  haemorrhage, 159–163, 426–427
  saluresis effect, 420
  vasopressor action, 427
  water intake control, 440–442
Adipose tissue
  cAMP, 529–530
  insulin control of, 528–532
Adipsia, 282, 440
Adipsic dehydratic aphagia, 282
Adrenal cortex
  aldosterone, 411–415
  gastric acid section, 340
  potassium and kidney, 481
  renin actions, 412–415
  sodium control, 411–415
Adrenal gland
  angiotensin, effect on, 163
  bradykinin, action on, 163
  temperature regulation, 46–47, 52–58
Adrenal medulla,
  glycogenolysis, 519–520
  reflex gut inhibition, 300–301
Adrenaline (epinephrine), 137–140
  bronchodilatation, 221
  cerebral blood flow, 613
  coronary blood flow, 172–173
  fatty acid metabolism, 528–532

623